MECHANISMS OF ANIMAL BEHAVIOR

PETER MARLER
THE ROCKEFELLER UNIVERSITY
AND THE NEW YORK ZOOLOGICAL SOCIETY

WILLIAM J. HAMILTON III
DEPARTMENTS OF ZOOLOGY
AND AGRICULTURAL ZOOLOGY
UNIVERSITY OF CALIFORNIA, DAVIS

JOHN WILEY & SONS, INC. NEW YORK • LONDON • SYDNEY

MECHANISMS OF ANIMAL BEHAVIOR

10　9　8　7　6　5

Library of Congress Catalog Card Number: 66–21043
Printed in the United States of America

To Judith and Marian

PREFACE

This book is about the processes that determine when behavior will occur and what form it will take. The relative importance of exogenous versus endogenous contributions to behavior recurs as a central issue in many of the historical controversies in behavioral science. Our aim is to elucidate the *interplay* of such factors in the control and development of animal behavior. We believe this approach, which Tinbergen characterizes in his classic introduction to *The Study of Instinct* as being concerned with the physiology of behavior, provides a suitable vehicle for conveying some sense of the ferment of ideas and experiments that prevails in animal behavior today.

Many topics in animal behavior have been omitted. Some, such as social behavior and the relationships between animal behavior and ecology, seemed to demand quite a different treatment. There is no general coverage of the evolution of behavior. Apart from these intended omissions, there are undoubtedly many inadvertent ones. For this we ask the reader's forbearance and cooperation. The book has been written for use at the senior undergraduate and graduate student level. One of us (WJH) has taken prime responsibility for the chapters on orientation (Chapters 13 through 16), the other for the remainder. The compromise between the introduction of facts on one hand and speculative interpretation on the other is in many sections an uneasy one, but we have found no effective alternative. Perhaps we shall stimulate others to find better solutions to this problem.

The book is an outcome of lectures and seminars on animal behavior given between 1957 and 1966 in the Department of Zoology at the University of California at Berkeley. As a direct consequence of stimulating discussion with many students, both in zoology and in the Departments of Anthropology and Psychology, the lecture outline has changed over the years, gradually taking the form indicated in the chapter headings. We are also deeply indebted to the following, who have criticized one or more chapters of the book: Norman Adler, Stuart Altmann, Howard Bern, Melvin J. Cohen, Reginald H. Dadd, John Davis, John Eisenberg, James T. Enright, Beatrice Gardner, Donald R. Griffin, Cadet Hand,

Jürgen Jacobs, Mark Konishi, Jean Moller, Keith Nelson, Floyd Ratliff, Mark Rosenzweig, Johann Schwartzkopff, Robert Selander, Curt Stern, Donald Wilson, and Edward O. Wilson. We are very grateful for the pains taken in reading the material and for the many constructive suggestions for improvement that resulted. Special thanks are due to George Barlow who gave time that he could ill afford to a thorough reading of the whole manuscript and who generated many improvements in both style and content. Those who helped in reading, typing, proofing, and indexing also made many thoughtful improvements, particularly June Elliot, Elizabeth Klekowski, Sandra Lesh, Barbara Licht, Anita Pearson, Miwako Tamura, and Patricia Warner. Again, our grateful thanks.

Many authors have allowed us to reproduce figures from their work, as acknowledged in the legends. We are similarly indebted to the following publishers for permission to reproduce material: Academic Press, Acta Psychologica Gothoburgensia, American Association for the Advancement of Science, American Institute of Biological Sciences, American Midland Naturalist, American Museum of Natural History, American Ornithologists' Union, American Philosophical Society, American Physiological Society, American Psychological Association Inc., American Scientist, American Society of Ichthyologists and Herpetologists, American Society of Limnology and Oceanography, American Society of Mammalogists, Annual Reviews, Appleton-Century-Crofts, Archives Neerlandaises de Zoologie, Bailliere, Tindall and Cassell, Biological Bulletin, Bird-Banding, Birkhäuser Verlag Basel, E. J. Brill Ltd., British Ornithologists' Union, Cambridge University Press, Chatto and Windus Ltd., Walter De Gruyter and Company, Doubleday and Company, Dover Publications, Ecological Society of America, Elsevier Publishing Company, Entomological Society of America, The Entomological Society of Canada, Fortschritte der Zoologie, Harper and Row, Publishers, Harvard University Press, Houghton Mifflin Company, Imperial Chemical Industries, Henry Kimpton (Medical Book Department of Hirschfeld Brothers Ltd.), Alfred A. Knopf, Long Island Biological Association, McGraw-Hill Book Company, The Macmillan Company, Methuen and Company, National Research Council of Canada, New York Academy of Science, North-Holland Publishing Company, Oxford University Press, Pergamon Press, Physiological and Comparative Oecology, Princeton University Press, Proceedings 13th International Ornithological Congress, The Ronald Press Company, Royal Society of London, W. B. Saunders Company, E. Schweizerbarts'che Verlagsbuchhandlung, Smithsonian Institution, Society for the Study of Evolution, Springer Verlag, Stechert Hafner, Texas Academy of Science, Time, Inc., University of California Press, University of Chicago Press, University of Illinois

Press, University of Oregon Publications, University of Texas Press, Verlag Paul Parey, Williams and Wilkins Company, Wisconsin University Press, The Wistar Institute of Anatomy and Biology, H. F. and G. Witherby Ltd., Yale University Press, and The Zoological Society of London.

PETER MARLER
WILLIAM J. HAMILTON III

March 1966

CONTENTS

one

SOME PRINCIPLES OF
BEHAVIORAL ORGANIZATION

Spontaneity in the behavior of coelenterates • Reflex theory and endogenous influences • Coelenterate feeding behavior • Vitalism versus
mechanism • Stimulus control of behavior • Describing and classifying
motor activities • Present responsiveness and past stimulation • Nature
and nurture.

Simple, sessile invertebrate animals, such as sea anemones, are not usually
thought of as having a rich spectrum of activities. It is true that some
species seem to do little more than contract when disturbed and feed
when a suitable object touches the tentacles. Others have a more varied
set of behavior patterns, but even in these more active forms the full range
may only be revealed by time-lapse photography, because many of the
activities are too slow to be detected by simple observation. Careful study
has in fact disclosed a great variety of 'postures' in resting, hungry, satiated, defecating, walking, swimming, and shriveling sea anemones. The
contortions by which one species attaches itself to a whelk shell containing
a hermit crab are among the most elaborate (Batham and Pantin 1950a,
b, c, Yentsch and Pierce 1955, Ross 1960, Figure 1–1).

In 1938 Karl S. Lashley, one of the most distinguished and influential
of the biologically oriented psychologists of the past generation, began an
historic analysis of instinctive behavior with an account of Kepner's
(1925) experiments on a planarian, *Microstoma.* After reviewing its methods of capturing *Hydra* and putting to use the nematocysts which it ingests

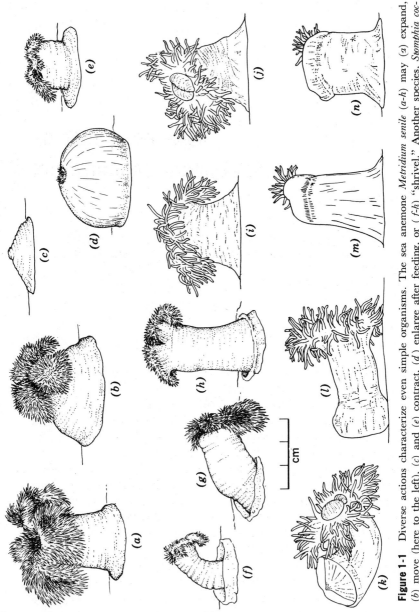

Figure 1-1 Diverse actions characterize even simple organisms. The sea anemone *Metridium senile* (*a-h*) may (*a*) expand, (*b*) move (here to the left), (*c*) and (*e*) contract, (*d*) enlarge after feeding, or (*f-h*) "shrivel." Another species, *Stomphia coccinea* (*i-n*) holds a (*i*) normal posture, (*j*) bends, (*k*) swims, (*l*) rests after swimming, (*m*) extends after contracting, and (*n*) responds to a starfish. After Batham and Pantin 1950a, Sund 1958.

for purposes of prey capture and defense, he concluded that here in this small flatworm "are encompassed all of the major problems of dynamic psychology." The relatively elementary behavior of simple organisms such as sea anemones and other coelenterates can serve as a useful approach to the principles of behavioral organization. The structural and behavioral simplicity of such animals brings the basic issues into particularly clear relief. Although different physiological processes underlie the behavior it can be shown that the same principles and issues are involved as in the study of higher organisms.

◆ *Spontaneous Activity.* Early zoologists who studied the behavior of animals such as sea anemones inclined to the view that all responses were directly evoked by external stimuli. The animal was believed to participate only as a passive recipient of environmental forces. But careful study of animals under controlled conditions has shown that movements in a sea anemone such as *Metridium* are occurring constantly and apparently spontaneously (Batham and Pantin 1950b). In this anemone there are three main systems of muscles. One system in the foot is seldom active. Another in the oral disk commonly shows some activity and a third in the vertical column is continuously active. Kymograph recordings obtained by linking small hooks to various points on the body show that the activity is often rhythmical, with an interval of about 10 minutes between contractions (Figure 1–2).

Can this be explained as a response to some rhythmical external stimulus? The experimenters could not detect one. Nor did animals

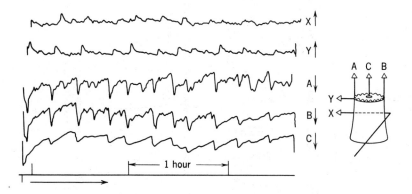

Figure 1-2 Short-term rhythm of muscular action of *Metridium senile*. Arrows indicate the direction of contraction. The activity records are direct kymograph tracings. After Batham and Pantin 1950a, 1950b.

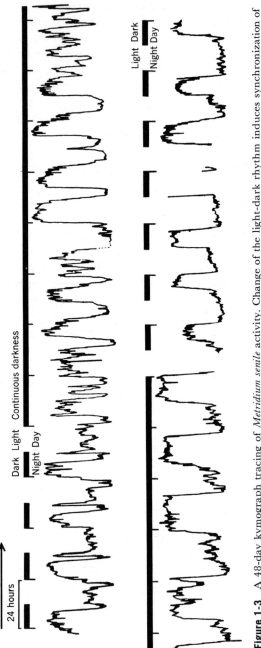

Figure 1-3 A 48-day kymograph tracing of *Metridium senile* activity. Change of the light-dark rhythm induces synchronization of activity, but a rhythm persists in continuous darkness. After Batham and Pantin 1950c.

placed side by side in the same aquarium show any synchrony in their patterns of activity. Another possibility is that the rhythmicity is based on a series of interacting 'reverberations,' with some past stimulus triggering one muscular system. By its contraction this system might then stimulate a second muscular system which would again stimulate the first and so on. This idea is somewhat inconsistent with the finding that there are occasions when different muscular systems are simultaneously active with different rhythms which shift in form and phase without any apparent effect on each other. The conclusion that some active, internal, physiological rhythm must be responsible seems inescapable.

If activity is registered for days rather than minutes, a new characteristic appears. An anemone exposed to the normal day-night cycle regularly contracted during the day and expanded at night. In the experiment depicted in Figure 1–3, two weeks with a normal light-dark cycle were followed by continuous darkness for 22 days and nights. Then the original light-dark rhythm was resumed, but in reverse, so that the animals were in darkness during the day and illuminated at night. A response to external stimuli imposed by the day-night rhythm was clearly shown. The activity cycle quickly came into phase with the reversed external conditions in the third part of the experiment. Surprisingly, during the 22 days of darkness the animal continued to show activity cycles. The extent to which the period varied from 24 hours soon carried the animal out of step with the original cycle. But remarkably, the rhythm persisted under relatively constant conditions.

Persistence of tidal rhythms has been recorded under constant conditions (see page 25). Evidently patterns of activity are more than passive responses to the alternating stimuli of day and night and the rise and fall of the tides. Moreover, Batham and Pantin could show that a new light-dark rhythm did not necessarily impose an immediate phase shift upon the activity cycle. Complete adjustment often took several days. Another intriguing discovery was that animals with a clearly defined rhythm often began to expand just *before* nightfall, before the onset of the appropriate external stimulus. Once again it appeared that the animal was by no means a passive respondent to the external stimuli. It participated in the interaction in a positive way. The normal behavior resulted from the combined effect of external stimuli and inherent physiological rhythms.

REFLEX THEORY AND ENDOGENOUS FACTORS IN BEHAVIOR

The major issues that concern modern investigators of animal behavior seem to have emerged during a period of rapid and exciting development.

Around the turn of the century the American psychologists William James and E. L. Thorndike and the Russian physiologists V. M. Bekhterev and I. P. Pavlov led a large and active group of workers who began to question the tactical value of introspective methods in the analysis of behavior. They substituted a variety of more direct techniques for describing behavior. The flood of research that followed helped formulate new problems which were the focus for another series of theoretical discussions in the 'twenties and 'thirties.

The central issues were the relationship of the external environment to behavior and the question of spontaneity. Pavlov came to the analysis of behavior as a physiologist who had already won a Nobel prize for his work on gastric physiology. Intensely concerned with the tactics of experimentation, he felt that the preoccupation of natural philosophers with the introspective aspects of behavior had been a hindrance to research. His discovery of the conditioned reflex convinced him of the importance of the external environment in the control and development of behavior. Moreover, he was able to frame his ideas in terms that could be tested by experiment. Pavlov's influence spread as his work became known in Germany and America. Thorndike (1898) had already prepared the ground with his important monograph, *Animal Intelligence*, which also criticized introspective methods. The two influences merged to encourage a strong emphasis on the role of external factors in behavioral control. Jacques Loeb (1900, 1918, 1964), a zoologist, and John B. Watson (1913, 1930), a psychologist, became central figures in the application and advocacy of this method of behavioral analysis.

It was perhaps inevitable that the fruitful exploration of environmental control of behavior should lead to a neglect of the importance of changes generated from within. Loeb, Watson, and the school of 'behaviorism' became vulnerable to the criticism that their approach was 'mechanistic.' There was open conflict with workers, such as the psychologist McDougall (1908, 1923, etc.), who felt endogenous influences to be supremely important in behavior. In common with a whole generation of biologists (see Thorpe 1963), McDougall was impressed by the apparent 'purposiveness' or 'goal-directedness' of much behavior. This quality, he felt, could not be reconciled with the subordination of behavior to the environment that the mechanists proposed. In different ways Freud and the 'Gestalt' psychologists also brought out limitations of the mechanistic approach.

The impasse generated by this conflict between the mechanistic point of view and the position of the so-called vitalists persisted in one form or another for a long time. Properly interpreted, it generated valuable research. The effect may still be discernible in the works of such distinguished investigators as D. O. Hebb and T. C. Schneirla, who are strong advocates of tactical emphasis upon environmental factors in behavioral control. But in the hands of those more concerned with arguing about problems than with doing research, the issue became sterile.

One reason why the conflict persisted for so long is that a great deal of behavior is indeed under close environmental control. Nevertheless, any attempt at a comprehensive theory of behavior was bound to fail if it did not take into account both exogenous and endogenous factors. The occurrence of cycles of activity in sea anemones in the absence of any synchronized, triggering, external stimuli implies the participation of internal changes. The biologist H. S. Jennings, a protozoologist at Johns Hopkins University and a contemporary of John B. Watson and Karl Lashley, was able to present another line of evidence in this direction. Jennings was well aware of the value of careful analysis of the external stimulus conditions which trigger behavior. Among his subjects was the ciliate, *Stentor,* which has a remarkably wide range of behavior patterns, many of them dependent on external triggers (Jennings 1906). The same external stimulus did not always elicit the same action, however. A cloud of carmine particles might evoke as many as five different reactions from the same individual *Stentor.*

Jennings placed strong emphasis upon the dynamic relationship between organisms and their surrounding environment. He pointed out that often the effect of an external stimulus upon an organism can be predicted only if the physiological state of the animal at the moment of stimulation is known. This and other issues led Jennings into a long and often bitter feud with Loeb, a feud which was continued in later years by his pupil Lashley and by Pavlov. In retrospect the extreme mechanist position seems to have been more at fault. To understand the mechanisms underlying behavior it is equally important to analyze external and internal factors.

ENDOGENOUS FACTORS AND FEEDING BEHAVIOR

The importance of internal factors is seen in the feeding of sea anemones and other coelenterates. The feeding behavior of *Hydra* depends on the physiological condition of the animal, which in turn is affected by the period of food deprivation. Jennings (1906, p. 219) cites an example from the work of E. B. Wilson (1891).

Hydras usually remain, as we have seen, in the upper layers of the water, on account of the oxygen there found. But when the Crustacea on which the animals feed have become very scarce, so that little food is obtained, *Hydra* detaches itself, and with tentacles outspread sinks slowly to the bottom. Here it feeds upon the debris composed of dead organic matter which collects at the bottom, often gorging itself with this material. It then moves towards the light, and at the lighted side again upward to the surface. Here it remains for a time, then sinks again and feeds upon the material at the bottom. This cycle may be repeated indefinitely, requiring usually some days for its completion.

The behavior is obviously closely dependent on external conditions, but endogenous changes in responsiveness to external stimuli are implicated as well.

The feeding behavior of a sea anemone (e.g. *Anemonia sulcata*, Pantin and Pantin 1943) involves the coordination of movements of several parts of the body. First, the cnidae discharge their threads into the food, attaching it to the tentacles. Then the tentacles close around the food and carry it to the mouth, which begins to turn and then to open. The food is thrust in and carried through the pharynx by muscular contractions. It is then digested, and finally the indigestible portions are expelled through the mouth.

In the course of these movements the pattern of rhythmical spontaneous activity is broken. In *Metridium* feeding is followed by elongation of the body, which continues for several hours (Figure 1–4a), overriding the finer spontaneous contractions which can still be detected as small inflections on the record. Then a new phase of movement begins. At the time of defecation, about 24 to 48 hours after feeding, there is another burst of activity overriding both the small-scale spontaneous movements and the pattern of diurnal activity.

This sequence of activities could result from a chain of reflexes, with each action mechanically stimulating the next movement. Thus food on the tentacles could elicit movement to the mouth, food in the mouth could trigger swallowing, and so on. A solution of food extract alone, however, evoked a similar pattern of activity (Figure 1–4b). Furthermore, the pattern persisted even when this chemical stimulus was removed by changing the water of the aquarium before the cycle had been completed. Thus the feeding pattern does not depend on a chain of external stimuli. "Even when an external stimulus initiates a phase, it merely releases a pattern of activity which the animal is quite capable of executing in its absence. The stimulus as it were, pulls a trigger" (Pantin 1950).

Other factors affecting the feeding response have to be accounted for. Whether food stimuli will in fact evoke feeding depends on the state of the animal which may be partly a function of its posture at the time. There is reason to think that the tentacles are especially responsive to food stimuli. When they are retracted there is, inevitably, less chance that a feeding response will be evoked. There are, however, variations in the responsiveness of expanded anemones. Starvation lowers the threshold

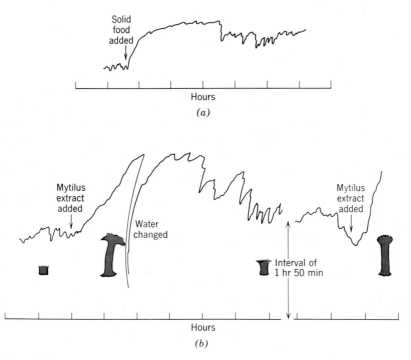

Figure 1-4   Elongation response of *Metridium senile* to solid food and to a fluid extract of food. After Batham and Pantin 1950c.

for the response and satiation raises it. A partially satiated animal will wait longer before responding to food and may have to be presented with several pieces of food before it will show a complete response. A completely satiated individual refuses all food. Conversely, a starved animal may show complete responses to inappropriate objects such as grains of sand. After prolonged starvation the pattern of feeding activity may even occur without any apparent trigger from the environment. It appears that the onset of feeding behavior is a function of a complex of factors, both internal and external.

VITALISM VERSUS MECHANISM

Interaction of exogenous and endogenous factors is a major topic of this book. The position we shall try to establish is that both internal and external factors are involved in *any* behavior pattern. No animal is a passive respondent to environmental commands. Rather, there is a process of interaction between the organism and its environment in which both have an active role. By the same token, it can be seen that completely endogenous control is equally illusive, for even when actions begin without any external trigger, the behavior is still affected by the other ongoing external conditions. Nevertheless, there are some behavior patterns, such as circadian activity rhythms, in which endogenous control is extensive. In others, such as escape behavior and the simple patterns of skin scratching in a frog or a dog, the external environment is dominant. Many types of behavior, including feeding and reproductive patterns, fall somewhere between these extremes. The controversy between the mechanists and vitalists is thus resolved. Both were right, depending to some extent on the type of behavior with which they were working. This position is close to that taken by some of the less extreme mechanists such as Karl Lashley. After he died in 1958 a memorial volume of his papers was edited by four of his former students and colleagues (Beach, Hebb, Morgan, and Nissen 1960). Their own work confirms the fruitfulness of Lashley's approach to the methodology of behavioral analysis. Even Loeb, whose reputation perhaps suffered most in the conflict, contributed a great deal to the understanding not only of tropisms but also of events in fertilization and cell division. In many ways he anticipated modern physico-chemical analyses of cellular and subcellular mechanisms.

THE MINIMUM ADEQUATE EXTERNAL STIMULUS

The mechanists strongly emphasized definition of the properties of an external stimulus which are necessary to change behavior. They were also concerned with specifying just how a given stimulus affected behavior —by eliciting it, steering it, and so on. Both problems arise in the behavior of sea anemones and *Hydra*. There is first the question of the specificity of external stimuli that will elicit responses. On the one hand, some actions are elicited by light or a touch—stimuli which are rather unspecific in nature. Other behavior patterns are only evoked by highly specific stimuli. The swimming behavior of the swimming sea anemone, *Stomphia*, cannot normally be evoked by disturbance or mechanical stimuli of any kind, other than contact with certain species of starfish. Sund (1958) carried out extensive tests with eleven species of starfish. Only two of them evoked a significant number of responses (Table 1). Ward (1962) has confirmed these results and shown that the effective substance is present only in the coelomic fluid and the tissues of the aboral surface of the starfish. The precise nature of the stimuli involved has yet to be determined, but there is no doubt about their specificity. The functional significance

Table 1-1   Effectiveness of Different Starfish in Evoking Swimming in the Sea Anemone, *Stomphia*

Starfish	+ Responses	− Responses	Number of trials
Crossaster papposus	1	69	70
Pteraster tesselatus	0	8	8
Hippasteria spinosa	200+	0	200+
Henricia leviuscula	0	53	53
Lepasteria hexactis	0	23	23
Orthasterias koehleri	0	48	48
Solaster stimpsoni	2	46	48
Evasterias troschellii	0	47	47
Pisaster ochraceus	0	25	25
P. brevispinus	0	26	26
Dermasterias imbricata	200+	few	200+

After Sund 1958.

of the response remains somewhat mysterious, for although some of the effective stimuli come from known predators on *Stomphia* (Robson 1962), others do not.

Sea anemones are often found attached to the shells of gastropods. In *Calliactis parasitica* the shell is usually occupied by a hermit crab. Selection of a suitable shell seems to depend on chemoreception, both in *Calliactis* and in *Stomphia* (Ross 1965).

The external stimuli evoking feeding behavior in anemones have been analyzed in some detail. There are at least two distinct phases. First there is the discharge of the nematocysts or cnidae and secondly the actual grasping and ingestion of the food. Earlier workers thought that simple mechanical stimulation triggered nematocyst discharge. Pantin (1942) showed that in *Anemonia sulcata* a mechanical stimulus is usually not enough. Normal discharge also requires sensitization by chemical stimuli which lower the threshold of response to tactile stimuli without actually eliciting discharge.

Only a trace of the chemical was necessary. A clean glass bead was ineffective. But if it was treated with a 0.1% dry-weight solution of human saliva in seawater for 5 minutes, there was extensive discharge (Figure 1–5). Pantin attempted to identify the compounds involved. His provisional conclusion was that a surface-active lipoid, widely present in potential food substances, was the significant constituent. The observation that detergents and other highly surface-active compounds were effec-

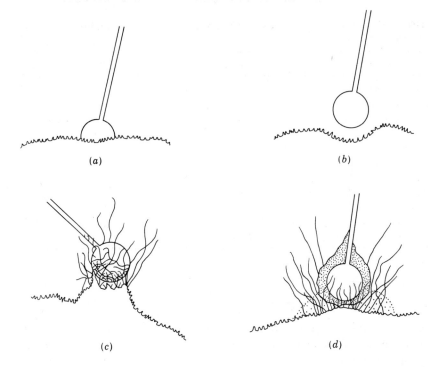

Figure 1-5   A carefully cleaned glass bead (*a, b*) elicits no nematocyst discharge on contact. A bead immersed for 5 minutes in 0.1 percent dry-weight of saliva in seawater (*c*) evokes extensive discharge. So does a bead smeared with alcoholic extract of *Pecten* mantle (*d*). After Pantin 1942.

tive in evoking discharge reinforced this conclusion, which can be extended to the nematocysts of free-swimming medusae (Yanagita 1960).

The situation in *Hydra* is complicated by the presence of four kinds of nematocysts. One type attaches the tentacles to the substrate during walking, another apparently protects the *Hydra* against collision with animals which are unsuitable for food, and two more types serve to capture prey of varying size and activity. After a detailed study of factors evoking discharge, Ewer (1947) concluded that different stimuli trigger each type. The two used in feeding are sensitized by chemical stimuli from food objects and are triggered by mechanical contact. One has a higher threshold than the other and is used on larger and more violent prey. The locomotory nematocysts are inhibited by food substances. In the absence of food stimuli, they have the lowest threshold of all to mechanical stimulation. They are triggered by steady pressure, which is provided by contact with the substrate but not by collision with a moving object. The protection nematocysts are unaffected by food substances and have a rather high mechanical threshold, but they are discharged by a colliding *Paramecium.* Since they are not discharged during locomotion, something more than a mechanical stimulus may be required; Ewer suggests that a sensitizing chemical different from that concerned with food capture may be involved. Thus a remarkably elaborate sensory organization ensures the appropriate response in the right context.

Nematocyst discharge has also been studied in two sea anemones, *Calliactis,* and the swimming anemone, *Stomphia* (Figure 1–1). In *Stomphia* nematocyst discharge can be triggered by flooding the surrounding water with food extract. Similar flooding has much less effect, however, when *Stomphia* is detached and swimming (Ross and Sutton 1964). By contrast, the threshold for nematocyst discharge in *Calliactis* is highest when the pedal disk is attached to a shell containing a hermit crab (Davenport et al. 1961). In these cases nematocyst discharge seems to be subject to control which is related to the activity state of the individual.

Several artificial compounds are effective in evoking nematocyst discharge in *Hydra,* sea anemones, and medusae, though the specificity of the chemical stimuli has yet to be precisely determined. The chemical stimuli for the next stage of the feeding response are highly specific, at least in *Hydra* and *Physalia,* the Portuguese man-of-war.

In 1955, Loomis discovered that reduced glutathione is a specific stimulus for feeding in *Hydra littoralis.* This substance is widely present in the fresh body fluid of prey animals and is released when the body wall is punctured by prey-catching nematocysts. Other compounds were ineffective, even closely related chemicals. Thus aspartathione, which resembles reduced glutathione so closely that it demonstrates coenzyme activity in the glyoxalate reaction, otherwise specific to reduced glutathione, was ineffective. Administration of a synthetic preparation of reduced glutathione in varying concentrations evoked a series of responses which culminated in the body turning inside out, attempts to ingest the glass wall of the container, and cannibalism (Figure 1–6). These abnormalities evidently arise in part because *Hydra* usually locates prey by the concentration gradient of the glutathione diffusing from the wounded area. In a homogeneous solution *Hydra* is naturally disoriented.

Lenhoff and Schneiderman (1959) have subsequently shown a similar effect of reduced glutathione on feeding responses of the gastrozoids of *Physalia physalia.* They add a further point which is relevant to *Hydra* as well: reduced glutathione alone cannot evoke a complete feeding response. A contact stimulus is also required. In the absence of tactile stimuli there is only extension and waving of the tentacles (or in *Physalia* of the entire gastrozoid) and opening of the mouth. The glutathione evokes

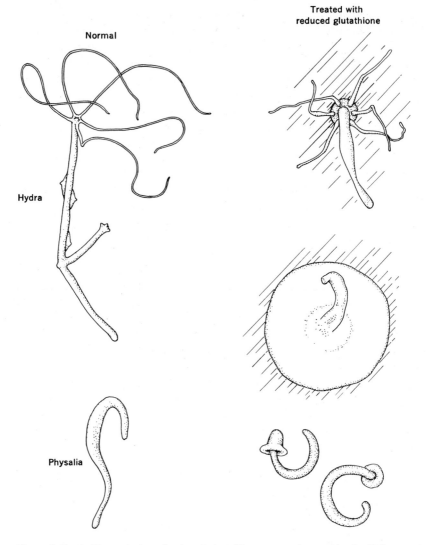

Figure 1-6   A dilute solution of reduced glutathione causes the mouth of a *Hydra* or a *Physalia* polyp to enlarge. There may be partial eversion of the body cavity (bottom). Contact with the vessel may lead to attempts to ingest the wall (top, middle). After Loomis 1955, Lenhoff and Schneiderman 1959.

something we might call 'searching' behavior. This term is appropriate enough since the behavior increases the chance of tactile contact with the prey.

THE CONTROL OF BEHAVIOR BY EXTERNAL STIMULI

Analysis of the stimulus properties responsible for the environmental control of different action patterns is a central concern in the study of animal behavior. We shall encounter wide variation in the specificity of the effective external stimuli. Some behavior patterns are triggered by several types of stimuli, and in others the relationship is more specific. But in every case a given behavior pattern is controlled by only a portion of the vast array of external stimuli that the animal can perceive.

This variation from specific to unspecific may at first seem paradoxical until we consider the biological requirements for survival in various situations. Each animal appears to focus responsiveness on what Jennings (1906) calls 'representative stimuli.' The animal does not respond to 'food' or to 'danger' but to some feature of the environment which is a predictable concomitant of these more general phenomena. At times a very specific stimulus may be representative of all the required situations and becomes the sole effective stimulus. This seems to be the case with glutathione, which is present in any prey animal that has vascular, coelomic, or pseudocoelomic fluids within the body wall. In *Cordylophora*, proline, another widely distributed substance, seems to be the trigger (Fulton 1963). In *Corymorpha* reduced glutathione, glycine, and several other compounds are effective (Wyman 1965).

Situations potentially dangerous to coelenterates are less readily reduced to a specific common denominator. Here natural selection will favor responsiveness to a broader range of unspecific stimuli. However, where a particular group of predators dominates the scene, specific responsiveness may result. The swimming sea anemone, *Stomphia*, flees only in response to chemical stimuli from certain species of starfish, although the predator-prey relationships here are still obscure.

Restriction of responsiveness to a small portion of the total perceptible spectrum, so-called 'representative,' 'token,' or 'sign' stimuli (Tinbergen 1951), implies some mechanism for sieving or filtering the incoming stimuli. Jacob von Uexküll, a contemporary of Jennings and teacher of Konrad Lorenz, repeatedly emphasized this point (see Schiller 1957). There are many sensory mechanisms by which this stimulus filtering can be achieved. Some, like the sensitization of the anemone's nematocysts by surface-active compounds, are relatively simple devices for filtering stimuli at the animal's periphery. Other mechanisms, which we shall find to be typical of vertebrates, involve subtle and complex integration of receptor and central nervous elements.

The study of stimulus-filtering mechanisms is complicated by variations in the type of contribution that stimulus properties make to behavioral control. Reduced glutathione causes *Hydra* to expand and wave about. But while it sensitizes the animal to triggering by tactile stimuli, it cannot elicit a complete feeding reaction. The cooperation of two stimulus types is needed for the full response.

In addition to the sensitizing and triggering functions of external stimuli, orientation of movements is often intimately related to environmental stimulation. In *Hydra* the diffusion gradient of the reduced glutathione and the location of tactile stimulation both contribute to the orientation of the different phases of the feeding response. Their contributions differ in an interesting way. The triggering and orienting effects of a touch on the tentacle of *Hydra* are achieved by the very same stimulus property— contact with a certain point on the body surface. The sensitizing and orienting effects of reduced glutathione, on the other hand, result from different stimulus properties. Perception of the presence of the compound is sufficient for sensitization, but detection of the gradient of diffusion from the source is needed for orientation. Thus under certain conditions a *Hydra* can detect the substance and yet be unable to orient to it.

In addition to having positive or facilitating consequences, some stimuli are inhibiting. They achieve their effect either by arresting a particular behavior pattern or by desensitizing the animal to certain external stimuli. For example, the threshold for discharge of *Hydra's* locomotory nematocysts is raised by the presence of food. A full description of the mechanisms of stimulus control must take these subtleties into account, not only for the sake of completeness but also because different physiological mechanisms may be involved in mediating the separate effects of external stimuli.

CLASSIFYING MOTOR ACTIVITIES

Description raises special problems in the study of all but the simplest behavior patterns. When confronted with complex and changeable phenomena, the investigator must abstract certain aspects of the situation and focus his attention on them. In this respect, the subject of animal behavior is no different from other types of scientific endeavor. However, concentration upon a single property of a complex behavioral situation is especially likely to lead to deceptive generalizations. It is important to remember that the initial selection of the limited part of the behavior pattern that is to be measured is based on the theoretical premises of the investigator.

Many early psychologists, inspired by Darwin's point of view on the relationship between animals and man, sought to determine whether the behavioral abilities of animals and man were confluent. The capacity to learn thus became a prime concern. The attention of Pavlov and Thorndike and their followers focused largely upon the modifiability of behavior in laboratory situations and definition of the laws that govern its lability.

Meanwhile another group of investigators, also following Darwin, became preoccupied with the patterns of behavior used by animals under natural conditions, and with the possibility that comparative study might illuminate problems of phylogeny just as studies of animal structure had done. In their attempts to find behavioral characteristics which might fortify and illuminate phylogeny, they were less concerned with the potential lability of behavior than with stereotypy and predictability. Jennings suggested that a start could be made by describing the 'action system' of behavior, asserting that "the action system of an organism determines to a considerable extent the way it shall behave under given external conditions" (1906, p. 300). Other zoologists, particularly Charles Whitman (1899, 1919) at the University of Chicago and Oskar Heinroth (1911) at the Berlin Zoo, were also placing emphasis at this time on the existence of consistent differences between the behavior patterns of species of birds. This viewpoint was crystallized some years later by Konrad Lorenz (1937, 1950) in the expression 'fixed action patterns,' a term which expresses the relative stereotypy of a significant proportion of the natural behavior of animals.

With some investigators emphasizing stereotypy and others stressing variability, the seeds of controversy were sown. The conflict was resolved by Wallace Craig, a pupil of Whitman also working with doves. He influenced a number of subsequent investigators, including the zoologist Lorenz and the psychologist Edward C. Tolman. In 1918 Craig wrote a paper which at one stroke put questions of stereotypy and variability into perspective and showed a way of incorporating both mechanist and vitalist points of view in a single more comprehensive theory (see Lorenz 1937, 1950, 1960). In this paper, which was titled "Appetites and Aversions as Constituents of Instincts," Craig sought to distinguish between two types of behavior that he called 'appetitive' and 'consummatory.' Appetitive behavior is the more variable, searching phase of behavioral sequences (e.g. looking for food); consummatory behavior is the more stereotyped phase which often leads to termination of the sequence (e.g. eating the food). A similar separation is to be found in the work of the neurophysiologist, Sherrington (1906). His 'precurrent' reactions embody much the same idea. They are responses that come before the consummatory events in a behavioral sequence. Psychologists have acknowledged the need for similar concepts (Woodworth 1958, Miller, Galanter, and Pribram 1960).

The distinction between appetitive and consummatory behavior is not universally applicable. There are some patterns, such as escape behavior and simple actions like scratching and preening, which lack an appetitive phase. The differences are not absolute but are matters of degree (Hinde 1953). Nevertheless, a classification of this type greatly aided Craig, Lorenz, and others in reaching their balanced perspective. These later workers focused especially on stereotyped patterns, consisting largely of consummatory actions. Psychologists and others continued to be more concerned with the variable patterns, consisting largely of appetitive behavior.

One reason already noted for the persistence of the vitalist-mechanist controversy is that some behavior patterns are much less dependent on external triggering stimuli than others. The appetitive-consummatory dichotomy also helped to resolve this difficulty. Although consummatory behavior is often dependent on particular, immediate, external stimulation for its occurrence, appetitive behavior often occurs without any immediate external trigger. This behavior is thus endowed with a spontaneous character that typifies certain types of activity. Moreover, the sensitization of an animal, in the appetitive phase of a behavioral sequence, to the particular external stimuli that elicit the consummatory phase embodies much of the 'purposiveness' that the vitalists felt was being neglected by the mechanists.

Craig's work also had a bearing on the development of behavior. While the mechanists emphasized the importance of environmental influences in causing variations in development, vitalists and others were stressing genetic factors. Whitman, Heinroth, and Lorenz pointed out that, within the same sequence of behavior, variations in appetitive behavior are often a result of learning—that is, of environmental control—but variations in consummatory behavior are more often under genetic control. Realization that the answers to developmental questions depend very much on the particular facet of a behavior pattern that is being studied was a considerable advance.

PRESENT RESPONSIVENESS AND PAST STIMULATION

The need to take account of the present physiological state of an animal in predicting what the effect of a given external stimulus will be on its behavior, relates in part to the appetitive-consummatory dichotomy. In the appetitive phase of a sequence the animal is predisposed to respond to a particular set of external stimuli, especially those that elicit the consummatory phase of the sequence. The appetitive phase may in turn be a function of external stimulation, not so much at present but at some time in the past. The time at which many animals start looking for food or water is affected by the time at which they last fed or drank. The duration of this interval since the last performance of consummatory activity and the experience of the accompanying external stimuli is an important variable.

The feeding behavior of a sea anemone, which is normally evoked only by objects which present chemical and tactile stimuli appropriate to food, can be elicited by grains of sand if the animal has been starved. Conversely, there are times when food fails to elicit the feeding response. The animal is satiated. Similarly, a well-fed *Hydra* will reject food, even through the nematocysts, which seem to be independent effectors, continue to discharge (Burnett, Lentz, and Warren 1960). If these changes in responsiveness are analyzed as sequences in time, we find that they have a cyclic quality. A period of satiation is followed by feeding, which is followed by satiation, etc. With an adequate food supply there are not normally variations in the specificity of the eliciting stimulus—either the response is given to the appropriate stimuli, or it is not given at all. Under conditions of extreme deprivation, however, there is a loss of selectivity in responsiveness which might make the difference between life and death. Inferior food is better than none at all, as man himself has often discovered.

Together with changes in responsiveness to external stimulation that follow a period of deprivation, the animal shows an increasing readiness to perform particular motor activities. This cyclical resurgence of a predisposition to perform certain activities was a special concern of the vitalistically inclined psychologist, William McDougall. He postulated some source of 'instinctive energy,' constantly accumulating and periodically discharging, specific to each major set of behavior patterns. Some years later Konrad Lorenz expounded a rather similar notion of 'action-specific energy.' Whatever type of hypothesis is adopted to explain the cyclic predisposition to perform certain actions—and there are reasons to distrust motivational concepts which are based upon the idea of energy flow (Hinde 1960)—the phenomenon of cyclic recurrence is of central importance in discussions of the 'motivation' of behavior.

Past stimulation can also influence responsiveness in a very different way. It may cause changes which are much less readily reversible and which lack the capacity for repeated cyclic recovery. This is the case when an animal learns to respond to a previously neutral stimulus—or learns not to respond to a previously effective stimulus.

Relatively irreversible change of responsiveness after previous stimulation has been noted in coelenterates. Consider the behavior of the anemone, *Aiptasia annulata,* when disturbed by water dripping from a height into an aquarium (Jennings 1906). A drop falls and the animal contracts. We wait for it to expand and then allow another drop to fall. After this sequence is repeated two or three times the animal fails to contract. As long as this stimulation is continued there is no further response. This type of change is different from the refusal of a satiated animal to feed. We are not saying that recovery of responsiveness cannot occur, but it may take a relatively long time and, more significantly, the stimulus must be discontinued in the interim.

Coelenterates also show a change in the form of motor activity as a result of prior stimulation. The column of the sea anemone, *Aiptasia,* is often bent into strange shapes through living in irregular crevices between rocks (Jennings 1906). When the anemone is moved to an aquarium these strange shapes persist, even though the animal is no longer restrained. Jennings found it was possible with appropriate stimulation to induce new shapes which would persist long after the restrictions had been removed.

The relatively irreversible effects that external stimuli can have on subsequent behavior are immensely varied, ranging from changes in the rate or nature of growth processes to learning complex new patterns of behavior. It is a moot point whether the changes in coelenterate behavior that we have described can usefully be thought of as a result of learning. Even in higher animals the limits of learning are not easy to define. Nevertheless, coelenterates display phenomena of the general type that includes learning, namely a relatively irreversible change of responsiveness following prior stimulation. Learning is free of the spontaneous cyclical reversibility that we associate with changes in responsiveness to such external stimuli as food and water.

NATURE VERSUS NURTURE

The conflict between vitalism and mechanism, originating in disagreement about the control of behavior in adult animals, had inevitable repercussions on the approach to problems of behavioral development. The emphasis of Pavlov on the exogenous control of reflexes is mirrored in Watson's conviction that environmental factors are supremely important in shaping behavioral development. This point of view is epitomized in his often quoted challenge: "Give me a dozen healthy infants, well-formed, and my own specified world to bring them up in and I'll guarantee to take any one at random and train him to become any type of specialist I might select" (Watson 1930). A similarly provocative brand of environmentalism is found in the work of Zin Yang Kuo, whose papers have such titles as "A Psychology without Heredity" (1924).

The opposing view sought to emphasize the contribution of endogenous factors to development. Concepts of 'instinct' were embraced by some (e.g. McDougall 1912) in a manner that was perhaps uncritical enough to justify the extreme counter position that the Watsonian behaviorists felt compelled to take. Nevertheless, there was a real danger of losing sight of the importance of genetic factors in behavioral development. Some signs of this bias still persist in the writings of certain workers, though amply corrected by such modern behavioral geneticists as Hirsch (1962) and McClearn (1963).

Among zoological behaviorists, Konrad Lorenz was especially influential in establishing a compromise point of view. He sought to emphasize environmental factors in the development of some activities, especially those of an appetitive nature. In consummatory behavior on the other hand, often highly stereotyped and species-specific, it seemed logical to stress genetic factors. Being very much interested in problems of animal phylogeny and classification, as Whitman and Heinroth had been, Lorenz and his associates concentrated on the study of those stereotyped, so-called 'innate' patterns of activity, types of behavior so completely ignored by many comparative psychologists that their very existence was barely acknowledged.

In more recent years the validity of the absolute dichotomy between 'innate' and 'learned' patterns of behavior was challenged (e.g. Lehrman 1953), generating in turn a fruitful reexamination of behavioral development from many points of view. In fact genetic and environmental factors have roles to play in the development of all behavior, and such terms as 'inherited' or 'learned' can properly be applied only to *differences* in behavior. Once more the issue is not one of supremacy of either exogenous or endogenous factors, but rather of the way in which the two kinds of factors interact with each other. It is as a consequence of the processes of interaction that behavior develops.

DESCRIPTION AND DESCRIPTION

To conclude this discussion of general problems of behavioral organization, we return to the task of describing behavior. We are told (Gantt 1941) that Pavlov had inscribed over his laboratory at Koltushy the words "Description and Description," thus throwing appropriate emphasis on what is perhaps still the most important single issue in many studies of animal behavior.

For the scientist confronted with the task of describing a complex phenomenon, the initial selection from the total array of possible characters may be the most difficult stage of an investigation. It can also be the most momentous, for the success of whatever is to follow stands or falls according to the appropriateness of the particular characters selected to the hypotheses being tested. In a young science tradition can be an even less reliable guide than usual in deciding what to record. Description of the dynamic and changing patterns of behavior will always be a challenge, for the possible measures are almost infinite. Some are correlated with one another, others vary independently. Some can be recorded directly by human senses, others require instruments to reveal them. Temporal relationships are often critical, as we have seen in sea anemones, and the limitations in our ability to relate events that occur very quickly or very slowly again call for instrumental aids. But one cannot record everything. Some selection must be made. Should it be random? Surely not, for to select in this way would be to deny a role to the intuition which plays such a vital role in scientific research. The alternative is to base the selection on a hypothesis, either unconscious or explicit.

In taking this inevitable course, there is danger in leaving the basis for selection uninspected. Yet the inductive thinking that is required at the initial stages of many behavioral investigations is necessarily but poorly understood by the observer himself—hence the critical importance of proceeding further to quantified measurement and experimentation. The interdependence is a mutual one, for quantification of blindly chosen characters, although never completely useless, can be more a waste of time than intuitive judgments which are never subjected to critical testing. The most fruitful contributions come from a wedding of both methods. The European ethologists have raised a compelling voice for the importance of inductive observation of the natural behavior of animals. Comparative psychologists cast their vote for quantified experimentation, exploiting to the maximum the progress of modern statistical methods. The union between these two approaches, the invocation to which has been set out in the writings of such men as Frank A. Beach (1950, 1960), may well lead to another major revolution in the methodology and content of the discipline of animal behavior.

REFERENCES

Batham, E. J. and C. F. A. Pantin. 1950a. Muscular and hydrostatic action in the sea-anemone, *Metridium senile* (L.). *J. Exp. Biol.*, **27**:264–289.
———— and ————. 1950b. Inherent activity in the sea-anemone, *Metridium senile* (L.). *J. Exp. Biol.*, **27**:290–301.

——— and ———. 1950c. Phases of activity in the sea-anemone, *Metridium senile* (L.), and their relation to external stimuli. *J. Exp. Biol.*, **27**:377–399.

Beach, F. A. 1950. The snark was a boojum. *Amer. Psychologist*, **5**:115–124.

———. 1960. Experimental investigations of species-specific behavior. *Amer. Psychologist*, **15**:1–18.

———, D. O. Hebb, C. T. Morgan, and H. W. Nissen (Eds.). 1960. *The Neuropsychology of Lashley*. McGraw-Hill Book Company, New York.

Burnett, A. S., T. Lentz, and M. Warren. 1960. The nematocyst of hydra (Part I). The question of control of the nematocyst discharge reaction by fully fed hydra. *Ann. Soc. Roy. Zool. Belg.*, **90**:247–267.

Craig, W. 1918. Appetites and aversions as constituents of instincts. *Biol. Bull.*, **34**:91–107.

Davenport, D., D. M. Ross, and L. Sutton. 1961. The remote control of nematocyst-discharge in the attachment of *Calliactis parasitica* to shells of hermit crabs. *Vie et Milieu*, **12**:197–209.

Ewer, R. F. 1947. On the functions and mode of action of the nematocysts of hydra. *Proc. Zool. Soc. Lond.*, **117**:365–376.

Fulton, C. 1963. Proline control of the feeding reaction of *Cordylophora*. *J. Gen. Physiol.*, **46**:823–837.

Gantt, W. H. 1941. *Introduction to Lectures on Conditioned Reflexes*, by I. Pavlov (trans. and ed. by W. H. Gantt), Vol. 2:11–35. International Publishers, New York.

Heinroth, O. 1911. Beiträge zur Biologie, namentlich Ethologie und Psychologie der Anatiden. *Proc. 5th Int. Orn. Congr.* (1910):589–702.

Hinde, R. A. 1953. Appetitive behaviour, consummatory act, and the hierarchial organisation of behaviour—with special reference to the great tit (*Parus major*). *Behaviour*, **5**:189–224.

———. 1960. Energy models of motivation. *Symp. Soc. Exp. Biol.*, **14**:199–213.

Hirsch, J. 1962. Individual differences in behavior and their genetic basis. In *Roots of Behavior*, ed. by E. L. Bliss: 3–23. Harper and Row, Publishers, New York.

Jennings, H. S. 1906. *Behavior of the Lower Organisms*. Columbia University Press, New York.

Kepner, W. A. 1925. *Animals Looking into the Future*. The Macmillan Company, New York.

Kuo, Z. Y. 1924. A psychology without heredity. *Psychol. Rev.*, **31**:427–448.

Lashley, K. S. 1938. Experimental analysis of instinctive behavior. *Psychol. Rev.*, **45**:445–471.

Lehrman, D. S. 1953. A critique of Konrad Lorenz's theory of instinctive behavior. *Quart. Rev. Biol.*, **28**:337–363.

Lenhoff, H. M. and H. A. Schneiderman. 1959. The chemical control of feeding in the Portuguese man-of-war, *Physalia physalia* L., and its bearing on the evolution of the Cnidaria. *Biol. Bull.*, **116**:452–460.

Loeb, J. 1900. *Comparative Physiology of the Brain and Comparative Psychology*. G. P. Putnam's Sons, New York.

———. 1918. *Forced Movements, Tropisms, and Animal Conduct*. J. B. Lippincott Company, Philadelphia.

———. 1964. *The Mechanistic Conception of Life*. Harvard University Press, Cambridge.

Loomis, W. F. 1955. Glutathione control of the specific feeding reactions of hydra. *Ann. N. Y. Acad. Sci.*, **62**:209–228.

Lorenz, K. Z. 1937. Über die Bildung des Instinktbergiffes. *Naturwissenschaften*, **25**:289–300, 307–318, 324–331.

———. 1950. The comparative method in studying innate behavior patterns. *Symp. Soc. Exp. Biol.*, **4**:221–268.

———. 1960. Methods of approach to the problems of behavior. *The Harvey Lectures* (1958–1959):60–103.

McClearn, G. E. 1963. The inheritance of behavior. In *Psychology in the Making*, ed. by L. Postman: 144–252. Alfred A. Knopf, New York.

McDougall, W. 1908. *An Introduction to Social Psychology*. Methuen and Company, London.

———. 1912. *Psychology. The Study of Behaviour*. Henry Holt and Company, New York.

———. 1923. *Outline of Psychology*. Charles Scribner's Sons, New York.

Miller, G. A., E. Galanter, and K. H. Pribram. 1960. *Plans and the Structure of Behavior*. Henry Holt and Company, New York.

Pantin, C. F. A. 1942. The excitation of nematocysts. *J. Exp. Biol.*, 19:294–310.

———. 1950. Behaviour patterns in lower invertebrates. *Symp. Soc. Exp. Biol.*, 4:175–195.

Pantin, A. M. P. and C. F. A. Pantin. 1943. The stimulus to feeding in *Anemonia sulcata*. *J. Exp. Biol.*, 20:6–13.

Robson, E. A. 1962. The swimming response and its pacemaker in the anemone, *Stomphia coccinea*. *J. Exp. Biol.*, 38:685–694.

Ross, D. M. 1960. The association between the hermit crab, *Eupagurus bernhardus* (L.), and the sea anemone, *Calliactis parasitica* (Couch). *Proc. Zool. Soc. Lond.*, 134:43–57.

———. 1965. Complex and modifiable behavior patterns in *Calliactis* and *Stomphia*. *Am. Zoologist*, 5:573–580.

——— and L. Sutton. 1964. Inhibition of the swimming response by food and of nematocyst discharge during swimming in the sea anemone, *Stomphia coccinea*. *J. Exp. Biol.*, 41:751–757.

Schiller, C. H. (Ed.). 1957. *Instinctive Behavior*. International Universities Press, New York.

Sherrington, C. 1906. *The Integrative Action of the Nervous System*. Charles Scribner's Sons, London.

Sund, P. N. 1958. A study of the muscular antomy and swimming behaviour of the sea anemone, *Stomphia coccinea*. *Quart. J. Micr. Sci.*, 99:401–420.

Thorndike, E. L. 1898. Animal intelligence. An experimental study of the associative processes in animals. *Psychol. Rev., Monogr. Suppl.* 2, No. 4 (whole No. 8):1–109.

Thorpe, W. H. 1963. *Learning and Instinct in Animals*. Harvard University Press, Cambridge.

Tinbergen, N. 1951. *The Study of Instinct*. Oxford University Press, London.

Ward, J. 1962. A further investigation of the swimming reaction of *Stomphia coccinea*. *Am. Zoologist*, 2:567.

Watson, J. B. 1913. Psychology as the behaviorist views it. *Psychol. Rev.*, 20:158–177.

———. 1930. *Behaviorism*. W. W. Norton and Company, New York.

Whitman, C. O. 1899. Animal behavior. Biological Lectures, Marine Biological Laboratory, Wood's Hole, Massachusetts, Boston.

———. 1919. The behavior of pigeons. Carnegie Inst. Washington Publ., No. 257:1–161.

Wilson, E. B. 1891. The heliotropism of *Hydra*. *Amer. Nat.*, 25:413–433.

Woodworth, R. S. 1958. *Dynamics of Behavior*. Henry Holt and Company, New York.

Wyman, R. 1965. Notes on the behavior of the hydroid, *Corymorpha palma*. *Am. Zoologist* 5:491–497.

Yanagita, T. M. 1960. Physiological mechanism of nematocyst responses in sea-anemone—III. *Comp. Biochem. Physiol.*, 1:123–139.

Yentsch, C. S. and D. C. Pierce. 1955. "Swimming" anemone from Puget Sound. *Science*, 122:1231–1233.

two

CIRCADIAN RHYTHMS: EXOGENOUS OR
ENDOGENOUS CONTROL?

Cyclic behavior and external stimuli • Translocation experiments •
Stopping the clock • The role of inheritance • Conclusions on independence from cyclic external stimuli • Effects of temperature and
light intensity • Entrainment and resetting • Internal structure and
physiological control • Circadian rhythms as examples of cyclic behavior.

Wallace Craig (1918) *opened his classic paper* on appetites and aversions
by stating that "the overt behavior of adult animals occurs largely in
rather definite chains and cycles . . . ." Rhythmicity of behavior is the
dominant theme of his discussion. He culminates with the conclusion
that "the active behavior of the human being is, like that of the bird, a
vast system of cycles and epicycles, the longest extending through life,
the shortest ones being measured in seconds."

The problems of explaining the mechanisms underlying such behavioral cycles are essentially the same whether the period is a year or
a fraction of a second. Annual reproductive cycles are considered by some
to be 'exogenous,' timed by external environmental stimuli. Others feel
they are 'endogenous,' originating within the animal and thus being to
some degree spontaneous (see Marshall 1960 and Wolfson 1960). There
are activity cycles associated with the phases of the moon and the tides
(Naylor 1958, Brown 1959, Fingerman 1960, Hauenschild 1960, Enright
1963a, b, Chandrashekaran 1965, Figure 2–1). The same questions have

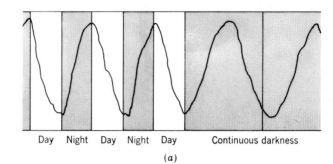

Day   Night   Day   Night   Day   Continuous darkness

(a)

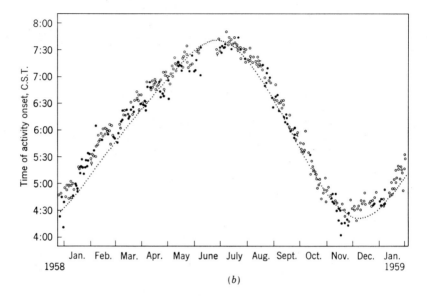

(b)

Figure 2-1   Circadian and tidal rhythms in plants and animals. (a) Kymograph records of leaf movements of *Phaseolus multiflorus* under normal day and night and continuous darkness. After Bünning 1957. (b) Time of onset of wheel running activity of a flying squirrel in natural daylight conditions throughout the year. After DeCoursey 1960. (c) Rhythm of emergence from pupae in a population of *Drosophila* under normal day and night and in continuous darkness. After Pittendrigh and Bruce, 1957. (d) Swimming activity of the amphipod *Synchelidium* in the laboratory. Activity corresponds closely to the height of the tide in their natural environment. The arrows indicate peaks of swimming activity. After Enright 1963a.

been asked about the timing of these rhythms. More progress has been made in the analysis of daily rhythms, and in this chapter we shall concentrate on them.

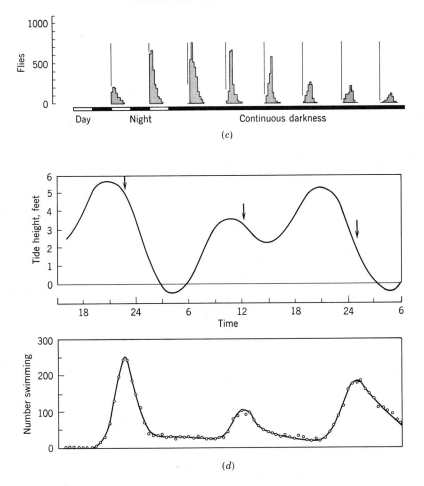

(c)

(d)

EXTERNAL STIMULI AND CYCLIC BEHAVIOR

The role of external stimuli in controlling rhythmical behavior patterns can be explored in several different ways. Does the cyclic patterning of the behavior depend on rhythmical external stimuli? Do steady external stimulus conditions affect the properties of the rhythm? What effects do rhythmical external stimuli have when they are presented, and how does responsiveness to these external stimuli vary in different phases of the cycle? Do external stimuli partially or completely control the characteristics of an activity sequence—do they time its onset, continuation, and termination and do they underlie differences between cycles? Are deviations from the average pattern such as bouts of activity that are longer or shorter than usual, accompanied by changes in responsiveness? We shall try to answer these questions as they relate to activity rhythms associated with the daily light-dark cycle.

CIRCADIAN RHYTHMS

The behavior of most animals in some way reflects the cycle of day and night. This influence can be seen in gross locomotor activity, in the pattern of feeding and drinking, in vocalizations and in other recurring

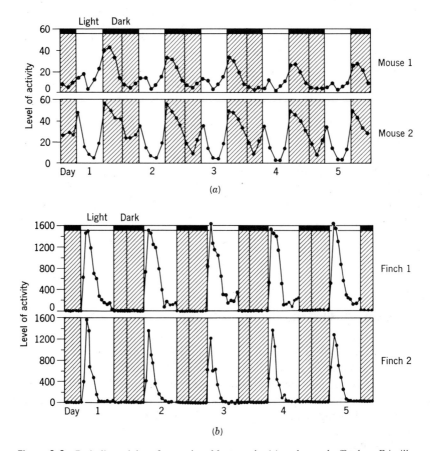

Figure 2-2   Periodic activity of two mice, *Mus musculus* (*a*) and two chaffinches, *Fringilla coelebs* (*b*) on a 24-hour light-dark schedule in the laboratory. After Aschoff and Honma 1959.

activities. It may also affect events which occur only once in a lifetime, such as the emergence of an imaginal insect from the pupal case (Aschoff 1960, Brown 1959, Pittendrigh 1960). It is easy to demonstrate these cycles when they recur day after day in the activity of an individual. A mouse cage can be outfitted with a device that records all movements. When the records are summarized in the form of a graph with appropriate units for the time axis, the graph reveals a cycle of activity which often reaches a major peak just after sunset and a minor peak around sunrise. There is little activity in the middle of the day (Figure 2–2). A diurnal animal such as a finch shows a similar pattern, but maximal activity occurs during the day. For the moment let us ignore the detailed internal structure of such a cycle and concentrate on its overall properties. These activity patterns are perfect examples of rhythmical behavior, recurring regularly with sessions of activity separated by intervals of reduced activity or of no activity at all. What has been revealed by analysis of such daily or circadian rhythms (*circa* about, *diem*–day, so called because these cycles approximate 24 hours under constant conditions)?

CIRCADIAN RHYTHMS IN THE ABSENCE OF SYNCHRONOUS RHYTHMICAL EXTERNAL STIMULI

To what extent is the cyclical pattern dependent on environmental triggers? We can start by placing the animal under conditions as constant as we can make them, eliminating all rhythmical cues related to the diurnal cycle that we can control. These may include such variables as changes of light and temperature. The result of such an experiment is generally unequivocal—a cyclic pattern persists (Figure 2–3). Some properties of the pattern may change—the peaks, for example, may rapidly dwindle in size—but a detectable rhythm generally persists for at least several cycles. We have already seen an example from the behavior of sea anemones (page 4), and there are many others (Figure 2–3).

Apparently the rhythmical pattern can continue endogenously, in the absence of any rhythmical eliciting stimuli from the external environment. We must be cautious, however, for Brown (1959, 1960) has pointed out many characteristics of the environment other than light and temperature which vary in the course of the day, characteristics such as pressure, humidity, and cosmic radiation which are seldom controlled in experiments of this kind. Until an experiment is conducted in the absence of all these cues, it is difficult to prove beyond all doubt that a circadian rhythm is in fact endogenous (Brown 1960). Nevertheless, endogeneity is also indicated by other kinds of experiments.

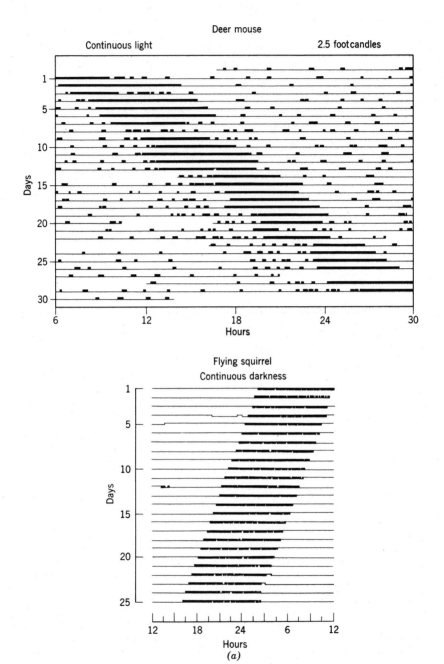

Deer mouse

Continuous light   2.5 footcandles

Flying squirrel
Continuous darkness

(a)

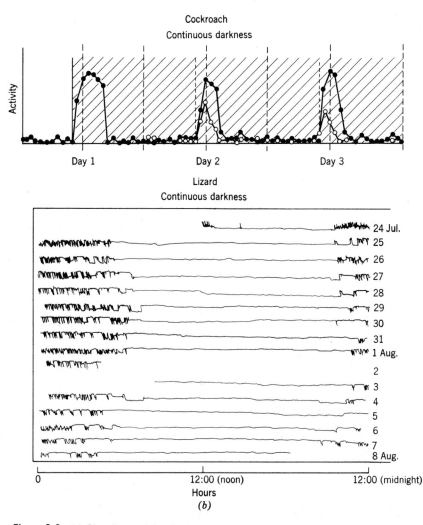

Figure 2-3 (*a*) Circadian activity rhythms persist under constant conditions but drift out of phase with the natural light-dark cycle. The record for the deer mouse was made under constant dim light and that for the flying squirrel was made in constant darkness. (*b*) Activity in continuous darkness. The cockroach (Harker 1960a) with the dark circles is untreated, having been under normal light-dark conditions previously. The open circles chart the action of an aphasic individual with a transplanted suboesophageal ganglion from a phasic animal (see page 65). The lizard, *Lacerta,* was hatched from an egg held under constant conditions. From Johnson 1939, DeCoursey 1960a, Harker 1960a, and Hoffmann 1959.

31

➤ *Translocation Experiments.* A circadian rhythm occurring under supposedly constant conditions might conceivably in fact be timed by some uncontrolled external stimulus temporally related to the earth's cycle of rotation. Transportation of the animal latitudinally around the earth to a new location should then result in immediate resynchronization of the rhythm to the new local time. When such experiments are performed the circadian rhythm does not reset at once, if light and temperature are kept constant. Instead it persists with the original timing for a number of cycles.

The circadian cycle of color change in the integument of fiddler crabs, which persists in continuous darkness, has been extensively studied by Brown (1959) and his colleagues (Brown and Webb 1948). When crabs were flown in darkened boxes from the Atlantic coast of the United States to the Pacific coast, the rhythm of color change maintained the original timing, despite the 51 degrees of longitudinal translocation, equivalent to a time change of 3.3 hours (Brown, Webb, and Bennett 1955). A similar result was obtained with a tidal rhythm of water propulsion in mussels (Rao 1954).

The most elaborate translocation experiments are those conducted by Renner with bees. Instead of working with bouts of activity throughout the day, Renner exploited the tendency of individual honeybees to visit flowers or a feeder regularly at a particular time of day. Earlier Beling (1929) and Wahl (1932) had already established that this circadian feeding rhythm can be conditioned by training, and that it persists under conditions which were as constant as they could make them. One experiment was even conducted in a salt mine, 180 meters below the earth's surface. Renner (1957) constructed a small portable room with constant light and temperature. A colony of bees placed inside could forage in the completely enclosed room at artificial feeders. In such a room in Paris a group of bees was trained to come to a feeder at a particular time of day. Then the hive was sealed and flown overnight to New York. A replicate room was set up in advance in New York, and after an overnight flight the bees were released in it. For three days the bees continued to visit the empty feeder at intervals of approximately 24 hours and at the hour they were accustomed to feeding in Paris. Local conditions imposed no immediate change of timing, thus demonstrating the independence of the circadian rhythm from local time. Translocation in the opposite direction gave the same result (Figure 2–4).

How would the results differ if the bees were allowed to see the sun by conducting the experiment outdoors? Renner (1959, 1960) trained bees in New York to visit a feeder at a certain time. The feeder was placed in a field some distance from the hive. Then the bees were flown overnight

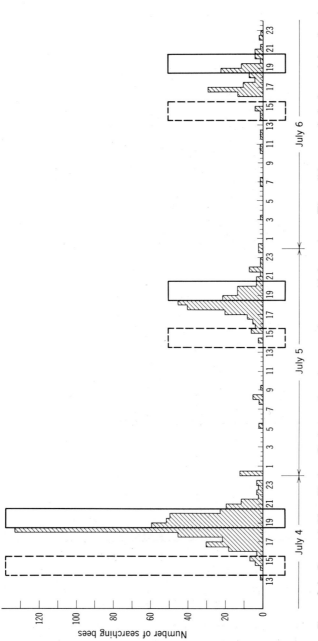

Figure 2-4 Renner's New York to Paris translocation experiment with honeybees. The solid rectangle is the training time in New York, the dotted rectangle the equivalent celestial time in Paris. In Paris the bees visited the feeder on New York time. After Renner 1957.

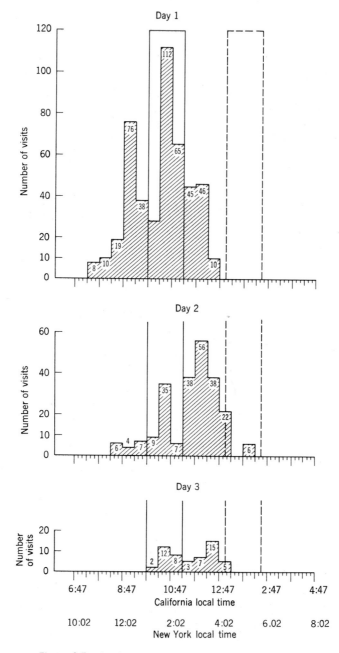

Figure 2-5 Another bee translocation experiment, this time with exposure to the natural sky after overnight translocation west across the United States. The solid rectangle is the training time in New York, the dotted rectangle the equivalent time in California. The shaded histogram is the number of visits made to automatic recorders in subsequent days following displacement to California. After Renner 1959.

to a field near Davis, California. The following morning they began visiting the empty feeders about 24 hours after the training time at New York. Their arrival times were already shifted slightly in the direction of local time, however. On the two subsequent days the bees still making unrewarded visits to the empty feeders in dwindling numbers came later and later, strongly suggesting that the rhythm was resetting to local conditions (Figure 2–5). Such translocation experiments demonstrate both the existence of an endogenous element and the gradual resetting of circadian rhythms when they are placed out of phase with the cycle of day and night.

◆ *Stopping the Clock.* It is customary to speak of circadian rhythms as implying the existence of a kind of biological clock. Another way to test the effect of external stimuli on circadian rhythms is to 'stop the clock' in some way and start it again later, thus changing its relationship with the local solar cycle. If we find that the clock continues to run after resetting and remains out of phase by the same amount, we shall have acquired additional evidence for a degree of independence of the clock from external eliciting stimuli. Cooling is one possible method. Temperature independence is a prerequisite for a good clock, and we shall see that the clock is unaffected over a wide range of temperatures. But cooling to near freezing can sometimes stop the clock, apparently. Renner (1957) did this, again with time-trained honeybees. After 5 hours of chilling the bees came to the food dish 5 hours late (Figure 2–6), suggesting that they were not relying upon external timing cues. But Renner (1960) points out that the result may be ambiguous, for the chilling may also have hindered the bees' perception of external stimuli that time the rhythm. If the clock could also be speeded up the result would be less equivocal, but this has yet to be done.

◆ *Deviation of the Clock from 24 Hours.* The period length of activity cycles performed under constant conditions is rarely exactly 24 hours (Aschoff 1960). Instead there is usually a slight but consistent deviation (Figures 2–3a, 2–7). If a 24-hour cycle of light and dark is superimposed the activity cycle synchronizes with it, but when the rhythmical stimulation of light and dark is removed, the original 'free-running' period is resumed (Rawson 1959, Fig. 2–7). Deviation of free-running period lengths from 24 hours is additional evidence for independence of the persistent rhythm from external triggering stimuli, as are the occasional spontaneous changes in the period of the cycle (Figure 2–8).

The cycles observed under constant conditions are often remarkably regular. Such constancy implies the existence of a very accurate clock.

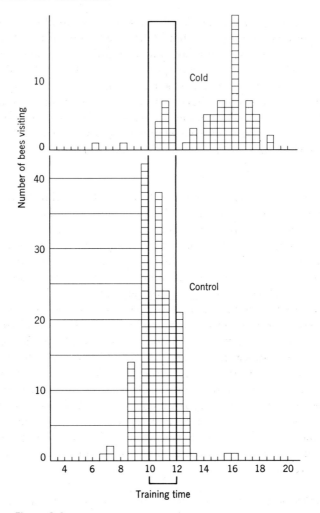

Figure 2-6   Bees time-trained to a honey reward, then chilled to about 5°C for 5 hours, arrived at the reward approximately 5 hours later than the controls. After Renner 1950.

In continuous darkness flying squirrels show a circadian activity rhythm which for many days may deviate only ±2 minutes from its mean value (DeCoursey 1961, Figure 2–3*a*). Consistent deviation from a 24-hour rhythm seems to imply an independence of circadian rhythms from the solar cycle.

◆ *Inheritance of Circadian Rhythms.* Several kinds of animals raised under constant conditions, in some instances for several generations, show a

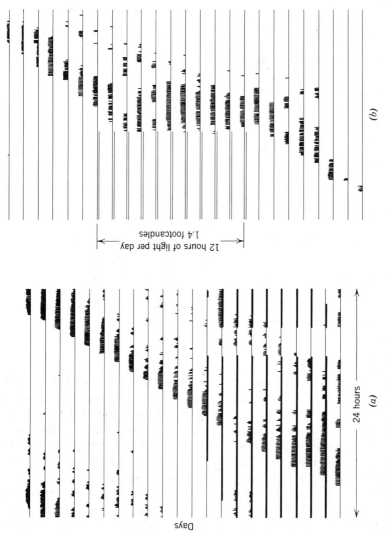

Figure 2-7 The activity rhythm of a deer mouse, *Peromyscus*, in constant darkness drifts continuously (*a*). When the animal is exposed to 12 hours of light per day (*b*) the activity becomes synchronized with the imposed light cycle. But when constant darkness is again imposed the cycle begins to drift once more. After Rawson 1959.

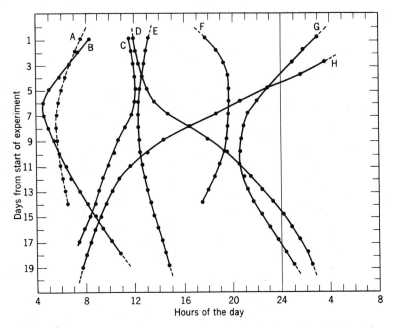

Figure 2-8   Eight experiments with lizards showing the time of maximal activity under various sets of constant conditions. Changes in period length of the cycles occurred without any change in the external conditions. The constant conditions were, A and B, 35°C and 60 lux; C, 16°C and 60 lux; D and F, 25°C and 5.5 lux; E, 25°C and 60 lux; G and H, 25°C and 42 lux. After Hoffmann 1960.

circadian rhythm at some stage in their life cycle. Domestic chicks, hatched in an incubator with constant light and temperature, showed a circadian activity cycle when they hatched (Aschoff and Meyer-Lohmann 1954b, Figure 2–9a). Similarly, lizards hatched from eggs incubated under constant conditions showed a clear circadian activity rhythm (Hoffmann 1957, Figure 2–3b). The impression of endogeneity is reinforced by Hoffmann's (1959) studies of lizards. Lizard eggs were kept on 18-hour (9 light, 9 dark) and 36-hour (18 light, 18 dark) days with corresponding temperature cycles. When the lizards were transferred to constant light and temperature the various treatments were found to have had no effect on subsequent activity cycles (Figure 2–9b). There were marked and consistent differences in the lengths of activity rhythm periods of different members of the same group. This variation is inconsistent with the idea of timing by uncontrolled cyclic external stimuli.

When a group of experimental animals remains in close synchrony, the case against influence by rhythmical external stimuli is less clear.

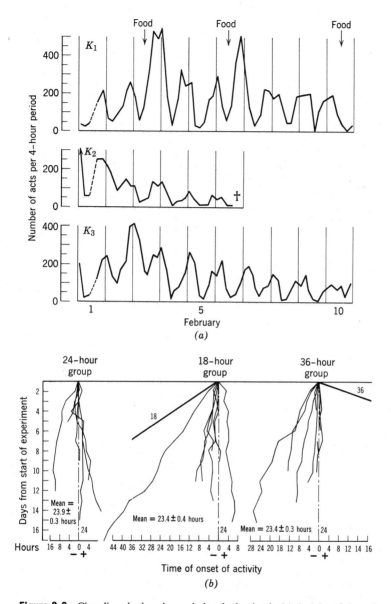

Figure 2-9 Circadian rhythms in newly hatched animals. (*a*) Activity of three domestic chicks hatched under constant conditions. (*b*) Graphs of the time of maximal activity in newly hatched lizards on consecutive days, kept under constant conditions. The lizards were hatched from eggs kept under day-night cycles of three types—a 24-hour day, with 12 hours of light and 12 hours of dark, an 18-hour day, with 9 hours of light and 9 hours of dark, and a 36-hour day, with 18 hours of light and 18 hours of dark. These prior treatments had no effect on the period length of activity occurring after hatching, under constant conditions. After Aschoff and Meyer-Lohmann 1954b, Hoffmann 1959.

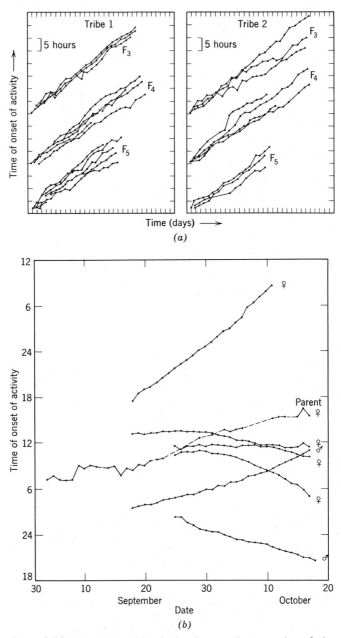

Figure 2-10 Circadian activity rhythms in successive generations of mice. (*a*) Two inbred lines of house mice, *Mus*, tested through the fourth, fifth, and sixth generations, show a consistent period length of activity under constant conditions (100 lux). (*b*) Times of onset of activity in constant darkness of a female *Peromyscus* and her litter of six young, all caged separately. There are consistent individual differences in the period of the activity cycle. After Aschoff 1960, Rawson 1959.

This was the situation in one study of house mice, in which a rather regular circadian activity rhythm was maintained through several generations (Aschoff 1960). On the other hand, an analysis of activity in two generations of deer mice revealed wide divergence in individual cycles under similar constant conditions (Rawson 1959, Figure 2–10*a*, *b*).

These studies suggest heritable variability in circadian rhythms, but the genetic mechanism involved remains to be worked out. No studies have been made of the activity of animals born to parents with different circadian rhythms. Only breeding experiments of this type can lead to definite statements about the contributions of inheritance to behavior.

◆ *Conclusions on the Independence of Circadian Rhythms from Cyclic External Stimuli.* The question of endogeneity of circadian rhythms is a controversial issue (see Aschoff 1960, 1963, Brown 1960, Pittendrigh 1960). Disagreements arise partly because of experimental difficulties and partly because complete proof of endogeneity is impossible to come by (Brown 1960). Translocation experiments suggest that some circadian rhythms can persist for several cycles out of phase with local time and with local phasic stimuli related to the solar cycle. Unfortunately, few such experiments have been conducted. Retarding of the general metabolic cycle by chilling puts the animal out of phase with local cues. The fact that the circadian cycle persists under these conditions even though it is out of phase hints once more at endogeneity. But as mentioned, interference with receptor processes could have a similar effect, confusing the interpretation of these experiments. The drifting of the rhythm away from the 24-hour cycle of the earth's rotation under constant conditions seems strong evidence for endogeneity. Individual variation in circadian rhythms under similar conditions also indicates the existence of an endogenous component.

EFFECTS OF TEMPERATURE AND LIGHT INTENSITY
UPON CIRCADIAN RHYTHMS

Even if animals can be experimentally isolated from rhythmical eliciting stimuli, they are exposed to other external influences imposed by the constant conditions of the experiment. What effects do these sustained stimuli have on activity rhythms?

Effects on the amplitude of rhythms can occur, either positive or negative (Harker 1958). The circadian rhythm of expansion and contraction of a sea anemone under constant conditions disappears if the lighting is too bright and reappears if the light is dimmed (Batham and Pantin 1950). The rhythm vanishes because the anemone remains contracted for long periods. If flies emerge from the pupae into continuous darkness, they are active in a circadian rhythm. Hatched into continuous light, their activity is arhythmic (Green 1964, Figure 2–11). Bright light also inhibits the circadian rhythm of deer mice; activity is scattered throughout the record, and its periodic property almost disappears (Johnson 1939, Figure 2–11). The rhythm of phototactic sensitivity of *Euglena* ceases in continuous light (Bruce and Pittendrigh 1956). In general, continuous light appears to inhibit the circadian rhythms of nocturnal animals. It facilitates those of diurnal animals, though very bright light can have an inhibiting effect here as well. Warming facilitates the expression of the circadian cycles of poikilotherms, and cooling inhibits them (e.g. lizards, Hoffmann 1957).

Light intensity and temperature also influence the periodic properties of circadian cycles. The period length of the activity cycles of deer mice increases with an increase in the intensity of the continuous lighting (Johnson 1939, Figure 2–12). A striking difference is seen when Johnson's study is compared with a similar experiment on lizards (Hoffmann 1960, Figure 2–12). The period of the activity cycle of deer mice increases in brighter light; that of the lizards decreases. Sufficient data are available to suggest what has become known as Aschoff's rule. Diurnal animals such as most birds react to increasing light intensity in the same way as

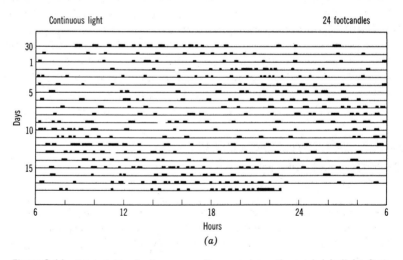

Figure 2-11   (*a*) Activity of a deer mouse, *Peromyscus,* in continuous bright light. Compare with Figure 2-3*a*. After Johnson 1939. (*b*) Activity of flies, *Phormia regina,* from time of emergence from pupae to time of death by starvation, under conditions of constant light and constant darkness. Activity is aperiodic in light. After Green 1964.

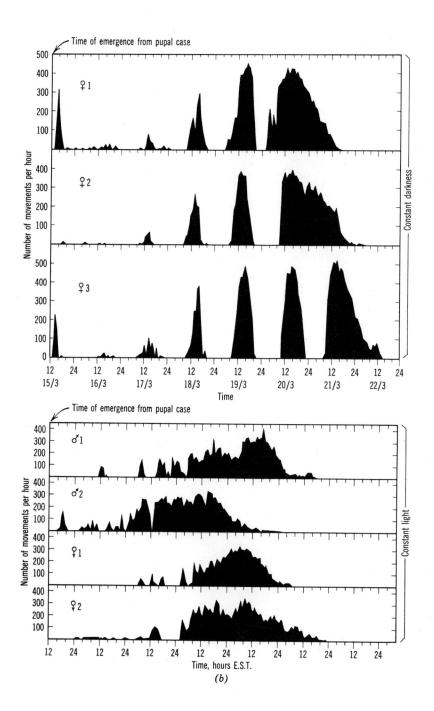

(b)

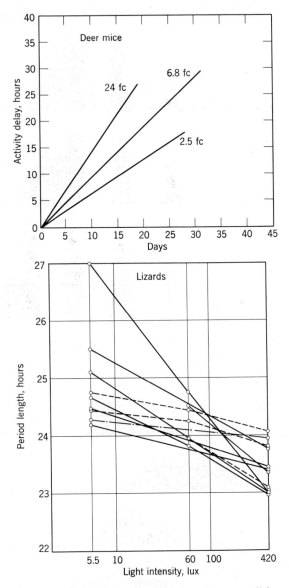

Figure 2-12 When a deer mouse is kept in constant light and the light intensity is increased, the period of the circadian rhythm lengthens. After Johnson 1939. A lizard shortens the period length of its circadian rhythm with increasing light intensity. After Hoffmann 1960.

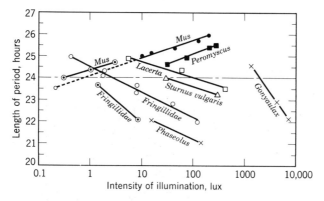

Figure 2-13   Period length of circadian rhythms as a function of light intensity. Cycles of locomotion, leaf movement (*Phaseolus*), and luminescence (*Gonyaulax*) are represented. After Aschoff 1960.

lizards, with a decreased period length. In contrast, flying squirrels and house mice which, like deer mice, are nocturnal show an increased period length in brighter light (Aschoff 1960, Hoffmann 1960, 1965, DeCoursey 1961, Figure 2–13).

Lighting conditions may have a variable effect on individual animals. This is certainly one interpretation of the individual rhythms which characterize a group of animals exposed to the same constant conditions.

The effect of temperature upon circadian cycles under constant conditions has been studied intensively for a good reason. Early workers (Bünning 1931, Wahl 1932, Kalmus 1934) found the period length to have a remarkable degree of independence from temperature under steady conditions (Figure 2–14). Since the rate of many physiological processes increases appreciably with rising temperature, the limited temperature dependence of circadian rhythms is of special interest. Studies of fiddler crabs (e.g. Brown and Webb 1948), fruit flies (Pittendrigh 1954), lizards (Hoffmann 1957), and many other species (Sweeney and Hastings 1960) have consistently revealed small but distinct shifts in period length within certain ranges of temperature change. Even homeotherms, which might be expected to lack such temperature compensation, show the same slight effect when they adopt a poikilothermous condition (e.g. hibernating deer mice and bats, Rawson 1960).

The relative temperature independence of circadian rhythms is presumably significant under natural conditions. If circadian rhythms serve primarily to concentrate appropriate behavior at certain times of day, change with temperature would hinder accurate timing. Although con-

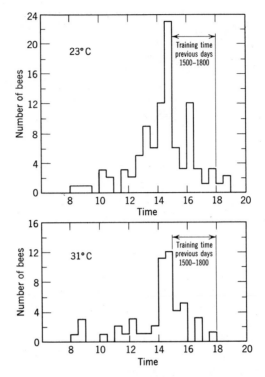

Figure 2-14   Bees trained to come to feeders at a particular time return at the same time on subsequent days within a wide range of ambient temperatures. The arrival of the majority before the training time is typical behavior of time-trained bees. After Wahl 1932.

stant temperatures cause little change in period length, a regular cycle of temperature change is quite effective in synchronizing some circadian rhythms (Roberts 1960, Aschoff 1963).

Temperature and light may also have interacting effects, even in a homeotherm. Enright (in press) finds that the extent to which low temperatures retard the free-running activity rhythm of the house finch depends on the intensity of the constant light.

In conclusion, light and temperature under constant conditions have general inhibitory or facilitating effects on the amplitude of circadian rhythms, and they can have definite effects on period length. With light the sign of the change depends on whether the animal is diurnal or nocturnal. What happens if these same stimuli are presented in a cyclic manner rather than as a steady state?

CYCLIC EXTERNAL STIMULI AND CIRCADIAN RHYTHMS:
THE PROBLEM OF ENTRAINMENT

Under constant experimental conditions circadian rhythms do not have periods of exactly 24 hours. Usually the period length is consistently longer or shorter so that an animal originally active at night eventually becomes active during the earth's day. When an animal which has drifted out of phase with the earth's day is exposed once more to a rhythm of night and day, it rapidly becomes synchronized again. Its activity cycle becomes locked to the cycle of external conditions and maintains an accurate 24-hour periodicity. The circadian rhythm thus becomes 'entrained' to the 24-hour day.

There are several questions to be asked about this process of entrainment. What are the effective stimuli? If entrainment to a 24-hour cycle is possible, what about an 18- or 36-hour cycle? Does entrainment take place in one jump or a series of changes? If the latter, is the degree of change related to the phase relationship between the new stimulus conditions and the original circadian cycle—in other words is there a changing cycle of responsiveness during the existing rhythm?

"Entrainment of circadian rhythms is defined as the phenomenon whereby a periodic repetition of light and dark (a light cycle) or a periodic temperature cycle, or, more rarely, a periodically repeated stimulus of some other type causes an overt persistent rhythm to become periodic with the same period as the entraining cycle" (Bruce 1960). This definition assumes the dominant role of light and temperature as entraining stimuli in experimental situations. Homeotherms appear to be particularly responsive to 24-hour cycles of light and dark. Poikilotherms such as lizards and insects respond to a cycle of temperature change as well as to light (Harker 1964). Activity of the beach isopod, *Excirolana chiltoni,* seems to become entrained to the rhythm of the tides as a result of mechanical stimulation by waves on the shore (Enright 1965a).

What happens if we attempt to entrain the rhythm to a period other than 24 hours? It rarely seems possible to entrain animals to day lengths shorter than about 16 hours (Harker 1964). The most thorough study of this question comes from the work of Tribukait (1956) who subjected domestic mice to light-dark cycles ranging from a 16-hour day to a 29-hour day, with half of each day dark, the other half light. He found that the mice could be entrained to day lengths of from 21 to 27 hours. Activity rhythms failed to synchronize with days longer or shorter than this. Instead the mice reverted to an approximately 24-hour cycle (Figure 2–15). The imposed regime, however, was not totally without effect during these

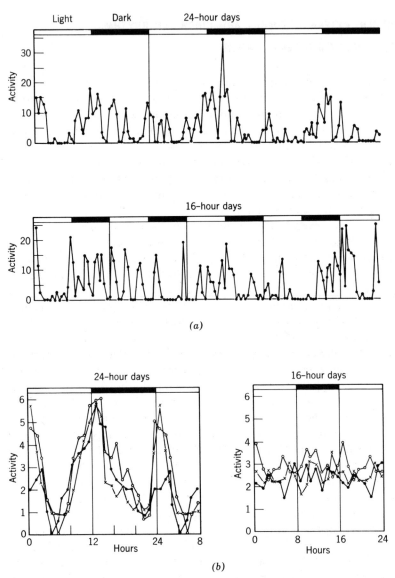

Figure 2-15   The activity of a mouse, *Mus musculus,* is recorded (*a*) on a 24-hour day with 12 hours of light and 12 hours of darkness and for a 16-hour day with equal light and dark periods. When these records are superimposed (*b*) it is clear that there is a rhythm with the 24-hour cycle but that it is lost on the 16-hour schedule.

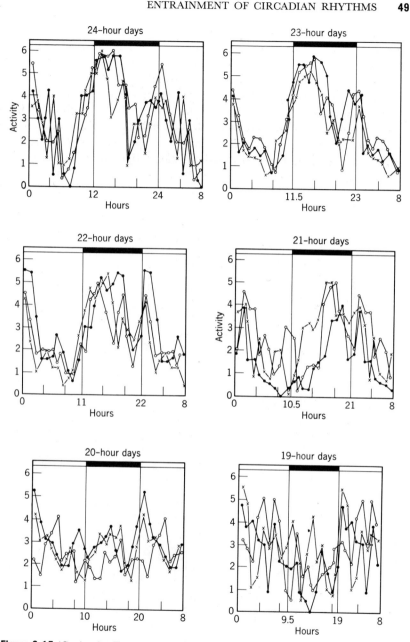

Figure 2-15 (*Continued*)   Tested with cycles of gradually decreasing length (*c*) synchrony of the activity rhythm breaks down around 21 hours. After Tribukait 1956.

very long and very short days. What was normally one rhythm of activity broke into two. The evening activity peak tended to follow the endogenous 24-hour rhythm, while the morning peak followed the timing imposed by the artificial conditions. Evidently the overall activity rhythm cannot be entrained by a simple on-off lighting schedule if rhythms deviate from 24 hours by more than a certain amount (Figure 2–23b). Similar results have been obtained with hamsters (Bruce 1960).

In contrast, Kavanau (1962a, b) has entrained activity, feeding and drinking cycles of deer mice to a 16-hour day (8 light, 8 dark), using artificial twilight transitions rather than simple on-off light control (Figure

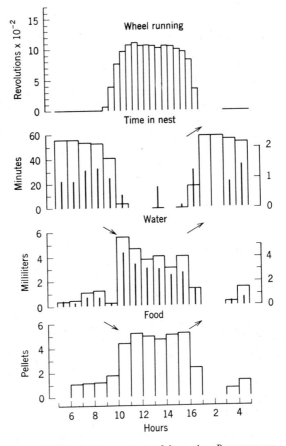

Figure 2-16   Activity patterns of deer mice, *Peromyscus,* on a 16-hour artificial day. Artificial twilight transitions are indicated by the slanting arrows. After Kavanau 1962a.

2–16). More systematic analyses of activity cycles of the same species under different day-night regimes are needed, both with and without simulated twilight.

When an animal is provided with a 24-hour day composed of a series of light-dark cycles, it will often maintain a 24-hour rhythm by responding only to certain cycles. A hamster exposed to a 6-hour day, consisting of 2 hours of light and 4 of dark, extracts a 24-hour rhythm by responding only to every fourth cycle. With a 4-hour day it responds only to every sixth cycle, and so on. Deer mice and cockroaches behave similarly (Bruce 1960). This phenomenon, called 'frequency demultiplication,' demonstrates again the predisposition to respond to stimulus cycles with a period length of about 24 hours.

If the problem is approached in a different way by trying to train an animal to perform some activity at a particular time of day, essentially the same result is obtained. "Even after weeks of training it was not possible to induce bees to look for food, say, every 19 or 48 hours," but they will readily come every 24 hours (Renner 1960).

These unsuccessful attempts to entrain circadian rhythms suggest a mechanism that restricts entrainment to cycles which approximate 24 hours. Within limits entrainment is clear and accurate. Beyond them it is difficult or impossible. An apparently endogenous component in circadian rhythms contributes to normal behavior by restricting responsiveness to rhythmical external stimuli with certain characteristics.

◆ *Sensitivity to Resetting.* Suppose that an animal is exposed to a 24-hour cycle of light and dark which is appreciably out of phase with its activity cycle. Observation of its subsequent behavior shows that the process of resetting is not sudden. Instead the cycle goes through a series of daily phase shifts which eventually bring it into line with the pattern of rhythmical stimulation. When synchrony with the external cycle is achieved, phase shifts end (Figure 2–17).

The extent and direction of the phase shifts are found to vary with the phase of stimulation in the existing cycle. The clearest demonstrations of this resetting process have exploited the fact that in nocturnal rodents a single brief stimulus of light in otherwise continuous darkness causes a phase shift in the next cycle of activity. The most elegant study of this type is by DeCoursey (1960, 1961). She interrupted the continuous darkness of flying squirrels with 10-minute periods of light. The daily cycle of responsiveness was clearly related to the rhythm of locomotor activity (Figure 2–17). The greatest delay of the next cycle occurred if the light stimulus was presented close to the time of onset of running. The delaying effect declined gradually as the stimulus was presented later in the activity

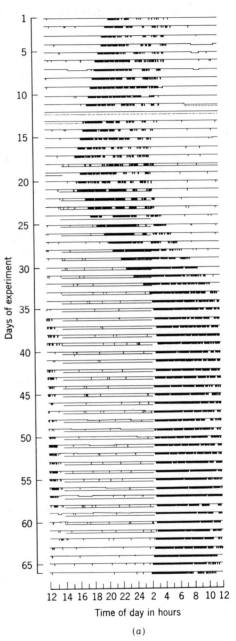

Figure 2-17 (*a*) The activity cycle of a flying squirrel, *Glaucomys,* drifts in constant darkness (days 1 to 17). When an artificial daylight schedule (double line, days 21 to 61) is imposed, the activity rhythm gradually comes into phase with it. When continuous darkness is resumed, the cycle again begins to drift. (*b*) A light shock (dark arrow) 3¾ hours before the expected onset of activity (*i*) has no effect on subsequent cycles. A light shock one hour after the onset of activity (*ii*) causes subsequent cycles to start later, and a light shock 9 hours after the onset of activity (*iii*) induces a shift to an earlier start of subsequent activity cycles. After DeCoursey 1961.

Days of experiment

Time of day in hours

12 14 16 18 20 22 24 2 4 6 8 10 12

(*a*)

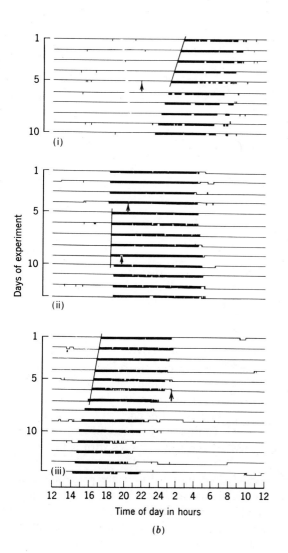

(i)

(ii)

Days of experiment

(iii)

12 14 16 18 20 22 24   2   4   6   8 10 12
Time of day in hours

(b)

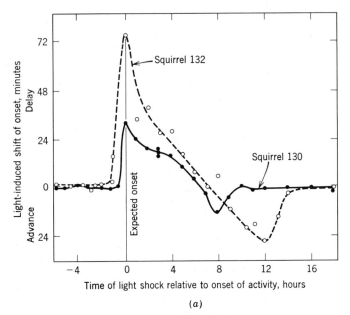

Figure 2-18   (*a*) The daily rhythm of resetting by 10-minute light exposures in the flying squirrel, *Glaucomys*. After DeCoursey 1961. (*b*) Diagrammatic resetting curves for locomotor activity cycles of a hamster and a cockroach, and for the luminescent activity of *Gonyaulax*. After Harker 1964, DeCoursey 1964.

cycle, until several hours after the onset of activity. Beyond this point light stimuli caused an advance of the cycle instead of a delay. Light stimuli had no effect throughout the inactive part of the cycle, until an hour or two before the expected onset of running (DeCoursey 1961).

A graph (Figure 2–18) reveals the rhythm of changing responsiveness in the course of the activity cycle. Comparable studies of responsiveness to brief light exposures in other species reveal curves with a rather different shape.

Maximal phase shifts occur when light stimuli are presented near the time of onset of activity, which in nature is at dusk for a flying squirrel. There is reason to consider sunset the most critical stimulus in setting rhythms of activities for other nocturnal animals. In diurnal animals dawn is more significant (DeCoursey 1961). The effects of a more prolonged light period are likely to be more complicated. The extent of resetting may be a compromise between different effects at onset and cessation of the light period.

Brown (1959, 1960) has pointed out the possibility that an animal exposed to constant light may be constantly resetting. If the magnitude of

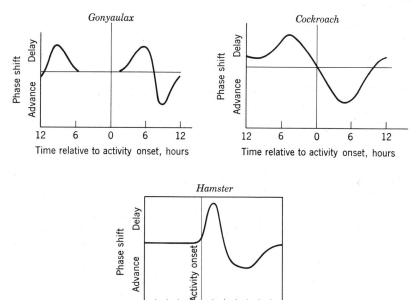

(b)

the response to light at the onset of activity differs from that at the end
of the cycle, the overall rhythm will show a consistent drift from day to
day. In flying squirrels the delaying effect at the start of the cycle is greater
than the advancing effect at the end of the cycle. Thus constant light
might result in repeated delays in the onset of activity, lengthening the
period of the activity cycle. Moreover, the delaying effect of a light stimulus increases with greater light intensities. This could explain the increase in the period of the cycle with brighter light, which is apparently
general in nocturnal animals (see page 45). It remains to be shown
whether the converse effect of constant light in diurnal animals is associated with dominance of the advancing effect over the delay.

So the deviation of a circadian rhythm from 24 hours under constant
conditions becomes subject to a new interpretation. An endogenous
rhythm of motor activity, whatever its period, may be subject to continual
resetting by the constant external conditions. Resetting alone cannot
explain all deviation from 24 hours in circadian rhythms. Thus Pittendrigh (1960) found that hamsters kept on a 23-hour day and then placed
under constant conditions had a shorter free-running rhythm than siblings kept on a 25-hour day and then similarly treated. Harker (1964)
was able to modify the period length of the free-running activity cycle

in cockroaches by prior light treatments. The persistence of such changes under constant conditions cannot readily be related to resetting, unless the prior treatment modifies the resetting mechanism in some durable fashion. Probably there are two kinds of endogenous components, one motor and the other sensory (Aschoff 1960, DeCoursey 1961). Further critical experiments along the lines of DeCoursey's work are needed for an appreciation of the relative contributions of these two types of endogeneity.

THE INTERNAL STRUCTURE OF CIRCADIAN ACTIVITY RHYTHMS

The manner in which circadian activity rhythms are often presented (e.g. Figure 2–1) gives only a gross picture of the actual pattern of activity in time because of the summation of data over long intervals. Presentation on a finer and finer time scale gives a quite different picture (Aschoff 1957, Figure 2–19). There are actually many short bouts of activity in the course of a day. The interval between these bouts varies somewhat. For example, in mice they may last 106 minutes in the nocturnal phase and 170 minutes in the diurnal phase (Aschoff and Meyer-Lohmann 1954a).

The circadian cycle results from variation in the intervals between bouts, which are shortest around dusk and dawn and longest in the middle of the day. There is in fact another minor cycle much shorter in length imposed on the major one of 24 hours. In rodents, for example, it varies between about 1.5 and 4 hours. There may even be a second rhythm imposed on the first, as indicated in Figure 2–19, where (*a*) suggests a 2-hour periodicity, and (*c*) a periodicity of 4 hours. It is the summation of these subcycles which gives the characteristic bimodal shape to the daily activity curve of mice as it is usually presented (Figure 2–19*d*). For this reason the short-term patterning of locomotion, feeding, and other activities is worthy of closer attention from students of circadian rhythms (see pages 117, 146).

◆ *Species Differences in Circadian Activity.* The average period of short-term cycles of activity varies from species to species. In shrews, Crowcroft (1953) has pointed out a correlation with body size. A comparison of daily activity in the large water shrew, the medium-sized common shrew, and the tiny pygmy shrew shows that there are shorter and more frequent bouts of activity in the smaller animals. In these shrews activity seems to be distributed evenly throughout the day. But if the data are plotted with longer time increments, the same type of bimodal activity curve

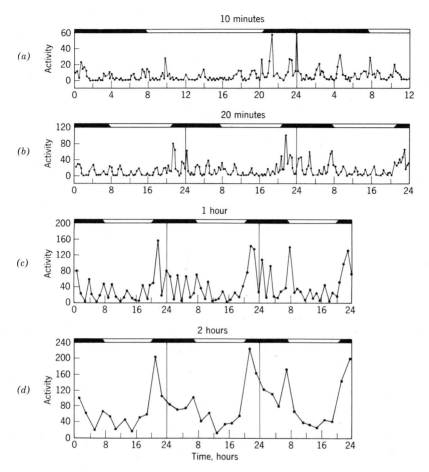

Figure 2-19   The same activity of a mouse is plotted in increments varying from 10 minutes to 2 hours. After Aschoff 1957.

which occurs in mice emerges. Interestingly enough, the pygmy shrew spends more of its total time resting than the common shrew, in spite of the greater frequency of activity bouts.

Variations of this kind lead to species-specific patterns of circadian activity. Different species of rodents may have strikingly distinct patterns (Aschoff and Honma 1959, Figure 2–20). There are insufficient data available even to guess at the ecological significance of these differences. Although members of the same species generally conform to the same overall pattern of activity, significant individual differences

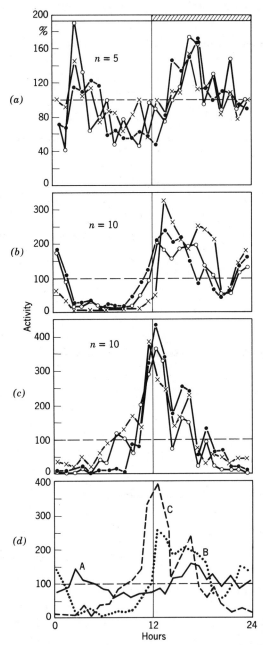

Figure 2-20 The superimposed activity of various animals (*a*) during five days for the shrew, *Sorex araneus*, (*b*) ten days for the mouse, *Mus musculus*, and (*c*) ten days for the hamster, *Mesocricetus auratus*. Each record is a summary for three individuals. (*d*) These performances show species differences when summed. The individual difference between the actions (*e*) of two mice, *Mus musculus*, and (*f*) two chaffinches, *Fringilla coelebs*. After Aschoff and Honma 1959.

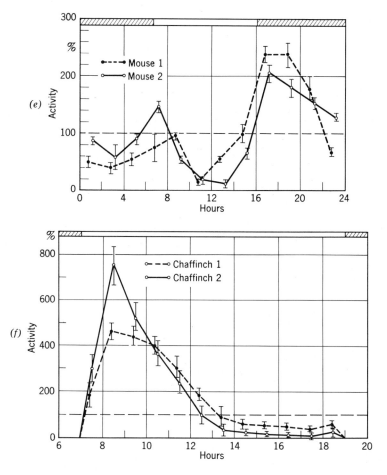

may appear (Figure 2–20). To explain the survival value of these variations and the mechanisms which underlie them, is still another problem.

◆ *Seasonal Variations.* Sometimes there are seasonal changes in the pattern of activity through the day (Eibl-Eibesfeldt 1958). Of the four shown in Figure 2–21, the winter circadian rhythms of a mouse, *Apodemus sylvaticus,* and the dormouse, *Glis glis,* are lower in amplitude but essentially similar in form to those seen in summer. The mice, *Clethrionomys glareolus* and *Microtus arvalis,* become largely diurnal in winter (Ostermann 1955).

The role of internal and external factors in causing these individual, specific, and seasonal differences in circadian rhythms is virtually unexplored. The significance of internal factors is revealed by experiments in

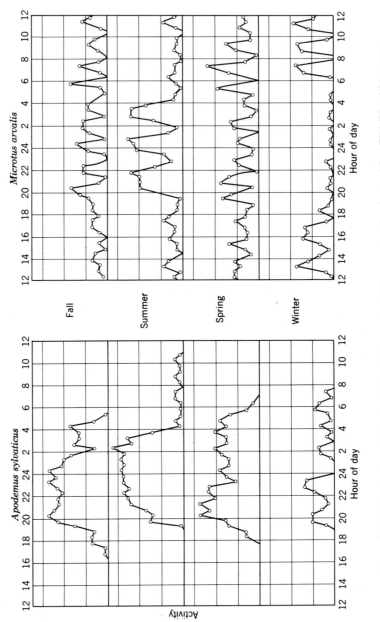

Figure 2-21   Seasonal variation in daily activity cycles of four species of rodents.   After Eibl-Eibesfeldt 1958.

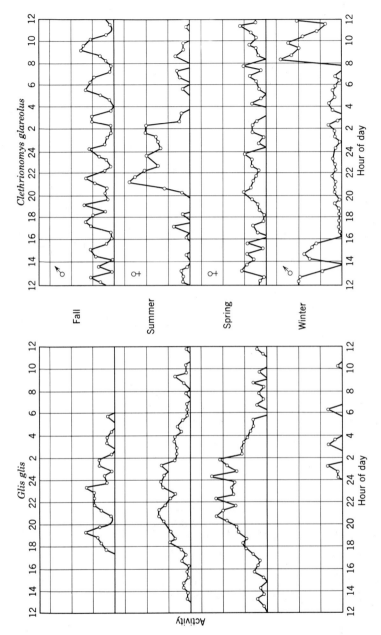

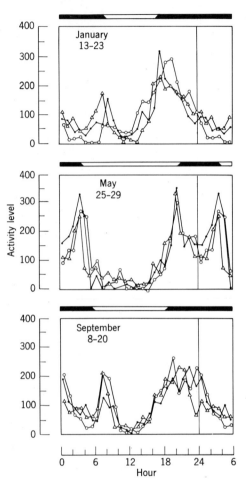

Figure 2-22 Activity of three mice at different seasons. The black and white bars at the top of each diagram indicate the approximate times of daylight and darkness. After Aschoff 1958.

which the long nights and short days of winter have been simulated to compare their effects with those of shorter nights and longer days (Aschoff 1958, 1960). Mice are active for longer periods of time on winter nights than on summer nights. But in winter, activity starts later in relation to 'sunset' and ceases earlier in relation to 'sunrise' than in summer (Figure 2–22), suggesting that the pattern throughout the year is to some degree independent of the external stimuli of sunrise and sunset. There is similar seasonal variation of the time of rising of birds (Dunnet and Hinde 1953). Nevertheless, effects of changes in the ratio of the periods of light and dark upon activity should not be underestimated. There is also evidence that the intensity of the light under both constant and alternating conditions may have profound effects upon the intensity of activity and upon the ratio of activity to resting (Aschoff 1960). We are still far from any complete explanation of the mechanisms underlying seasonal variations of activity rhythms, however. Nor can we explain the differences between individuals and species and the variations taking place during individual development (Aschoff and Honma 1959).

◆ *Mechanisms Underlying Circadian Rhythms.* There is little evidence on the physiological identity of mechanisms controlling circadian rhythms. Nevertheless, there is general consensus about the kind of thing to look for. Many investigators agree that at least two systems which behave differently in some degree must be involved. One is more strictly endogenous, and the other is more responsive to external stimuli. The overall behavior of the animal is a result of interaction between the two.

Brown and his associates (see Brown 1959) were led to this conclusion from their studies of color change in fiddler crabs. Work on the timing of emergence of the adult fruit flies from the pupae led to a similar hypothesis (Pittendrigh 1960). If a culture of *Drosophila* eggs was raised in the dark, the adults finally emerged asynchronously. If a light was presented briefly, subsequent emergence became synchronized. It took place at some multiple of 24 hours after light onset, which would have been dawn, the time of emergence in nature. This periodicity in the behavior of a population, involving a single event in the life of each individual, has many of the properties of a circadian rhythm and has been explored extensively from this point of view by Pittendrigh and his colleagues (Pittendrigh 1954, 1958, 1960, Pittendrigh, Bruce and Kaus 1958, etc.). That temperature changes can lead to a temporary resetting of the time of emergence, only to be overridden by the original cycle in the pupae that are still several days from emergence, again suggests that at least two systems are involved.

The experiments of Tribukait (1956) on the effects of very long and very short days on the activity of mice imply more than one system. The evening activity peak maintains a cycle of roughly 24 hours which is presumably endogenous, whereas the morning peak keeps time with the artificial cycle (Figure 2–23*b*). Here two systems are operating on the behavior of the same animal at different times.

In a general discussion of this problem, Pittendrigh (1960) concludes that we must "abandon the common current view that our problem is to isolate and analyze *the* endogenous rhythm, or *the* internal clock." In-

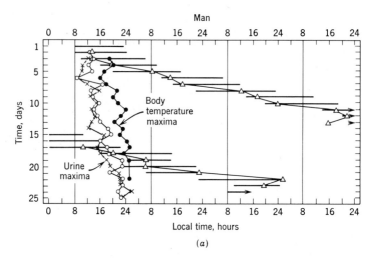

Figure 2-23 (*a*) Desynchronization of circadian rhythms in a man living in isolation without time cues. Black bars, times of wakefulness; open triangles, maxima of calcium excreted in urine; open circles and crosses, maxima of water and potassium excreted in urine; closed circles, maxima of body temperature. After Aschoff 1965. (*b*) Graphs of the time of morning and evening activity peaks in mice kept on different day lengths. As the day length deviates from 24 hours the evening peak tends to veer toward a 24-hour periodicity while the morning peak remains synchronized with the artificial light cycle. The figures denote mean period lengths for some of the cycles. After Tribukait 1956.

stead we are faced with the conclusion that "the organism comprises a population of quasi-autonomous oscillatory systems."

There are circadian rhythms of human activity under constant conditions (Kleitman 1963). Studies of circadian rhythms in human physiology suggest a multiplicity of mechanisms. Thus, for a man placed under constant conditions, the periodicities of maximal body temperature and production of water, calcium, and potassium in the urine are not necessarily the same as those of waking and sleeping (Aschoff 1965, Figure 2-23*a*). Richter (1965) has reviewed physiological cycles, ranging from minutes to hundreds of days in length, in both normal and diseased human patients. Evidently many cycles can run simultaneously.

PHYSIOLOGICAL CONTROL OF CIRCADIAN RHYTHMS IN COCKROACHES

Cockroaches show a diurnal cycle of activity which continues with an approximate 24-hour periodicity under constant light and temperature,

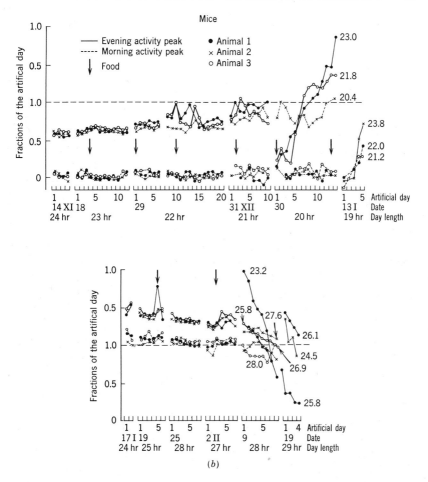

the exact period length depending on the conditions (Harker 1956, Roberts 1960). Harker's investigations of the physiological factors underlying this behavioral rhythm stemmed from a remarkable discovery. When the suboesophageal ganglion of a cockroach with a certain circadian rhythm is transplanted into another individual which is arhythmic, the arhythmic cockroach takes up the rhythm of the donor (Harker 1956, 1960a, b, c). The suboesophageal ganglion thus maintains a circadian rhythm of activity independent of any neural connections for several cycles. The group of neurosecretory cells in the ganglion responsible for the activity cycles has been located. These cells receive material from neurosecretory bodies, the corpora cardiaca, by way of a small nerve.

If this nerve is cut the circadian cycle breaks down, even in a normal light-dark cycle.

The phase of cyclic secretory activity in cockroaches is normally set by the alternation of light and dark. According to Harker, this light change is perceived not by the compound eyes but by the simple eyes or ocelli. These ocelli have direct nervous connections to the suboesophageal ganglia, which clearly carry the main responsibility for control of the circadian rhythm. Secretion normally begins at the onset of darkness and activity starts two to four hours later. However, study of resetting by external stimuli reveals that a second system is also involved.

If cockroaches are kept in 12 hours of light and 12 of darkness for several days, resetting can be demonstrated by changing the time of onset of darkness. Immediately after the first sunset at the new time, the suboesophageal ganglion is removed and implanted into an arhythmic animal which is kept in constant darkness. In this way the effects of darkness on the secretory cycle can be compared at different phases of the cycle. There is a definite rhythm of responsiveness. Secretion normally occurs for about 2 hours after sunset. If the new onset of darkness falls in this period there is no resetting. However, if it falls within about 2 hours before or after the secretory period, the periods of 'possible secretion,' the cycle is reset. The next cycle of activity in the implanted animal then begins about 24 hours after the new onset of darkness. At any other time during the period of 'impossible secretion,' the onset of darkness has no effect on the secretory rhythm. These relationships are summarized in Figure 2–24a.

If the same experiment is done without removal of the ganglia, to observe resetting in the intact animal, there is a striking difference. Onset of darkness in what Harker called the period of impossible secretion now causes resetting. This outcome suggests the existence of a second mechanism, also responsive to light-dark changes, that can influence the neurosecretory cycle of the suboesophageal ganglion. Harker was able to confirm the existence of this second system by localized chilling of the ganglion *in situ*. The circadian cycle of cockroaches, as of other insects, can be retarded by chilling at a temperature just above zero (see page 35). If the whole animal is chilled, all systems should be affected. But by chilling the ganglion alone Harker was able to place its cycle of activity out of phase with whatever other systems the animal might possess. When the chilled ganglion was left in position, the activity cycle was delayed after periods of chilling ranging from 5 to 17 hours. There was no delay after chilling durations of up to 4 to 5 hours. Thus if the secretory cycle is strongly out of phase with the unchanged second system, it cannot be reset; but if it is only slightly out of phase, with the second

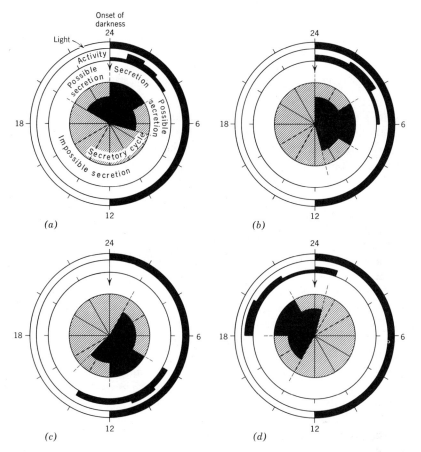

Figure 2-24   Locomotor activity and the neurosecretory cycle of the cockroach (*a*) under artificial lighting of a 24-hour light-dark cycle, (*b*) with chilling of the suboesophageal ganglion for 4 hours, (*c*) 8 hours, and (*d*) 18 hours. After Harker 1960c.

system indicating onset of secretory activity at a time still within the period of possible secretion, the secretory cycle is reset to its original phase relationship (Figure 2–24*b-d*). Complete resetting of the second system by light can be shown by combining chilling and light-dark experiments. The onset of darkness is simulated by covering the ocelli with paint. In this way the phase relationships can be adjusted so that 4 hours of chilling of the ganglion delay the cycle by 4 hours. This is possible because the second system, modified by the light-dark manipulation, now indicates onset of secretory activity at a time of impossible secretion.

Harker (1960c) concluded that there are at least two cycles which are light sensitive and which can influence each other. "One of these cycles, referred to as the secondary cycle, can be immediately reset at any time of day by the onset of darkness, whereas the other, the neurosecretory cycle, can be reset only when the stimulus occurs at a time fairly close to that when activity would normally occur." The usefulness of these two interacting systems to an animal living in normal field conditions seems to be that they allow for the gradual shift in the timing of the active peak with the change in day length but prevent the resetting of phase by incidental changes of light intensity at abnormal times. A similar explanation applies to the cycles of responsiveness considered earlier, but only in the cockroach has such progress been made in locating the structures involved.

CIRCADIAN RHYTHMS AS EXAMPLES OF CYCLIC BEHAVIOR

There are no clearer demonstrations of the contribution of endogenous factors to cyclic behavior than the examples we have been discussing. Activity appears in a regular periodic manner. Under constant conditions the rhythm continues. We infer that it can persist in the absence of rhythmical eliciting stimuli. Nevertheless, if periodic external stimuli are presented they evoke a response—the entrainment of the circadian rhythm. The kind of stimulus that will evoke a response is limited by certain criteria. The cycle length must not deviate too far from 24 hours. Enright (1965b) lists other relevant properties such as the ratio of intensities in the light and dark parts of the cycle and the relative durations of the light and dark periods. Endogenous factors thus impose a degree of specificity upon the triggering external stimuli, a characteristic which activity rhythms share with many other types of behavior. External stimulus conditions also play an obvious role. In addition to causing entrainment, they can have permissive effects, allowing the circadian rhythm to occur under some constant conditions and not others. They can also modulate the response to another stimulus that causes entrainment (Enright 1965b, in press).

The behavior of an animal which we see under natural conditions is thus a demonstrable result of positive interaction between the animal and its environment. Nowhere is this interaction more obvious than in the process by which a circadian rhythm becomes entrained to cyclic external stimuli. The rhythmic pattern of behavior is accompanied by an endogenous cycle of responsiveness. In rodents, for example, the response is minimal in the inactive period and maximal around the times of onset and termination of the active phase of the existing cycle. Here a general property of rhythmical behavior patterns is revealed in an exceptionally pure and simple form. It is most striking that this cycle of responsiveness continues under constant conditions. As a result, continuous resetting may contribute to the deviations of the cycle period from 24 hours.

We do not know as much about the internal structure of the cycles, partly because relatively little attention has been given to this aspect of circadian rhythms. There are often cycles within cycles, their intensity and frequency varying in different parts of the activity period. The role of endogenous and exogenous influences in controlling this fine structure has hardly been investigated, although such factors as light intensity and the ratio of light to dark in the course of a day seem to be involved. Studies of the fine structure of other types of cyclic behavior have gone further, but the broader characteristics of rhythmical behavior are nowhere better illustrated than in circadian rhythms.

The interaction between endogenous and exogenous factors in the control of behavior which Craig (1918), Lorenz (1960), and others emphasized, is well illustrated by circadian rhythms. The control of behavior is not the prerogative of external stimuli, nor of factors within the animal. It is a result of complex interaction between the two. And the lingering doubts about the exact nature of endogenous contributions to circadian rhythms can serve to remind us how difficult it is to disentangle the internal and external causes that underlie behavior, as it occurs under natural conditions.

REFERENCES

Aschoff, J. 1957. Aktivitätsmuster der Tagesperiodik. *Naturwissenschaften,* **13**:361–367.

———. 1958. Tierische Periodik unter dem Einfluss von Zeitgebern. *Z. Tierpsychol.,* **15**:1–30.

———. 1960. Exogenous and endogenous components in circadian rhythms. *Cold Spr. Harb. Symp. Quant. Biol.* (1960), **25**:11–28.

———. 1963. Comparative physiology: diurnal rhythms. *Ann. Rev. Physiol.,* **25**:581–600.

———. 1965. Circadian rhythms in man. *Science,* **148**:1427–1432.

——— and K. Honma. 1959. Art- und Individual-Muster der Tagesperiodik. *Z. vergl. Physiol.,* **42**:383–392.

——— and J. Meyer-Lohmann. 1954a. Die Schlussfolge der locomotorischen Aktivität bei Nagern. *Pflüg. Arch. Ges. Physiol.,* **260**:81–86.

——— and ———. 1954b. Angeborene 24—Stunden—Periodik beim Kücken. *Pflüg. Arch. ges. Physiol.,* **260**:170–176.

Batham, E. J. and C. F. A. Pantin. 1950. Phases of activity in the sea-anemone, *Metridium senile* (L.), and their relation to external stimuli. *J. Exp. Biol.,* **27**:377–399.

Beling, I. 1929. Über das Zeitgedächtnis der Bienen. *Z. vergl. Physiol.,* **9**:259–338.

Brown, F. A., Jr. 1959. Living clocks. *Science,* **130**:1535–1544.

———. 1960. Response to pervasive geophysical factors and the biological clock problem. *Cold Spr. Harb. Symp. Quant. Biol.*, **25**:57–71.

——— and H. M. Webb. 1948. Temperature relations of an endogenous daily rhythmicity in the fiddler crab, *Uca. Physiol. Zool.*, **21**:371–381.

———, ———, and M. F. Bennett. 1955. Proof for an endogenous component in persistent solar and lunar rhythmicity in organisms. *Proc. Nat. Acad. Sci.* (Wash.), **41**:93–100.

Bruce, V. G. 1960. Environmental entrainment of circadian rhythms. *Cold Spr. Harb. Symp. Quant. Biol.*, **25**:29–48.

——— and C. S. Pittendrigh. 1956. Temperature independence in a unicellular "clock." *Proc. Nat. Acad. Sci.* (Wash.), **42**:676–682.

Bünning, E. 1931. Untersuchungen über die autonomen tagesperiodischen Bewegungen der Primärblätter von *Phaseolus multiflorus. Jahrb. wiss. Bot.*, **75**:439–480.

———, 1957. Endogenous diurnal cycles of activity in plants. In *Rhythmic and Synthetic Processes in Growth*, ed. by D. Rudnick: 111–126. Princeton University Press, Princeton.

Chandrashekaran, M. K. 1965. Persistent tidal and diurnal rhythms of locomotory activity and oxygen consumption in *Emerita asiatica* (M—Edw.) *Z. vergl. Physiol.*, **50**:137–150.

Craig, W. 1918. Appetites and aversions as constituents of instincts. *Biol. Bull.*, **34**:91–107.

Crowcroft, P. 1953. The daily cycle of activity in British shrews. *Proc. Zool. Soc. Lond.*, **123**:715–729.

DeCoursey, P. 1960. Phase control of activity in a rodent. *Cold Spr. Harb. Symp. Quant. Biol.*, **25**:49–55.

———. 1961. Effect of light on the circadian activity rhythm of the flying squirrel, *Glaucomys volans. Z. vergl. Physiol.*, **44**:331–354.

———. 1964. Function of a light response rhythm in hamsters. *J. Cell. Comp. Physiol.*, **63**:189–196.

Dunnett, G. E. and R. A. Hinde. 1953. The winter roosting and awakening behavior of captive great tits. *Brit. J. Anim. Behav.*, **1**:91–95.

Eibl-Eibesfeldt, I. 1958. Das Verhalten der Nagetiere. *Handb. Zool. Berlin*, **8**(12):1–88.

Enright, J. T. 1963a. The tidal rhythm of activity of a sand-beach amphipod. *Z. vergl. Physiol.*, **46**:276–313.

———. 1963b. Endogenous tidal and lunar rhythms. *Proc. 16th Int. Congr. Zool.*, Washington, D.C., Vol. 4:355–359.

———. 1965a. Entrainment of a tidal rhythm. *Science*, **147**:864–867.

———. 1965b. Synchronization and ranges of entrainment. In *Circadian Clocks*, ed. by J. Aschoff. North-Holland Publishing Company, Amsterdam.

———. In press. Temperature and the free-running circadian rhythm of the house finch.

Fingerman, M. 1960. Tidal rhythmicity in marine organisms. *Cold Spr. Harb. Symp. Quant. Biol.*, **25**:481–489.

Green, G. W. 1964. The control of spontaneous locomotor activity in *Phormia regina* Meigen—I. Locomotor activity patterns of intact flies. *J. Insect Physiol.*, **10**:711–726.

Harker, J. E. 1956. Factors controlling the diurnal rhythm of activity in *Periplaneta americana* L. *J. Exp. Biol.*, **33**:224–234.

———. 1958. Diurnal rhythms in the animal kingdom. *Biol. Rev.*, **33**:1–52.

———. 1960a. The effect of perturbations in the environmental cycle on the diurnal rhythm of activity of *Periplaneta americana* L. *J. Exp. Biol.*, **37**:154–163.

———. 1960b. Internal factors controlling the suboesophageal ganglion neurosecretory cycle in *Periplaneta americana* L. *J. Exp. Biol.*, **37**:164–170.

———. 1960c. Endocrine and nervous factors in insect circadian rhythms. *Cold Spr. Harb. Symp. Quant. Biol.*, **25**:279–287.

————. 1964. *The Physiology of Diurnal Rhythms.* Cambridge Monogr. Exper. Biol., No. 13. Cambridge University Press, Cambridge.

Hauenschild, C. 1960. Lunar periodicity. *Cold Spr. Harb. Symp. Quant. Biol.,* **25**:491–497.

Hoffmann, K. 1957. Über den Einfluss der Temperatur auf die Tagesperiodik bei einem Poikilothermen. *Naturwissenschaften,* **44**:358.

————. 1959. Die Aktivitätsperiodik von im 18- und 36- Stunden-tag erbrüteten Eidechsen. *Z. vergl. Physiol.,* **42**:422–432.

————. 1960. Versuche zur Analyse der Tagesperiodik I. Der Einfluss der Lichtintensität. *Z. vergl. Physiol.,* **43**:544–566.

————. 1965. Overt circadian frequencies and the circadian rule. In *Circadian Clocks,* ed. by J. Aschoff. North-Holland Publishing Company, Amsterdam.

Johnson, M. S. 1939. Effect of continuous light on periodic spontaneous activity of white-footed mice (*Peromyscus*). *J. Exp. Zool.,* **82**:315–328.

Kalmus, H. 1934. Über die Natur des Zeitgedächtnisses der Bienen. *Z. vergl. Physiol.,* **20**:405–419.

Kavanau, J. L. 1962a. Activity patterns on regimes employing artificial twilight transitions. *Experientia,* **18**:382–384.

————. 1962b. Twilight transitions and biological rhythmicity. *Nature,* **194**:1293–1295.

Kleitman, N. 1963. *Sleep and Wakefulness* (revised edition). University of Chicago Press, Chicago.

Lorenz, K. Z. 1960. Methods of approach to the problems of behavior. *The Harvey Lectures* (1958–1959):60–103.

Marshall, A. J. 1960. Annual periodicity in the migration and reproduction of birds. *Cold Spr. Harb. Symp. Quant. Biol.,* **25**:499–505.

Naylor, E. 1958. Tidal and diurnal rhythms of locomotory activity in *Carcinus maenas* (L.). *J. Exp. Biol.,* **58**:602–610.

Ostermann, K. 1955. Zur Aktivität heimischer Muriden und Gliriden. *Zool. Jahrb., Abt. allg. Zool. Physiol.,* **66**:355–388.

Pittendrigh, C. S. 1954. On temperature independence in the clock system controlling emergence time in *Drosophila. Proc. Nat. Acad. Sci.* (Wash.), **40**:1018–1029.

————. 1958. Perspectives in the study of biological clocks. In *Perspectives in Marine Biology,* ed. by A. A. Buzzati-Traverso: 239–268. University of California Press, Berkeley.

————. 1960. Circadian rhythms and the circadian organization of living systems. *Cold Spr. Harb. Symp. Quant. Biol.,* **25**:159–184.

———— and V. G. Bruce. 1957. An oscillator model for biological clocks. In *Rhythmic and Synthetic Processes in Growth,* ed. by D. Rudnick: 75–109. Princeton University Press, Princeton.

————, V. G. Bruce, and P. Kaus. 1958. On the significance of transients in daily rhythms. *Proc. Nat. Acad. Sci.* (Wash.), **44**:965–973.

Rao, K. P. 1954. Tidal rhythmicity of rate of water propulsion in *Mytilus,* and its modifiability by transplantation. *Biol. Bull.,* **106**:353–359.

Rawson, K. S. 1959. Experimental modification of mammalian endogenous activity rhythms. In *Photoperiodism and Related Phenomena in Plants and Animals,* ed. by R. B. Withrow: 791–800. American Association for the Advancement of Science, Washington, D.C.

————. 1960. Effects of tissue temperature on mammalian activity rhythms. *Cold Spr. Harb. Symp. Quant. Biol.,* **25**:105–113.

Renner, M. 1957. Neue Versuche über den Zeitsinn der Honigbiene. *Z. vergl. Physiol.,* **40**:85–118.

————. 1959. Über ein weiteres Versetzungsexperiment zur Analyse des Zeitsinnes und der Sonnenorientierung der Honigbiene. *Z. vergl. Physiol.,* **42**:449–483.

————. 1960. The contribution of the honey bee to the study of time-sense and astronomical orientation. *Cold Spr. Harb. Symp. Quant. Biol.*, **25**:361–367.

Richter, C. P. 1965. *Biological Clocks in Medicine and Psychiatry*. Charles C Thomas, Publisher, Springfield.

Roberts, S. K. de F. 1960. Circadian activity rhythms in cockroaches. I. The free-running rhythm in steady-state. *J. Cell. Comp. Physiol.*, **55**:99–110.

Sweeney, B. M. and J. W. Hastings. 1960. Effects of temperature upon diurnal rhythms. *Cold Spr. Harb. Symp. Quant. Biol.*, **25**:87–104.

Tribukait, B. 1956. Die Aktivitätsperiodik der weissen Maus im Kunsttag von 16–29 Stunden Länge. *Z. vergl. Physiol.*, **38**:479–490.

Wahl, O. 1932. Neue Untersuchungen über das Zeitgedächtnis der Bienen. *Z. vergl. Physiol.*, **16**:529–589.

Wolfson, A. 1960. Regulation of annual periodicity in the migration and reproduction of birds. *Cold Spr. Harb. Symp. Quant. Biol.*, **25**:507–514.

three

REPRODUCTION:
HORMONES AND BEHAVIOR

Exogenous and endogenous factors in the timing of breeding seasons • Social systems and reproduction • Short-term cycles in sexual behavior of birds and mammals • Ovulation and clutch size • The role of nest building and courtship • Temporal organization of copulatory behavior • Parental behavior • Hormonal control of reproductive behavior.

The analysis of behavioral rhythms is concerned with the same problems of causal explanation whether the period length is measured in seconds, days, or years. The whole gamut of cycles is covered in reproductive behavior, from the timing of individual acts in a bout of sexual behavior to breeding seasons. Many investigators have attempted to explain the causation of these different levels of organization in reproductive behavior. In the process they have been confronted with the same difficulty which arises in all studies of motivation, the problem of trying to separate the roles of endogenous and exogenous stimuli.

The controversies about factors responsible for the timing of breeding seasons (e.g. A. J. Marshall 1960, Wolfson 1960) parallel to a remarkable degree those that studies of circadian rhythms have provoked. Here the case will be argued that this parallel is more than coincidental, and that, like circadian rhythms, reproductive behavior illustrates many of these same principles of behavioral organization.

Precisely coordinated timing is more important in breeding than in any other kind of behavior, as Nalbandov (1958) has pointed out.

The shedding of eggs by the female frog, for example, must be closely followed by the shedding of sperm by the male. Here the problem is rather simple; all that is needed is a system that will assure the simultaneous shedding of gametes by two individuals of opposite sex [but of the same species] in the same vicinity of the pond at the most propitious season. In more complex animals a whole series of interlocking and synchronized events must follow one another if reproductive efficiency is to be attained. The shedding of gametes, fertilization, gestation, parturition, and lactation are all events that require accurate timing, and all of them must occur in such a way that the young life depending on them has a good chance of surviving. . . . Without synchronization and cyclic repeatability, reproduction would become a chaotic and completely inefficient game of chance.

Various physiological mechanisms, involving especially the endocrine system, are charged with coordinating this complex series of events.

LONG-TERM REPRODUCTIVE RHYTHMS

✦ *Seasonal Breeding*. No exhaustive account of the huge literature on the subject will be attempted, but we shall rely heavily on several recent reviews (Amoroso and F. H. A. Marshall 1960, Aronson 1957, 1959, Beach 1948, 1951, 1958, Bullough 1961, Farner 1959, Lehrman 1959, 1961, A. J. Marshall 1960, 1961, F. H. A. Marshall 1956, Wolfson 1959, 1960, and Young 1957, 1961).

Breeding seasons of most species have an annual basis. In the animal kingdom as a whole, reproduction may occur at any time of the year (Figure 3–1). The periods vary greatly in duration and synchrony. Although reproductive capacity often extends over three or four months of the year it is sometimes much more confined. The timing may be extremely restricted, as in the palolo worm that breeds primarily on one or two nights at a particular phase of the moon. Other polychaete annelids breed with similar precision.

The factors dictating the optimal moment for breeding vary widely from species to species. Correspondingly, variation may be expected in the mechanism by which timing is achieved. If the critical factors recur in a regular manner, as they do when they are related to the seasons, their predictability permits the evolution of endogenous timing mechanisms. When these factors are essentially unpredictable, as in areas with erratic rainfall, external eliciting stimuli may become extremely important.

In most animals the reproductive success is likely to be affected by a

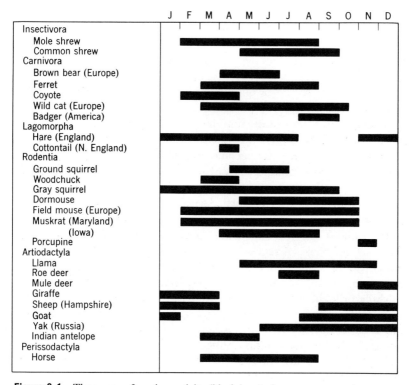

Figure 3-1   The season of mating activity (black bars) of some representative mammals. Southern hemisphere seasons have been converted to northern hemisphere equivalents. The records are for several locations. After Everett 1961.

variety of factors, some predictable, others not. Most species lie between the two extremes, and depend on both exogenous and endogenous timing mechanisms to set an appropriate time for reproduction.

As a further complication, there may be successive mechanisms for coarse and fine timing in the same animal. One set of factors may induce a permissive physiological state of readiness to breed. Another set may regulate the precise time of breeding. A long delay between fertilization and birth poses further problems, as in mammals with long gestation periods. An effective environmental trigger for breeding in such species must come at a different season than the optional time for birth of the young.

◆ *Aseasonal Breeding: Exogenous Control.* Seasonal breeding is the rule for terrestrial animals in temperate regions where much of the research on animal reproduction is done. It is easy to forget that there are parts of the world where a seasonal pattern is less appropriate. For example, in arid regions many birds and amphibians breed only after unpredictable rainfall. A year may pass with neither rain nor reproduction (Moreau 1950, Serventy and Marshall 1957).

The breeding season of birds inhabiting these areas, such as the red-billed dioch, *Quelea quelea*, of Africa and the zebra finch, *Poephila castanotis*, and other Australian birds, may be quite erratic, lacking any constant relationship to season (A. J. Marshall 1960, 1961). When rains are seasonal a more regular cycle becomes established. But here too it need not necessarily be an annual one, as Miller (1962) has shown in the Andean sparrow, *Zonotrichia capensis*, which breeds twice a year. A similar situation is believed to occur in some North African birds (F. H. A. Marshall 1956).

In several species living where rain is meager and sporadic, the gonads of both males and females remain large for long periods of time, apart from a brief phase of regression after a cycle of breeding. Breeding behavior appears only when the rains come. Then, within days or weeks, depending on the species, intensive reproductive activity begins. Young red-billed diochs begin breeding after rains, in response to the sudden availability of green grass with which they weave nests (A. J. Marshall and Disney 1957). Older birds seem to be stimulated by a complex of factors, including having an abundance of particular foods to eat, and perhaps even hearing the sound and feeling the contact of falling rain (A. J. Marshall 1960, 1961).

In these birds which respond to environmental stimuli reproductive behavior can begin within a remarkably short time. This is true both of red-billed diochs in Africa and of zebra finches in northwestern Australia. Immelmann (1963a, b) saw zebra finches which had passed through many months with no rain and no breeding activity at all, courting in the rain of a thunderstorm. Immelmann believes that the falling rain itself directly triggers a reproductive cycle. Some Australian ducks also depend on rains for reproduction, perhaps being stimulated by the level of the flood waters in which they breed (Frith 1960).

◆ *Evidence of Endogenous Rhythms.* A variety of animals go through a cycle of breeding and nonbreeding while kept under conditions which are constant throughout the year, with no cycle of day length. The list includes ferrets (Bissonnette 1936), ducks (Benoit 1938), golden-crowned and white-crowned sparrows (Miller 1955), red-billed diochs, budgerigars, zebra finches (see Marshall 1960, 1961), and greenfinches (Schildmacher 1956). There is no evidence of a precise annual rhythm under such conditions. There is clearly a capacity to cycle, however, which can apparently operate independently of the seasonal change in day length.

The reproduction of ants has been studied over many years by T. C. Schneirla (see 1953, 1957). Colonies of army ants, *Eciton*, are nomadic and spend much of their time on the move, setting up a new nest each night from which raiding parties go out in different directions in the course of the day. At the day's end there is a mass emigration to another nest site or bivouac. These periods of restless movement, the "nomadic" phase, alternate with a relatively sedentary "statary" phase in which the colony remains in one nest for some days. At this time the queen lays eggs, fertilized by sperm stored since mating at the time the colony was established.

Schneirla has shown that the timing of cycles between nomadic and statary conditions is relatively constant within a species. Egg laying occurs at rather precise intervals throughout the year—every 36 days or so in *Eciton hamatum*. Careful study of periodic changes within the colony shows that the cycle is largely self-generated. The appearance of the new brood excites the colony sufficiently to elicit the next nomadic phase which then continues until the brood has matured. At this time further egg laying by the queen is inhibited, the stimulating effect of the newcomers wanes, and a new statary phase begins. Activity in this phase, together with endogenous changes within the queen, in turn probably contributes to the timing of the next ovulation cycle (Schneirla 1957). The basic period length seems to be the result of interplay between processes and stimuli generated by the organisms themselves, rather than a result of a rhythm imposed by the physical environment.

◆ *Lunar Rhythmicities.* The Atlantic palolo worm, *Leodice fucata,* the Pacific palolo worm, *Eunice viridis,* and the fish known as the grunion, *Leuresthes tenuis,* breed annually at certain phases of the moon with almost unbelievably accurate timing. Their behavior illustrates the interaction of lunar, annual, and daily cycles.

Palolo worms live in deep coral crevices, feeding at night by extending part of the body from the hole (Clark and Hess 1942). Only once or twice each year do they leave the coral rocks to swim freely on the surface. The body breaks in two. The reproductive segment is left in great swarms on the surface, and the other part apparently returns to the coral crevices to regenerate the reproductive parts.

The Polynesian natives gather masses of palolo worms in specially made baskets, eating them raw and collecting great quantities for traditional feasts. Although a few animals may rise on different days and in different months, the bulk of the population swarms on a single day. The natives are reported to predict these occasions far in advance. Corney's (1922) long run of data on the date of this "great day" affords an insight into the mechanism of this rhythmicity, and allows us to examine the natives' accuracy, and our own for that matter, in predicting a rise in any particular year.

The average date of the great rise is November 27, with extremes of November 7 and December 22—an annual cycle of considerable regularity. During the months of November and December there is a subcycle, which is in some as yet unknown way timed to the lunar cycle. Swarming occurs seven, eight, or nine days after the full moon. Between the limiting dates of November 7 and December 22 this particular phase of the moon occurs once in some years and twice in others. The problem is to work out the mechanism of choice in cases where it occurs twice, for there seems to be no regular pattern. It may be that some additional exogenous factor is involved.

The Atlantic palolo also is most likely to swarm about eight days after the full moon. The time of swarming is in July and falls somewhere within a period of about 30 days in the Caribbean Tortugas. There is again a long run of information, covering 41 years with some gaps, with an intensive study of the actual swarming performances (Clark and Hess 1942). Environmental factors affect the timing. Wind is particularly important, and when it exceeds 8 miles per hour swarming is inhibited, though sheltered groups may swarm on schedule, out of synchrony with the unprotected population.

The time of day when palolos breed is also rather regular. Again Clark and Hess provide splendid data, demonstrating not only that there is a closely timed schedule within the circadian cycle, but that the schedule is sex dependent, the males preceding the females. Here is a parallel to the social systems of certain vertebrates (see page 82) in which a considerable advantage can sometimes be gained by males by arriving before females at the sexual arena.

A pattern of seasonal reproductive activity that has a lunar rhythmicity also occurs in the grunion. This fish leaves the water to deposit its eggs in the southern California sands. The overall season is long, extending from March through August, but the heaviest runs are in late spring and summer. During a spawning run the fish swim ashore after the high tide has turned, and if females are already there the males remain to mate with them. Milt from one or more males runs through the sand or down the sides of the wet female, the eggs are deposited two to three inches deep in the wet sand, and the next wave returns the fish to the ocean.

To be successful, spawning runs must coincide with the highest waters of each tide and with the highest tides of each month. Premature eggs are washed out almost at once. The eggs must develop during two weeks in the wet sand before hatching. Then they are wetted by the next high tide. The timing is usually quite accurate. An individual female may make from four to eight spawning runs on different occasions during the season; so there is a recurring lunar subcycle within the annual cycle (Walker 1952). So far nothing is known of the stimuli that time these runs, but the times of spawning are sufficiently predictable to be published in advance for sportsmen.

◆ *Day Length: The Interaction of Exogenous and Endogenous Factors.* A majority of animals breed on an annual basis, with breeding behavior suppressed and the gonads regressed for a large part of the year. In most species external timing stimuli play an important role. In nonequatorial species day length is often the paramount factor. Shortening days in the fall may be a cue, both in autumn-breeding animals such as brook trout, *Salvelinus fontinalis,* and in other groups such as ruminants, which begin reproductive behavior in response to shortening days but do not give birth to the young until a considerably later date. In many spring-breeding fish, mammals, and birds, the combination of long days and short nights in spring triggers the onset of gonad growth (Aronson 1959, Amoroso and F. H. A. Marshall 1960, Farner 1959, 1964). Experimental manipulation of day length simulating spring conditions can readily induce reproductive behavior out of season.

Interaction between day length and a circadian rhythm may prove to be the critical factor here. Hamner (1963, 1965) finds that house finches show testis recrudescence when a 6-hour light period is coupled with dark periods in a cycle length of 12, 36, and 60 hours but not in cycles of 24, 48, and 72 hours (Figure 3–2). Farner (1965) has similar evidence for white-crowned sparrows. Thus the endogenous circadian rhythm may contribute to photoperiodic responses in a very positive way.

Another subtle endogenous contribution to regulation of the photoperiodic response comes from the so-called refractory period which follows the breeding season in many birds; this period must be completed before day length changes can elicit another cycle. Its prime function is probably to prevent breeding at an unpropitious time, namely in the late summer and fall. The refractory period varies in duration from species to species. It may be important in spring-breeding birds which each year migrate across the equator to breed. With a simple photoperiodic response to lengthening days these transequatorial migrants might otherwise be triggered to a breeding response in their winter quarters. The refractory period may extend far enough into the northern spring to prevent this accident (Marshall 1960, 1961).

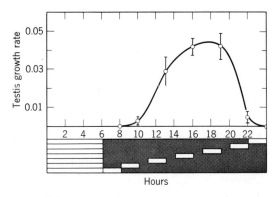

Figure 3-2   The rate of testicular growth in male white-crowned sparrows kept on 6 hours of light and 18 hours of dark, with 2 hours of light interrupting the dark period at various chosen times. Maximal growth occurs when the light is given at a certain phase of the circadian cycle, about 8 hours after the onset of darkness. After Farner 1965.

The existence of endogenous rhythms of breeding cannot be doubted. But we should not exaggerate the contribution they make to timing of the breeding season under natural conditions. Susceptibility to the influence of day length is well established. Even the refractory period is not entirely free of effect, for its duration can be varied by changing the pattern of photoperiodic stimulation. In juncos, *Junco hyemalis,* for example, the termination of the refractory period in the fall is hastened by premature exposure to short 'winter' days. If instead a bird is left on long 'summer' days, the refractory phase may continue into the following spring, so that it will not breed at the proper time. In this species it seems that once the refractory phase is completed a gradual regeneration of the gonads will occur, whatever the day length regime may be. Exposure to long days, however, will hasten regeneration and must provide the normal trigger for the breeding season in spring (Wolfson 1960).

Thus there are variations in the effects which a given day-night regime will have at different stages of the endogenous cycle. During the refractory phase, long days will postpone testicular development. A little later, when the refractory phase is passed, the same stimulus accelerates development of the breeding condition. The reverse is true of short days. If we view these phenomena as evidence of interaction between the endogenous cycle and the natural cycle of changing day length, we are immediately reminded of the entrainment of an endogenous circadian rhythm by the cycle of day and night (see page 51). Again there is a rhythm of changing responsiveness in the course of the endogenous cycle. With circadian rhythms, as with breeding seasons (see Marshall 1960, Wolfson 1960), there is a tendency for some investigators to exaggerate the role of endogenous factors, and for other investigators to minimize it. The solution is surely to be found in a compromise. Both types of influence are required to explain the natural behavior.

Cycles of reproductive behavior, like circadian rhythms, can be suppressed by certain constant conditions. A less than adequate food supply can inhibit seasonal growth of the gonads of a bird even when all other prerequisites are satisfied. A steady state, such as the intensity of constant light, has an effect on the period length of a circadian rhythm. We can at least see the possibility that the proportion of light to dark under a regime of constant day length of the breeding cycle might have a similar effect of extending or reducing the period length of the cycle, and in some cases of eliminating the cycle altogether (Farner 1959). Just as with circadian rhythms, experiments on the role of endogenous factors in breeding cycles must take careful account of the constant conditions under which the tests are run, for a rhythm may appear in one circumstance and be inhibited in another.

Many aspects of breeding seasons and their control have been omitted from this review. Weather plays a role in accelerating or retarding the spring breeding seasons of many birds which make their coarse adjustment to the season from photoperiodic cues. When it is fine and warm the breeding of birds begins earlier in the spring, and occasionally may even occur in the fall as well (Marshall 1952, Orians 1960, Selander and Nicholson 1962). Temperature is a critical factor in some mammals such as ground squirrels and, of course, in poikilotherms. An increased food supply may trigger breeding in some cases (e.g. crossbills, *Loxia curvirostra*, Tordoff and Dawson 1965), and there are many more complications to which attention has been drawn.

The basic principles presented here serve to reinforce our thesis. Erratic and unpredictable breeding seasons are triggered by external stimuli, with endogenous factors usually playing no more than a permissive role in the timing mechanism. In regular annual breeding seasons, endogenous factors assume a more prominent part. The effects are achieved in nature not so much by endogenous triggering of breeding as by endogenous modification of the response to day length and other external stimuli, at different phases of the cycle. In such cases the cycle cannot be regarded as either endogenous or exogenous but must be seen as the result of a combination of both. Thus it makes little sense to argue one side to the exclusion of the other.

SOCIAL SYSTEMS AND REPRODUCTIVE TIMING

To comprehend the short-term patterning of events which will be discussed later, some brief comments are needed on the social framework within which these events occur. Social organization has a special bearing on the matter of timing, since the overall social system determines to a large extent the amount of latitude that is permitted in sexual activities.

◆ *Mating Swarms.* The greatest premium on precise timing occurs when masses of individuals gather together with promiscuous shedding of gametes. For example, in the palolo worm, discussed earlier, mating is restricted to one or two days of the year, and the mating swarms form in the predawn hours. Pelagic fish may form similar promiscuous swarms, with mating synchronized to a particular part of the day. The sardine, *Sardina pirchondus,* for example, spawns in the early evening hours (Gamulin and Hure 1956). Pelagic invertebrates solve the problem by emitting vast numbers of male gametes almost continuously during the breeding season. The environment is thus saturated with male gametes, and the chances of released eggs being fertilized are high. The effectiveness of external fertilization depends largely on spatial distribution of the mating animals. This distribution is accomplished in numerous ways. In some marine organisms the male and female are attached to each other. Other mechanisms to ensure temporal synchronization of mating rely on either synchronizing environmental stimuli or direct communication between the sexes (see page 381). The fine adjustment in timing is often made by chemical signals or 'pheromones' (Karlson and Butenandt 1959, Wilson and Bossert 1963), emitted by ripe females, which cause the release of spermatozoa and guide them to the ovum of the female.

◆ *Mating Locations and Pair Bonds.* The males of some fish species establish locations where gravid females visit them for spawning; then the females are driven away (Aronson 1957, Fabricius and Gustafson 1955, etc.). Elaborate rituals can play a key role in such exchanges, and signals can be transmitted through several sensory modes (Aronson 1945, 1951; Tavolga 1954, 1956). Increased development of such rituals seems to be correlated with the use of smaller numbers of larger eggs. Nevertheless, there is seldom any extended mutual interaction between the sexes in most fish, such as is common in birds and mammals. Some degree of promiscuity seems to be the general rule.

Internal fertilization in vertebrate and invertebrate groups often involves a larger investment in particular acts of fertilization and a corresponding economy in the output of gametes. Frequently it demands a closer relationship between individual males and females. If the male drops a spermatophore which is picked up later by the female, as in some insects, there is less demand for precise sexual coordination than when gametes are transferred directly. Internal fertilization is most characteristic of terrestrial animals in which copulation transfers sperm from males to females. Other behavior is associated with embryo retention and maximal investment in the success of fewer young. Pair bonds may extend through a breeding cycle, a season, or sometimes through life. Males frequently protect the pregnant or incubating female, and in some species the involvement of both sexes in postnatal care of the young results in complex behavioral interactions among members of the family.

There are many exceptions to these generalizations. In some birds, certain grouse for example, the pairing bond between male and female is as brief as that in many fish (see page 388). In other birds the contact may last for several days during the laying of the eggs. Often it lasts for several weeks or months, and sometimes for life (review in Berger 1961). Similarly, among mammals there is a complete spectrum, from the brief contact between male and female and an exclusion of the male from the family in hamsters, to the persistent family group in beavers (Eisenberg 1966). But amphibians and fishes, even viviparous species with internal fertilization, rarely show the extended and elaborate sexual contacts that occur in mammals and birds.

◆ *Delayed Implantation.* Sheltering the embryo within the mother's body during early development involves a commitment to a long, intricate, and rather rigid series of physiological processes, which complicates the problem of timing the breeding season. Some mammals have evaded the problem by delaying the implantation of the embryo in the wall of the uterus for various periods of time after fertilization. In the fur seal, *Callorhinus*, for example, mating takes place immediately after the young are born on the summer breeding islands. Only eight months are needed for embryo growth. Development does not begin until implantation occurs, long after the events of ovulation and fertilization. Delayed implantation postpones the timing of partus until the return to land in the following year when copulation also occurs. In other species, such as some mice (Hamilton 1962), delayed implantation may delay the physiological burden of pregnancy while the female is still lactating. Yet mating occurs in the first two days after the birth of the young, as in mice which lack delayed implantation. Delayed implantation thus provides a mechanism whereby the timing of mating can be emancipated from the energy requirements of pregnancy.

Exogenous factors can intrude in determining the timing of implantation. In the mink, *Mustela vison,* and the marten, *Martes americana,* Pearson and Enders (1944, Enders 1952) have shown that the timing of the initiation of development of the unimplanted embryo is subject to photoperiodic manipulation. In the marten, for example, mating occurs in July and August. By artificially lengthening the days from September onward the time of birth can be advanced from April to the previous December, cutting short the implantation delay.

SHORT-TERM REPRODUCTIVE CYCLES

◆ *Patterns of Ovulation.* The temporal organization of ovulation in female vertebrates follows a number of different patterns. In amphibians and fish the female generally comes into seasonal reproductive condition, and then she ovulates and engages in sexual activity with the male for a limited part of the reproductive season. Her sexual receptivity rises in response to stimuli from a variety of sources, both environmental and social. In mammals ovulation and sexual receptivity recur periodically as a manifestation of the estrous cycle. The cyclic receptivity of certain fish (Amoroso and Marshall 1960) suggests the sort of step that may have anticipated this development. Embryo retention within the uterus may have been a primary factor favoring the development of this cyclicity since successful implantation requires a suitable condition of the uterine wall, and this has to be prepared beforehand.

◆ *Physiological Basis of Ovulation.* The physiological mechanisms underlying mammalian estrous cycles involve both endogenous and exogenous factors. There is a basic feedback relationship between estrogen from the ovaries and the follicle-stimulating hormone (FSH) from the anterior pituitary (see Everett 1961, Young 1961). Negative feedback results in a cycle of ovarian activity and sexual behavior in mammals which ovulate spontaneously (Figure 3–3). There is also evidence of a separate cycle of hypothalamo-hypophysial activity, for cycling of gonadotropin production has been recorded in female rats and mice after destruction or removal of all ovarian follicles (review in Everett 1961).

Some mammals have one period of heat per year. An example is the silver fox, *Vulpes fulva.* The females are receptive only during a period of from one to six days during February (Pearson and Bassett 1946). With some exceptions, such as the basenji with one annual heat, most domestic dogs have two periods of heat per year, one in the early spring and one in the fall. A bitch is then receptive for one or two weeks. Many mammals are polyestrous, having a series of receptive periods. These periods follow one another at regular intervals throughout the breeding season, varying in duration from a day or less in rodents to a week or more in primates.

The estrous cycle of the female rat lasts four to five days. It is associated not only with variations in sexual receptivity but with striking changes in overall activity which are readily detectable if the rat is placed in a running wheel (Figure 3–4). In most mammals the period of maximal receptivity seems to just precede the time when fertilization is most likely to occur, some hours before ovulation. For example, female golden hamsters, *Mesocricetus auratus,* kept on a 12-hour day-night schedule came into heat between 1 hour before the onset of darkness and about 5 hours after, and ovulated 8 or 9 hours later (Harvey et al. 1961). A precise temporal correlation between maximal receptivity and ovulation is not universal, however, as Rowell (1963) has shown with rhesus monkeys, *Macaca mulatta.* Female rats and hamsters, both 'spontaneous ovulators,' will shed the eggs whether they have copulated or not. As we shall see, there are mammals, called 'induced ovulators,' in which ovulation is triggered by external stimulation.

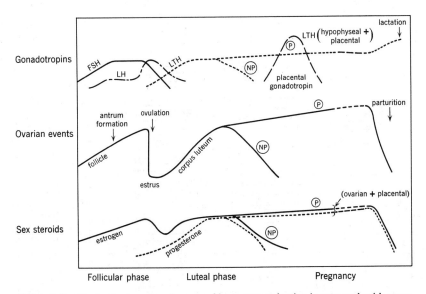

Figure 3-3 The cycle of ovarian change and hormone production in mammals with an active luteal phase. The cycle of events is indicated in pregnancy, P, and in a normal estrous cycle without pregnancy, NP. There are species differences in the life of the corpus luteum during pregnancy and in the duration of gonadotropin output. After Gorbman and Bern 1962.

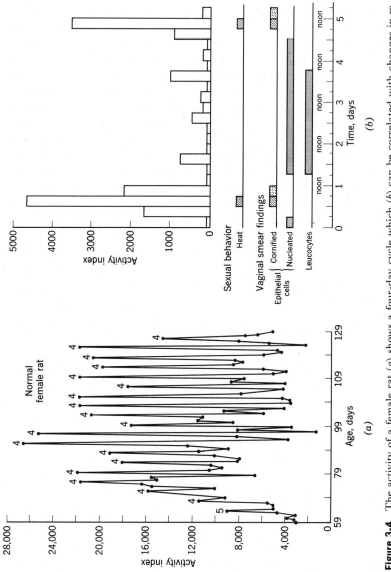

Figure 3-4 The activity of a female rat (*a*) shows a four-day cycle which (*b*) can be correlated with changes in reproductive physiology. After Sawyer 1960 and Munn 1950.

◆ *Ovulation in Birds.* Female birds differ from mammals in lacking any strict parallel to the estrous cycle. As already pointed out, the general season for breeding is dictated by one set of factors, both internal and external, and the precise timing is regulated by other factors. In birds the ultimate control of this detailed timing is largely the prerogative of the female. Such factors as weather, availability of nesting sites and food, and social stimuli from the male play a significant role in determining the actual day when a female bird will ovulate (Marshall 1960, 1961). Once a clutch of eggs is started, laying proceeds at a regular interval until the clutch is complete. The raising of a brood may be followed by a further cycle of ovulation. Another clutch may also be produced if a nest is destroyed.

Most of the evidence on the physiological basis of ovulation in birds is concerned with chickens, although Hinde, Lehrman, and others are extending our knowledge of other birds as well. Some intrinsic mechanism ensures that follicles mature in a graded series, even when follicular development is evoked by massive gonadotropin injections. The follicle-stimulating hormone, FSH, provides the stimulus for this maturation. We may assume its production through a large part of the breeding season (Tienhoven 1961, Lehrman 1961). Early in the season the growth of ovarian follicles is slow, but some days before laying occurs there is rapid acceleration, presumably in response to pituitary gonadotropins. External stimuli of various kinds control the timing of the events that lead to the laying of the first egg, special significance being attached to those stimuli generated in courtship and nest building activity (Lehrman 1959, 1964).

◆ *The Role of Courtship in Ovulation in Birds.* A number of social factors can contribute to the occurrence of ovulation in a female bird. The best evidence is from pigeons. An isolated female pigeon normally will not lay eggs, but she can be induced to do so by allowing her to see another pigeon, or even by giving her a mirror (Matthews 1939).

The relationship between external stimuli and the breeding cycle has been pursued further in a long and ingenious series of experiments by Lehrman and his colleagues (1961, etc., Figure 3–5). They have shown that participation of ring doves in courtship hastens the onset of nest building. Apparently this behavior evokes the release of estrogens from the ovarian follicles, an effect that must be mediated by the pituitary. Stimuli generated by male courtship are important for gonadal development of female doves. Caged females with a view of castrated, noncourting males show signs of less estrogen production than caged females with a view of normal, courting males (Erickson and Lehrman 1964). The next phase of the cycle, involving nest building, is induced by the secre-

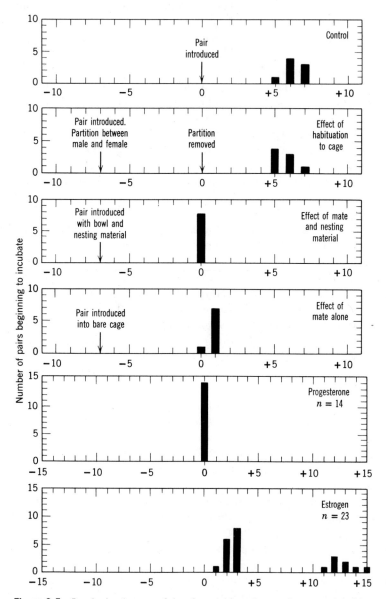

Figure 3-5 Incubation latency of ring doves with various environmental and hormonal pretreatments. A nest with eggs was introduced on day 0. After Lehrman 1958a, b.

tion of estrogens. The actions of nest building and the stimuli that they generate serve in turn to hasten ovulation, apparently by eliciting the release of luteinizing hormone (LH) from the pituitary; increasing production of progesterone by the ovaries may also occur. The stage is then set for ovulation. According to Lehrman, progesterone facilitates another burst of LH production, and the first egg is laid.

The rhythm of further egg laying until clutch completion varies in a characteristic manner from species to species. Evidently the presence of an egg in the oviduct inhibits the production of LH. As the egg is laid the release of LH follows rapidly (within a few minutes in the domestic hen), and the sequence of events leading to ovulation and laying of the next egg is initiated (Tienhoven 1961).

The cycle of laying is also influenced by a daily rhythm. Birds tend to lay eggs at a particular time of day which changes with a shift in the rhythm of light and dark.

➤ *The Incubation Patch.* Shortly before the start of incubation, many female birds develop one or more 'incubation patches' on the breast and belly. Down feathers are shed, the epidermis thickens, and there is a great increase in vascularity and edema in the underlying tissues (Figure 3–6, Bailey 1952). Increased production of estrogen, acting with luteotropin (LTH) from the anterior pituitary, and perhaps with progesterone (Bailey 1952, Selander and Kuich 1963, Steel and Hinde 1964), seems to cause these changes. Experimenters using hormone therapy have not yet been able to develop incubation patches comparable to those occurring in nature (Figure 3-6c). Selander and Yang (in press) suggest that full development may depend either on a special sequence of hormonal actions or on tactile stimulation of the patch, such as might be provided by the eggs during incubation.

In phalaropes some roles of male and female are reversed, and males incubate. In two species, *Steganopus tricolor* and *Lobipes lobatus,* Johns and Pfeiffer (1963) found that testosterone, rather than estrogen, is the effective gonadal hormone in incubation patch development and that it acts together with LTH. Although females do not normally develop an incubation patch, they do so if treated with testosterone and LTH. In a few passerine species both males and females have incubation patches (Selander 1963), but the hormonal mechanism remains to be worked out.

➤ *Clutch Size.* The number of eggs in a clutch, a species characteristic, seems to be controlled by two different mechanisms. In some species removal of eggs from the nest as they are laid results in the continued production of eggs. These species are called 'indeterminate layers.' Perhaps

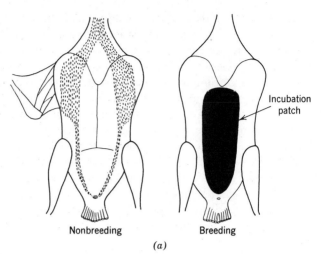

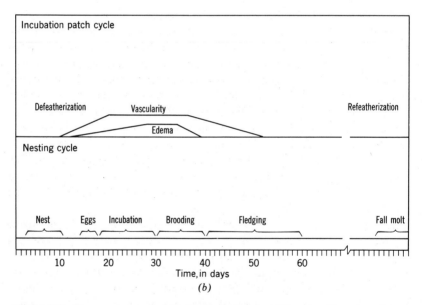

Figure 3-6 Hormonal control of the incubation patch. (*a*) Female white-crowned sparrow, showing the position of the patch. (*b*) Stages of the incubation patch cycle in the white-crowned sparrow. (*c*) Weight changes in the incubation patch of house sparrows in the wild and under various hormonal treatments. After Bailey 1952, Selander and Yang in press.

stimuli generated by the nest and eggs, received in part by the sensitive incubation patch, play a role in limiting the size of the clutch. Development of the incubation patch is accompanied by a measurable increase

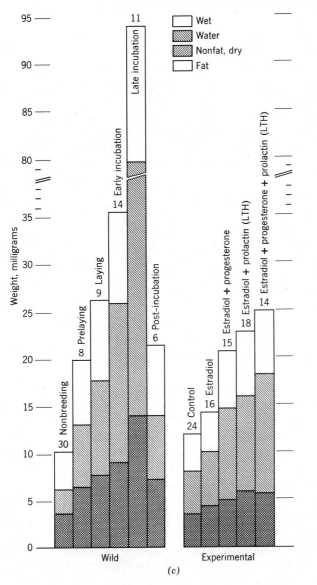

(c)

in tactile sensitivity (Bell and Hinde 1963, Hinde, Bell, and Steel 1963, Hinde and Steel 1964). Visual stimuli from the eggs may also play some part.

With 'determinate layers,' on the other hand, removal of the eggs does not increase the number of eggs laid, and endogenous factors are more prominent in determining clutch size. Like an indeterminate layer, however, such a bird will produce fewer eggs if some are introduced into the nest prematurely by the experimenter, and she may even refrain from laying altogether. Thus determinate layers are responsive to stimuli from the nest and from the eggs as well (review in Lehrman 1961).

In some species the situation is complicated by the commencement of incubation at the start of laying, not toward the end as is more usual. Laying seems to terminate after a certain number of days of incubation (Weidmann 1956).

This review of events leading up to completion of the clutch serves to emphasize the intricate experimentation that is required to disentangle the roles of internal and external factors in the natural sequence of behavior. The same is true of later stages of the cycle.

Progesterone seems to induce the start of incubation (Eisner 1960). As soon as incubation begins, the third pituitary gonadotropin, luteotropic hormone or prolactin (LTH), is released, facilitating further incubation. LTH also inhibits the production of FSH and LH and therefore inhibits the production of the gonadal hormones as well. Then the sexual phase gives way to the parental phase. LTH, acting with ovarian steroids, furthers development of the brood patch and also encourages care of the young after they hatch, particularly brooding behavior, feeding, and defense from predators.

Doves are specialized to produce 'crop milk' at this time, as a result of proliferation of the crop wall. The milk is regurgitated by members of both sexes directly into the mouth of the young. The production of crop milk is dependent on LTH and constitutes a standard bioassay for this hormone (Lehrman 1955, 1961). Although LTH provides the normal basis for parental behavior, some parental behavior can be evoked in its absence. Presenting adults with young will elicit parental behavior in some animals but does not produce crop milk in pigeons. In time, the young become independent and the level of LTH production declines. If the season permits, another cycle of FSH production and gonad growth may begin and a further breeding cycle will ensue. If not, the pituitary will not produce more gonadotropins until internal and external factors once more combine to instigate the next annual breeding cycle.

◆ *Precopulatory Behavior and Reproductive Isolation.* There are certain conditions that precopulatory behavior must satisfy. The need for synchronization of the reproductive physiology of male and female has already been mentioned. Before this is possible, the two sexes must find each other. If there is to be effective reproduction, each adult animal must locate a partner of the opposite sex and of the same species. In order to avoid wasting time and gametes there must be reproductive isolation.

In many animals the problem of reproductive isolation is settled well before the two sexes engage in reproductive behavior and copulation. A particular temporal or spatial distribution of activity may ensure minimal contact with other species. Mates may be selected from a pre-existing social group; this is often the case with mammals in nature. The processes by which the group became established at an earlier time may already have excluded other species. In many monogamous birds the pair bond is established some weeks before mating.

On the other hand, there are animals from all levels of the animal kingdom in which the sequence of behavior leading to copulation includes within its functions that of ensuring reproductive isolation. When the sexes have only a brief contact, we find the most extreme developments in precopulatory behavior of patterns of sound, odor, appearance, and physical contact. The requirement for strong specific distinctiveness seems to be at least one of the functions of the elaborate nature of precopulatory behavior (e.g. Mayr 1942, Sibley 1957, Marler 1957). Some insects may solve the problem at a later stage in a direct mechanical fashion, by the evolution of specific 'lock and key' types of genital apparatus, though the evidence for this is equivocal. But in most terrestrial organisms the mechanisms for reproductive isolation involve a complex of behavioral traits that are effective before actual mating, such as selection of habitat, timing of activity, and choice of a mate (Mayr 1963).

With some exceptions (e.g. Eisenberg 1963) most of the information about the structure of reproductive behavior in small mammals is necessarily derived from experiments in which two animals are placed in close contact in a small cage. This procedure bypasses whatever forms of distance communication may be involved in the establishment of contact, as well as environmental barriers in nature that might hinder it. We shall return to this subject in discussing external stimuli and reproductive behavior.

◆ *Copulation.* The problem of ensuring physiological synchrony between mating partners varies widely in different animals. Males of many species are ready to copulate at short notice during a long season. They must induce readiness in the female by various kinds of precopulatory courtship activity. The need may also be mutual. The contrast is well illustrated by comparing the precopulatory behavior of bulls and horses (Walton 1955, p. 604).

The stallion differs from the bull in having a typical vascular penis in marked contrast to the fibro-elastic penis of [the bull]. In the non-erect condition the horse's penis is quite flaccid and is withdrawn within the confines of the prepuce. The retractor penis muscle is relatively undeveloped and adherent to the ventral surface of the penis. There is no sigmoid flexure. Erection and protrusion of the penis are affected by gradually increasing tumescence of the erectile vascular tissue in the corpus cavernosum penis. Erection usually takes place rather slowly, and depends upon the continued reception of erotic stimuli derived from courtship and foreplay. Foreplay appears to be an essential accompaniment of vascular erection and this is well featured in the behaviour pattern of the stallion.

By contrast with the stallion the bull exhibits little or no foreplay prior to mounting and copulation. The penis of the bull is of the fibro-elastic type. It is of small diameter and relatively rigid even in the non-erect condition. The erectile tissue is small and the penis undergoes little enlargement on erection although it becomes more rigid. Protrusion is affected partly by erection but mostly by relaxation of the retractor muscle and by straightening of the sigmoid flexure. In mating with the cow there is little or no foreplay. The bull "tests" the cow by smelling or exploring the vulva with muzzle or tongue and by placing the chin on the [base of the] cow's tail. . . . If the cow is not [in] heat, she moves away rapidly and evades the bull's attempt to mount, if she is [in] heat she stands still and accepts service, which is performed with great rapidity.

In polyestrous mammals, which provide most of our data on copulatory behavior, precopulatory exchanges are relatively brief. They seem to function primarily to allow the female to reveal whether or not she is receptive and to provide sufficient mutual stimulation to bring both parties to the appropriate level of motivation for copulation to occur. After the preludes are completed copulation takes place. The actual temporal sequence of activities varies from species to species. During sustained association between a pair of animals a number of copulations is likely to occur during the estrous phase of the female, maximizing the possibility that fertilization will take place.

◆ *Induced and Spontaneous Ovulation.* In certain mammals, copulatory activity is necessary for ovulation. Such animals are referred to as induced ovulators rather than spontaneous ovulators. The domestic rabbit and cat are typical induced ovulators in which the ovarian follicles degenerate at the end of each estrous cycle if copulation does not occur. In the short-tailed shrew, *Blarina brevicauda,* several copulations are required before ovulation will occur. In the mink, *Mustela vison,* participation in precopulatory behavior may suffice (Enders 1952, Pearson 1944, Pearson and Enders 1944). In both species the courtship is a rather violent affair.

Immediately following copulation, some birds perform strikingly elaborate displays. In ducks these postcopulatory displays take the form of rapid swimming of the male, with head held high (Lorenz 1941). In the avocet the mating birds cross their bills and race side by side for several yards (Makkink 1936). No adequate explanation for these displays has been put forth, though it seems possible that elaborate and precise patterns such as these have an important function, possibly in triggering ovulation.

Other external stimuli can play a part. The characteristic beginning of estrus at a particular time of day has already been pointed out. Experiments with shifted day-night rhythms have shown that light-dark stimuli are important in establishing the timing of ovulation. A change in the day-night regime is followed by a gradual phase shift of ovulation to harmonize with the new circumstances (Everett 1961).

The importance of external stimuli to induced ovulators is obvious, although the female must be in the appropriate physiological state for ovulation to occur. In some mammals, the spontaneous ovulators, endogenous factors are dominant, and in others, the induced ovulators, the effects of external stimuli are more prominent.

SEQUENCES OF MATING BEHAVIOR

Having considered the organization of reproductive behavior on an annual basis, as well as the shorter cycles which are to be found within the breeding season, we can now turn to the temporal organization at the bout level. What are the preludes and sequels to the act of insemination in different types of animals? How is the whole sequence organized in time? And what is known of the mechanisms by which this temporal patterning is achieved? There is so much variation within the animal kingdom that it almost defies analysis, but there are some functional considerations, relating to the appetitive and consummatory properties of sexual behavior (see page 727), which help to introduce order into the wide range of possibilities.

In rats and guinea pigs copulatory activity is organized in bouts, in much the same ways as other types of behavior. In general, sequences of appetitive precopulatory behavior lead to the consummatory activity of copulation. This is followed by a period with sexual activity absent, perhaps with the intervention of other activities, before another bout of sexual behavior begins. Complications within this simple framework have occupied the researches of many investigators, notably F. A. Beach and W. C. Young, over a number of years.

In the guinea pig the sequence is fairly straightforward (review in Young 1961).

When a male encounters a female in heat, he follows her, sniffing at her anogenital region. The female is likely to adopt the lordosis posture if she is receptive; then he mounts her, and perhaps after some abortive attempts, achieves intromission and makes pelvic thrusts. He may dismount and repeat this sequence several times before he achieves ejaculation, when he falls back in a distinctive manner. Both animals clean their genitals and further sexual activity is then suspended for a variable length of time.

In rats and hamsters (Beach and Rabedeau 1959) the preliminaries to copulation are similar to those of the guinea pig. Grooming behavior is often included, an activity which is prevalent in the sexual activities of many rodents (Eisenberg 1962, 1963). The later stages are more complex. Mounting and pelvic thrusts are normally repeated several times before the male achieves ejaculation. Then the sequence comes to an end and is followed by 24 or more hours without sexual activity.

Careful quantitative description of the temporal sequence of events shows that the concepts of appetitive and consummatory behavior are applied less easily to rats and hamsters than to the guinea pig (Beach 1956, 1958, Larsson 1956). Successive ejaculations are indeed followed by increasingly long 'postejaculatory refractory periods' as the bout proceeds. However, we must also consider the paradoxical finding that successive ejaculations are achieved with fewer and fewer intromissions within the same series. There are in fact suggestions of increasing and decreasing motivation at the same time, reminding us once more of the dangers of considering motivation in unitary terms (Hinde 1959, see page 120). Evidently a sequence of intromissions and ejaculations has both inhibiting and facilitating effects on subsequent sexual activities (Beach 1956).

It is only when the inhibitory influences become completely dominant that the bout is terminated. Artificial separation of the pair between the first and second ejaculations for varying periods of time shows that the facilitating effects of the first ejaculation wane rapidly, returning to the original level after about 90 minutes (Larsson 1958, Beach and Whalen 1959). As the inhibitory effects of successive ejaculations increase, the refractory period presumably exceeds this period of facilitation, and the sequence terminates.

Beach (1948, 1956, 1958) proposes at least two distinct physiological mechanisms to explain the temporal patterning of mammalian sexual behavior, and other types of evidence point to a similar conclusion (Soulairac 1952, Larsson 1956, Rosenblatt and Aronson 1958a, b, Jakway 1959). Beach postulates an 'arousal mechanism' which mediates the initiation and maintenance of sexual excitement (Beach and Whalen 1959) and underlies the appetitive phase of the sequence. The execution of copulatory and ejaculatory reactions is held to depend on the 'copulatory mechanism' called into play when activity in the arousal mechanism becomes sufficiently intense.

No doubt a multiplicity of physiological effects will prove to be involved. Beach (1958) believes that the copulatory mechanism in rodents is particularly involved with spinal and autonomic elements and the hypothalamus, and that the arousal mechanism involves the cerebral cortex, especially in males. The latter point is suggested by the ease with which learning can affect the arousal responses of male rodents to external stimuli. In higher mammals cortical involvement becomes still more extensive. As we shall see later, the sex hormones may even be dispensable in experienced males.

◆ *Mechanisms of Terminating Sequences of Reproductive Behavior.* In sexual activities, as in other types of behavior, there is need for a combination of facilitating effects to sustain bouts of activity and inhibitory effects to bring sequences to an end. The mechanisms available are as varied as, for example, those that regulate feeding behavior. Intrinsic consequences of sexual activity, both facilitating and inhibitory, seem to contribute to the control of behavioral sequences in rats. Other factors play a part as well (Beach 1956).

The account thus far has been of a sequence of responses of a male rat or hamster to the same estrous female. In fact, many such experiments involve the repeated substitution of one estrous female for another. These substitutions provide the maximum intensity of external stimulation for the male, necessary because males become habituated to repeated contacts with the same female. The effect was clearly demonstrated in guinea pigs (Grunt and Young 1952, Figure 3–7) and rats (Wilson, Beach, and Kuehn 1963, Fisher 1962, Fowler and Whalen 1961) by allowing a male to mate with one estrous female and then reviving sexual activity to some extent by substituting a new female.

Habituation makes a definite contribution to termination of a bout of sexual activity involving the same two animals. In rats and guinea pigs the effects evidently act in concert with intrinsic consequences of copulation. In some other animals habituation seems to take on a still more dominant role. For example, experiments designed to obtain large quantities of semen from bulls for artificial insemination have shown that bulls too wane rapidly in their responsiveness to the same stimulus object —a cow or a dummy (Hale and Almquist 1960). If on the other hand the stimulus situation is constantly changed by using a new animal as the dummy, or by presenting the old one in a new situation, a bull will continue to perform a remarkable number of consecutive ejaculations. "Sexual satiation to one stimulus provides negligible interference with a

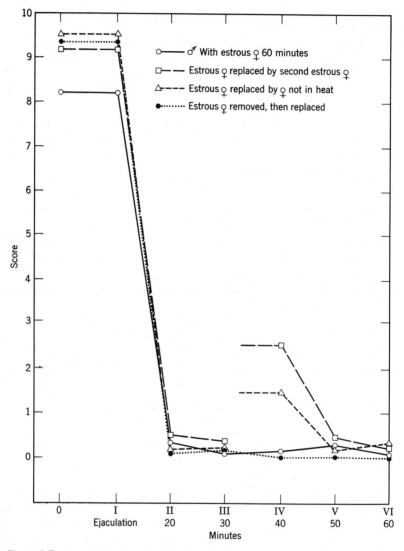

Figure 3-7   Sexual behavior of male guinea pigs in various test conditions. After Grunt and Young 1952.

subsequent response to a new stimulus animal" (Hale and Almquist 1960). Evidently intrinsic consequences of motor sexual activity contribute little to the normal termination of a sequence in this case.

Barrass (1960, 1961) has described a somewhat similar phenomenon in an insect, the chalcid hymenopteran *Mormionella vitripennis*. A female normally ceases to be receptive after a male has successfully copulated with her. So a particular bout of sexual behavior is naturally terminated in this way. The provision of new receptive females revives the male's sexual activity, however, and Barrass concludes that "mating in this insect does not result in reduced ability to repeat the same behavior immediately." New nonreceptive females will also elicit some revival of male courtship, but the effect gradually wanes with a series of presentations. In this species habituation cooperates with postcopulatory changes in the behavior of the female to terminate a bout of sexual activity between a given pair of animals.

Changes in the external stimulus situation generated by sexual activity contribute to the termination of bouts of sexual behavior in other species. Some of the best-established cases occur in fishes. Eggs laid by the female at the climax of a courtship sequence provide stimuli which inhibit any further sexual activity by the male; he is now aggressive toward the female. In the bitterling, *Rhodeus amarus,* the male defends a territory around a mussel and is visited by the female, who lays the eggs in the mantle cavity. Wiepkema (1961) has shown that it is not the act of sperm ejection which terminates a bout of male courtship. Rather it is the presence of eggs in the host mussel. In the three-spined stickleback, *Gasterosteus aculeatus,* deposition of eggs in the male's nest inhibits further male courtship of the female (Bol 1959, Sevenster-Bol 1962). The same change in the external stimulus situation also facilitates other patterns of behavior, including sperm ejection over the eggs and attack upon the female. This example is a reminder that the same sequence can be appetitive with respect to some behavior patterns and consummatory with respect to others (see page 729).

We have already reviewed Lehrman's demonstration of the way stimuli generated at one phase of behavior can lead to the next phase in the reproductive behavior of ring doves (see page 87). Another example is provided by Hinde's analysis of nest building in canaries. Nest building is a complex task involving the selection of several types of material. This selection shifts from grass to feathers as the day of the first egg approaches, and is paralleled by a change in the frequency of different nest-building movements. Hinde (1958, 1962, Warren and Hinde 1961, Hinde and Steel, 1962, 1964) has shown that the progressive changes can be explained partly in terms of endogenous hormonal changes and partly as a result of stimuli received from the decrease in the size of the nest cup during construction. The texture of the nest material also plays a part, and so apparently does the increasing tactile sensitivity of the bird's incubation patch.

The interactions between changing exogenous and endogenous factors are so complex that a simple application of the ideas of appetitive and consummatory behavior is not often easy. Nevertheless, there is a widespread general pattern to bouts of sexual behavior, and there are various means of ending or consummating a sequence. Many different mechanisms can contribute to the emergence of a similar system of temporal organization in the overt behavior (Table 3–1).

Table 3-1 Mechanisms for Termination of a Bout of Male Copulatory Activity with a Given Female

Animal	Habituation of male to individual female	Some change in female after mating	Change in environment after mating	Consequence of performing sexual motor activities
Rat and guinea pig	+	–	–	+
Bull	+	–	–	–
Stickleback	–	–	+ (eggs in nest)	–
Mormionella	+	+	–	–

MATERNAL BEHAVIOR

◆ *Pregnancy in Mammals.* In the absence of fertilization, estrous cycling in polyestrous female mammals continues. If mating occurs, the course of the cycle is broken. The series of changes which follows leads to implantation of the embryo in the uterine wall and the provision for nutrition, birth, and suckling of the young together with all the associated behavior patterns of nest building, defense, and care of the young. The timing of these events varies widely from species to species.

The break in the estrous cycle results from a change in the relationships between the anterior pituitary and the corpus luteum, a structure derived from the ruptured follicle left behind after ovulation. In some mammals there is no functional (i.e. progesterone-secreting) luteal phase in a normal estrous cycle. In others the corpus luteum persists for some days. Under the influence of LTH it produces progesterone which, together with estrogen, prepares the uterine wall for the implantation of embryos. Eventually the corpus luteum ceases to secrete, and cycling begins again. The effect of fertilization is to instigate or prolong the development of the corpus luteum. It may persist either until the end of the gestation period or until the placenta is producing sufficient quantities of estrogen and progesterone to take over the functions of maintaining the condition of the uterus and inhibiting further estrous cycles. Normally, persistence of the corpus luteum results from arrival of the embryo in the uterus. The embryo causes a persistence of LTH production by the anterior pituitary which then influences the corpus luteum. The further production of LTH also combines with estrogen and progesterone in encouraging the growth of the mammary glands, together with a host of other influences.

◆ *Birth in Mammals.* Behavior of the mother after birth has been widely studied (Rheingold 1963), but the physiological mechanisms underlying parental behavior are by no means clear. For example, the behavior of rodents retrieving young displaced from the nest is easily quantified. Several investigators have shown that the female's retrieving response is maximal in the latter part of pregnancy and around the time of birth, suggesting a link with the hormones of pregnancy. Injections of LTH increase retrieving. But hypophysectomized and gonadectomized animals will retrieve young, showing that the physiological basis for this behavior is more complex than it at first appears.

In rats a variety of stimuli, olfactory, auditory, visual, and tactile, are involved in eliciting the retrieving response (Beach and Jaynes 1956a, b). Hamsters perform a certain amount of retrieving, whatever their physiological condition. On occasion, they may attack or eat the young instead (Rowell 1961). Careful experimentation with this species shows that the age of young presented in relation to the age of the female's own young is a critical factor. The effectiveness of the young varies with their age (Rowell 1960). Rowell found that the increasing age of the young is also responsible for the gradual decline in frequency of maternal licking and other changes in maternal behavior. A mother provided each day with young of a constant age continues to lick them with the same frequency. The same procedure perpetuates milk production; removal of the young curtails it.

External stimuli play a particularly large role in maternal behavior. Nonpregnant rats retrieve freely when they are simply enclosed with young. Very young rodents will retrieve nestmates from an earlier litter, or even from the same one. Although the predisposition to retrieve is clearly affected by hormones, it may also occur to some extent independently of hormonal control, in the presence of certain external stimuli.

Similarly in the production of milk, changes in hormones and other internal factors play a key role. This holds true especially in initiating the general physiological readiness for lactation. But tactile stimulation of the mother's nipples is required for the actual 'letdown' of the milk, which is mediated by the release of oxytocin from the neural lobe of the pituitary. Once more the behavior is a result of interaction between endogenous and exogenous factors.

THE ROLE OF HORMONES

◆ *Hormonal Basis of Breeding Seasons.* The onset of the breeding season is heralded by changes in the structure and physiology of the gonads. Either as an endogenous change, or through the influence of external stimuli, the anterior pituitary begins secreting gonadotropic hormones (FSH and LH), which in turn induce growth of the gonads. These hormones also induce the production of the gonadal or sex hormones, mostly androgens in the male and estrogens in the female. The sex hormones elicit changes in structure, modifying the reproductive tract and some of the secondary sex characters, and are the main cause of the onset of reproductive behavior.

The sex hormones are not the only physiological mediators of the onset of the breeding season. The pituitary gonadotropins have direct effects in some cases. Migratory behavior, which preludes the breeding season in many species of birds, appears unchanged in castrated finches. Thus it can occur independently of gonadal hormones. Whether gonadotropins, or some extragonadal source of androgens and estrogens such as the adrenal cortex, are responsible has yet to be determined (Farner 1955, Lofts and Marshall 1961, Morton and Mewaldt 1962).

The gonadotropin LH is responsible for the cycling of reproductive and nonreproductive male plumage patterns in weaver finches (Witschi 1961), and antler growth in deer may be similarly effected (review in Amoroso and Marshall 1960). In fishes the thyroid has been implicated in the onset of migration. Spring movement of three-spined sticklebacks, *Gasterosteus aculeatus,* from salt to fresh water occurs normally in castrated animals and can be elicited out of season by thyroxine treatment. In this case the production of the thyrotropic hormone by the anterior pituitary, induced by the lengthening days of spring, is claimed to be responsible for onset of the first phase of the breeding cycle (Baggerman 1957, 1959).

Even in these exceptional cases the breeding cycle can hardly proceed far without involvement of the gonads. Arthropods are exceptional in that sexual behavior and secondary sexual characters seem to be less dependent on direct gonadal control than on activity of the corpora allata (Schneirla 1953, Barth 1962, Gorbman and Bern 1962).

In vertebrates the process of release of gonadotropins by the anterior pituitary is initiated in the hypothalamus, which is ideally placed to receive sensory information about external conditions and to respond to endogenous changes within the central nervous system. Neurosecretory cells become active and their products are transported by the hypothalamo-hypophyseal portal system to the pituitary. These hormones are released into the circulatory system (Gorbman and Bern 1962). Breeding behavior is then maintained by several complex interactions between gonads, pituitary, and the environment (see page 84).

◆ *Termination of the Breeding Cycle.* How the breeding season is brought to an end is not entirely understood. A key role is probably played by the pituitary gonadotropin, LTH. It is implicated in the parental phases toward the end of the breeding cycle, and it is known to cause gonad regression in some male birds. The thyroid gland may also be involved, especially in birds that molt after the breeding season. Whatever the cause, the pituitary enters a refractory phase at the end of the breeding season. During this phase gonadotropin production cannot be elicited. In time the pituitary again becomes responsive to external stimuli which can again trigger the cycle of secretory activity. The stage is set for the next breeding season (Wolfson 1959, Farner 1959).

◆ *Sites of Hormone Action.* The effectiveness of hormones in eliciting reproductive behavior is readily illustrated by the standard techniques of removal and replacement therapy (review in Sawyer 1960). A male rat or guinea pig is castrated. The effect of the operation upon his mating behavior is determined with standard females in a test situation. After the test he is injected with an androgen preparation which restores the deficit in his mating behavior (Figure 3–8).

The loss of mating behavior following castration is even more immediate in females. In some female mammals estrogen alone suffices to restore estrous behavior. In others, a combination of estrogen and progesterone is required. Several lines of evidence show that the gonadal hormones are not the only factors involved. Although male hormones injected into females can and normally do induce male sexual behavior, they may also cause female patterns, especially at high dosages. The same duality emerges when males are injected with ovarian hormones. Furthermore, behavior patterns of the opposite sex often appear in the course of natural reproductive behavior (Beach 1948). The mechanisms for male and female behavior patterns are thus present in both sexes and are subject to facilitation or inhibition by several factors.

Individuality plays a part in the varying effects of hormone administration. Castrated male guinea pigs show individual differences in sexual

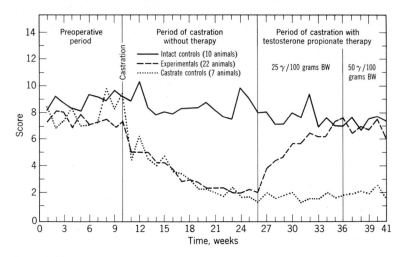

Figure 3-8   In a test of sexual behavior, the scores made by male rats declined as a result of castration. Experimental testosterone therapy restored sexual behavior to near preoperative level. From Sawyer 1960 after Grunt and Young.

performance after identical testosterone therapy corresponding to differences they exhibited before castration (Young 1957). Beach and Holz (1946) and Beach and Fowler (1959) also found that the castrate male rats most active sexually before the operation needed the least testosterone to restore their ability to copulate. An element of individuality is also implied by observations that individual female silver foxes and mink are somewhat consistent from year to year in the date of mating (Pearson and Bassett 1946, Enders 1952).

◆ *Mechanisms of Hormone Action.* How do gonadal hormones achieve their customary effect? Various lines of evidence show that parts of the central nervous system, particularly in the hypothalamus, respond to the sex hormones by facilitating one pattern of sexual behavior or the other (review in Sawyer 1960).

Higher centers are also involved. The cerebral cortex is more dispensable for sexual behavior in female mammals than in males, though it is more important in the parental behavior of the female. The rhinencephalon and the reticular system are also implicated, and the former in particular seems to have inhibitory effects, so that lesions may cause hypersexuality (Sawyer 1960, Beach 1964). And of course the mid- and hindbrain and the spinal cord are intimately concerned with the spatial and temporal organizations of the behavior patterns used, as they are with all motor activities.

→ *Peripheral Hormonal Effects.* Hormones act not only upon the central nervous system to condition or trigger behavior but also peripherally upon sensory and motor structures. These peripheral effects in turn have direct repercussions on behavior. Consider, for example, the effect of testosterone on the penis of the male rat. One of the changes that takes place after castration of an adult is a reduction in the development of papillae on the glans penis. Testosterone therapy restores the papillae, and Beach and Levinson (1950) demonstrated quantitative correspondence between the rate of their reappearance and the onset of renewed mating activity (Figure 3–9). There are sensory nerve endings immediately below these papillae. It seems reasonable to suppose that their increased sensitivity contributes to the resurgence of sexual activity. Their contribution is dispensable, because mounting and other phases of sexual activity can persist after the genitalia are anesthetized, even though intromission and ejaculation are impossible (Adler and Bermant in press).

Peripheral hormonal effects have been invoked to explain other behavior patterns as well. Lehrman (1955) has shown that in ring doves regurgitation of crop milk to the young, induced by LTH, is in part the result of sensitization of the external wall of the crop to emetic stimuli created by pecking movements of the young. Similarly, the nest-building

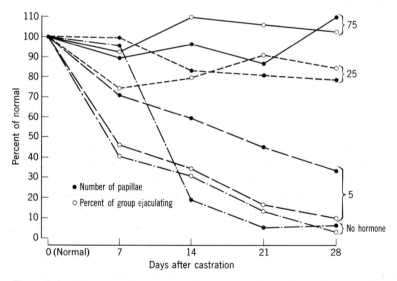

Figure 3-9 The effect of testosterone therapy upon the papillae of the penis of a castrated rat. The dosage of testosterone in micrograms per day is indicated in the brackets to the right. Sexual performance and number of papillae relative to intact animals are indicated as percent of normal. After Beach and Levinson 1950.

behavior of rats is affected by a variety of hormones and other factors, all apparently connected with the threshold of response to temperature change in the environment. Although hypophysectomy increases nest building, it is the relationship with the thyroid rather than the gonads that is significant, because of its role in the control of body temperature (review in Lehrman 1961).

The incubation patch of some birds, induced by the combined effects of gonadal steroids and LTH, may serve as a modified receptor surface with consequent effects on behavior. There is greater tactile sensitivity and possibly increased sensitivity to the temperature of the eggs and young. Tactile stimulation of the ventral integument may even be needed for complete morphological development of the incubation patch (Selander and Kuich 1963, see page 89). This sensitivity seems to be related to the timing of changes in the selection of nesting material and mode of construction of the nest (Hinde 1962, Hinde and Steel 1962, Hinde, Bell and Steel 1963).

The dichotomy between central and peripheral hormonal effects is not complete (Lehrman 1961). After all, the nervous system is necessarily involved whenever behavior occurs. Efferent control of the function of many receptors (see page 421) makes the distinction between central and peripheral effects still less absolute. Nevertheless, the theoretical emphasis on peripheral effects by Lehrman, Schneirla (1956), Rosenblatt and Aronson (1958a, b), and others has illuminated a previously neglected aspect of the problem. To understand the behavior completely, the environment in which the animal is placed, as well as its internal physiological state, must be considered.

◆ *Variation in the Degree of Hormonal Control.* Castration of adult animals generally eliminates sexual behavior, quickly in females, more gradually in males. The exceptions to this rule have a special theoretical interest (Beach 1948, 1958, 1964, Aronson 1959, etc.). Some men and women continue to engage in sexual behavior after loss of the gonads. The same is true of various lower primate males, but females generally cease sexual activity after castration. In intact female primates, however, sexual behavior is not completely restricted to estrus. Male cats and dogs sometimes continue to engage in sexual activity long after castration (Rosenblatt and Aronson 1958a, b), but castrated females do not. Moreover, the sexual activity of intact female cats, and indeed of all nonprimate female mammals, is restricted to estrus (Beach 1964, Michael 1961). In rodents castration tends to eliminate the sexual behavior of both sexes, although there are exceptions.

Beach (1958) has suggested a phylogenetic series. Going up the scale there is gradual emancipation of sexual behavior from complete dependence on gonadal hormones, most evident in the male but perceptible in the female. This series is paralleled by changes in the role of the cerebral cortex. Removal of large portions of the cerebral cortex has more effect on the sexual behavior of male rats than of female rats, but males can still mate after very extensive ablations. In cats there is a similar contrast between males and females. But the sexual behavior of male cats is more affected by limited cortical ablations than that of male rats.

The suggestion is that in some carnivores and primates the cerebral cortex has taken over functions which in lower mammals can be performed only under the influence of gonadal hormones. There is generally a greater involvement of the cerebral cortex in the sexual behavior of males than of females, irrespective of phylogenetic level (Beach 1958, 1964).

The prominence of cortical involvement, especially in males, suggests that learning may be important in this emancipation from hormonal control. The influence of learning on the sexual behavior of men has long been recognized. It is also generally agreed that women are less affected in this regard (Beach 1958, 1964, Ford and Beach 1951).

Careful experiments by Rosenblatt and Aronson (1958a, b) have established the importance of learning in the sexual behavior of male cats. Persistence of sexual behavior after castration is dependent upon prior sexual experience. The possible substitution for gonadal effects of sex hormone secretion from sources other than the gonads, such as the adrenal cortex, has been disposed of effectively (review in Aronson 1959). Androgens are necessary for the initiation of sexual behavior during ontogeny, however. Beach (1958) has presented evidence that experience plays a part in shaping the sexual behavior of other higher mammals as well. The general case is well established for the partial replacement of hormonal control of sexual behavior by neural control, as a result of experience in certain species of mammals.

Aronson (1959) has drawn attention to many variations in sexual behavior throughout the animal kingdom that remain unexplained. The sexual behavior of some male fish persists for a time after castration; in others it quickly ceases. Aronson suggests that there may be cases of parallel evolution among teleost fishes, and there is good reason for taking care in deciding exactly what constitutes a phylogenetic series. Certainly experience can play a very crucial role in the development of sexual behavior of vertebrates at many phylogenetic levels (e.g. Young 1961).

REFERENCES

Adler, N. and G. Bermant in press. Sexual behavior of male rats: effects of reduced sensory feedback.

Amoroso, E. C. and F. H. A. Marshall. 1960. External factors in sexual periodicity. In *Marshall's Physiology of Reproduction*, ed. by A. S. Parkes, Vol. 1, Part 2 (3rd edition):707–831. Longmans, Green and Company, London.

Aronson, L. R. 1945. Influence of the stimuli provided by the male cichlid fish, *Tilapia macrocephala*, on the spawning frequency of the female. *Physiol. Zool.*, **18**:403–415.

———. 1951. Factors influencing the spawning frequency in the female cichlid fish *Tilapia macrocephala*. *Amer. Mus. Novit.*, No. 1484:1–26.

———. 1957. Reproductive and parental behavior. In *The Physiology of Fishes*, ed. by M. E. Brown, Vol. **2**:271–304. The Academic Press, New York.

———. 1959. Hormones and reproductive behavior: some phylogenetic considerations. In *Comparative Endocrinology*, ed. by A. Gorbman: 98–120. John Wiley and Sons, New York.

Baggerman, B. 1957. An experimental study on the timing of breeding and migration in the three-spined stickleback (*Gasterosteus aculeatus* L.). *Archiv. Néerl. Zool.*, **12**:105–317.

———. 1959. The role of external factors and hormones in migration of sticklebacks and juvenile salmon. In *Comparative Endocrinology*, ed. by A. Gorbman: 24–70. John Wiley and Sons, New York.

Bailey, R. E. 1952. The incubation patch of passerine birds. *Condor*, **54**:121–136.

Barrass, R. 1960. The courtship behavior of *Mormoniella vitripennis* Walk. (Hymenoptera, Pteromalidae). *Behaviour*, **15**:185–209.

———. 1961. A quantitative study of the behaviour of the male *Mormoniella vitripennis* (Walker) (Hymenoptera, Pteromalidae) towards two constant stimulus-situations. *Behaviour*, **18**:288–312.

Barth, R. H., Jr. 1962. The endocrine control of mating behavior in the cockroach *Byrsotria fumigata* (Guérin). *Gen. Comp. Endocrinol.*, **2**:53–69.

Beach, F. A. 1948. *Hormones and Behavior*. Paul B. Hoeber, New York.

———. 1951. Instinctive behavior: reproductive activities. In *Handbook of Experimental Psychology*, ed. by S. S. Stevens: 387–434. John Wiley and Sons, New York.

———. 1956. Characteristics of masculine "sex drive." *Neb. Symp. Motiv.*, **4**:1–32.

———. 1958. Neural and chemical regulation of behavior. In *Biological and Biochemical Bases of Behavior*, ed. by H. F. Harlow and C. N. Woolsey: 263–284. University of Wisconsin Press, Madison.

———. 1964. Biological bases for reproductive behavior. In *Social Behavior and Organization Among Vertebrates*, ed. by W. Etkin: 117–142. University of Chicago Press, Chicago.

——— and H. Fowler. 1959. Individual differences in the response of male rats to androgen. *J. comp. physiol. Psychol.*, **52**:50–52.

——— and A. M. Holz. 1946. Mating behavior in male rats castrated at various ages and injected with androgen. *J. Exp. Zool.*, **101**:91–142.

——— and J. Jaynes. 1956a. Studies of maternal retrieving in rats. I: Recognition of young. *J. Mammal.*, **37**:177–180.

——— and ———. 1956b. Studies of maternal retrieving in rats. III. Sensory cues involved in the lactating female's response to her young. *Behaviour*, **10**:104–125.

——— and G. Levinson. 1950. Effects of androgen on the glans penis and mating behavior of castrated male rats. *J. Exp. Zool.*, **114**:159–171.

——— and R. G. Rabedeau. 1959. Sexual exhaustion and recovery in the male hamster. *J. comp. physiol. Psychol.*, **52**:56–61.

———— and R. E. Whalen. 1959. Effects of intromission without ejaculation upon sexual behavior in male rats. *J. comp. physiol. Psychol.,* **52:**476–481.

Bell, R. Q. and R. A. Hinde. 1963. Brood patch sensitivity of female canaries brought into reproductive condition in winter. *Anim. Behav.,* **11:**561–565.

Benoit, J. 1938. Rôle des yeux et de la voie nerveuse oculo-hypophysaire dans la gonado-stimulation par la lumière artificielle chez le canard domestique. *Comp. Rend. Séanc. Soc. Biol.,* **129:**231–234.

Berger, A. J. 1961. *Bird Study.* John Wiley and Sons, New York.

Bissonnette, T. H. 1936. Sexual photoperiodicity. *Quart. Rev. Biol.,* **11:**371–386.

Bol, A. C. A. 1959. A consummatory situation. The effect of eggs on the sexual behaviour of the male three-spined stickleback *(Gasterosteus aculeatus* L.). *Experientia,* **15:**115.

Bullough, W. S. 1961. *Vertebrate Sexual Cycles.* Methuen and Company, London.

Clark, L. B. and W. N. Hess. 1942 (1940). Swarming of the Atlantic palolo worm, *Leodice fucata* (Ehlers). Papers from Tortugas Laboratory, **33:**21–70. Carnegie Institute of Washington, Publ. 524.

Corney, B. C. 1922. Abstract of a paper on the periodicity of the swarming palolo *(Eunice viridis,* Gr.). *J. Torquay Nat. Hist. Soc.,* **3:**126–130.

Eisenberg, J. 1962. Studies on the behavior of *Peromyscus maniculatus gambelii* and *Peromyscus californicus parasiticus. Behaviour,* **19:**177–207.

————. 1963. The behavior of heteromyid rodents. *Univ. Calif. Publ. Zool.,* **69:**1–114.

————. 1966. The social organizations of mammals. *Handb. Zool. Berlin,* **10**(7):1–92.

Eisner, E. 1960. The relationship of hormones to the reproductive behaviour of birds, referring especially to parental behaviour: a review. *Anim. Behav.,* **8:**155–179.

Enders, R. K. 1952. Reproduction in the mink *(Mustela vison). Proc. Amer. Philos. Soc.,* **96:**691–755.

Erickson, C. J. and D. S. Lehrman. 1964. Effect of castration of male ring doves upon ovarian activity of females. *J. comp. physiol. Psychol.,* **58:**164–166.

Everett, J. W. 1961. The mammalian female reproductive cycle and its controlling mechanisms. In *Sex and Internal Secretions,* ed. by W. C. Young, Vol. **1:**497–555. The Williams and Wilkins Company, Baltimore.

Fabricius, E. and K.-J. Gustafson. 1955. Observations on the spawning behaviour of the grayling, *Thymallus thymallus* (L.). *Inst. Freshwater Res. Rep.,* No. **36:**75–103.

Farner, D. S. 1955. The annual stimulus for migration: experimental and physiologic aspects. In *Recent Studies in Avian Biology,* ed. by A. Wolfson: 198–237. University of Illinois Press, Urbana.

————. 1959. Photoperiodic control of annual gonadal cycles in birds. In *Photoperiodism and Related Phenomena in Plants and Animals,* ed. by R. B. Withrow: 717–750. American Association for the Advancement of Science, Washington.

————. 1964. The photoperiodic control of reproductive cycles in birds. *Amer. Scient.,* **52:**137–156.

————. 1965. Circadian systems in the photoperiodic responses of vertebrates. In *Circadian Clocks,* ed. by J. Aschoff: 357–369. North-Holland Publishing Company, Amsterdam.

Fisher, A. E. 1962. Effects of stimulus variation on sexual satiation in the male rat. *J. comp. physiol. Psychol.,* **55:**614–620.

Ford, C. S. and F. A. Beach. 1951. *Patterns of Sexual Behavior.* Harper and Brothers, New York.

Fowler, H. and R. E. Whalen. 1961. Variation in incentive stimulus and sexual behavior in the male rat. *J. comp. physiol. Psychol.,* **54:**68–71.

Frith, J. H. 1960. The ecology of wild ducks in New South Wales. IV. Breeding. Commonwealth Scientific and Industrial Research Organization, *Wildlife Res.,* **4:**156–172.

Gamulin, T. and J. Hure. 1956. Spawning of the sardine at a definite time of day. *Nature* (London), **177**:193–194.

Gorbman, A. and H. A. Bern. 1962. *A Textbook of Comparative Endocrinology*. John Wiley and Sons, New York.

Grunt, J. A. and W. C. Young. 1952. Psychological modification of fatigue following orgasm (ejaculation) in the male guinea pig. *J. comp. physiol. Psychol.*, **45**:508–510.

Hale, E. B. and J. O. Almquist. 1960. Relation of sexual behavior to germ cell output in farm animals. *J. Dairy Sci.* Suppl., **43**:145–169.

Hamilton, W. J. III. 1962. Reproductive adaptations of the red tree mouse. *J. Mammal.*, **43**:486–504.

Hamner, W. M. 1963. Diurnal rhythm and photoperiodism in testicular recrudescence of the house finch. *Science*, **142**:1294–1295.

———. 1965. Avian photoperiodic response-rhythms: evidence and inference. In *Circadian Clocks*, ed. by J. Aschoff: 379–384. North-Holland Publishing Company, Amsterdam.

Harvey, E. B., R. Yanagimachi, and M. C. Chang. 1961. Onset of estrus and ovulation in the golden hamster. *J. Exp. Zool.*, **146**:231–236.

Hinde, R. A. 1958. The nest-building behaviour of domesticated canaries. *Proc. Zool. Soc. Lond.*, **131**:1–48.

———. 1959. Unitary drives. *Anim. Behav.*, **7**:130–141.

———. 1962. Temporal relations of brood patch development in domesticated canaries. *Ibis*, **104**:90–97.

———, R. Q. Bell, and E. Steel. 1963. Changes in sensitivity of the canary brood patch during the natural breeding season. *Anim. Behav.*, **11**:553–560.

——— and E. A. Steel. 1962. Selection of nest material by female canaries. *Anim. Behav.*, **10**:67–75.

——— and ———. 1964. Effect of exogenous hormones on the tactile sensitivity of the canary brood patch. *J. Endocrin.*, **30**:355–359.

Immelmann, K. 1963a. Tierische Jahresperiodik in ökologischer Sicht. *Zool. Jahrb., Abt. Syst. Ökol. Geogr.*, **91**:91–200.

———. 1963b. Drought adaptations in Australian desert birds. *Proc. 13th Int. Orn. Congr.*: 649–657.

Jakway, J. S. 1959. Inheritance of patterns of mating behaviour in the male guinea pig. *Anim. Behav.*, **7**:150–162.

Johns, J. E. and E. W. Pfeiffer. 1963. Testosterone-induced incubation patches of phalarope birds. *Science*, **140**:1225–1226.

Karlson, P. and A. Butenandt. 1959. Pheromones (ectohormones) in insects. *Ann. Rev. Ent.*, **4**:39–58.

Larsson, K. 1956. Conditioning and sexual behavior in the male albino rat. *Acta Psychol. Gothoburg.*, **1**:1–269.

———. 1958. Aftereffects of copulatory activity of the male rat: II. *J. comp. physiol. Psychol.*, **51**:417–420.

Lehrman, D. S. 1955. The physiological basis of parental feeding behavior in the ring dove (*Streptopelia risoria*). *Behaviour*, **7**:241–286.

———. 1958a. Induction of broodiness by participation in courtship and nestbuilding in the ring dove (*Streptopelia risoria*). *J. comp. physiol. Psychol.*, **51**:32–36.

———. 1958b. Effect of female sex hormones on incubation behavior in the ring dove (*Streptopelia risoria*). *J. comp. physiol. Psychol.*, **51**:142–145.

———. 1959. Hormonal responses to external stimuli in birds. *Ibis*, **101**:478–496.

———. 1961. Hormonal regulation of parental behavior in birds and infrahuman mammals.

In *Sex and Internal Secretions*, ed. by W. C. Young, Vol. 2:1268–1382. The Williams and Wilkins Company, Baltimore.

———. 1964. Control of behavior cycles in reproduction. In *Social Behavior and Organization among Vertebrates*, ed. by W. Etkin: 143–166. University of Chicago Press, Chicago.

Lofts, B. and A. J. Marshall. 1961. Zugunruhe activity in castrated bramblings *Fringilla montifringilla*. *Ibis*, **103a**:189–194.

Lorenz, K. Z. 1941. Vergleichende Bewegungsstudien an Anatinen. *J. Orn.*, **89** (Suppl. 3): 194–293.

Makkink, G. F. 1936. An attempt at an ethogram of the European avocet (*Recurvirostra avosetta* L.) with ethological and psychological remarks. *Ardea*, **25**:1–62.

Marler, P. 1957. Specific distinctiveness in the communication signals of birds. *Behaviour*, **11**:13–39.

Marshall, A. J. 1952. The interstitial cycle in relation to autumn and winter sexual behaviour in birds. *Proc. Zool. Soc. Lond.*, **121**:727–740.

———. 1960. Annual periodicity in the migration and reproduction of birds. *Cold Spr. Harb. Symp. Quant. Biol.*, **25**:499–505.

———. 1961. Breeding seasons and migration. In *Biology and Comparative Physiology of Birds*, ed. by A. J. Marshall, Vol. 2;307–339. The Academic Press, New York.

——— and H. J. de S. Disney. 1957. Experimental induction of the breeding season in a xerophilous bird. *Nature*, **180**:647–649.

Marshall, F. H. A. 1956. The breeding season. In *Marshall's Physiology of Reproduction* (3rd edition), ed. by A. S. Parkes, Vol. I, Part 1:1–42. Longmans, Green and Company, London.

Matthews, L. H. 1939. Visual stimulation and ovulation in pigeons. *Proc. Roy. Soc. Lond., B,* **126**:557–560.

Mayr, E. 1942. *Systematics and the Origin of Species*. Columbia University Press, New York.

———. 1963. *Animal Species and Evolution*. Harvard University Press, Cambridge.

Michael, R. P. 1961. Observations upon the sexual behaviour of the domestic cat (*Felis catus* L.) under laboratory conditions. *Behaviour*, **18**:1–24.

Miller, A. H. 1955. The expression of innate reproductive rhythm under conditions of winter lighting. *Auk*, **72**:260–264.

———. 1962. Bimodal occurrence of breeding in an equatorial sparrow. *Proc. Nat. Acad. Sci.*, (Wash.), **48**:396–400.

Moreau, R. E. 1950. The breeding seasons of African birds—I. Land birds. *Ibis*, **92**:223–267.

Morton, M. L. and L. R. Mewaldt. 1962. Some effects of castration on a migratory sparrow (*Zonotrichia atricapilla*). *Physiol. Zool.*, **35**:237–247.

Munn, N. L. 1950. *Handbook of Psychological Research on the Rat*. Houghton Mifflin Company, Boston.

Nalbandov, A. V. 1958. *Reproductive Physiology*. W. H. Freeman and Company, Publishers, San Francisco.

Orians, G. 1960. Autumnal breeding in the tricolored blackbird. *Auk*, **77**:379–398.

Pearson, O. P. 1944. Reproduction in the shrew (*Blarina brevicauda* Say). *Amer. J. Anat.*, **75**:39–93.

——— and R. K. Enders. 1944. Duration of pregnancy in certain mustelids. *J. Exp. Zool.*, **95**:21–35.

——— and C. F. Bassett. 1946. Certain aspects of reproduction in a herd of silver foxes. *Amer. Nat.*, **80**:45–67.

Rheingold, H. L. 1963. *Maternal Behavior in Mammals*. John Wiley and Sons, New York.

Rosenblatt, J. S. and L. R. Aronson. 1958a. The decline of sexual behavior in male cats after castration with special reference to the role of prior sexual experience. *Behaviour*, **12**:285–338.

——— and ———. 1958b. The influence of experience on the behavioural effects of androgen in prepuberally castrated male cats. *Brit. J. Anim. Behav.*, **6**:171–182.

Rowell, T. E. 1960. On the retrieving of young and other behaviour in lactating golden hamsters *Proc. Zool. Soc. Lond.*, **135**:265–282.

———. 1961. Maternal behaviour in non-maternal golden hamsters (*Mesocricetus auratus*). *Anim. Behav.*, **9**:11–15.

———. 1963. Behaviour and female reproductive cycles of rhesus macaques. *J. Reprod. Fertil.*, **6**:193–203.

Sawyer, C. H. 1960. Reproductive behavior. In *Handbook of Physiology*, ed. by J. Field, Sec. 1, Vol. 2:1225–1240. American Physiological Society, Washington, D.C.

Schildmacher, H. 1956. Physiologische Untersuchungen am Grünfinken *Chloris chloris* (L.) im künstlichem Kurztag und nach 'hormonaler Sterilisierung.' *Biol. Zbl.*, **75**:327–355.

Schneirla, T. C. 1953. Collective activities and social patterns among insects. In *Insect Physiology*, ed. by K. D. Roeder: 748–779. John Wiley and Sons, New York.

———. 1956. Interrelationships of the 'innate' and the 'acquired' in instinctive behavior. In *L'Instinct dans le Comportement des Animaux et de l'Homme:* 387–439. Fondation Singer-Polignac. Masson et Cie Editeurs, Paris.

———. 1957. Theoretical consideration of cyclic processes in doryline ants. *Proc. Amer. Phil. Soc.*, **101**:106–133.

Selander, R. K. 1963. The problem of timing of development of the incubation patch in male birds. *Condor*, **66**:75–76.

——— and L. L. Kuich. 1963. Hormonal control and development of the incubation patch in icterids, with notes on behavior of cowbirds. *Condor*, **65**:73–90.

——— and D. J. Nicholson. 1962. Autumnal breeding of boat-tailed grackles in Florida. *Condor*, **64**:81–91.

——— and S. Y. Yang. In press. The incubation patch of the house sparrow, *Passer domesticus* Linnaeus.

Serventy, D. L. and A. J. Marshall. 1957. Breeding periodicity in Western Australian birds: with an account of unseasonal nestings in 1953 and 1955. *Emu*, **57**:99–126.

Sevenster-Bol, A. C. A. 1962. On the causation of drive reduction after a consummatory act. *Arch. Néerl. Zool.*, **15**:175–236.

Sibley, C. G. 1957. The evolutionary and taxonomic significance of sexual dimorphism and hybridization in birds. *Condor*, **59**:166–191.

Soulairac, A. 1952. Étude expérimentale du comportement sexuel male. Indépendance relative des diverse éléments moteurs chez le rat male normal. *Ann. Endocr.*, **13**:775–780.

Steel, E. A. and R. A. Hinde. 1964. Effect of exogenous oestrogen on brood patch development of intact and ovariectomized canaries. *Nature*, **202**:718–719.

Tavolga, W. N. 1954. Reproductive behavior in the gobiid fish *Bathygobius soporator*. *Bull. Amer. Mus. Nat. Hist.*, **104**:427–460.

———. 1956. Visual, chemical and sound stimuli as cues in the sex discriminatory behavior of gobiid fish, *Bathygobius soporator*. *Zoologica*, **41**:49–64.

Tienhoven, A. van. 1961. Endocrinology of reproduction in birds. In *Sex and Internal Secretion*, ed. by W. C. Young, Vol. 2:1088–1170. The Williams and Wilkins Company, Baltimore.

Tordoff, H. B. and W. R. Dawson. 1965. The influence of daylength on reproductive timing in the red crossbill. *Condor*, **67**:416–422.

Walker, B. W. 1952. A guide to the grunion. *Calif. Fish and Game*, **38**:409–420.

Walton, A. 1955. Sexual behaviour. In *Progress in the Physiology of Farm Animals*, ed. by J. Hammond, Vol. 2:603–616. Butterworth and Company (Publishers), London.

Warren, R. P. and R. A. Hinde. 1961. Roles of the male and the nest-cup in controlling the reproduction of female canaries. *Anim. Behav.*, **9**:64–67.

Weidmann, U. 1956. Observations and experiments on egg-laying in the blackheaded gull (*Larus ridibundus* L.). *Brit. J. Anim. Behav.*, **4**:150–161.

Wiepkema, P. R. 1961. An ethological analysis of the reproductive behaviour of the bitterling (*Rhodeus amarus* Bloch). *Arch. Néerl. Zool.*, **14**:103–199.

Wilson, E. O. and W. H. Bossert. 1963. Chemical communication among animals. *Recent Prog. Hormone Res.*, **19**:673–716.

Wilson, J. R., R. E. Kuehn, and F. A. Beach. 1963. Modification in the sexual behavior of male rats produced by changing the stimulus female. *J. comp. physiol. Psychol.*, **56**:636–644.

Witschi, E. 1961. Sex and secondary sexual characters. In *Biology and Comparative Physiology of Birds*, ed. by A. J. Marshall, Vol. 2:115–168. The Academic Press, New York.

Wolfson, A. 1959. The role of light and darkness in the regulation of spring migration and reproductive cycles in birds. In *Photoperiodism and Related Phenomena in Plants and Animals*, ed. by R. B. Withrow: 679–716. American Association for the Advancement of Science, Washington, D.C.

———. 1960. Regulation of annual periodicity in the migration and reproduction of birds. *Cold Spr. Harb. Symp. Quant. Biol.*, **25**:507–514.

Young, W. C. 1957. Genetic and psychological determinants of sexual behavior patterns. In *Hormones, Brain Function and Behavior*, ed. by H. Hoagland: 75–98. Proceedings of a conference in neuroendocrinology held at Harriman, New York in 1956. The Academic Press, New York.

———. 1961. Hormones and mating behavior. In *Sex and Internal Secretions*, ed. by W. C. Young, Vol. 2:1173–1239. The Williams and Wilkins Company, Baltimore.

four

FEEDING, DRINKING, AND BREATHING

Approaches to the study of motivation • Temporal organization of feeding • The problem of 'hunger' • Centers in the hypothalamus • External stimuli and the dynamics of food selection • Feeding behavior of flies • Parallels with drinking and breathing.

The analysis of motivation is the hub of behavior study. To understand completely the motivation of a particular behavior pattern, it is necessary to know all the factors that influence its predictability. What will be its timing, its completeness, its frequency of occurrence, and its duration? What kinds of barriers will be overcome in order to achieve it? What effect does it have on the readiness to learn? Described in this way, the reason for the central position of motivation analysis is clear, for it encompasses a large sector of behavioral science. For this same reason the subject is intimidating in its extent, covering both the effects of external stimuli and changing internal states.

THE HOMEOSTATIC APPROACH TO MOTIVATION ANALYSIS

The concept most frequently used to unify these diverse phenomena is homeostasis (e.g. Hull 1943, Dempsey 1951, Lindsley 1957, Hebb 1958, Young 1961). The physiologists Bernard (1878) and Cannon (1932) drew attention to the remarkable capacity of living organisms to maintain a constant internal environment in the face of diverse disruptive influences from the external world. The chemical composition of mammalian blood, for example, varies within remarkably narrow limits. If these limits are exceeded death is likely. Normally excessive deviation from the normal condition is prevented by an array of homeostatic physiological response mechanisms that come into play when the concentration of some substance changes significantly. These responses serve to counteract the change and return the composition of the blood to its equilibrium state.

The concept of homeostasis has been extended to include behavioral responses as well. Direct support for this approach to motivation analysis came from C. P. Richter (1942). He showed how behavior could be involved in the same physiological mechanisms that Bernard investigated. The loss of sodium chloride in the urine is normally restricted by adrenocortical hormones. When the adrenal cortex of a rat is removed, control of the salt levels fails and sodium chloride is excreted rapidly in the urine. Such an animal will normally die. But Richter found that if it was given access to salt solutions, it would seek them out and make up the deficit by drinking them in large quantities (see Bare 1949). Thus it might remain alive and in good health, behavior substituting for the physiological mechanisms of homeostasis.

The loss of calcium from the blood of mammals is controlled mainly by the parathyroid glands. When the calcium level drops too low, the animal dies. Richter found that a rat whose parathyroid glands had been removed could avoid death if it was given access to calcium salts. It ate these in large quantities, counterbalancing urinary losses of calcium. Behavioral responses to excessive heat or cold parallel the physiological mechanisms of the thyroid gland and the autonomic nervous system in the same way.

The homeostatic approach is less appropriate for the analysis of some other types of behavior (Young 1961) that cannot readily be related to physiological deficit or excess. Expressed in psychological terms, motives are by no means always coincident with bodily needs. Reproductive behavior, for example, cannot be regarded in the same terms as respiration. If an animal does not respire, it will die but, as Beach (1956) points out, "no one ever died for the lack of sex." Even in feeding behavior the homeostatic approach has limited value. Obviously, the overall pattern of food consumption is related to the maintenance of a stable internal environment. But if we are also concerned with understanding the detailed structure of feeding behavior, a homeostatic framework is less useful as a guide to experimental design. An alternative approach is to start by describing the temporal organization of the behavior, and then to try to explain the various characteristics of the pattern.

PATTERNS OF FEEDING BEHAVIOR

Feeding behavior is incredibly varied and complex throughout the animal kingdom. There is a complete spectrum of temporal patterning, from animals that feed almost continuously, such as certain filter feeding invertebrates, to others, such as some parasitic insects and carnivorous vertebrates, that feed rarely, at intervals of many hours, days, or weeks. There are phases in the life cycle of some animals when there is no feeding at all, such as in the adult of some insects and in the male fur seal while he is ashore defending his territory. Most animals are somewhere between these extremes, feeding at relatively short intervals measured in minutes or a few hours. Among the many examples are rats (Richter 1927, Teitelbaum and Campbell 1958), mice (Anliker and Mayer 1956), cattle (Hafez and Schein 1962), birds (Hamilton and Cutler in press), fish (Tugendhat 1960), and flies (Evans and Barton Browne 1960). Discussion will be restricted to animals in this more familiar condition.

Rats feed at average intervals of about 2 to 4 hours (Richter 1927). There are wide variations and individual differences, and the interval can be changed by training (Bindra 1959). Nevertheless, a cyclic pattern of one kind or another persists, with statistically predictable intervals between feeding bouts (Figure 4–1). Cattle feed with a fairly regular pattern of distinct bouts during the course of the day (review in Hafez and Schein 1962). A small passerine bird (Figure 4–1), the bobolink, *Dolichonyx oryzivorus* (Hamilton and Cutler in press), also has a rhythmical feeding pattern.

If we expand the time scale and look at the behavior that makes up one cycle of feeding activity, more details of the pattern are revealed. The prelude to a bout of eating is often locomotion, either in free exploration of the environment or in movement to a location where food is habitually found. This appetitive phase is followed by the behavior associated with selecting, preparing, and ingesting food—the consummatory phase. After one or more such sequences, sometimes interspersed with further searching which may make up a regular pattern of subcycles, the bout ends. The interval that follows may be occupied with a variety of other activities such as locomotion, resting, sleeping, drinking, and social encounters. Between bouts of feeding, cattle spend much of the time ruminating, i.e. regurgitating food, chewing it, and swallowing it again (review in Hafez and Schein 1962).

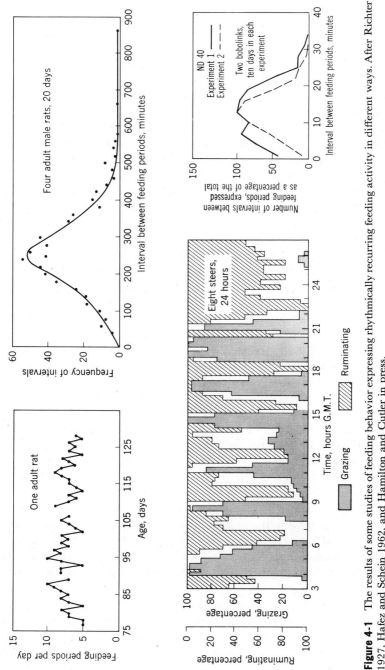

Figure 4-1 The results of some studies of feeding behavior expressing rhythmically recurring feeding activity in different ways. After Richter 1927, Hafez and Schein 1962, and Hamilton and Cutler in press.

ENDOGENOUS FACTORS: THE PROBLEM OF 'HUNGER'

◆ *Feeding Patterns in Cattle.* During a session of feeding there are often hints of variation in the vigor or persistence with which the behavior is performed. As a cow goes through a bout of feeding, "subtle changes in pattern are evident. . . . Initially, grazing is intermittent and selectivity is low: grass stems are ingested along with the leafy pasture. As the period progresses grazing becomes steady and selectivity gradually increases. Towards the end, grazing again becomes intermittent and selectivity is marked with grass stems being completely avoided" (Hafez and Schein 1962). There are also variations in the periodic pattern of feeding. Some sessions are short, others are longer. The rate of feeding behavior can vary from bout to bout. One's initial inclination is to assume that such changes in the intensity of feeding behavior reflect something equivalent to a state of 'hunger' in the animal.

Such an inference can be misleading when considered in detail, but taken at a simple level it suggests some useful questions. For example, we might expect that an exceptionally long interval between feeding bouts would leave an animal hungrier than usual and would thus be followed by an unusually long feeding bout.

◆ *Feeding Patterns in Birds.* Bobolinks do indeed have long feeding bouts after not eating for a considerable period of time (Hamilton and Cutler in press). The relationship is not a simple, linear one, however. Increasing intervals between feeding bouts are followed by longer bouts only up to a certain point. Beyond this the duration of the feeding bout tends to level out. If it were assumed that hunger increases with length of the interval between bouts, the duration of feeding bouts would be a poor measure of the level of hunger over most of the range of variation. Actually, when there is free access to food, as was the case with the bobolinks, a long pause might simply be a consequence of an unusually large meal beforehand, leaving the animal not much hungrier than usual. Without experimental manipulation of the interval between bouts, the issue remains inconclusive. We are still left with the problem of deciding how the notion of hunger as commonly used can be applied in feeding studies.

◆ *Stickleback Feeding.* Two independent studies have been made of the feeding behavior of the three-spined stickleback, *Gasterosteus aculeatus.* Beukema (1963) has described six basic elements in the feeding behavior of the stickleback: (1) turning eyes toward the prey, (2) orienting the body axis to the prey, (3) approaching, (4) picking up, (5) eating, or (6) rejecting. He made a special study of the relationship of the behavior to such factors as familiarity of the prey object (see later). Both he and Tugendhat (1960) also studied the effects of enforced deprivation.

Tugendhat selected two items for special study. Visual fixation of food is regarded as an 'initiated feeding response.' The act of snapping food up is called a 'completed feeding response.' In a normal feeding bout a stickleback fixates three or four times and then takes a worm into its mouth and swallows it. After a pause the responses are repeated. If a fish is deprived of food for some time and is then given a supply of worms, the pattern of feeding behavior changes. The rate of eating worms increases and then declines with satiation. In goldfish, Rozin and Mayer (1961) were able to show that the increased food intake balances the deficit.

After a long interval of enforced deprivation between feeding bouts in sticklebacks, the feeding which follows is in some respects more rapid, suggesting increased motivation. If the same 'hunger drive' energizes all feeding, any behavior related to the acquisition of food might be expected to occur more often, more persistently, and more vigorously when the drive increases.

As Tugendhat increased the length of the deprivation period, the number of completed feeding responses per hour increased when the fish were returned to an aquarium with an abundant supply of food, as might have been predicted. However, the total amount of time spent performing feeding movements was not greater after longer periods of deprivation because the feeding responses following longer deprivation were performed more rapidly.

Similar anomalies appeared in different measures of the decline of feeding during the course of 'satiation.' The frequency of completed feeding responses decreased, but the frequency of initiated feeding responses remained about the same, and sometimes even increased. The duration of feeding responses increased, so that the total time spent in feeding behavior remained steady and sometimes even increased.

A detailed view of the process of satiation reveals further complications (Figure 4–2). Although the number of completed feeding responses does decline at first, as we might expect, a recovery follows which is greatest after long periods of deprivation. Starved fish begin feeding at a high rate when they are returned to the test situation. A regrouping of the data into three classes according to the rate of feeding in the first 3 minutes rather than according to deprivation duration brings out the correlation between the rate of the initial decline and the subsequent recovery of the number of completed feeding responses (Figure 4–2b, 4–2c). For example, a high initial feeding rate may decline rapidly to a value below that observed in a fish which began at a lower rate (compare curves 2 and 3, arrow). Thus even the most straightforward measure of feeding behavior, the rate of eating, can give paradoxical results at certain stages in the process of satiation.

Finally, examination of the eating rates of individual fish during the process of satiation revealed that the rates at the bottom of the dip and at the top of the second high point correlated with the overall rate of eating in the whole session. Thus a fish which characteristically ate more rapidly had higher rates than one that ate more slowly. A comparison with the initial rate of eating revealed no correlation, so that a fish which ate rapidly on the average for the entire session might begin eating either slowly or rapidly.

These results on the feeding behavior of sticklebacks have been reviewed in detail because they reveal clearly the difficulties of drawing inferences about the underlying physiological mechanism from behavior studies. One measure of feeding behavior, the rate of completed feeding responses, may lead us to infer that a single relatively simple mechanism underlies it; by this measure the 'feeding drive' increases progressively after greater periods of deprivation and declines during the process of satiation. Other measures show that the simplicity of this inference is an illusion. If the total time spent feeding is used as a measure, deprivation has no effect. Yet both can be regarded as measures of motivation. They must be related to underlying physiological states that are in some respects different.

Study of the process of satiation is equally complex. The initial rate of eating after deprivation is apparently affected by different processes than those that determine the rate at a later stage and the overall rate. Finally, there is the paradox that even the most direct measure of feeding, the rate of completed responses, indicates an *increase* in feeding motivation at one stage of the satiation process.

We cannot say what physiological mechanisms underlie these complex changes in the rates of different measures of feeding behavior, although Tugendhat has offered an explanatory model (Figure 4–3). Clearly a single 'unitary' mechanism, a feeding drive, will not suffice. Studies of motivation concepts derived from other types of behavior (Hinde 1959b) lead to a similar conclusion. There is a danger in basing hypotheses about motivation on a single measure of behavior. Accurate models of motivation must eventually be based on sophisticated descriptions of the physiological mechanisms which underlie the temporal pattern of behavior. Models based on behavior studies may suggest how these physiological studies should proceed, however.

Feeding behavior must satisfy certain nutritional requirements if the animal is to survive. From this point of view the homeostatic require-

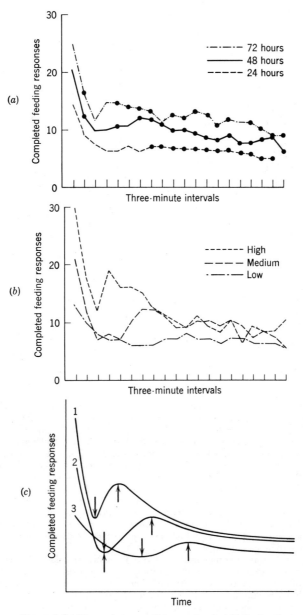

Figure 4-2 The eating rate of three-spined sticklebacks, *Gasterosteus aculeatus* after 24, 48, and 72 hours of food deprivation in the hour after they were returned to an aquarium with abundant food. (*a*) The fish are grouped according to duration of deprivation. (*b*) They are grouped according to initial rate of eating regardless of the deprivation period. (*c*) The results of (*b*) are presented as smooth curves. After Tugendhat 1960.

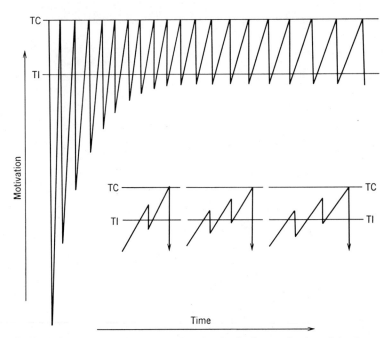

Figure 4-3 Tugendhat's model to describe the feeding motivation of the three-spined stickleback, *Gasterosteus aculeatus,* during a feeding session following starvation. From Tugendhat 1960, p. 301.

A model that describes the changes in feeding behavior occurring in the course of a feeding session. When motivation is below the threshold for initiations (TI) no feeding behavior appears, when it is above the threshold the fish initiate feeding responses, and when the threshold TC is reached the initiated feeding response will be completed. Feeding motivation then drops abruptly and builds up less steeply for each successive bout of feeding. The values to which motivation falls before building up again are very low early in the feeding session and less low later in the session. The effect of this change is shown in the spacing of completed responses in time. At first, the interval between successive completed responses grows longer, then it is shortened, and finally, for the remainder of the feeding session, the inter-response interval gradually lengthens. For successive completed responses there is more time during which motivation is above TI. There is also more time above the initiation threshold when equal units of time in the middle and very early in the feeding session are compared.

During the time that motivation is above TI, many initiations of short duration or fewer initiations of long duration may appear. The smaller diagrams suggest how frequency and duration are interrelated. These represent bouts of feeding behavior early, in the middle, and late in the session. The average rate of build-up is becoming less steep. Feeding motivation is represented as rising to TC in fluctuations that exceed the average rate of build-up and then fall proportionately below it. A feeding response will last for as long as motivation is above TI and some initiated feeding responses can be completed. The ratio of initiated to completed responses and the duration of all feeding responses increases with time in the feeding session.

To describe the difference between two deprivation groups, the early portions of the main diagram, with very steep rates of buildup, are omitted if deprivation time is shorter. A different decay function for the drop in motivation after completed responses, with a lesser rate of change, must be used.

ment is a simple one. Yet a variety of physiological mechanisms may be interposed between the response to deprivation of food and the eventual elimination of the deficit by food ingestion.

◆ *Feeding in Rats.* Different measures of the feeding behavior of rats reveal unexpected complexities. Rats deprived of food for varying periods of time and then presented with food, consisting of an enriched milk solution, were subjected to a series of different tests (Miller 1957). In one test group, the volume of milk drunk was measured. In another, the amount of quinine necessary to inhibit drinking was determined. In a third group, the measure of readiness to feed was the rate of bar pressing to obtain food in a Skinner box. In a fourth group, the measure of motivation was the frequency of stomach contractions, a response to starvation, as determined by inserting a balloon into the stomach.

The effects of different periods of deprivation on these four measures were by no means the same (Figure 4–4). The amount of milk drunk reached a maximum after 6 hours of deprivation and then declined, and the frequency of stomach contractions followed a similar course. The curves for the other measures continued to increase after as many as 54 hours of deprivation. Evidently the different measures of feeding in rats, as in sticklebacks, were influenced by somewhat different factors.

Other studies of feeding motivation in rats have focused on the characteristics of the overeating which resulted from certain brain lesions

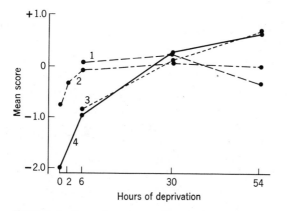

Figure 4-4   Several measures of hunger in starved rats. (1) The amount of milk drunk, (2) rate of stomach contractions, (3) amount of quinine in food before it will be rejected, and (4) the amount of bar pressing the rat will perform to obtain food. After Miller 1957.

(next section). Rats with such lesions ate more than usual and became very obese. Their motivation for feeding was stronger than usual if the amount of food eaten per day was used as a measure. Tests in a Skinner box, however, revealed the surprising fact that a 'hyperphagic' rat did not work as hard as a normal rat for his food by pressing a lever (Teitelbaum 1957). In another test a lid was placed over the food dish. The hyperphagic animals pushed unweighted lids off the food dishes and ate more than did the controls. But if the lid was weighted they ate less. Less quinine was necessary to inhibit feeding in the operated animals than in the controls, and they were more easily kept from food by an electric shock. Finally, they did not run as fast to reach food and did not pull as hard on a harness as did the controls. Once more we are reminded that conclusions derived from a single behavioral measure can be deceptive. The hyperphagic rats are less "hungry" than normal by some measures.

BRAIN CENTERS AND FEEDING IN MAMMALS

◆ *Hypothalamic Lesions.* The hypothalamus, lying in the floor of the third ventricle of the forebrain of mammals, has important functions regulating the coordination of feeding and many other types of behavior. Damage to the hypothalamus in rats, cats, mice, monkeys, or dogs (Morgane and Kosman 1960) may have quite different effects on feeding behavior, depending on the location of the lesion.

A rat with a lesion in the region of the ventromedial nucleus of the hypothalamus overeats until it becomes excessively obese; a 250-gram rat may consume food until it weighs more than 600 grams. On the other hand, a rat with damage or anaesthesia localized in the lateral portions of the hypothalamus will stop feeding and, unless it is kept alive by stomach tube feeding, will starve to death. Electrical stimulation of these areas has the opposite effect—medial stimulation inhibits feeding and lateral stimulation elicits it (reviews in Brobeck 1960, Anand 1961, Teitelbaum 1961). Thus there seem to be separate mechanisms for starting and terminating a bout of feeding.

The onset of feeding is associated with activity of the 'feeding centers' in the lateral hypothalamus. This activity involves not only the acts of eating and increased responsiveness to food stimuli but also the appetitive phase of locomotion; lesions in the lateral area result in both cessation of feeding and reduction of locomotion (Anand 1961).

Eating results in consequences which include activation of the 'satiety centers' in the medial hypothalamus. These centers inhibit the feeding center, and the bout of feeding behavior is terminated. Later the inhibition is relaxed, the feeding center becomes active, and another feeding bout ensues.

The reciprocal relationship between the feeding and satiety centers has been confirmed by an elegant experiment using intracranial self-stimulation. In a series of studies made by Olds (Olds and Milner 1954, Olds 1958), rats repeatedly stimulated themselves by pressing a lever in a Skinner box. With electrodes in the first position, the area of the lateral hypothalamus including the feeding centers, stimulation was rewarding in a learning situation. With electrodes in the second position, the area of the medial hypothalamus including the satiety centers, stimulation was either neutral or punishing.

By preparing rats with several electrode cannulas permitting both electrical stimulation and administration of a local anaesthetic, Hoebel and Teitelbaum (1962) were able to study directly the effects of one system on the other. They concluded that the medial and lateral centers control self-stimulation in a manner analogous to their control of feeding. Anaesthetization of the satiety centers resulted both in more feeding and in more self-stimulation in the feeding areas. Stimulation of the medial satiety center inhibited feeding and also inhibited self-stimulation of the lateral feeding centers. Previous feeding to satiation also inhibited lateral self-stimulation for periods from 30 minutes to 2 hours. A hungry animal engaged in more lateral self-stimulation, presumably with minimal activity of the satiety centers.

Although the hypothalamus clearly plays a major role in regulating food intake in mammals, it is not the only brain center concerned with this function in mammals. Lesions in the amygdala may also result in overeating in cats, although the hyperphagia is only one-third of that caused by medial hypothalamic lesions in the same species (Morgane and Kosman 1960). Other areas of the brain may be more concerned with discrimination and a predilection for certain food items.

◆ *Onset of Feeding.* We know from behavioral evidence that the activity of centers controlling the facilitation and inhibition of feeding must be related to the nutritive state of the animal. There is still doubt about how this balance is maintained. Consider the onset of a feeding bout that begins with appetitive behavior, rather than one that is immediately elicited by external stimuli from food. What activates the feeding center and leads to the onset of locomotion which results in feeding?

Early workers (Cannon 1929, Carlson 1916) thought that stomach contractions, which occur after a period without food, were instrumental in starting feeding behavior. After long periods of food deprivation they may have an important influence (Quigley 1955). But various lines of evidence suggest that their rate of contraction is unimportant in normal feeding. A man with a denervated stomach still eats regularly (Grossman 1955). Moreover, studies of the effects of various stomach conditions on electrical activity in the hypothalamic centers have shown that stomach contractions are not correlated with activity in the feeding centers, though they are inhibited during activity of the satiety centers (Sharma et al. 1961).

The evidence indicates that some parts of the brain, perhaps the feeding and satiety centers, respond directly to properties of the circulating blood and so instigate feeding behavior. Alternative or complementary suggestions about the eliciting stimuli, often well supported by evidence, include: a small difference in concentrations of glucose and other metabolites in the arterial and venous circulations, slight drops in body temperature, an increased availability of water in the body, and fluctuations in the concentration of a hormone (review in Anand 1961). Brobeck (1960) concludes that several of these factors and perhaps all will prove to be involved, but that it is not possible at the present time to assess quantitatively the relative significance of each (see also Rosenzweig 1963, de Ruiter 1963).

◆ *Duration of Feeding and its Cessation.* Once the hungry animal has located food, feeding behavior is elicited by the external stimuli provided by the food. What factors determine how long feeding will continue before the bout is terminated? Various consequences of feeding are involved. In the first place, the repeated eating and swallowing may itself eventually be self-exhausting as a result either of performance of the motor activity, or of stimulation of receptors in the head and throat. Thus an animal with a fistula which discharges food from the esophagus to the outside rather than to the stomach eats much more than usual. But it does not eat continuously; there are still bouts of feeding. A given quantity of food eaten through the mouth is more effective in reducing subsequent feeding than the same quantity of food given directly into the stomach (Grossman 1955, Miller 1957, Figure 4–5*a*). As a corollary, it has been established that an animal which is stomach-fed through a fistula with as much or more food than it normally eats in a meal still shows an appreciable amount of feeding behavior (Grossman 1955). It is therefore clear that oropharyngeal factors participate in terminating a bout of feeding behavior, though seldom with a dominant role.

Arrival of food in the stomach is critical in the process of satiation. Distension of the stomach wall stimulates stretch receptors which activate the satiety centers in the hypothalamus (Sharma et al. 1961). Partial inhibition of further feeding can be induced by filling the stomach

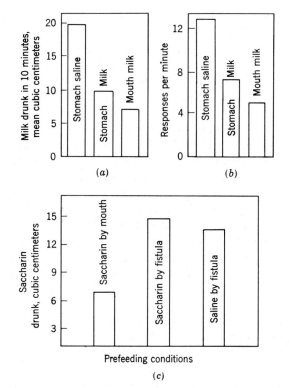

Figure 4-5 The amount of milk drunk by a rat in a 10-minute test period is affected by previous treatments. (*a*) Injection of 14 milliliters of milk directly into the stomach reduces subsequent milk uptake more than pretreatment with the same volume of saline. But the same volume of milk taken orally reduces subsequent uptake most of all. (*b*) The amount of bar pressing is the measure of motivation following pretreatments and the results are similar. (*c*) If a saccharin solution is injected directly into the stomach, it has an effect on subsequent drinking of saccharin solution similar to that of the same amount of normal saline. The same volume of saccharin solution taken by mouth reduces subsequent uptake. After Miller 1957.

with inert material. Food is more effective, however. Miller (1957) has shown this by comparing the effects on subsequent drinking of enriched milk, of injecting similar quantities of milk or isotonic saline directly into the stomach (Figure 4–5*b*). Furthermore, an animal given food that is diluted by varying amounts of inert material will compensate to some extent by eating more (e.g. Adolph 1947). The amount of stomach distension permitted before feeding stops must somehow be related to the nutritive properties of the food; chemoreceptors in the stomach may be responsible. Some further consequences of eating may come rapidly into play, such as the flow of fluids into the digestive tracts accompanying eating, the consequent dehydration of certain tissues, and the release of acetylcholine and other chemical mediators during intestinal absorption (Soulairac 1963).

In general, the assimilation of food is too slow to play a direct role in terminating feeding. Several investigators have pointed out the lack of relationship between the nutritive value of food consumed in a given bout of feeding behavior and the termination of that bout. A longer-term relationship necessarily exists, resulting in an overall correlation between the nutritive state of the animal and food intake. In this general maintenance of homeostasis, such factors as levels of glucose and other metabolites in the blood presumably come into play. The rise in temperature consequent upon assimilation of a meal may also play a part. In a number of animals warmth and hyperthermia inhibit eating while cold environments encourage it.

◆ *Body Weight and Feeding.* A possible relationship between body weight and food intake is suggested by Teitelbaum's (1957, 1961) studies of hyperphagic rats. The specific effects of lesions in the satiety centers in causing overeating have already been discussed (see page 124). In one of the few studies of the detailed temporal patterning of feeding behavior which have been published, he found that hyperphagic rats given an enriched fluid diet eat larger meals, but that they drink at a normal rate and eat meals with the usual frequency (Figure 4–6). With a solid diet, the increased food consumption in hyperphagia is associated with more frequent and larger meals. Teitelbaum associated this difference with the greater caloric value of the liquid diet. He went on to show that dilution of the liquid diet induced a predicted increase in the frequency of meals in both hyperphagic and normal rats.

Evidently the hyperphagic rat, though it overeats, still regulates the caloric intake of food. Lesions in the satiation centers do not cause completely unregulated feeding behavior, but something more subtle. Teitelbaum notes that the behavior of a hyperphagic rat changes strikingly when it reaches a certain degree of obesity, and its feeding behavior comes to resemble that of a normal rat (Figure 4–6). An obese hyperphagic rat ceases to overeat and consumes only enough to maintain its overweight condition in a steady state. This behavior suggests that body weight or some correlate of it is another factor related to the organization of feeding behavior and that this relationship is disrupted by lesions in the satiety

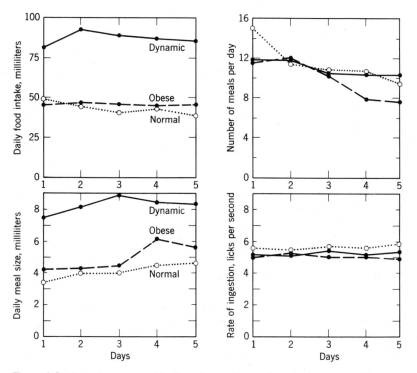

Figure 4-6   Several measures of feeding of normal rats, of rats in the process of becoming obese as a result of hypothalamic lesions (dynamic), and of already obese rats. The diet is liquid. After Teitelbaum and Campbell 1958.

centers. As Teitelbaum puts it, "one might say that the hyperphagic animal overeats to get fat. Once it is fat, it no longer overeats." This notion is reinforced by the demonstration that in rats which have been made excessively overweight by other means, lesions cause no hyperphagia. Teitelbaum concludes, with Kennedy (1950, 1953), that the satiety centers may be directly or indirectly responsive to some circulating metabolite related to the state of fat deposits in the animal's body.

◆ *General Pattern of Feeding Mechanisms in Mammals.* The tentative picture drawn from these studies of the physiological mechanisms underlying feeding behavior is as follows. A bout of feeding behavior starts with locomotion in search of food—the appetitive phase. This phase is triggered by activity in the lateral hypothalamic feeding centers and inactivity in the medial satiety centers. The release of the feeding centers from inhibition by the satiety centers, a response to a wide variety of changes in the body associated with deprivation of food, may be the primary step. Changes in higher brain centers may also release feeding areas from inhibition (Soulairac 1963), allowing for the demonstrable influence of learning on periodic patterns of feeding. After repeated acts of eating and swallowing, followed by arrival of food in the stomach—the consummatory phase—the bout of feeding eventually terminates. Oropharyngeal factors play an undetermined but definite role. Stomach distension plays a critical role, directly activating the satiety center, which then inhibits the feeding center. Passage of fluids into the gut may have a similar effect. The maximum stomach distension permitted varies with the nature of the food material, so that diluted food is taken in greater quantities. The general nutritive state of the animal may also determine, within limits, the degree of stomach distension permitted and thus the duration of the feeding bout. Perhaps the nutritive state directly affects the threshold of responsiveness of the satiety center.

The animal then refrains from feeding for a time, even though it may still be exposed to external stimuli from food materials. The length of the interval before another bout of feeding begins seems to depend on a wide variety of factors including temperature, body weight, and concentration of several metabolites in the blood. In general, it appears that the greater the nutritive deficit, the more rapidly the activity of the satiety center wanes. Feeding resumes more rapidly, and more food is consumed in each bout. Although the duration of feeding bouts and of intervals between bouts varies with the nutritive state of the animal, the rate of actual feeding movements seems to vary relatively little under normal conditions.

We are now in a better position to understand the apparent inconsistencies found by Miller and Tugendhat in the changes of motivation during cycles of feeding and satiation. There is no single, unitary, underlying mechanism but a multiplicity of mechanisms which are at least in some degree independent of one another. The contrasting results obtained by applying different measures to the same sequence of feeding are no longer paradoxical if we know that many or all of these various physiological factors can influence the animal's behavior with relative degrees of independence. The sum of their effects is the rhythmical pattern of bouts of feeding separated by periods of other kinds of activity.

This repetitive cycle has no simple basis in exogenous or endogenous influences. The underlying mechanism involves a subtle integration of effects of stimuli impinging on organisms from without and changes taking place within the organism. External influences do of course loom large, for the behavior is designed as part of a homeostatic mechanism which must make allowances for variations in the availability, palatability, and nutritive value of different types of food. It is appropriate to consider their contribution in more detail.

EXOGENOUS FACTORS

◆ *Food Preferences.* All animals are selective in choosing food in their natural habitat, some more so than others. No two species living together at the same time and place eat exactly the same staple food. This is the competitive exclusion principle (see Lack 1954, Mayr 1963). So feeding selectivity is a subject of major biological importance, not only because it has a bearing upon studies of nutrition, but also because of its relationship to problems of interspecific competition. When animals are given a choice they show preferences. "Cattle exhibit preferences not only for certain plant species but for the same species at different stages of growth, and even for the various parts of an individual plant and for individual plants within a species" (Hafez and Schein 1962). The preferences of seed-eating birds (Morris 1955, Wood–Gush 1955, Kear 1962), rats (Barnett 1963) and primates (Harlow and Meyer 1952, Berkson 1962) are equally clear.

The mechanisms underlying such preferences are not well understood. In seed-eating birds ability to husk a seed quickly and efficiently may determine what seeds are selected. The choice of particular seeds for food correlates well with the size and structure of the bill as in, for example, the Galapagos finches (Lack 1947, Bowman 1961). Experience with different kinds of seeds leads each species to concentrate upon the seeds with the largest and most nutritious kernel which it can efficiently handle (Kear 1962). Body size and locomotor ability may play just as important a role as structure of the actual feeding equipment (Davis 1957, Hinde 1959a). But within a species a strong element of individuality has been noted by many workers, indicating that a wide latitude in selection of food items is possible.

◆ *External Stimuli and Feeding Behavior.* What is the role of external stimuli in the selection of food and in control of the structure of the feeding bout that ensues? Some external stimuli tend to stop feeding behavior, encouraging rejection or even vomiting. Features such as texture, hardness, and shape may play a part, but chemical characteristics, both smell and taste, are especially important (e.g. Le Magnen 1963).

Cattle reject food with a bitter flavor, and grasses with a high coumarin content are often avoided. Food soiled with feces deters feeding in many species (Hafez and Schein 1962). Among phytophagous insects the selection of host plants is often controlled by the presence or absence of inhibitory and often lethal chemicals (see page 233).

Visual characters are sometimes equally important in discouraging feeding. The 'warning coloration' of many animals, various conspicuous colors and patterns which repel predators, are a good example. These features are often coupled with a noxious taste, smell, or texture, or an effective weapon such as a sting, and predators learn to avoid the warning colors by experience (Poulton 1898, Swynnerton 1919, Mostler 1935, Cott 1957). Sometimes harmless species mimic noxious ones and thus avoid being preyed upon (e.g. Sibley 1955, Hecht and Marien 1956, Brower 1958). Certain color patterns, such as the eye spots on the wings of moths, will even deter a naïve predator (Blest 1957).

The effectiveness of inhibiting stimuli on feeding depends on the state of the animal. It is minimal after long periods of food deprivation and maximal after a bout of feeding. Competition between eliciting stimuli of varying effectiveness may also affect the outcome. Thus, although repulsive stimuli are significant in determining food preferences (e.g. in rats, Barnett 1963), rejection of certain food objects in favor of others may also occur through a variety of other mechanisms, with availability playing an important role.

Facilitating stimuli are not normally thought of as having inhibiting properties. Yet there is a sense in which such effects can accrue when the stimuli are encountered in a certain temporal pattern either by loss of the power to elicit responses or by more positive inhibitory effects.

External stimuli facilitate feeding behavior in several ways. An animal may be sensitized to food stimuli in such a way that contact with one stimulus lowers the threshold of responsiveness to others. Olfactory stimuli often have sensitizing effects (Le Magnen 1963), and other senses may work this way as well. In gregarious species social stimuli may facilitate feeding. The presence of another chicken causes a hen to eat more grain, and properties of the food, such as the size of the pile, have a similar effect (Bayer 1929). Other typically gregarious species such as certain schooling fish (Welty 1934), rats (Harlow 1932), sheep (Tribe 1955), and primates (Harlow and Yudin 1933) also change their feeding habits and eat more when they are with other members of the same species.

The eliciting function of stimuli is that most commonly investigated by behaviorists and physiologists. External stimuli also orient responses in space, an important fact often overlooked in laboratory studies of feeding behavior. The range of effective eliciting stimuli is broad in some species and narrow in others (Hinde 1960). But we still have astonishingly little comparative information on the specificity of stimuli which elicit feeding behavior (see page 230). Both quantitative and qualitative properties of eliciting stimuli are important. The concentration of compounds that can be tasted in food, for example, is an important variable. Several experiments have shown that the effectiveness of substances in eliciting drinking rises with increasing concentration in a solution and then declines (Stellar 1960, Figure 4–7). These parallels do not imply that the same physiological processes are involved. The rejection of strong solutions of saccharin is probably a response to its bitter taste. The more frequent rejection of strong salt solutions, on the other hand, seems to be at least partly related to the dehydration resulting from its ingestion (Stellar 1960).

An example of the qualitative properties of external stimuli that are important in sensitizing and eliciting feeding behavior is found in the larva of the diamond-backed moth, *Plutella maculipennis,* which responds only to the mustard oil glucosides found in certain cruciferous plants (Thorsteinson 1960, see page 231). Chemicals play a prominent role as facilitating cues in plant-eating animals but vision can be significant. Aphids, for example, are attracted to leaves from a distance, distinguishing them from blue sky by a preference for light with a wavelength above about 500 mμ (Kennedy, Booth, and Kershaw 1961). Vision is especially important to predators.

The varying valence of qualitatively different food stimuli in evoking feeding provides a potential tool for exploring the motivation of feeding behavior. If we consider eliciting stimuli as either strong or weak, their effectiveness in eliciting feeding should vary with changing motivation to feed. In the interval following a bout of feeding only the strongest eliciting stimuli will induce feeding. As the interval since the last meal increases, strong stimuli are more likely to elicit feeding and eventually weak stimuli will become effective as well. In the extreme case, after extended food deprivation, even stimuli which would never normally be effective may acquire eliciting properties. In these circumstances the effectiveness of inhibitory stimuli will decrease. Once feeding has taken place the cycle will begin again. Such an experiment might provide an ideal example of rhythmical changes of responsiveness accompanying a cyclic pattern of behavior.

◆ *Specific Hunger in Mammals.* Hunger for specific ingredients may become the basis for variations in responsiveness to eliciting stimuli. An adrenalectomized rat, lacking salt, will seek out even very low concentrations of salt in water that a normal rat does not bother to distinguish, and it will accept higher concentrations than a normal rat. If certain crucial nutrients are eliminated from the diet an animal may shift its preference to other diets which provide the necessary ingredients (Richter 1942,

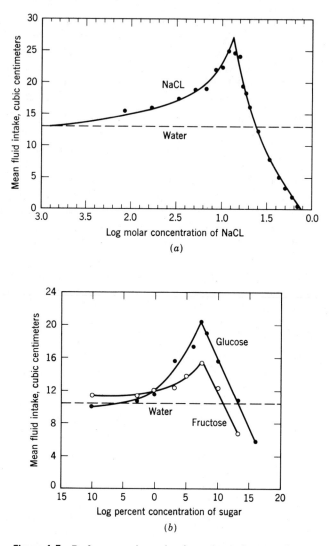

Figure 4-7   Preference and aversion for various substances changes with concentration. In diagrams (*a*), (*b*), and (*c*) the preference is based on the average amount of water drunk from the test solution in one hour. In (*d*) the score is based on intake in 24 hours when bottles of water and alcohol of the indicated concentration were presented as a choice. The subjects are rats. After Stellar 1960.

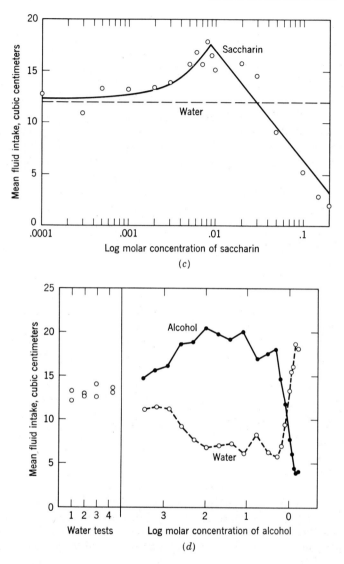

Log molar concentration of saccharin

(c)

Water tests

Log molar concentration of alcohol

(d)

Young 1961). Female mammals may develop new food preferences when they are pregnant. Some birds do the same thing when they are laying eggs. Seasonal changes in food preferences are probably widespread, but there is little evidence to distinguish the relative roles of changes in preference and availability of various food items.

◆ *External Stimuli and Brain-Damaged Rats.* The importance of considering the properties of eliciting stimuli in feeding behavior was recognized early in studies of hypothalamic hyperphagic rats (Miller, Bailey, and Stevenson 1950). Paradoxically, animals that ate more than usual were more dependent on optimal eliciting stimuli than normal rats. They were also more responsive to inhibitory stimuli. Thus while sugar increased their food intake, addition of quinine or dilution of the food with cellulose actually caused them to eat less than normal (Teitelbaum 1961).

A later series of elegant experiments was conducted with rats that could be fed directly by a stomach tube. Elimination of the opportunity for taste or smell has clarified the role of external stimuli (Epstein and Teitelbaum 1962, Teitelbaum and Epstein 1963). A normal rat can readily maintain its natural feeding patterns when fed intragastrically. Thus taste and smell can be dispensed with. Not so with animals made hyperphagic by lesions in the ventromedial nuclei.

When an animal is switched from oral feeding to intragastric feeding, taste and smell are removed as a reinforcement from the diet. Normal animals are sufficiently motivated to overcome the decrease in reinforcement and therefore they continue to regulate their intake without lag when feeding themselves intragastrically. Hyperphagic animals, however, with their impaired motivation, react exaggeratedly to the removal of taste and smell from their diet. They do not press the bar frequently enough to obtain sufficient food. It is only after they have had a long period of experience with the diet that they will work for it and demonstrate adequate regulation when they are fed intragastrically. This can be very clearly shown by providing the taste of food in addition to its injection into the stomach. If a tiny amount of food is injected into their food cup while they receive their full amount of intragastric injection, hyperphagic animals that are demonstrating this motivational inertia when first beginning to work for food will immediately display vigorous hyperphagia. They will work hard for food only if they get a slight taste of the diet in addition to the intragastric injection. They regulate precisely, work vigorously, overeat and gain weight rapidly. If the taste is removed again, however, they immediately relapse into a state of sluggish motivation. Therefore, the regulation that they could display is concealed because they are not adequately motivated. This shows clearly that taste acts as a powerful motivating stimulus to enable animals with impaired motivation to regulate normally (Teitelbaum and Epstein 1963, p. 356–357).

Aphagic rats, with lateral hypothalamic lesions, refuse their usual food and die if they are not force-fed. But they can be persuaded to eat highly palatable substances such as a liquid diet, milk chocolate, or wet cookies. It would be difficult to find better proof of the powerful effects of stimuli of taste and smell in eliciting feeding, a prerequisite in these brain-damaged animals, and a significant but apparently dispensable factor in the feeding of normal animals.

DYNAMICS OF NATURAL FOOD SELECTION

➤ *Selection of a Varied Diet.* In nature the matter of food selection is more complicated for most animals than it is in the laboratory. Some species do live on a limited array of foods, such as some insect larvae, and the red tree mouse that feeds only on leaves of certain coniferous trees (Hamilton 1962). The koala restricts its diet to eucalyptus leaves, and certain birds may eat only particular species of snails. But most animals take a variety of foods. Often variety is needed in order to remain healthy. Some means must exist to program the homeostatic intake of different foodstuffs. All foods are not equally available, however. And the varying amount of work that must be done to find, capture, and eat a given food will be an important consideration in the feeding program. The density of any one food varies from time to time. Furthermore, this availability may change drastically under natural conditions, from day to day and week to week, calling for rapid adjustments in feeding tactics.

Although there is little information on the dynamics of natural feeding patterns, some outstanding studies, particularly of insects and birds, point the way to further understanding. Consider first the behavior of an animal when confronted with a new source of food. Holling has studied the predation by deer mice and shrews on the cocooned pupae of certain sawflies. The eggs of the European pine sawfly "laid in pine needles the previous fall, hatch in early spring and the larvae emerge and feed upon the foliage. During the first two weeks of June the larvae drop from the trees and spin cocoons within the dust of the forest floor," the adults emerging in the fall some four months later (Holling 1959). The cocoons are eagerly eaten by mice and shrews.

By collecting cocoons in the field and presenting them buried in sand to the predators in captivity, Holling (1958, 1959) was able to explore various aspects of this feeding situation. Healthy cocoons were buried two centimeters deep in sand. Soon the shrew or mouse began digging; holes were accurately placed from the start. When the cocoons were removed, the digging rapidly declined in frequency and the animal resumed feeding on the canned meat that was present throughout the experiment (Figure 4-8a). Although accurate digging occurred from the beginning, there was a lag of three or four days before the rate of cocoon capture reached a maximum (Figure 4-8b). Evidently learning plays a part in developing the pattern of full exploitation.

What external stimuli do these shrews use to locate the cocoons? Olfactory and auditory stimuli are the possible candidates, and careful experiments showed that olfaction is of paramount importance. The digging is evoked and oriented by a wide variety of novel olfactory stimuli. Re-

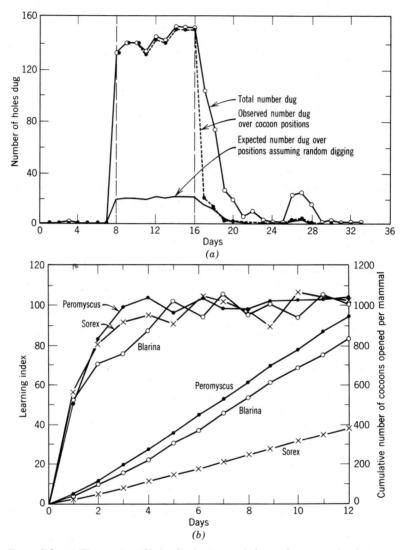

Figure 4-8 (*a*) The number of holes dug by mammals for sawfly coccons. Sawfly larvae were present only from the eighth to the sixteenth days. (*b*) The cumulative number of cocoons opened per mammal during twelve days in another set of experiments (three lower curves). These may be compared with scores on a learning index which expresses the number of cocoons taken as a percentage of the average number opened in the last six days of the experiment, when learning was assumed to be complete. After Holling 1958.

sponsiveness to these novel stimuli normally wanes rapidly. After being rewarded by cocoons, however, shrews are sensitized to their smell and will orient toward them in an olfactometer. They also learn to distinguish healthy cocoons from those infected with fungal and other parasites. The cocoons of females are larger than those of males, and thus make a bigger

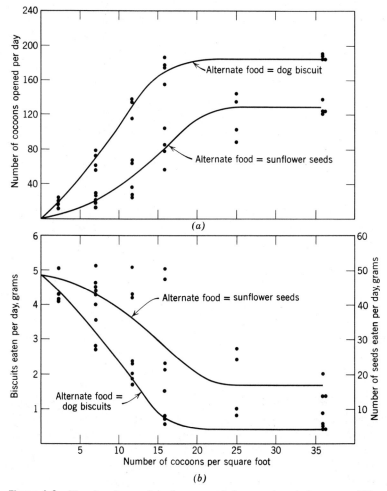

Figure 4-9 The abundance of sawfly cocoons influences the relative acceptability of two alternate foods to a deer mouse, *Peromyscus*. (*a*) The number of sawfly cocoons dug out and eaten is plotted against cocoon density, with alternate foods present in abundance. (*b*) The amount of alternate food taken is compared with cocoon density. After Holling 1959.

meal. Under field conditions the mice and shrews opened more female than male cocoons, again apparently making use of olfactory cues.

In nature the mice and shrews are confronted with a wide choice of foodstuffs. Some of these are more abundant than others; some are highly palatable, others less so.

The number of sawfly cocoons that a deer mouse takes at a given cocoon density varies if an alternate food supply is provided. Holling (1959) used two alternative foods provided in abundance, one highly palatable (sunflower seeds), the other less palatable (dog biscuits). At low cocoon densities few were taken, and the animal relied almost entirely on the alternate food. With increasing densities more were taken, and the animal ate less of the alternate food. But a plateau was soon reached, beyond which the number of cocoons opened per day remained more or less constant (Figure 4-9). The level of this plateau varied with the alternate food, being higher with the dog biscuit (less palatable) than with the sunflower seeds (more palatable). Even with dog biscuit, however, consumption of this less preferred food never dropped to zero. A varied diet was maintained, even with abundance of a highly preferred food source.

There is a similar mechanism for maintaining a varied diet in two species of monkeys and chimpanzees (Katz 1937). The relative preference for seven different foods was determined, and then the monkey was given all it could eat of one type of food for half an hour. When the selection was presented again the preference rating of the prefed food dropped. After such a surfeit a monkey might refuse to eat the test food for up to two days, although it would freely accept other foodstuffs.

A temporary loss in the eliciting value of certain foods (Morgan 1959) contributes to the termination of bouts of feeding in insects (see page 143), and perhaps in other animals as well. This satiation with certain foods parallels the role of habituation to a particular female in terminating bouts of male sexual behavior (see page 97).

◆ *Feeding Predispositions and Prey Density.* Let us consider the relationship between number of sawfly cocoons eaten by mice and shrews and density of cocoons in more detail (Figure 4-10). The behavior at low prey densities has special interest (Holling 1959). The ratio of predation to cocoon density shows that predation is by no means random. Rather, at very low prey densities these predators take fewer cocoons than might be expected, almost as though they constitute a food source that is not worth exploiting. However, as cocoon densities increase, the proportion taken rises dramatically. They now become the object of special search.

This shift to searching out a food source when it reaches a certain abun-

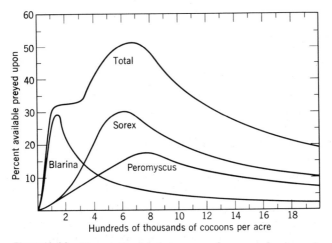

Figure 4-10   The relationship between sawfly cocoon density and the proportion taken by a predator. After Holling 1959.

dance has also been described by L. Tinbergen (1960) in Holland and confirmed by other workers (Mook et al. 1960, Gibb 1962). In the breeding season the great tit feeds largely on the larvae of moths and sawflies found in pine trees. The numbers of each prey species fluctuate greatly in the course of the great tit's breeding season. Tinbergen studied the effect of these variations on the diet the great tits fed their nestlings. When a new prey species appeared it was neglected in favor of other foods until it reached a certain density. Then it was heavily exploited, though never to the exclusion of other prey species. Often this exploitation required a new pattern of searching behavior that remained part of the feeding strategy as long as that food was favored.

The behavior suggested to Tinbergen the notion that when conditions are right the great tit adopts a 'specific searching image' adjusted to that particular prey species. This image is maintained through conditioning, by a complex interplay of characteristics of the prey species. The list of factors that bear on the predisposition to search for a particular prey animal include not only the population density of the prey but also its size, palatability, and the ease with which it can be found, as well as the same characteristics of alternate food species. Tinbergen assumed that an individual great tit can possess only a limited number of specific searching images at one time so that it concentrates on a few food items which provide the greatest yield.

Here, too, there is a check on overspecialization. With rising prey density the number of prey taken reaches a plateau so that even when one food is superabundant some other foods are always taken as well. Not only is a varied diet ensured, but there is also a continued sampling of different food sources so that the bird is in touch with the total food situation and can adjust its feeding strategy rapidly when necessary.

This elaborate organization of feeding behavior in insect-eating birds has in turn led to the evolution of complex adjustments in the larvae they prey upon. One trend characteristic of relatively palatable caterpillars has been to cryptic appearance and behavior and a dispersed population. Other species have developed means of defense such as hairs, bristles, and distasteful substances. These caterpillars tend to be conspicuous in appearance, and they may give distinctive displays when disturbed. They are often large in size and their distribution is frequently clumped. The variations in palatability are only relative. Unpalatable species may become a staple diet in times of food shortage. In this circumstance their relative conspicuousness becomes a disadvantage (de Ruiter 1952, 1956, Prop 1960, Tinbergen 1960).

There is evidently a subtle and dynamic balance between these different evasive characteristics of the prey species on the one hand and the abilities of the predators to overcome them on the other. The predators may evolve ability either to locate hidden prey or to tolerate noxious properties that certain conspicuous prey species have evolved. Similar relationships exist in other predator-prey situations (Cott 1957). There are especially close parallels in the evolution of noxious or toxic substances in plants and the evolution of tolerance, or even a preference for them, by plant-eating insects (see page 233).

FEEDING BEHAVIOR OF FLIES

Flies have much the same basic pattern of feeding behavior as mammals. Given free access to food, the pattern is typically cyclic, with periods of feeding activity alternating with longer intervals without feeding. The combined efforts of a number of investigators have provided a comprehensive picture of the physiological basis of this behavior which has great intrinsic interest. In addition to the parallels with mammalian feeding behavior there are certain striking contrasts.

◆ *External Stimuli.* The role of external stimuli in triggering feeding behavior in flies is well worked out. Feeding responses are elicited by a limited class of compounds, primarily certain sugars but also certain proteins (see page 145).

Contact chemoreceptors on the tarsi are stimulated. This sensory input results in extension of the proboscis. Extension brings the chemosensory hairs on the aboral surface of the labellum into contact with the sugar. In response to this stimulation the labellar lobes open, thus bringing the receptors on the oral surface into contact with the sugar. Stimulation of these receptors, as well as of the labellar hairs, initiates sucking. Feeding is thus initiated and driven by input from oral receptors (Dethier and Bodenstein 1958, p. 134).

Receptors within the pharynx or esophagus may also be involved (Arab 1957, quoted in Evans and Barton Browne 1960). There is some evidence of various groups of chemoreceptors with slightly different functions, perhaps having somewhat different thresholds from one another (Dethier, Evans, and Rhoades 1956). In addition to eliciting feeding behavior, chemical stimuli may also orient the fly to food. Alcohol attracts flies from a distance (Dethier 1961a). Whether chemical stimuli can sensitize flies to eliciting stimuli is uncertain and perhaps unlikely, in view of Evans and Barton Browne's (1960) demonstration that removal of the antennae and palps, which bear the olfactory receptors, does not influence the threshold of responsiveness to beef liver (see also Dethier 1961b).

◆ *Continuation of the Feeding Bout.* Once feeding has been elicited it continues for a certain time and certain rate. Both the rate and the duration of the bout of feeding are controlled by external stimuli. Rate seems to be a function of the intensity of the eliciting stimulus, increasing with the sugar solution concentration but declining with the strongest solutions of all. In addition to taste, viscosity limits the rate, especially at the highest concentrations of sugar solutions (Dethier et al. 1956).

The duration of a given feeding bout is a function of the time taken for the contact chemoreceptors to become adapted to the eliciting stimulus. Consummation is thus the simple result of loss of responsiveness to the eliciting stimulus resulting from continued exposure to it.

The stronger the stimulus, the longer the bout of feeding. The initial threshold of responsiveness of the animal is an additional variable to consider. Evans and Barton Browne (1960) measured feeding bouts lasting on the average from 51 to 133 seconds, depending on the length of time the animal had been deprived of food.

◆ *Feeding Thresholds.* After a bout of feeding, the threshold of responsiveness to eliciting stimuli remains high for a time and then gradually declines to a level at which feeding will occur again. The shape of the recovery curve depends on the kind of sugar used (Figure 4-11). The threshold declines somewhat 20 minutes after the end of the previous bout, probably because the effects of adaptation are waning. Then the

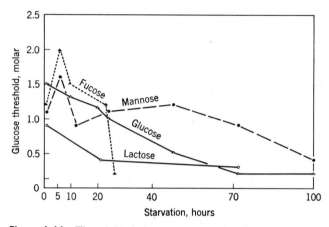

Figure 4-11 The minimal glucose concentrations for eliciting feeding in flies after varying periods of starvation, following feeding to satiation with four different sugars. After Evans and Barton Browne 1960 from Evans and Dethier 1957.

threshold rises again to a maximum before declining once more. This second recovery phase lasts too long to be related to sensory adaptation and suggests a mechanism differing from that involved in the initial threshold decline. This conclusion is confirmed by the discovery that sugars which normally do not elicit feeding and are thus assumed not to be tasted by the tarsal receptors have the same effect of changing the threshold of responsiveness to glucose for a long time (Evans and Dethier 1957). Some consequence of feeding has resulted in a prolonged change in the threshold of responsiveness to eliciting stimuli.

Feeding thresholds are unrelated to the nutritive value of assimilated food (Evans and Dethier 1957, Dethier and Bodenstein 1958, Evans and Barton Browne 1960). Ingestion of sugars which have no nutritive value for flies, such as fucose, for example, still causes elevation of the feeding threshold. Injection of nutritive sugars into the haemocoel of a starved fly has no effect on the threshold. Furthermore, threshold changes are not related to the timing of changes in the level of normal blood sugar, trehalose. Nor is the simple performance of the motor activity of feeding responsible for satiation, since the detached head of a satiated fly will feed. Experiments involving delicate surgery have localized the origin of inhibition of feeding somewhere in the foregut other than the crop. How the effect is mediated is still uncertain. Evans and Barton Browne (1960) suggest a possible hormonal link. Chemoreceptors in the wall of the foregut may also play a role (Arab 1957).

Locomotory appetitive behavior for feeding is closely related to changes in the threshold of the feeding response. Locomotion is minimal after feeding on nutritive or non-nutritive sugars and gradually rises to a maximum about 24 hours after feeding. A hormone from the corpus cardiacum is believed to be involved, its release being triggered by receptors in the foregut that register the presence or absence of food (Green 1964a, b). The recovery curve varies with the type and concentration of sugar fed but not in the same way as the sensory thresholds. This fact led Evans and Barton Browne (1960) to emphasize the diversity of physiological mechanisms underlying the whole complex of feeding behavior. They suggest that the term hunger should be used with caution, if it is taken to imply a unitary phenomenon. As such it has little relevance to these studies of flies which show several aspects of feeding behavior to be relatively independent functions. This conclusion is strikingly similar to that reached in studies of hunger in mammals and fish.

➤ *Specific Hunger in Flies.* As a final parallel with vertebrates, Strangeways-Dixon (1961) and Dethier (1961b) have demonstrated a specific hunger in flies. Many female insects including the blowfly change their diet at the time of egg laying. Both males and females continue to increase their protein uptake for about a week after emergence. After this males take little more, but mated females increase their protein uptake again after laying each batch of eggs. Just as a female rat seeks out foods which will relieve her deficiency, so a protein-starved female fly comes to prefer protein over the normal basic diet of carbohydrate.

CONCLUSIONS ON FEEDING BEHAVIOR

The contributions of external stimuli to the control of feeding behavior are as varied and as complex as those initiated by endogenous mechanisms. Many stimulus properties interact in determining the readiness of an animal to take a given food at any time. Some properties tend to facilitate feeding, others inhibit it. Palatability, abundance, and ease of access are especially important. The intrinsic properties of a food tell only part of the story, however. In nature it is the relationship between these properties and those of other potential foods sampled by the animal that determines the final choice. The immediate past history of the animal has profound effects on its present responsiveness. Such effects must be mediated by changes in its internal state. Once more the overt behavior can only be understood in terms of interaction between exogenous and endogenous factors.

DRINKING BEHAVIOR

In many of the studies we have been discussing, the distinction between feeding and drinking is blurred. This is no accident, for the two behavioral groupings are closely related. Deprivation of water has effects on feeding behavior, and vice versa (see Anand 1961). In young mammals the two behavior patterns are indistinguishable. No one has yet explained how the transition to normal feeding and drinking behavior takes place (Brobeck 1960).

◆ *Temporal Pattern of Drinking.* In one of the few temporal analyses of drinking behavior, Stellar and Hill (1952) found that the pattern of drinking in rats has the same cyclic property that we have seen in feeding. Rats drink at a rate of about six or seven laps per second, in bouts of varying duration. As a rough estimate, a rat drinks for one minute and then waits about an hour before drinking again under normal cage conditions. Previous deprivation of water affects both the duration of

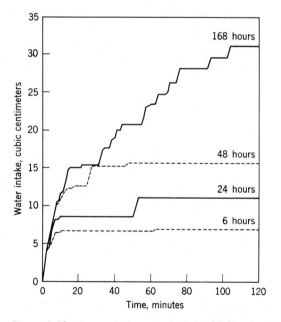

Figure 4-12   A cumulative record of the drinking behavior of a rat which has been deprived of water for periods up to 168 hours. After Stellar 1960 from Stellar and Hill 1952.

drinking bouts and the interval between them (Figure 4-12). After long deprivation drinking bouts are longer and more closely spaced, but they slowly return to the characteristic pattern.

The deer mouse, *Peromyscus maniculatus*, a smaller mammal than the rat, drinks more frequently (Kavanau 1962, 1963). For two mice the duration of most drinking bouts was from 3 to 6 seconds in one mouse and less than 3 seconds in another. The interval between drinks was from 10 to 40 minutes in one animal and 5 to 15 minutes in the other (Figure 4-13). In both there was a clear but highly variable rhythm. As with feeding, the details of the pattern of drinking depend on the time of day (Wolf 1930, Meyer–Lohmann 1955). Kavanau recorded long sequences of action with automated activity recorders. Auto- and cross-correlation analyses of these results (Figure 4–13) showed that eating and drinking are indeed closely linked. The animals tend to eat within one minute of drinking. Drinking follows eating by a longer interval that rarely exceeds 10 minutes. Thus eating and drinking tend to be clustered in time. The data also show that elimination (urination and defecation together) is closely associated in time with both eating and drinking. These data are, of course, obtained from caged mice which have free access to food and water. Under natural conditions food and water supplies are often spatially separated.

What is the physiological basis of this cyclic pattern? Dryness of the mouth and throat seems to play a part in eliciting drinking behavior in mammals. The prime trigger for drinking seems to arise in lateral centers in the hypothalamus, close to the feeding centers but apparently separate from them (Anand 1961). Electrical stimulation of these centers elicits drinking behavior, and destruction of them inhibits it. There are assumed to be osmoreceptors within them which monitor the osmotic concentration of the blood. Administration of tiny amounts of hypertonic saline into the centers is equally effective in evoking drinking (Andersson 1953).

◆ *Terminating Drinking Bouts.* The factors that terminate a bout of drinking behavior are not as well understood. No inhibitory or satiety center for drinking has been discovered. Stomach distension certainly plays a part. An animal with an esophageal fistula still drinks intermittently, however. The motor activity of drinking may play a role in terminating this behavior (Stellar 1960), and Cannon's (1929) assumption that elimination of the stimuli associated with throat dryness plays a role seems reasonable.

The situation is different in insects. For them the loss of responsiveness to water after drinking is apparently controlled by increased blood

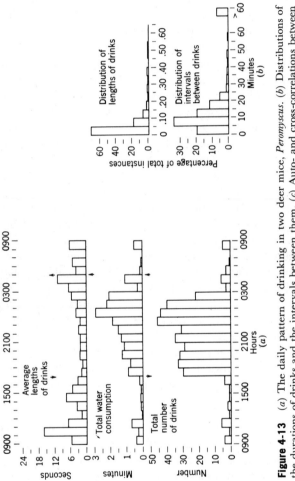

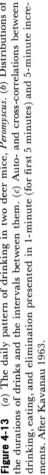

Figure 4-13 (*a*) The daily pattern of drinking in two deer mice, *Peromyscus*. (*b*) Distributions of the durations of drinks and the intervals between them. (*c*) Auto- and cross-correlations between drinking, eating, and elimination presented in 1-minute (for first 5 minutes) and 5-minute increments. After Kavanau 1963.

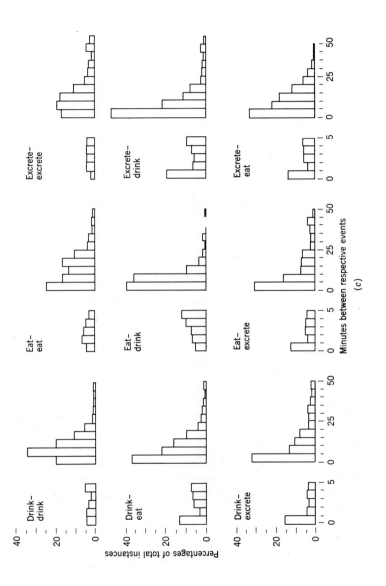

(c)

volume and pressure rather than osmotic changes. This is another illustration of similar temporal patterns of behavior resulting from different physiological mechanisms (Dethier and Evans 1961).

BREATHING BEHAVIOR

Along with food and water, oxygen is another basic requirement for the maintenance of homeostasis. The study of breathing behavior is nearer the realm of the comparative physiologist than that of the behaviorist: there is a large and excellent literature on the subject (e.g. Krogh 1941, Hughes 1963). Breathing is particularly susceptible to physiological analysis because of its continuous and repetitive nature in most species, whether the organs involved are gills, trachae, or lungs. The exceptions will be of special interest to us. Physiologists have long been interested in unraveling the mechanisms underlying this rhythmical activity, which serves to maintain a steady concentration of oxygen and carbon dioxide in the body fluids.

In terrestrial mammals the breathing process is comparatively well understood, although some points in the account which follows, from Oberholzer and Tofani (1960), remain to be fully verified. We shall find the same difficulty in resolving the relative contributions of neural and somatic factors that we have encountered with feeding behavior, illustrating yet another version of the controversy over exogenous (i.e. somatic) versus endogenous (i.e. neural) control.

◆ *Breathing Mechanisms in Mammals.* In mammals records of activity in the motor nerves to the diaphragm and intercostal muscles reveal that inspiration is triggered by a burst of action potentials which cease at the end of the inspiratory phase and resume following expiration (Bronk and Ferguson 1935). Here, at the level of the motor pathway, we see the physiological counterpart of the externally observable behavior. Is this rhythmic discharge the manifestation of some intrinsically active neural center, or is the true explanation more complex than this?

The primary respiratory rhythm results from the interaction of several centers in different parts of the hindbrain. The paired respiratory centers on each side of the medulla oblongata each include zones responsible for inspiration and expiration. The inspiration zone tends to be active continuously. If it is isolated from the other mechanisms it causes sustained, convulsive inspiration. Rhythmicity is introduced by reciprocal interaction with the expiratory center which is excited by activity of the inspiratory center. As a result the inspiratory muscles relax and expiration occurs, sometimes with the aid of active expiratory musculature. The high degree of summation required to activate the expiratory center allows for the necessary delay, thus permitting inspiration to be completed before inhibition of the inspiratory center occurs. After discharge of the expiratory center, the inspiratory center is released from inhibition and inspiration occurs once more. There is also an inhibiting area in the pons which seems to function as a second expiratory center with somewhat similar properties.

The three centers cooperate to provide the basic properties of the respiratory rhythm. But they alone are not sufficient. The demands of the body for oxygen vary from time to time, and these fluctuations must somehow be compensated for by the pattern of breathing. It appears that an increased concentration of carbon dioxide in the blood has a direct facilitating influence on the inspiratory center, causing deeper and more rapid breathing. A similar effect is also exerted by chemoreceptors in the carotid bodies which are stimulated by dissolved carbon dioxide. They exert a tonic facilitating effect on the inspiratory center through the vagus nerves, as well as inducing responses to high concentrations of carbon dioxide.

The degree of distension of the lungs also plays a complex role in respiratory control. When the stretch receptors in the lungs are highly stimulated they cause, by way of the vagus nerves, both inhibition of the inspiratory center and facilitation of the expiratory center, so that breathing becomes rapid and more shallow. When the stretch receptors are less strongly stimulated they exert a tonic facilitating effect on the inspiratory center. This complication perplexed physiologists for many years until the varying role of stretch receptors at different levels of stimulation was ascertained.

In addition to these mechanisms for the direct coordination of breathing with carbon dioxide levels, there are many other factors which can have some effect on respiration. Changes in the resistance to air flow in the respiratory passages cause appropriate adjustments in the vigor of contraction of the inspiratory and expiratory muscles. During the act of swallowing food or water, closure of the glottis causes the temporary arrest of respiration at any phase, so that for a brief moment feeding and drinking behavior take precedence over respiration. Noxious, irritating odors may also cause a suspension of respiratory activity. A variety of aromatic odors, on the other hand, may facilitate respiration and cause sniffing. Thermal and emotional disturbances are often accompanied by changes in respiration, effects which have all been directly associated with the hypothalamus and other fore and midbrain structures. Finally, there is the clear involvement of the forebrain in the integration of respiration and vocal behavior.

As Oberholzer and Tofani (1960) point out at the conclusion of their review, "the number of factors that can influence respiration in the intact animal is so great that virtually the entire organism can be said to contribute something to the control of respiration." Brobeck (1960) has reminded us of the many parallels Sherrington found between feeding and breathing behavior—parallels that evidently reappear in the physiological mechanisms which underlie them. A hypothetical unitary drive is surely inappropriate here.

◆ *Air-Breathing Aquatic Animals.* Breathing activity is usually continuous, without any patterning into bouts. The respiratory behavior of most aquatic animals has the same type of structure as that of terrestrial animals. The same sorts of physiological mechanisms are involved, though carbon dioxide levels play a less critical role. Carbon dioxide is readily soluble in water and easily disposed of. Oxygen is often a limiting factor, and oxygen tension becomes a prime regulator of activity in the respiratory centers of aquatic animals (Prosser and Brown 1961). Unlike feeding, drinking, and reproductive behavior, breathing permits no ready subdivision into appetitive and consummatory behavior. Most animals have no need to search for their respiratory medium; it surrounds them constantly. When oxygen is lacking, however, such appetitive behavior does appear, as anyone who has swum for long underwater can attest. Spurway and Haldane (1953) have pointed out the interest of air-breathing aquatic animals from this point of view.

In aquatic animals that live below the water surface and have to move to the surface to collect air, the requirements of respiration are similar to those of feeding behavior. The animal cannot spend all its time at the surface; respiration must be interrupted by other activities which take it to other parts of the environment. Thus breathing becomes organized into bouts, and there is a clear division into appetitive and consummatory elements. An aquatic salamander, the newt, for example, will rise to the surface at regular intervals, gulp air, and then descend. The properties of this rhythm are affected by a number of factors. At a reduced temperature or when oxygen is substituted for air, the newt rises less frequently. If the air is replaced with nitrogen the newt rises more frequently. By such manipulations Spurway and Haldane (1953) could demonstrate parallels with more typical types of cyclic activity such as feeding.

CONCLUSIONS

What generalizations can be drawn from this survey of breathing, feeding, and drinking behavior? First, we have seen that organization into rhythmically recurring bouts is widespread, particularly when the motor equipment is required for several different activities. The rhythmical pattern allows the animal to allot proportions of its time to the different activities necessary for survival. Actions which involve only a limited portion of the animal's motor equipment and can proceed without interfering with other types of behavior are free from these restraints. Examples are breathing in many animals, drinking in aquatic animals, and perhaps even feeding in some types of organisms such as filter feeders. Use of motor equipment for multiple purposes, such as occurs in many animal groups, limits the kinds of activities that can go on continuously and favors organization into rhythmic bouts instead.

The existence in the behavioral repertoire of different patterns that use the same motor equipment also raises the question of priority. If conditions appropriate for more than one activity occur, one must take precedence over the other. There is a hierarchy of behavior patterns, noted by Sherrington (1906) and recognized by many subsequent workers, which establishes a basic order of priority. Sherrington cites the example of the precedence that responses to painful stimuli have over other responses involving the same motor equipment, and there are many others. The hierarchy must be a dynamic one if the principles of homeostasis are to be served. In an unusual shortage of food or water, for example, feeding or drinking must take precedence over activities that might otherwise have priority.

Such a mechanism exists in the organization of rhythmical bouts of activity. During the appetitive phase of the bout the animal is ready to perform the appropriate motor activities and is also sensitized to certain external stimuli. The greater any particular homeostatic imbalance, the stronger the predisposition to perform the appropriate behavior. Thus the hierarchical relationship is adjusted to other types of behavior.

Perhaps the most remarkable characteristic of these principles of behavioral organization is the variety of physiological mechanisms associated with them. In breathing, feeding, and drinking, different mechanisms achieve similar ends. The temporal patterning of the feeding behavior of flies and mammals is much the same, but the patterns are brought about by quite different physiological mechanisms. Moreover, in any one organism not just one but many physiological factors influence the readiness to perform a behavior pattern. From a homeostatic point of view, this is perhaps to be expected. Multiple control mechanisms provide a wider margin of safety in allowing for the effective expression of behavior which satisfies a wide variety of bodily needs.

With this diversity of physiological mechanisms it is perhaps not surprising that detailed measures of behavior—the frequency or completeness of the component acts, latency measures, or the readiness to overcome obstacles—often fail to correlate with one another perfectly. We know that the various physiological substrates may vary independently to some degree. When these physiological variables result in behavior, the pattern of organization a behaviorist observes will depend in a critical way on which facet of behavior he records. This is perhaps the strongest reason of all for not relying on one behavioral measure in motivation studies. The more aspects one considers, the better chance there is of deriving models which can illuminate the problems of the physiologist. Of course everything cannot be recorded, for the possibilities are infinite. Hence hypotheses become extremely important in making behavioral descriptions (see page 712). The details of the temporal patterning of feeding and drinking behavior are worthy of more attention than they have had in the past. The more customary records of the amounts of food eaten or water drunk are of course necessary. But descriptions of the temporal organization of individual actions provide a source of data which are in some ways easier to translate into principles of physiological organization.

REFERENCES

Adolph, E. F. 1947. Urges to eat and drink in rats. *Amer. J. Physiol.*, **151**:110–125.

Anand, B. K. 1961. Nervous regulation of food intake. *Physiol. Rev.*, **41**:677–708.

Andersson, B. 1953. The effects of injections of hypertonic NaCl-solutions into different parts of the hypothalamus of goats. *Acta Physiol. Scand.*, **28**:188–201.

Anliker, J. and J. Mayer. 1956. An operant conditioning technique for studying feeding-fasting patterns in normal and obese mice. *J. Appl. Physiol.*, **8**:667–670.

Arab, Y. M. 1957. A study of some aspects of contact chemoreception in the blowfly. Ph.D. Thesis. Johns Hopkins University. Quoted in Evans and Barton Browne 1960.

Bare, J. K. 1949. The specific hunger for sodium chloride in normal and adrenalectomized white rats. *J. comp. physiol. Psychol.*, **42**:242–253.

Barnett, S. A. 1963. *A Study in Behaviour*. Methuen and Company, London.

Bayer, E. 1929. Beiträge zur Zweikompononentheorie des Hungers. *Z. Psychol.*, **112**:1–54.

Beach, F. A. 1956. Characteristics of masculine "sex drive." *Neb. Symp. Motiv.*, **4**:1–32.

Bernard, C. 1878. *Leçons sur les Phénomènes de la Vie Communs aux Animaux et aux Végétaux.* J. B. Baillière et fils, Paris.

Berkson, G. 1962. Food motivation and delayed response in gibbons. *J. comp. physiol. Psychol.*, **55**:1040–1043.

Beukema, J. J. 1963. Experiments on the effects of the hunger state and of a learning process on the risk of prey of the three-spined stickleback (*Gasterosteus aculeatus* L.). *Arch. Néerl. Zool.*, **15**:358–361.

Bindra, D. 1959. *Motivation. A Systematic Reinterpretation*. The Ronald Press Company, New York.

Blest, A. D. 1957. The function of eyespot patterns in the Lepidoptera. *Behaviour*, **11**:209–256.

Bowman, R. I. 1961. Morphological differentiation and adaptation in the Galapagos finches. *Univ. Calif. Publ. Zool.*, **58**:1–26.

Brobeck, J. R. 1960. Regulation of feeding and drinking. In *Handbook of Physiology*, ed. by J. Field, Sec. 1, Vol. 2:1197–1206. American Physiological Society, Washington, D.C.

Bronk, D. W. and L. K. Ferguson. 1935. The nervous control of intercostal respiration. *Amer. J. Physiol.*, **110**:700–707.

Brower, J. van Z. 1958. Experimental studies of mimicry in some North American butterflies. I. The monarch, *Danaus plexippus*, and viceroy, *Limenitis archippus archippus*. *Evolution*, **12**: 32–47.

Cannon, W. B. 1929. *Bodily Changes in Pain, Hunger, Fear and Rage*. Appleton-Century Company, New York.

———. 1932. *Wisdom of the Body*. W. W. Norton and Company, New York.

Carlson, A. J. 1916. *The Control of Hunger in Health and Disease*. University of Chicago Press, Chicago.

Cott, H. B. 1957. *Adaptive Coloration in Animals*. Methuen and Company, London.

Davis, J. 1957. Comparative foraging behavior of the spotted and brown towhees. *Auk*, **74**:129–166.

Dempsey, E. W. 1951. Homeostasis. In *Handbook of Experimental Psychology*, ed. by S. S. Stevens: 209–235. John Wiley and Sons, New York.

Dethier, V. G. 1961a. The role of olfaction in alcohol ingestion by the blowfly. *J. Insect Physiol.*, **6**:222–230.

———. 1961b. Behavioral aspects of protein ingestion by the blowfly *Phormia regina* Meigen. *Biol. Bull.*, **121**:456–470.

——— and D. Bodenstein. 1958. Hunger in the blowfly. *Z. Tierpsychol.*, **15**:129–140.

——— and D. R. Evans. 1961. The physiological control of water ingestion in the blowfly. *Biol. Bull.*, **121**:108–116.

———, ———, and M. V. Rhoades. 1956. Some factors controlling the ingestion of carbohydrates by the blowfly. *Biol. Bull.*, **111**:204–222.

Epstein, A. N. and P. Teitelbaum. 1962. Regulation of food intake in the absence of taste, smell, and other oropharyngeal sensations. *J. comp. physiol. Psychol.*, **55**:753–759.

Evans, D. R. and L. Barton Browne. 1960. The physiology of hunger in the blowfly. *Amer. Midl. Nat.*, **64**:282–300.

——— and V. G. Dethier. 1957. The regulation of taste thresholds for sugars in the blowfly. *J. Insect Physiol.*, **1**:3–17.

Gibb, J. A. 1962. L. Tinbergen's hypothesis of the role of specific search images. *Ibis*, **104**:106–111.

Green, G. W. 1964a. The control of spontaneous locomotor activity in *Phormia regina* Meigen. I. Locomotor activity patterns of intact flies. *J. Insect Physiol.*, **10**:711–726.

———. 1964b. The control of spontaneous locomotor activity in *Phormia regina* Meigen. II. Experiments to determine the mechanism involved. *J. Insect Physiol.*, **10**:727–752.

Grossman, M. I. 1955. Integration of current views on the regulation of hunger and appetite. *Ann. N.Y. Acad. Sci.*, **63**:76–91.

Hafez, E. S. E. and M. W. Schein. 1962. The behaviour of cattle. In *The Behaviour of Domestic Animals*, ed. by E. S. E. Hafez: 247–296. Balliere, Tindall and Cassel, Limited, London.

Hamilton, W. J. III. 1962. Reproductive adaptations of the red tree mouse. *J. Mammal.*, **43**:486–504.

—— and B. D. Cutler. In press. Exogenous and endogenous components of the temporal pattern of feeding in caged bobolinks.

Harlow, H. F. 1932. Social facilitation of feeding in the albino rat. *J. Gen. Psychol.*, **41**:430–438.

—— and D. R. Meyer. 1952. Paired comparisons scales for monkey rewards. *J. comp. physiol. Psychol.*, **45**:73–79.

—— and H. C. Yudin. 1933. Social behavior of primates. I. Social facilitation of feeding in the monkey and its relation to attitudes of ascendance and submission. *J. Comp. Psychol.*, **16**:171–185.

Hebb, D. O. 1958. *A Textbook of Psychology.* W. B. Saunders Company, Philadelphia.

Hecht, M. K. and D. Marien. 1956. The coral snake mimic problem: a reinterpretation. *J. Morph.*, **98**:335–365.

Hinde, R. A. 1959a. Behaviour and speciation in birds and lower vertebrates. *Biol. Rev.*, **34**:85–128.

——. 1959b. Unitary drives. *Anim. Behav.*, **7**:130–141.

——. 1960. Energy models of motivation. *Symp. Soc. Exp. Biol.*, **14**:199–213.

Hoebel, B. G. and P. Teitelbaum. 1962. Hypothalamic control of feeding and self-stimulation. *Science,* **135**:375–377.

Holling, C. S. 1958. Sensory stimuli involved in the location and selection of sawfly cocoons by small mammals. *Can. J. Zool.*, **36**:633–653.

——. 1959. The componets of predation as revealed by a study of the small-mammal predation of the European pine sawfly. *Can. Ent.*, **91**:293–320.

Hughes, G. M. 1963. *Comparative Physiology of Vertebrate Respiration.* William Heinemann, London.

Hull, C. L. 1943. *Principles of Behavior.* Appleton-Century-Crofts, New York.

Katz, D. 1937. *Animals and Men.* Longmans, Green and Company, London.

Kavanau, J. L. 1962. Precise monitoring of drinking behavior in small mammals. *J. Mammal.*, **43**:345–351.

——. 1963. Continuous automatic monitoring of the activities of small captive animals. *Ecology,* **44**:95–110.

Kear, J. 1962. Food selection in finches with special reference to interspecific differences. *Proc. Zool. Soc. Lond.*, **138**:163–204.

Kennedy, G. C. 1950. The hypothalamic control of food intake in rats. *Proc. Roy. Soc. Lond., B.*, **137**:535–549.

——. 1953. The role of depot fat in the hypothalamic control of food intake in the rat. *Proc. Roy. Soc. Lond., B.*, **140**:578–592.

Kennedy, J. S., C. O. Booth, and W. J. S. Kershaw. 1961. Host finding by aphids in the field. III. Visual attraction. *Ann. app. Biol.*, **49**:1–21.

Krogh, A. 1941. *The Comparative Physiology of Respiratory Mechanisms.* University of Pennsylvania Press, Philadelphia.

Lack, D. 1947. *Darwin's Finches.* Cambridge University Press, Cambridge.

——. 1954. *The Natural Regulation of Animal Numbers.* Oxford University Press, London.

Le Magnen, J. 1963. Olfactory identification of chemical units and mixtures and its role in behaviour. In *Olfaction and Taste,* ed. by Y. Zotterman, Vol. 1:337–345. The Macmillan Company, New York.

Lindsley, D. B. 1957. Psychophysiology and motivation. *Neb. Symp. Motiv.*, **5**:44–105.

Mayr, E. 1963. *Animal Species and Evolution.* Harvard University Press, Cambridge.

Meyer-Lohmann, J. 1955. Über den Einfluss täglicher Futtergaben auf die 24- Stunden-

Periodik der lokomotorischen Aktivität weisser Mäuse. *Pflüg. Arch. ges. Physiol.*, **260**:292–305.

Miller, N. E. 1957. Experiments on motivation. *Science*, **126**:1271–1278.

―――, C. J. Bailey, and J. A. F. Stevenson. 1950. Decreased "hunger" but increased food intake resulting from hypothalamic lesions. *Science*, **112**:256–259.

Mook, J. H., L. J. Mook, and H. S. Heikens. 1960. Further evidence for the role of "searching images" in the hunting behaviour of titmice. *Arch. Néerl. Zool.*, **13**:448–465.

Morgan, C. T. 1959. Physiological theory of drive. In *Psychology: A Study of a Science*, ed. by S. Koch, Vol. 1:644–671. McGraw-Hill Book Company, New York.

Morgane, P. J. and A. J. Kosman. 1960. Relationship of the middle hypothalamus to amygdalar hyperphagia. *Amer. J. Physiol.*, **198**:1315–1318.

Morris, D. 1955. The seed preferences of certain finches under controlled conditions. *Avicult. Mag.*, **61**:271–287.

Mostler, G. 1935. Beobachtungen zur Frage des Wespenmimikry. *Z. Morph. Ökol. Tiere.*, **29**:381–454.

Oberholzer, R. J. H. and W. O. Tofani. 1960. The neural control of respiration. In *Handbook of Physiology*, ed. by J. Field, Sec. 1, Vol. 2:1111–1129. American Physiological Society, Washington, D. C.

Olds, J. 1958. Self-stimulation of the brain: its use to study local effects of hunger, sex and drugs. *Science*, **127**:315–324.

―――― and P. Milner. 1954. Positive reinforcement produced by electrical stimulation of septal area and other regions of rat brain. *J. comp. physiol. Psychol.*, **47**:419–427.

Poulton, E. B. 1898. Natural selection the cause of mimetic resemblance and common warning colors. *J. Linn. Soc. Lond.* (Zool.), **26**:558–612.

Prop, N. 1960. Protection against birds and parasites in some species of tenthredinid larvae. *Arch. Néerl. Zool.*, **13**:380–447.

Prosser, C. L. and F. A. Brown, Jr. 1961. *Comparative Animal Physiology* (2nd edition). W. B. Saunders and Company, Philadelphia.

Quigley, J. P. 1955. The role of the digestive tract in regulating the ingestion of food. *Ann. N.Y. Acad. Sci.*, **63**:6–14.

Richter, C. P. 1927. Animal behavior and internal drives. *Quart. Rev. Biol.*, **2**:307–343.

――――. 1942. Total self regulatory functions in animals and human beings. *Harvey Lectures* (1942–1943), Series **38**:63–103.

Rosenzweig, M. R. 1963. Mechanisms of hunger and thirst. In *Psychology in the Making*, ed. by L. Postman: 73–143. Alfred A. Knopf, New York.

Rozin, P. and J. Mayer. 1961. Regulation of food intake in the goldfish. *Amer. J. Physiol.*, **201**:968–974.

Ruiter, L. de. 1952. Some experiments on the camouflage of stick caterpillars. *Behaviour*, **4**:222–232.

――――. 1956. Countershading in caterpillars. An analysis of its adaptive significance. *Arch. Néerl. Zool.*, **11**:285–341.

――――. 1963. The physiology of vertebrate feeding behaviour: towards a synthesis of the ethological and physiological approaches to problems of behaviour. *Z. Tierpsychol.*, **20**:498–516.

Sharma, K. N., B. K. Anand, S. Dua, and B. Singh. 1961. Role of stomach in regulation of activities of hypothalamic feeding centers. *Amer. J. Physiol.*, **201**:593–598.

Sherrington, C. 1906. *The Integrative Action of the Nervous System*. Charles Scribner's Sons, London.

Sibley, C. G. 1955. Behavioral mimicry in the titmice (Paridae) and certain other birds. *Wilson Bull.*, **67**:128–132.

Soulairac, A. 1963. Neurological factors in the control of the appetite. *Int. Rev. Neurobiol.,* **5**:303–346.

Spurway, H. and J. B. S. Haldane. 1953. The comparative ethology of vertebrate breathing. I. Breathing in newts, with a general survey. *Behaviour,* **6**:8–34.

Stellar, E. 1960. Drive and motivation. In *Handbook of Physiology,* ed. by J. Field, Sec. 1, Vol. III:1501–1527. American Physiological Society, Washington, D.C.

——— and J. H. Hill. 1952. The rat's rate of drinking as a function of water deprivation. *J. comp. physiol. Psychol.,* **45**:96–102.

Strangeways-Dixon, J. 1961. The relationship between nutrition, hormones and reproduction in the blowfly *Calliphora erythrocephala* (Meigen). I. Selective feeding in relation to the reproductive cycle, the corpus allatum volume and fertilization. *J. Exp. Biol.,* **38**:225–235.

Swynnerton, F. L. S. 1919. Experiments and observations bearing on the explanation of form and colouring, 1908–1913. *J. Linn. Soc. Lond.* (Zool.), **33**:203–385.

Teitelbaum, P. 1957. Random and food-directed activity in hyperphagic and normal rats. *J. comp. physiol. Psychol.,* **50**:486–490.

———. 1961. Disturbances in feeding and drinking behavior after hypothalamic lesions. *Neb. Symp. Motiv.,* **9**:39–65.

——— and B. A. Campbell. 1958. Ingestion patterns in hyperphagic and normal rats. *J. comp. physiol. Psychol.,* **51**:135–141.

——— and A. N. Epstein. 1963. The role of taste and smell in the regulation of food and water intake. In *Olfaction and Taste,* ed. by Y. Zotterman, Vol. 1:347–360. The Macmillan Company, New York.

Thorsteinson, A. J. 1960. Host selection in phytophagous insects. *Ann. Rev. Ent.,* **5**:193–218.

Tinbergen, L. 1960. The natural control of insects in pinewoods. I. Factors influencing the intensity of predation by songbirds. *Arch. Néerl. Zool.,* **13**:266–336.

Tribe, D. E. 1955. The behaviour of grazing animals. In *Progress in the Physiology of Farm Animals,* ed. by J. Hammond, Vol. **2**:585–602. Butterworth and Company (Publishers), London.

Tugendhat, B. 1960. The normal feeding behavior of the three-spined stickleback (*Gasterosteus aculeatus* L.). *Behaviour,* **15**:284–318.

Welty, J. C. 1934. Experiments in group behavior of fishes. *Physiol. Zool.,* **7**:85–128.

Wood-Gush, D. G. M. 1955. The behaviour of the domestic chicken: a review of the literature. *Brit. J. Anim. Behav.,* **3**:81–110.

Wolf, E. 1930. Die Aktivität der japanischen Tanzmaus und ihre rhythmische Verteilung. *Z. vergl. Physiol.,* **11**:321–344.

Young, P. T. 1961. *Motivation and Emotion.* John Wiley and Sons, New York.

five

EXPLORATION, AGGRESSION, CONFLICT, AND PLAY

Measures of exploratory behavior • The relation to external stimuli • Exploration, withdrawal, and aggression: examples of nonrhythmic behavior • Personal space and dominance relations • The reduction of aggression • Conflict and displacement • Characteristics and functions of play.

Animals spend much of their time in motor activity, the function of which is often difficult to identify. Sometimes the temporal patterning of the activity may help in this identification; at other times it is a hindrance.

Circadian rhythms ensure the beginning and ending of activities at appropriate times of day. Predictable timing of a significant change in the environment—rising and setting of the sun—is accompanied by a predictable pattern of behavior, and the pattern gives us a hint about its function. Similarly, predictable changes in the needs of the organism for environmental commodities such as air, food, or water are met at least in part by predictable rhythms in the behavior associated with their provision.

The timing of many significant events in the relationship between animals and their environments lacks this quality of predictability. To a mouse the strike of a hawk is unexpected. Although the mouse is more likely to stray from the protection of its burrow at dawn or dusk, the hawk cannot precisely anticipate this event. Both predator and prey are confronted with problems in timing which endogenous mechanisms cannot solve. In this circumstance they must rely heavily on evocation of behavior by external stimuli. The timing of the behavior so evoked will lack any regular, inherent rhythmicity and by itself may not reveal anything of its function.

The point to emphasize is the degree to which animals must sometimes rely on external stimuli to control the timing of certain kinds of behavior. Yet the role of the animal is not passive. It must be constantly alert. Generally, only limited portions of the environment can be perceived from any one place; active exploration of the surroundings is often called for. The animal may either move through the environment as in locomotor exploration or displace parts of the environment in activities such as manual examination. Such behavior can display an element of spontaneity, raising the possibility that endogenous factors make some contribution to its control. To be sure, the contribution is less than in circadian rhythms. Nevertheless, we will see that a complete explanation of exploratory behavior must take account of both endogenous and exogenous components.

EXPLORATORY BEHAVIOR

◆ *Measures of Exploration.* A variety of measures can be used as indices of the amount of exploratory behavior shown in different circumstances. Perhaps the most direct way is to record the frequency and duration of occasions when an animal takes a position to examine test objects. For example, Berlyne (1955) placed objects in an alcove in a rat's cage with a beam of infrared light passing across it to a photoelectric cell. When the rat approached to examine the object or sniff at it, it interrupted the beam, triggering a counter and a timer. By direct observation Darchen (1952, 1955) recorded the approach of cockroaches to objects placed in the cage. Butler (1953, 1954) recorded the numbers of times rhesus monkeys opened a small window to view a scene on the other side. In other experiments the frequency of manual exploration of objects has been measured (Harlow and McClearn 1954). Each experiment may reasonably be regarded as measuring 'perceptual exploration' (Berlyne 1960).

Another index is provided by measures of the amount of locomotion in different situations. An arena or 'open field' is marked out with a lattice, so that the number of squares entered by a rat or mouse in a given period of time can be recorded. Often the animal is required to negotiate a system of incomplete barriers placed across the arena (Thompson 1953, McClearn 1959). Running activity in a more typical maze is also used as a measure (e.g. Montgomery 1953). Sometimes gross activity is recorded, without reference to its spatial characteristics. All these measures are related to something that might be described as 'locomotor exploration.'

As another index of exploratory behavior, the animal is given the opportunity for either locomotor or perceptual exploration as a reward in a learning situation. The rate at which learning takes place permits some of the properties of exploratory behavior to be compared in different situations. By such methods it has been shown that rats learn to enter the parts of a maze that allow the maximum chance for exploration (Montgomery 1954). The opportunity for manual exploration of objects is an adequate reward for rhesus monkeys and chimpanzees (e.g. Harlow and McClearn 1954).

The relationship of learning to exploration can be tested in a different way. Animals will learn to perform a simple mechanical task if the experimenter makes the task effect some change in the perceptual environment. Thus rats and monkeys quickly acquire the habit of pressing a lever in a Skinner box when this results in a sound or a change in light intensity (review in Berlyne 1960), or when it allows them to explore a new portion of the environment (Butler 1958, 1960).

→ *Relation of Exploration to External Stimuli.* The results of investigations of exploratory behavior all reinforce the impression that this is a prominent and distinctive form of behavior. In the appropriate circumstances it can be as intense and as persistent as feeding or sexual behavior and can readily lead to rapid learning. Nissen (1954) asserts the need to postulate an actual drive to perceive and to explore. Woodworth (1947) and Thorpe (1963) have expressed similar convictions. These investigators thus emphasize the endogenous aspects of exploratory behavior.

But there is evidence that much exploratory behavior is elicited by external stimuli. The key stimulus properties seem to be 'novelty' and 'complexity' (Berlyne 1960). Their effects can be demonstrated in simple experiments. Rats will approach and investigate an unfamiliar object placed in the cage. Berlyne (1955) found that rats confronted with a gray cube as a stimulus object in his automatic registration cage showed a maximum number of approaches in the first minute. During the rest of a 10-minute exposure, the frequency of approaches declined. In tests with the same stimulus object on subsequent days, a further decline appeared (Table 5-1), suggesting that less perceptual exploration was evoked by a familiar object. Cockroaches approach a stick in an arena less frequently with time (Darchen 1952, 1955). Replacement of the test object with something new, such as a green stick instead of a white one in the cockroach experiments, resulted in renewed vigor of investigation.

Table 5-1   The Number of Approaches of a Rat to a Test Object per Minute During Three Consecutive Trials

Interval	Trial 1	Trial 2	Trial 3	Total
First minute	3.3	2.5	1.7	2.52
Minutes 2, 3	2.0	0.5	0.3	0.95
Minutes 4–10	1.2	0.3	0.6	0.72
Whole trial	1.58	0.59	0.68	0.95

Berlyne 1955.

Reviewing the evidence, Berlyne (1960) concludes that "exploration of an object has a special role during the first minute or two of each exposure to a situation, and during the very first exposure to it." Measures of manual exploration such as the amount of handling of novel and familiar objects by chimpanzees (Welker 1956) yield a similar picture.

Novelty of external stimuli and exploratory behavior are intimately related. There is equally convincing evidence that the most complex external stimuli evoke the most exploration, whether the subject be rat, chimpanzee, or man. The most novel and complex stimuli lead to the fastest rates of learning (e.g. Berlyne and Slater 1957). Novel stimuli evoke both increased locomotor activity and increased investigation of the stimulus object. The susceptibility of exploratory behavior to external stimulation is thus well established.

There is an important point that should not be overlooked. In none of the experiments involving repeated presentation of the same stimuli did exploratory behavior and activity fall to zero. However familiar an object may be, it is still investigated occasionally. In a simple and monotonous environment exploration still occurs. It is well known that deprivation of the opportunity for such exploration in an excessively homogenous environment can lead to grossly abnormal behavior in man (e.g. Solomon et al. 1961). Again there is suggestion of spontaneous exploratory behavior, implying that the natural behavior is a result of interaction between internal and external factors.

◆ *Exploration and Withdrawal.* The same stimulus properties that evoke exploratory behavior may also evoke withdrawal. Novelty, either in the form of a stimulus which is qualitatively unusual, or as a stimulus of unaccustomed intensity, may cause an animal either to flee or to investigate. Thorpe (1944, 1950) notes that escape responses to such stimuli are almost ubiquitous. He suggests that they provide one of the most elementary adaptations for survival, supplemented in special cases by responsiveness to more specific stimuli (see page 245).

There is a close relationship between 'curiosity' and 'fear' in wild Norway rats (Barnett 1958). A relatively minor change in a familiar environment may result first in flight, then in approach and investigation. Degrees of novelty are thus critical in determining which response will be given. Berlyne (1960) suggests that the novelty of a particular pattern is inversely related to (1) how often patterns that are similar enough to be relevant have been experienced before, (2) how recently they have been experienced, and (3) how similar they are to the new stimulus. He further points out that novelty effects are elicited most strongly by stimuli with an intermediate degree of novelty, like something rather well known, but distinct enough to be "interesting." There are many examples from human experience in art, humor, sports, and other activities. A similar principle probably prevails in animals (Hinde 1954b, Schleidt 1961a, b, see page 134). Schneirla (1959, Maier and Schneirla 1935) emphasizes the general rule that "low intensities of stimulation tend to evoke approach reactions, high intensities withdrawal reactions with reference to the source." There are close parallels in the subjective judgments of acceptability and rejection for increasing concentrations of taste stimuli in man (review in Berlyne 1960), a phenomenon summarized by Wundt (1874) in the curve shown in Figure 5-1.

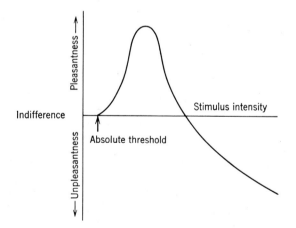

Figure 5-1   The relationship of stimulus intensity to pleasantness and unpleasantness of sensation. After Wundt 1896 in Berlyne 1960.

The balance between withdrawal and exploratory approach established in a novel situation seems to be strongly affected by the degree of novelty involved. And since novelty dwindles with the time of exposure of the organism, we may expect temporal changes of response of the kind which Barnett has described in rats.

Birds may show similar behavior. Chaffinches first respond to a strange object placed in their cage by avoiding it. Later they will approach and investigate it, then avoid it, and finally ignore it (Marler 1956a). The postures, movements, and calls given during the investigation are similar to those used in the process of 'owl mobbing.' Hinde (1954b) experimented with the responses of chaffinches to a stuffed owl. The caged chaffinch was placed at various distances from the owl, and the proportion of movements toward and away from it were recorded. At closer ranges most movements are made away from the owl; further away, movements toward the owl predominate. The transition takes place at a distance of about 17 feet (Figure 5-2). Thus there are both approach and withdrawal elements to the same stimulus object. In nature mobbing chaffinches and other birds vacillate between approach and withdrawal.

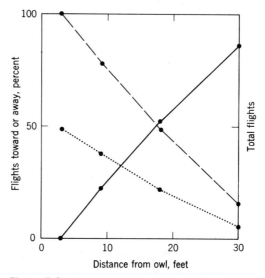

Figure 5-2 The responses of caged chaffinches to a stuffed owl. The dashed curve is the proportion of flights away from the owl, the continuous curve the proportion toward it. The dotted curve is the total number of flights. After Hinde 1954b.

Other workers have emphasized this intermingling of withdrawal elements with what is usually classified as exploratory behavior both in rats (e.g. Montgomery 1955, Welker 1959) and in birds (Rand 1941).

The following quotation which Berlyne (1960, p. 123) gives from Lorenz (1956) illustrates the same point.

A young raven, confronted with a new object, which may be a camera, an old bottle, a stuffed polecat or anything else, first reacts with escape responses. He will fly up to an elevated perch and, from this point of vantage, stare at the object literally for hours. After this, he will begin to approach the object very gradually, maintaining all the while a maximum of caution, and the expressive attitude of intense fear. He will cover the last distance from the object hopping sideways with half-raised wings, in the utmost readiness to flee. At last, he will deliver a single fearful blow with his powerful beak at the object and forthwith fly back to his safe perch. If nothing happens he will repeat the same procedure in much quicker sequence and with more confidence. If the object is an animal that flees, the raven loses all fear in the fraction of a second and will start in pursuit instantly. If it is an animal that charges, he will either try to get behind it or, if the charge is sufficiently unimpressive, lose interest in a very short time.

In discussing the factors that determine whether the response to a novel stimulus will be exploration or escape, Berlyne (1960, p. 126) concludes that

it seems to be a matter of how novel or complex the stimulation is. Extreme novelty or complexity tends to induce avoidance, and moderate novelty or complexity to induce approach. But another factor that evidently makes a great deal of difference is whether an animal is plunged into the midst of a totally unfamiliar environment or whether its environment contains both relatively novel and relatively familiar elements. In the latter case, the general tendency is for the animal to keep its distance from the novel elements at first, with perhaps a few scattered exploratory forays, and then to become more and more inclined to expose itself to novelty as time goes on. But when an animal is attacked by novel stimuli from all sides, it does not have the same choice. There is then likely to be intensive exploratory activity initially, with a subsequent rapid decline.

Much exploratory behavior is associated with a rapid and repeated alternation between approach and withdrawal, implying a 'conflict.' From a functional point of view the withdrawal responses to the same stimulus situation serve to hold exploratory behavior in check, restraining the animal from approach beyond safe limits. The sum of these effects is that the strongest exploratory approach is evoked by situations presenting a moderate degree of novelty and complexity. Responsiveness of this sort, characterized by Berlyne (1960) as "the quest for intermediate arousal potential," is widespread throughout the animal kingdom (Maier and Schneirla 1935, Schneirla 1959).

WITHDRAWAL AND AGGRESSION:
EXAMPLES OF NONRHYTHMIC BEHAVIOR

In his paper on appetites and aversions Wallace Craig (1918) countered the emphasis on the cyclic recurrence of many activities with a reminder that there are certain types of behavior that lack any regular rhythm. An obvious appetitive or searching phase is lacking. Instead these behaviors are triggered largely or entirely by external stimuli. Craig associated them with 'aversions' rather than with 'appetites'; they continue until external stimulation ceases.

Many simple reflexes fall into this category—the scratch reflex of dogs, the wiping reflex of frogs, the eye blink, and a host of other responses that are elicited by noxious, irritating, or disturbing stimuli, including much of the behavior that is concerned with care of the body surface. The outstanding examples of this nonrhythmical type of organization in more complex behavior patterns come from escape behavior and aggression. In neither is there clear evidence of an appetitive phase. A bout is normally terminated by eliminating the eliciting stimulus in some way. In escape behavior the external stimulus is avoided or the animal becomes habituated to it. In aggressive behavior, in which we include both combat and aggressive display, the same end is gained by driving the stimulus object away or otherwise modifying it by intimidating, injuring, or even killing it.

◆ *External Stimuli and Personal Space.* A comprehensive review of the diverse social systems within which aggressive behavior takes place cannot be attempted here (Collias 1944). We shall consider only some of the most elementary examples. A simple type of aggression occurs in the maintenance of a free space around the individual as it moves about. This 'personal space' characterizes so-called 'distance' animals, as contrasted with 'contact' animals that are much more ready to permit proximity and even bodily contact (Hediger 1950). Distance animals generally maintain a certain personal space or 'individual distance' around them by limiting the approach to another individual, withdrawing from it, or driving it away. The dimensions of this space have been described in a number of bird species. It is variable to some extent according to circumstances, and yet definitely measurable (e.g. Burckhardt 1944, Conder 1949, Emlen 1952a, b, Hinde 1952, Crook 1953, 1961, Sabine 1959). Consider the chaffinch, a species for which the personal space has been precisely measured in captive flocks (Marler 1955a, b, 1956b, 1957).

In a flock of chaffinches in nonreproductive condition, violation of the personal space by another chaffinch is the main stimulus for fighting behavior. It may occur at a localized source of food, water, or perching space. Experiments with movable food hoppers show that a male chaffinch is more likely than not to either attack another male or withdraw from it, if it approaches closer than about 20 centimeters (Figure 5-3). Females can approach a male to within half this distance before they are attacked.

Male and female chaffinches differ in appearance: the female's breast is gray-brown, and the male's breast is orange-brown. The significance of this difference in eliciting aggression can be shown by coloring the breasts of females orange. These disguised females are attacked at the same distance as males would be (Figure 5-3e, f, curve 2). Other females are also hesitant to approach them too closely. More subtle characters of appearance and behavior play a part, so that some individuals are allowed closer proximity than others. The adoption of certain postures also permits a close approach.

Personal space is thus a dynamic phenomenon. Its properties depend on the stimuli presented by an intruding animal. An aggressive posture elicits responses at a greater distance than a peaceful one. The orientation of the stimuli may be important. In chickens the zone of intolerance is greater ahead than behind (McBride et al. 1963).

In mammals, where similar phenomena probably occur, olfactory stimuli may be as important as visual ones (e.g. Barnett 1963, Eisenberg 1963). However, many mammals permit contact, at least with familiar members of the same species. In such circumstances aggressive behavior is more commonly elicited by threatening behavior, physical restraint, or pain-inflicting stimuli than by simple proximity (Scott and Fredericson 1951). The infliction of pain or restraint may also generate aggression in distance animals, particularly in predator-prey relationships, when the aggressive postures used in intraspecific encounters are ineffectual.

◆ *Dominance Relationships.* Individual characteristics are immensely important in eliciting or inhibiting aggression. In animal societies composed of individuals which recognize one another a stranger elicits aggression more readily than a familiar individual. Recognition can be primarily visual (e.g. chickens, Guhl and Ortman 1953), auditory (e.g. the ovenbird, Weeden and Falls 1959), olfactory (e.g. fish and dogs, Schmid 1935, Göz 1954), or it can depend on some combination of the senses. The significance of individuality is observed to be most dramatic when a stranger intrudes. It can play an equally important role in social relationships within a familiar group of animals, however, particularly in the organization of so-called dominance hierarchies. Schjelderup-Ebbe (1922) and Allee (1938), working with domestic hens and a wide

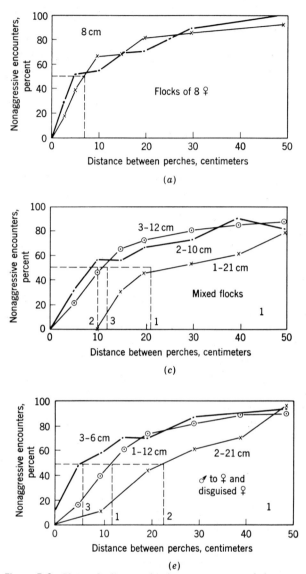

Figure 5-3 If two feeding perches in a cage are moved closer together, the probability that perching chaffinches, *Fringilla coelebs*, will fight when they encounter one another increases. The distance at which 50 percent of the encounters result in fights is indicated for each condition. (*a*) Flock of eight females, curves for two different flocks. (*b*) Two flocks of eight males. (*c* and *d*) Two flocks of mixed males and females; 1, male to male encounters; 2, female to female; and 3, male to female and female to male encounters. (*e* and *f*) Two mixed flocks; 1, males with females; 2, males with females disguised as males; and 3, subsequent tests with normal females. After Marler 1956b.

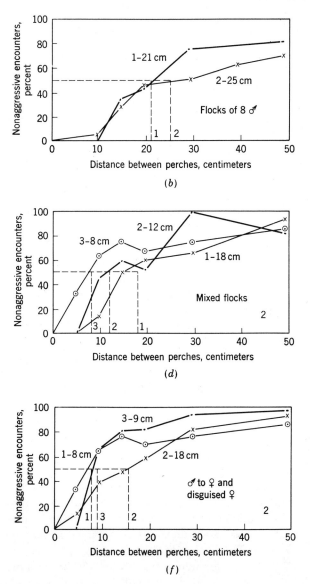

(b)

(d)

(f)

variety of other animals, were pioneers in the analysis of dominance relationships in animal societies (review in Collias 1944, Wynne-Edwards 1962).

In established groups of many species the outcome of aggressive encounters is predictable. Some individuals are consistently dominated by

Table 5-2   The Dominance Hierarchy of a Flock of Hens

	2	3	4	5	6	7	8	9	10	11	12	13
Bird 1 pecks	2	3	4	5	6	7	8	9	10	11	12	13
Bird 2 pecks		3	4	5	6	7	8	9	10	11	12	13
Bird 3 pecks			4	5	6	7	8	9	10	11	12	13
· · ·				·	·	·	·	·	·	·	·	·
· · ·					·	·	·	·	·	·	·	·
· · ·						·	·	·	·	·	·	·
· · ·							·	·	·	·	·	·
· · · 8↘							·	———	·	·	·	·
· · · ↑ 9							·		·	·	·	·
· · · 10↙							·		·	·	·	·
· · ·									·	·	·	·
· · ·										·	·	·
Bird 13 pecks none												

The hierarchy is linear except for one triangular relationship near the bottom of the hierarchy. After Allee 1938.

others. The simplest case is the linear 'peck-right' hierarchy in which one animal dominates all others, the one below dominates all except the despot, and so on down the hierarchy to the bottom animal that dominates none (Table 5-2). In large groups linearity is rare; triangular relationships develop. Monarchial systems also exist, with one despot dominating the whole social group and aggression virtually suspended among the rest. Other types of hierarchy are possible depending in part on the degree of crowding of the group (Uhrich 1938).

In these examples the observer's key to the prediction of the outcome of aggressive encounters is the identification of the individuals involved. Even when individual identification is not possible, the sex or age class of the participants will permit some prediction. Older animals commonly dominate younger ones, larger animals dominate smaller ones, and males dominate females, though there are exceptions. In birds and primates there are well-documented cases of reversal of the dominance relationships between the sexes at certain stages of the breeding season or estrous cycle (Yerkes 1940, Thompson 1960).

An unusual type of dominance hierarchy has been found in wild baboons. The troop is dominated by a small number of males who depend on one another to subordinate the rest of the members (Washburn and DeVore 1961, DeVore and Washburn 1963). A member of this 'central hierarchy' may be subordinate to some other members of the troop when he is separated from his supporters. This rarely happens, since they usually keep together. To predict accurately the outcome of aggressive encounters in this hierarchy it is necessary to know not only the individual identity of the members of the group but also their relative spatial position. Coalitions also occur in macaques, where one animal may actively cooperate with another in maintaining its dominance over a third individual (Imanishi 1960, Altmann 1962). Thus an observer may need to know where an encounter is taking place in relation to other animals or objects in the environment before a prediction of the outcome can be made. For example, an animal with prior experience of the area is likely to assume higher status in a dominance hierarchy than a stranger to the area.

⟋ External referents play a still more important role in some dominance systems. Some male birds and fishes dominate and chase other males from a small area around their mates (Hinde 1956b, Wickler 1957). Their position in relation to the female becomes a crucial determinant of the outcome of such aggressive encounters. In geese the whole family may become the external reference for such dominance (Jenkins 1944, Boyd 1953). For hummingbirds a group of flowers serving as a food source sometimes becomes the focus of domination and eviction of other birds (Pitelka 1942, 1951).

A place for sleeping, mating, laying eggs and raising young, or feeding, or simply a space in the habitat that can be used for many things can become an external reference for dominance (Nice 1941, Bourlière 1955, Hinde 1956b, Wynne-Edwards 1962, Carrick 1963, Brown 1964). When the external reference for dominance is more or less fixed in space it is commonly spoken of as a 'territory.' The habitats of many species of animals are mosaics of such territories (Figure 5-4). In each one a single animal, a pair, a family, or a larger group of animals dominates the others. Such dominance is usually exerted over members of the same species and often of the same sex. Sometimes it may be extended to other species as well (Orians and Willson 1964). Interspecific territoriality has special interest for ecologists because territorial defense is an important means of dividing the natural resources of an area among the resident animals.

Active defense is not a necessary condition for the maintenance of some degree of exclusive occupation of an area—the most important ecological consequence of territoriality (Pitelka 1959). For example, a combination of attachment to a particular place, 'philopatry' (Mayr 1963), and mutual avoidance between individuals can result in a similar type of spatial distribution (Hutchinson 1953). The concept of 'home range' is often used here (Burt 1943) to refer to the space that an animal occupies during the annual cycle or a part of it, without suggesting the particular means by which the space is maintained.

Complete dominance over other members of the same species within

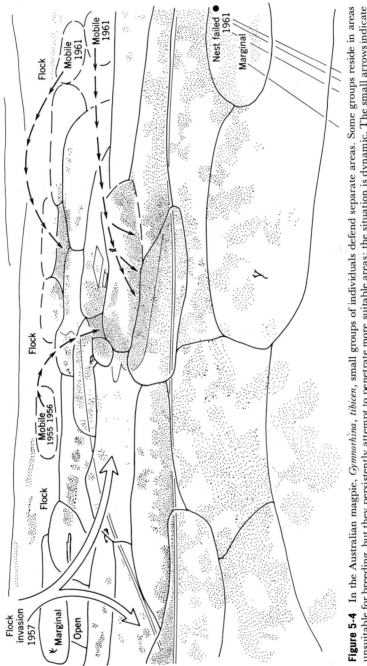

Figure 5-4 In the Australian magpie, *Gymnorhina, tibicen*, small groups of individuals defend separate areas. Some groups reside in areas unsuitable for breeding, but they persistently attempt to penetrate more suitable areas; the situation is dynamic. The small arrows indicate the penetration of these marginal flocks in the breeding season. The broad arrow shows the invasion of winter flocks from marginal areas during especially cold conditions. Most territories ranged from 10 to 20 acres, and the number of birds in each was from two to ten magpies. There were 650 magpies individually color banded in this study. After Carrick 1963.

the territory is the most striking characteristic of this type of social system. But the influence of the territory may extend more widely. Brown (1963) has found a situation in the Steller's jay that may occur in other species as well. Studies of the dominance hierarchy at several feeding stations revealed that the status of an individual depends on the distance of the station from the nesting area (Figure 5-5). At each station there is a peck-right hierarchy. Only by wider study was the territorial nature of the dominance system revealed (see Diebschlag 1941, Ritchey 1951 for a study of dominance in captive pigeons). Brown concludes that the situation in Steller's jays "may be conceived as a series of concentric zones of diminishing dominance rank from the center of its nesting area outward." Often individual activity is largely confined to the area where dominance is complete so that extension of the influence of the territory may have been missed in the study of other territorial species.

Dominance relationships are dynamic in many species of animals. Some animals maintain territories throughout the year, as do the fish, *Badis badis* (Barlow 1962b), the European robin (Lack 1943), and hamsters (Eibl-Eibesfeldt 1958). Many animals oscillate between individual dominance in the nonreproductive phase and territorial dominance in the reproductive phase. The dominance relationships between different classes of individuals may also oscillate; males can dominate females at one phase and be subordinate to them at another.

◆ *Crowding and Aggressive Organization.* The degree of crowding may affect the type of dominance system. In captive populations of fish (Fabricius and Gustafson 1954), birds (Bennet 1940, Davis 1959), and mammals (Crowcroft 1955, Davis 1958), a shift from territorial dominance at low densities to individual dominance at high densities has been demonstrated. Individual dominance may in fact be an artifact of captivity in some species, induced by the inability of defeated animals to escape as they would in nature. Even the provision of a localized food source for wild animals, often used to obtain data on dominance under 'natural' conditions, may lead to a deceptive impression of the frequency and nature of dominance interactions in nature. Variations in population density are known to be associated with drastic physiological changes, particularly in the activity of the adrenal cortex (Christian 1959, Thiessen and Rodgers 1961). Other physiological variables also influence dominance relations and the whole pattern of aggressive behavior.

◆ *Endogenous Factors and Aggression.* Although the role of external stimuli is crucial in triggering aggressive actions, internal variables can raise, lower, or otherwise modulate responsiveness to these stimuli. The most drastic changes are associated with cycles of breeding activity. Males are

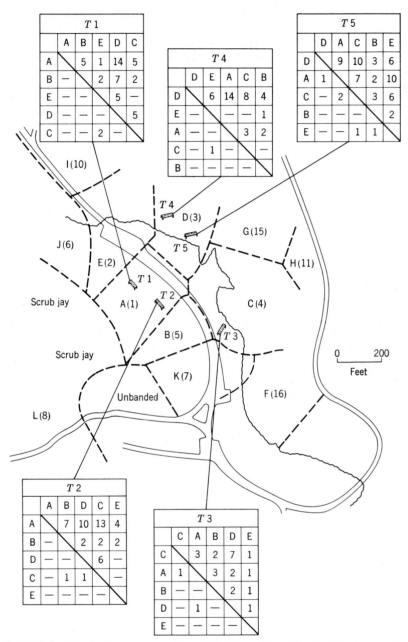

Figure 5-5 The dominance status of five Steller's jays, *Cyanocitta stelleri*, in winter varies with the position of the encounter in relation to the site of the nesting territory in the previous summer. The nesting territories are shown by dotted lines. The winter hierarchies as determined at picnic tables, *T*1 to *T*5, are shown by the insets. The hierarchical rank of each individual at *T*1 is shown in parentheses following the letters A to E that identify each individual in its territory. After Brown 1963.

generally the more aggressive and become increasingly so with the onset of the breeding season. Abundant evidence shows that in vertebrates the increase marches with the growth of the testes, is eliminated by castration and can be induced by injections of the male gonadal hormone (Beach 1948, Collias 1950, Guhl 1961). It is clear that androgens lower the threshold for aggression in many species. Often this lowered threshold is accompanied by an increase in the distance at which the eliciting stimuli are effective and a tendency for dominance to become linked with environmental references such as a territory.

We have already reviewed many of the factors that bear on this rhythm of gonad growth and regression (see page 102). But the sensitizing effect of androgens on aggression does not imply that aggressive behavior is completely dependent on androgens for its appearance—far from it. Castrated males often show some signs of aggressiveness. Castrated male starlings are barely less aggressive than intact ones (Davis 1957).

Female sex hormones may also influence aggressiveness, though the effects are more variable (Guhl 1961). In many species they seem to lower aggressiveness. In others they increase it, presumably in species in which the female comes to dominate the male as the breeding season advances (see page 170). The effects of the hormones must be mediated by the brain, and many parts of the brain are implicated, including the amygdala, hypothalamus, and the midbrain (Brady 1960, Brown and Hunsperger 1963), controlling changes in both motor and sensory processes.

Endogenous influences associated with other types of behavior may also modify aggression. For example, fighting becomes more frequent among some animals when they are hungry. Such is the case with captive flocks of chaffinches (Marler 1955a, 1956b, 1957) in which fighting over food becomes more frequent after a period of starvation (Table 5-3).

Table 5-3 The Ratio of Nonaggressive Encounters to Total Encounters in a Flock of Eight Captive Male Chaffinches, after Various Intervals of Starvation

Starvation time, minutes	Experiment 1		Experiment 2		Experiment 3		Totals	
	U	S	U	S	U	S	U	S
45	.64	.62	.59	.63	.64	.62	$.62(N = 229)$	$.62(N = 335)$
90	.62	.63	.69	.64	.65	.70	$.65(N = 162)$	$.65(N = 345)$
180	.66	.65	.66	.75	.69	.70	$.67(N = 120)$	$.70(N = 356)$

The food dishes were 20 cm apart. The birds were observed for 30 minutes on one day without starvation and for 30 minutes after starvation on the next day. The totals show the increase in the number of encounters at the food after starvation. U, unstarved; S, starved. After Marler 1956b.

Table 5-4   Ratio of Dominant-to-Subordinate to Subordinate-to-Dominant Approaches to Food after Starvation.

	Starvation, minutes						
	0	15	30	45	60	90	120
8 ♂ ♂	10.4	2.1	5.5	0.73	1.6	0.8	1.3
8 ♀ ♀	3.9	2.3	1.4	0.55	0.80	0.75	0.97
4 ♂ ♂, 4 ♀ ♀	0.79	0.74	0.63	0.49	0.66	0.29	

The effect of starvation on the ratio (d/s) of approaches by dominant chaffinches to a food dish occupied by a subordinate (d) to approaches by subordinates to food occupied by a dominant (s). After Marler 1955a.

Studies of the distance at which starved chaffinches attack each other reveals no change from the normal, however (Table 5-3). The increased frequency of fighting actually results from a greater readiness among subordinate birds to approach dominant individuals at the food when starved (Table 5-4). Andrew (1957) obtained similar results with captive yellow buntings, *Emberiza citrinella*.

Evidently starvation raises the threshold for withdrawal responses, both in these birds and in other animals (e.g. rats, Hall 1941). This seems an adequate explanation for the increased frequency of fighting after starvation, at least in some species. The dominance of starved or thirsty rats (Bruce 1941), chimpanzees (Nowlis 1941), and birds (Andrew 1957, Marler 1957) at a food or water source may be similarly explained. In some species, such as the corn bunting, *Emberiza calandra*, there is actually less fighting over food after starvation (Andrew 1957). A similar effect is sometimes seen in female chaffinches and other birds (Sabine 1959).

Increased fighting among starved animals has been used to support the contention that 'frustration' is the source of motivation for aggressive behavior. Frustration may be defined as 'interference with the occurrence of an instigated goal response at its proper time in the behavior sequence.' The concept of frustration has often been linked with aggression in studies of human psychology with ample supporting evidence (Dollard et al. 1939, Miller 1941, Jackson 1954). In many studies of animals the increase in fighting seems better explained as a result of increased exposure to external stimuli eliciting aggression, induced by crowding around a food or water source, than by the somewhat vaguer notion of frustration (e.g. Ginsburg and Allee 1942, Seward 1945–1946).

Yet a special relationship between aggression and frustration can develop through experience. For example, in one crowded flock of chaffinches a male with somewhat unstable rank in the hierarchy showed unusual behavior during some starvation experiments. "He developed the habit of making infrequent visits to the food remaining there longer than normal, and defending himself violently against all who approached. For some weeks after the experiment, as this male became hungry, he showed aggressive postures and attacked others at considerable distances" (Marler 1957). Similar behavior has been reported in rats and mice (Scott and Fredericson 1951).

These instances are some of the few in which there is clear evidence of animals seeking fights. Unusual aggressiveness can be a short-term effect of immediately previous fighting experience. Aggression aroused by one opponent is transferred or redirected to another individual. This redirection has been described in groups of many animals, often passing down the hierarchy from dominant to subordinate (e.g. Schjelderup-Ebbe 1935, Tompkins 1933, Maslow 1936, Colquhoun 1942, Bastock, Morris, and Moynihan 1953, Andrew 1957, Marler 1957). In a territorial bird society, clearly defined appetitive behavior for aggression in male chaffinches has been recorded in recently contested parts of the territory, but not otherwise (Marler 1957). The regular patrolling of territories seems to have a more general function than aggression alone. Questions concerning the actuality of appetitive behavior for aggression persist, and existing evidence cannot be considered conclusive. It is possible that in territorial birds the seeking of fights is temporary, stemming from relatively recent aggressive experience.

Wallace Craig (1918) made this point in characterizing aggression as an 'aversion' rather than an 'appetite.' He expanded this view later in an essay called "Why do animals fight?" (Craig 1928). His discussion leads to the conclusion that "fundamentally, among animals, fighting is not sought nor valued for its own sake; it is resorted to rather as a means . . . of defending the agent's interests." With obviously intended human overtones he continues: "Even when an animal does fight, he aims, not to destroy the enemy, but only to get rid of his presence and his interference." Essentially similar conclusions, phrased in different terms, have been drawn from studies of fighting in rats and mice (Scott and Frederickson 1951, Scott 1958) and birds (Andrew 1957, Marler 1957, Sabine 1959).

Aggressive behavior is usually instigated by contact with eliciting external stimuli and not by endogenously triggered appetitive actions such as we see in many other behavior patterns. Only rarely is such appetitive behavior induced by the experience of correlation between fighting and some other kind of activity. Endogenous influences on aggression are thus usually achieved by sensitization of the animal to certain classes of external stimuli. Spatial relationships with the external stimulus are especially important, the critical distances varying with the nature of the stimulus and with the internal state of the animal. Increasing testosterone levels are associated with the extension of dominance to greater distances and to external referents. Genotypic differences in aggressiveness found in certain strains of rats and mice (e.g. Ginsburg and Allee 1942, Hall and Klein 1942, Scott and Fredericson 1951, Marler 1957) also seem to be the result of differences in responsiveness to external stimuli.

The rarity of seeking for fights in animals is not altogether unexpected. Fighting is basically a means of competing more effectively for any commodity in short supply—food, water, nesting sites, mates, or space. Unless something is gained, fighting is at best a waste of time. At worst it engenders the possibility of distraction from other dangers, or of injury, or of death. An endogenous tendency to seek out fights would thus have hazardous consequences. Unnecessary fighting may be reduced by restricting aggressive behavior to situations in which animals are drawn into proximity for some other reason. Searching for fights may develop subsequently through learning if the animal gains some reward by it.

◆ *External Stimuli and Reduction of Aggression.* Fighting is a means of spacing animals. Exchanges of aggressive display achieve the same end, without danger of physical damage. Many species have evolved methods of reducing the frequency of combat and aggressive display in certain special social situations, thus permitting a closer spacing of individuals than would otherwise be possible. There is an extensive literature on occurrence of such distance-reducing behavior patterns (Tinbergen 1959) in a variety of animals.

Certain external stimuli greatly increase the probability of aggression, their nature depending on the species, strain, sex, age, reproductive state, past experience, position in space, and current behavior of the subject. Aggressive gestures by the opponent are an especially effective stimulus. One evolutionary trend that has decreased the probability of fighting and aggressive display when eliciting stimuli are present is the reduction of aggressive gestures to a minimum. This strategy has been exploited in the evolution of submissive or appeasement behavior, employed to achieve a closer proximity of individuals without provoking aggression (Moynihan 1955). The elements of aggressive behavior are often eliminated by the adoption of postures which are in many respects the opposite or antithesis of the positions of attack (Darwin 1872, Hinde 1952, 1955–1956a, Tinbergen and Moynihan 1952, Morris 1954, 1956, Chance 1962, Barnett 1963, Figures 5-6, 5-7).

Darwin's principle of antithesis (Figure 5-7) seems to explain these postures better than the notion that submissive animals expose some vulnerable part of their body. For example, in many mammals, birds,

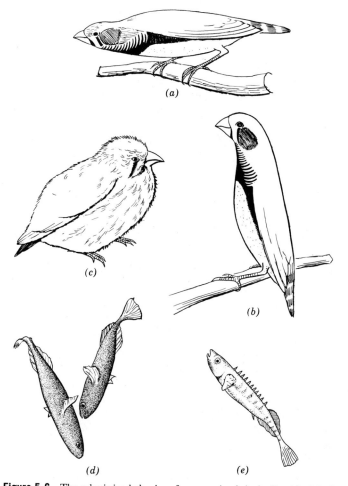

Figure 5-6   The submissive behavior of many animals is the "antithesis" of aggressive postures. In the zebra finch, *Poephila guttata,* the intensely aggressive posture (*a*) with plumage sleeked, that a male takes when facing a rival, contrasts with the submissive posture of the hunched female (*c*) with plumage fluffed out. In (*b*) a male stands in another less aggressive posture. In (*d*) two male ten-spined sticklebacks, *Pygosteus pungitius,* assume aggressive postures, accompanied by dark coloration. A submissive individual (*e*) blanches and assumes a head-up instead of a head-down position. After Morris 1954, 1958.

and fish a direct frontal gaze at the opponent is one characteristic of threat. In submissive behavior the eyes gaze in any direction other than that of the opponent. Submissive signals also involve subdued movement

(a)

(b)

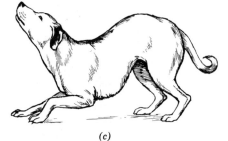

(c)

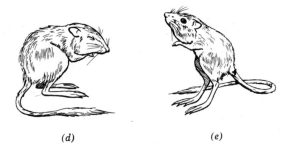

(d)   (e)

Figure 5-7   Darwin's illustrations of the expressive movements of dogs. The threat postures (*a* and *b*) include both 'serviceable associated habits' (e.g. withdrawal of the lips from the teeth) and 'movements due to direct action of the nervous system' (e.g. erection of hair on the back). The submissive posture (*c*) is the reverse of threat behavior in many respects illustrating Darwin's principle of antithesis. A similar contrast is seen between aggressive and submissive postures of kangaroo rats (*d* and *e*). After Darwin 1872, and Eisenberg 1963.

or even motionlessness, postures lacking the signs of muscular tension that characterize threat behavior, and so on. The parts of the body that are presented in threat, sometimes with conspicuous visual adornments, are often hidden from the opponent (Figure 5-8). In fish they may even change in color (Barlow 1962b, c, 1963). The bill of black-headed gulls

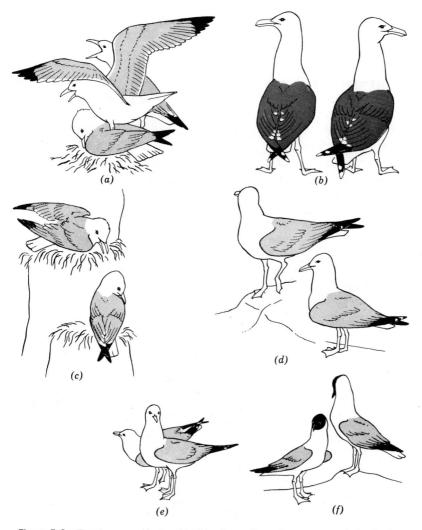

Figure 5-8 Turning away the head and beak as a form of appeasement behavior in a variety of gull species. (*a*) Kittiwake (the lower bird, which is an intruder on the nest of the pair); (*b*) lesser black-backed gull, female (left) and male; (*c*) kittiwake (the lower bird—the other bird jabs); (*d*) common gull (the bird on left—the other adopts the aggressive upright); (*e*) Hartlaub's gull—female (left) and male; (*f*) black-headed gull—female (front) and male. From Tinbergen 1959.

is thrust forward in aggressive behavior and turned away during the form of appeasement behavior known as head flagging (Tinbergen 1959).

These actions are by no means those of an animal preparing to flee. Precipitant flight by the opponent is a very effective stimulus for attack (Marler 1956a, Barlow 1962b). Submissive behavior often involves the elimination of escape behavior as well as aggressive postures. In this way defeated animals may slip away without pursuit, reducing the violence of resolving a conflict. Thus submissive behavior may increase spacing as well as reduce it.

An alternative method of reducing aggression is to elicit some other activity (Moynihan 1955). Immobility or withdrawal may be induced. The squeaking or squealing of defeated mammals and birds has much the same effect as a strong threat display, quelling the opponent's aggressiveness directly and eliciting withdrawal. Frequently submissive animals divert the opponent to some activity other than aggression or withdrawal

(a)

(b)

(c)

(d)

Figure 5-9 Postures used by gulls in potentially aggressive situations, perhaps to divert the companion to some nonaggressive activity. The hunched posture of (*a*) a young herring gull, (*b*) a black-headed gull, and (*c*) a kittiwake often evokes the presentation of food. Head tossing, shown in (*d*) a herring gull, is often a prelude either to food presentation or to copulation. After Tinbergen 1959.

(Figure 5-9). In many mammals the diversion is to mutual grooming (e.g. rodents, Eibl-Eibesfeldt 1958, Eisenberg 1962, 1963, primates, Altmann 1962, Hall and DeVore 1965, Marler 1965). In some primates sexual presentation seems to have a submissive effect by eliciting mounting by the opponent (Altmann 1962, Hall and DeVore 1965). Patterns of this type not only reduce the incidence of aggression but also provide a positive incentive for the maintenance of proximity or contact. Thus they assume a particularly important role in maintaining peace and cohesion in groups of some highly social species.

In the most complex societies such signals are not restricted to occasions when subordinate animals appease dominants. Dominant rhesus monkeys sometimes use similar behavior to achieve proximity with a subordinate (Altmann 1962). The head-flagging movement of black-headed gulls is not associated with dominance and subordination; it is given by both males and females in forming pairs (Tinbergen and Moynihan 1952). There is thus a spectrum from a mutual exchange of signals which reduce aggression to unilateral exchange in which one participant regularly takes the initiative in assuaging the disturbance of the other.

This cursory survey of aggression and related patterns of behavior has neglected many of the social and ecological aspects of the problem. The main point is to emphasize the dependence of both aggressive and withdrawal behavior on the external stimulus situation. This is not to say that endogenous variables can be ignored. The behavior is as much the outcome of interaction between internal and external factors as any other type of activity. Nevertheless, as Wallace Craig (1918) pointed out, control of the timing of the actions is largely the prerogative of external triggering stimuli, more so than in most other types of behavior.

SIMULTANEOUS OCCURRENCE OF MORE THAN ONE TYPE OF BEHAVIOR

There are many circumstances in which the same external stimulus situation can elicit more than one type of behavior. Complex social behavior often arises as a result of the multiple effects of certain situations (Baerends et al. 1955, Hinde 1955–1956a, Morris 1956, Tinbergen 1952, 1959 etc., see page 188). The simultaneous eliciting of more than one type of behavior may have a variety of outcomes.

Sometimes a free intermingling of different activities takes place, for example, in the locomotion of feeding fishes or of aerial insectivorous birds or in feeding and grooming crustacea. The elementary reflexes and simple behavior patterns may engage only a small portion of the animal's sensory and motor equipment. Most of what we speak of as behavior requires a major involvement of the whole organism at any one time to be effective, making it difficult to do several things at once.

When there is a possibility of such incompatibility, a mechanism is needed to program the use of motor equipment. The value of such programming can also be argued from another point of view. The constant barrage of varied stimuli upon receptors could result in confused and useless vacillation between one response and another. Some means is required to ensure that once a given type of behavior is under way, it is not "constantly tugged from its given course by the claims of rival processes" (Berlyne 1960).

There are inhibiting and facilitating mechanisms for ensuring an orderly outcome when more than one type of behavior is elicited. The problem is minimal when intermingling can take place, with or without changes in the frequency or completeness of the behavior patterns involved. A conflict may still arise in orientation of the behavior. The balancing of approach and withdrawal may come to be critical for survival. Such cases occur in exploratory behavior, and there are many others. The balance between withdrawal and approach has an important role in the control of fighting behavior (e.g. in the chaffinch, Marler 1956a) and in courtship behavior (review in Tinbergen 1954). Intermingling may involve more than two detectable types of behavior. Elements of fighting, withdrawal, and feeding may be present simultaneously in the behavior of wild great tits (Hinde 1952).

Instead of intermingling activities the animal may simply become immobile. When one of the conflicting patterns is withdrawal from danger, such immobility may have direct survival value, helping the animal to hide from a rival or predator. Inactivity would be dangerous in many circumstances, however. Sometimes conflict is resolved by a continuation of one behavior pattern with a new orientation, thus allowing withdrawal from the stimulus which evoked the conflict. This new behavior may include elements similar in form and orientation to those present in one or both of the conflicting patterns (Lind 1959). A fighting great tit, for instance, showing conflicting attack and withdrawal behavior may suddenly peck at a twig or bud with the same vigor that it might display in pecking at its opponent's head (Hinde 1952). This is a so-called 'redirection activity.' If a male black-headed gull evinces a conflict between withdrawal and attack when visited by a female, he may resolve it by assaulting another nearby gull that was not previously involved (Bastock, Morris, and Moynihan 1953). In other situations redirected aggression may be aimed at inanimate objects.

In conflict situations one type of behavior may inhibit the other altogether. Precedence depends in part on which actions the animal is most highly aroused to perform. There is a hierarchical ordering of behavior patterns so that, for example, intense withdrawal behavior tends to take precedence over other types of behavior.

Behavior emerging in conflicting situations does not necessarily share the motor patterns which the stimuli would normally elicit. But new stimuli generated within the conflicting situation may evoke the behavior. In many birds intense behavioral conflicts occur during copulation. Many ducks bathe after copulation. This bathing is probably elicited by disturbance of the feathers, perhaps by water splashed on the birds during the act of copulation, in which the female in particular is often completely submerged (Lind 1959). In passerine birds the elaborate preening that follows copulation may result in part from the inevitable disturbance of the feathers during the mating act (Andrew 1956b).

Activation of the autonomic nervous system commonly accompanies behavioral conflicts. Autonomic effects may determine in part the outcome of a conflict (Andrew 1956a, Morris 1956). Thus disturbance of the mechanisms for temperature control, which are autonomically regulated, provides a plausible explanation for the appearance of thermoregulatory behavior in such circumstances. Arousal of the sympathetic portion of the autonomic system can lower the threshold for tactile receptors in the skin of frogs to the extent that they may even discharge spontaneously (Loewenstein 1956). This phenomenon suggests a possible origin of grooming in mammals and preening in birds in conflict situations.

DISPLACEMENT ACTIVITIES

Occasionally a new kind of behavior emerges in conflict situations that seems to be quite unrelated to those that precede it, a so-called 'displacement activity.' The appearance in conflict situations of activities which to the observer appear irrelevant has been widely commented upon by observers of both animals and man (e.g. Huxley 1923, Makkink 1936, Kortlandt 1940, Tinbergen 1940, Armstrong 1947, Barnett 1955). Such activities frequently occur in the course of exploratory behavior. For example, when rats vacillate between withdrawal behavior and approach for investigation, they engage in excessive amounts of grooming (Bindra and Spinner 1958).

The primary characteristic of displacement activity is its apparent irrelevance to the immediate context. The behavior often seems to occur in the absence of the customary eliciting stimuli. The association of displacement activities with conflict situations led several investigators to interpret displacement activities as the result of 'overflow' or 'sparking over' of motivation from the conflicting behavior patterns into a new channel.

The overflow hypothesis is not the only possible interpretation of displacement activities. Van Iersel and Bol (1958) developed an alternative based on studies of the preening behavior of terns. This behavior occurs as an irrelevant activity in several different conflict situations. When a tern sitting on a nest of eggs is disturbed by another bird, an airplane, or a man, it shows signs both of withdrawal from the nest and of remaining to incubate. When these two types of behavior are more or less evenly balanced, the incubating bird often shows displacement feather preening. There may also be a conflict between incubating the eggs and attacking another bird. In this case displacement nest building often occurs.

Van Iersel and Bol conducted a careful study of the temporal relationships between preening behavior on the one hand and incubation and withdrawal behavior on the other, both in and out of conflict situations. This led them to interpret the so-called displacement as a result not of an overflow phenomenon but of what they called 'disinhibition' (see Sevenster 1961). This idea, developed by Andrew (1956b) to explain irrelevant preening behavior in finches, and by Sevenster (1961) to account for displacement fanning activity by the three-spined stickleback, is based on the concept of hierarchical arrangements of behavioral types, with some inhibiting others when they occur together. Preening has low status in this hierarchy; it is inhibited by many other behavior patterns. During incubation preening is inhibited even when external stimuli that might otherwise elicit it are present. Preening behavior is also inhibited in some degree during withdrawal behavior. What happens when incubation and withdrawal behavior come into conflict? If these two are about evenly balanced they tend to cancel each other. Van Iersel and Bol suggest that when this happens they also reduce or eliminate the inhibitory effects which they each have on other forms of behavior. Thus preening behavior is disinhibited and is free to be elicited by the appropriate external stimuli to occur as a displacement activity. The external stimuli are present at least in mild degree much of the time. Furthermore, incubating terns perform more displacement preening when light rain is falling, showing the susceptibility to external stimulation. A similar argument can explain displacement nest building.

Rowell (1961) also made use of temporal analysis in studies of displacement preening, bill wiping, and other comfort activities in chaffinches. Approach and withdrawal were induced simultaneously either by exposing the birds to an owl (see page 164) or by frightening them away from food when they were hungry. In this experiment preening was inhibited during the occurrence of other behavior patterns but appeared when such patterns came into conflict. Once elicited, the duration and vigor of preening were controlled by the appropriate external stimuli and by the available time. The role of the conflicting patterns can thus be regarded as a permissive one and nothing more. Rowell concludes that displacement activities are part of a much larger class of activities which "occur regularly at the transition between two types of mutually incompatible behavior." According to this interpretation displacement activities are an inevitable result of a hierarchical arrangement of behavior which confines subordinate patterns to occasions when dominant patterns are absent. If these hypotheses are correct, the inappropriateness of the behavior vanishes, and displacement activities become a special case of a more general phenomenon. Alternatively, the true explanation may be found in some combination of the overflow and disinhibition hypotheses.

CONFLICT BEHAVIOR IN RATS

In a review of experimental studies of conflict, N. E. Miller (1944) presents data of a different kind on the outcome of interaction between approach and withdrawal behavior in rats. By attaching a rat to a harness and placing it in a runway, the force exerted in locomotion in different directions can be measured. The performance has been assessed in various types of situations. One of these is an approach-withdrawal conflict, brought about by giving an electric shock at the feeding place several times and then observing the behavior after varying periods of food deprivation. Another situation involved approach-approach and withdrawal-withdrawal conflicts, arranged by presenting conditioned stimuli for feeding or withdrawal to hungry rats at both ends of a runway. Miller's conclusions were set forth as a series of principles which regulate approach-withdrawal behavior. The vigor of approach or withdrawal from stimuli is stronger the nearer the subject is to the source, and the vigor of avoidance increases more rapidly with nearness to the stimulus source than does that of approach (Figure 5-10). The balance point varies with the relative degree of arousal of the two behavior patterns, as one would predict. Near equilibrium, the rats often vacillate, especially when the conflicting tendencies are strong.

The tendency of rats in these approach-withdrawal situations is to reach an equilibrium which will be stable, at least for a time. In contrast, an approach-approach situation is unstable and is likely to be resolved quickly without vacillation. A withdrawal-withdrawal situa-

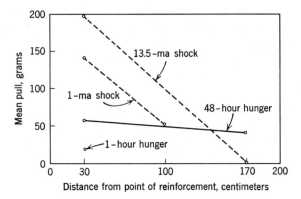

Figure 5-10 Studies of conflict behavior show that rats pull harder at a harness to avoid a shock the closer they are to it and the stronger the shock has been during training (broken lines). Approach to a feeding place increases in strength after prolonged starvation but is relatively independent of distance from the point of reinforcement (solid line). After Miller 1944.

tion is different again, and tends to result in attempts to withdraw from the whole situation. If this is not permitted, vacillation is likely.

The behavioral changes that occurred in these various harness experiments have not been described in detail. Thus it is difficult to generalize from this work to other kinds of investigation. Nevertheless, Miller points to methods for defining the characteristics of conflict behavior more precisely.

CONFLICT IN SOCIAL SITUATIONS

Whenever two animals come together for the purpose of social exchange, there is an increased possibility of aggression. Approach-withdrawal conflicts are therefore more likely than not to occur. Such conflicts have exerted a strong influence on the evolution of communicatory behavior (Tinbergen 1952, 1954). The so-called 'upright threat posture' of the herring gull was one of the first of a series of behavior patterns to be interpreted as the outcome of the intermingling of attack and withdrawal behavior. A similar posture occurs in the black-headed gull (Figure 5-11). Incomplete acts from both behavioral types are simultaneously present in the same individual. Furthermore, the temporal pattern of such behavior often includes oscillation between sequences of attack and withdrawal; threat is most prominent when the intensities of the two are evenly balanced. This pattern is widespread in the fighting behavior of many species (e.g. Hinde 1952, 1953, 1954a, 1955-1956a, Baerends et al. 1955, Moynihan 1955, Morris 1956, Marler 1956a, Andrew 1957, Wiepkema 1961).

Sometimes there are elements in the behavior that cannot be directly related to either attack or withdrawal behavior. It appears that in a particular state of conflict, defined both by the degree of arousal of the two types of behavior and by their relative states of balance, new behavior patterns occur. These have evolved from a variety of origins which often remain sufficiently distinctive to permit identification. Sometimes these beginnings were irrelevant acts in the context of attack-withdrawal situations which have been incorporated from other behavioral patterns.

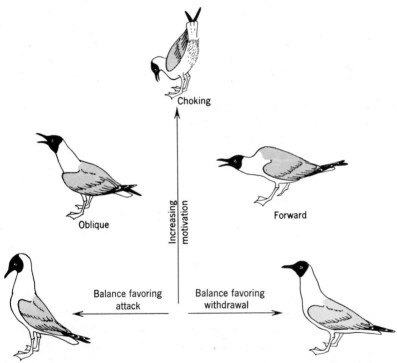

Figure 5-11 The displays of the black-headed gull used in courtship and fighting are thought to involve degrees of attack and withdrawal. In the 'oblique' and the 'aggressive upright' aggression predominates; but the oblique is relatively more intense. In the 'forward' and the 'anxiety upright' the balance favors withdrawal motivation. The 'choking' display seems to represent a balance of attack and withdrawal elements, also with very strong motivation. After Moynihan 1955.

Other patterns may be incomplete versions of behavior from one of the conflicting types of behavior. In the course of subsequent evolution they may come to have unique characteristics of their own. Distinct patterns representing different levels and degrees of balance between the attack and withdrawal behavior may emerge (Moynihan 1955, Figure 5-11).

Just as the simultaneous elicitation of approach and withdrawal by novel stimuli functions to provide a delicate adjustment of the distance from which a potentially dangerous object is surveyed, so in fighting behavior it allows the necessary compromise between headlong flight and overconfident attack. The balance is determined by many factors, both present and past, internal and external, and especially by the external stimuli generated by the changing behavior of the opponent.

An aggressive response to the presence of other individuals of the same species is deeply rooted. It often reappears in the relationship between the sexes. The courtship of many species is a modified version of the fighting behavior. This is so in many species of gulls (e.g. Tinbergen 1959), finches (e.g. Hinde 1955-1956a), and various groups of fishes (e.g. Baerends et al. 1955, Morris 1956). In addition to the aggression and withdrawal elements, a third element may enter, purely reproductive in function, centered around the act of copulation.

The method used by Moynihan (1955) to analyze the behavior of the black-headed gull involves the study of temporal sequences. By observing how often a gull shows withdrawal or attack just before or after a given posture, the degree of arousal of the two types of behavior is inferred (Figure 5-11, vertical axis). This same method has been applied to the analysis of courtship of finches (Hinde 1953, 1954a) and sticklebacks (Tinbergen 1954, Morris 1958). Thus the dancing performed by a courting male ten-spined stickleback is associated with frequent attacks on the female, and showing of the nest entrance is very likely to lead to some further sexual action (Figure 5-12).

The predominant behavioral pattern arising in encounters between animals of the opposite sex may vary strikingly on different occasions. Often the male attacks the female for much of the time but changes to withdrawal as the time for mating approaches. At the moment of copulation the competing behavior patterns in the male are those of withdrawal and approach (review in Hinde 1959, Thompson 1960). The female changes from an early predominance of withdrawal behavior to attacks upon the male which let up only at the moment of copulation. Parallel interpretations can be made of the courtship of cichlid fishes (Barlow in litt.), birds such as the chaffinch, and the chimpanzee (Yerkes 1940).

From a functional point of view, the multiplicity of responses elicited

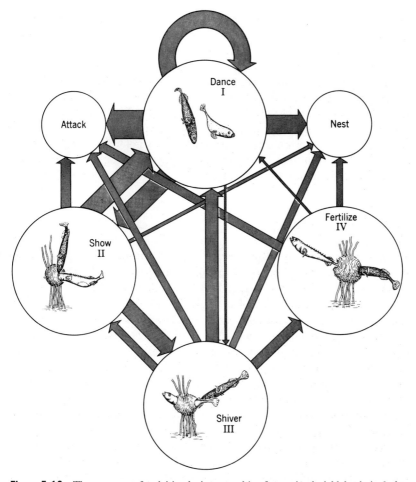

Figure 5-12   The sequence of activities during courtship of ten-spined sticklebacks includes much aggression. The male is the darker of the two. The sequences of male courtship activities from dancing to fertilization are shown. The number of times that these behavior patterns preceded or followed other actions is represented by the width of the connecting arrows. Attacks may follow any part of the sequence. Adapted from Morris, 1958.

by the mate, involving both approach and withdrawal, serves to achieve a delicate balance. The introduction of a conflict helps reduce the incidence of biologically unproductive indulgence and rape.

◆ *Conclusions on the Significance of Conflict in Behavior.* Attention has been focused mainly on conflicts arising from the temporal overlapping of different types of behavior. A similar phenomenon occurs at the level of individual acts (Andrew 1956a, Berlyne 1960). Conflicts may arise whenever there are functionally equivalent motor patterns as in activities such as locomotion (Barlow 1962a). Whenever different orientations of the same response are possible, conflicts occur. Indeed, conflicts are probably generated in all choice situations. They are difficult to analyze because their direct behavioral manifestations are slight. There may be measurable autonomic and other physiological consequences, however. A great deal of human emotional behavior is probably generated at this level—hence perhaps our lack of a thorough understanding of its behavioral significance (Lindsley 1951, Young 1961).

PLAY

◆ *The Characteristics of Play Behavior.* Many authors have pointed out the close relationship between exploration and playful behavior (e.g. Groos 1898, Beach 1945, Nissen 1951, Lorenz 1956, Bindra 1959, Berlyne 1960). The same objects can evoke both responses. Acts of exploration in which the animal actively changes the environment by manual or other means often have a playful quality. The effectiveness of novel objects in evoking both play and exploration wanes rapidly with time in much the same way (e.g. Inhelder 1955a). Playful activity, like exploration, is not entirely dependent on elicitation by novel external stimuli. Stimulus qualities other than novelty may be involved, especially in social situations, and it is in this context that endogenous factors become apparent. Young animals clearly seek opportunities to play.

Although there are qualities which exploratory and playful behavior share, it may be deceptive to conclude that this resemblance has any fundamental significance. Play behavior is more complex and variable than exploratory behavior. More kinds of external stimuli are involved in the control of play. The elicitation of both behavior patterns by similar external stimuli may be no more than another illustration of the multivalent properties of certain situations. Nor should we be misled by the conclusion that playful behavior has a similar function to exploratory behavior—namely familiarization of the individual with external conditions. Equivalence of function cannot be equated to equivalence of mechanism.

Play behavior cannot be discussed without defining it, and a definition is not easy to derive. The activities it encompasses include various types of locomotory behavior, prey-catching and feeding behavior, withdrawal, aggressive and sexual activities, as well as the manipulatory behavior which relates so closely to exploration (Beach 1945, Meyer-Holzapfel 1956). What ever other properties these activities may have in common, observers agree on the subjective judgment that lack of 'seriousness' is a key quality. The basis for this judgment is rarely made explicit, but it generally seems to relate to some aspect of the temporal patterning of the behavior concerned. The individual acts observed in play are often similar to those recurring in normal versions of the same major pattern (Figure 5-13). However, in the 'playful' version the normal sequences are replaced by a different pattern. The following characteristics of this pattern may serve as an approach to a definition of play.

1. The normal temporal groupings of functionally related actions break down, so that elements of a number of different types intermingle in the same behavioral sequence (Meyer-Holzapfel 1956). Rensch and Dücker (1959) draw attention to this in the play behavior of the mongoose, in which prey-catching and sexual movements often follow in

Figure 5-13 The play of mammals often includes acts which are parts of a sequence from another context, such as fighting behavior, as seen in this picture of play in captive young chimpanzees. After Meyer-Holzapfel 1956.

rapid succession. Polecats and badgers switch rapidly from prey-catching movements to aggressive behavior and back again. They may alternate rapidly between the dominant and submissive role (Eibl-Eibesfeldt 1950, 1956). There is a lack of proper inertia and momentum in play (Lorenz 1956). One element may become separated from its usual concomitants. In playful fighting in dogs, snarling may be dissociated from the pilo-erection which inevitably accompanies it in true fighting.

2. In addition to the mingling of different types of behavior, the sequences within a given type are also disrupted. Where a bout usually involves a sequence of appetitive and consummatory behavior, the playful version often lacks the regular pattern. Actions of prey capture may be divorced from the stalking behavior that usually precedes them.

3. The pattern of behavior in play is less dependent on the normal stimulus-response relationship. Less specific external stimuli often become effective. In cats, foxes, and mongooses, both adult and young, a wide variety of inappropriate objects, either animate (such as a companion's tail) or inanimate (a stone or leaf), may evoke playful prey-catching behavior (Leyhausen 1956, Tembrock 1957, Rensch and Dücker 1959). Aggressive and sexual responses can be given to equally inappropriate objects (e.g. Inhelder 1955a,b). Behavior may occur without any obvious external eliciting stimuli at all. Various types of withdrawal behavior occur spontaneously in the play of ungulates, especially the jumping and arching of the back used to throw off predators (Darling 1937, Lorenz 1956).

So far the picture we have of play behavior consists of elements drawn from other types of behavior and rearranged in new patterns of timing and sequence. In addition, there are behavior patterns which are evinced only in play. Hamsters and foxes use particular postures as a prelude to play (Eibl-Eibesfeldt 1953, Tembrock 1957). Rensch and Dücker (1959) describe a sudden vertical jump into the air with which a mongoose often prefaces a bout of play. In addition to such typical behavior, new patterns are constantly being invented, especially in play with inanimate objects (see page 689). Often such movements become stereotyped and are repeated again and again.

Behavior patterns taken from other temporal groupings can be modified in the context of play. The terminal movements of prey catching, for example, are often incomplete and lack the vigor of the same pattern in its usual context, especially if it is directed toward a companion. Similarly playful aggressive behavior differs from actual aggressiveness both in completeness and in timing, even though the majority of the movements are shared.

There are thus several reasons for thinking of play as a distinct, separate category of behavior. It consists largely of movements recurring in a number of other types of behavior. These are incorporated into a new and distinctive pattern of sequence and timing, often with slight but consistent qualitative changes. Some elements are unique. The overall patterning within sequences of play has been little studied, but it may be possible to speak of bouts of play in the same sense that we have spoken of bouts of other types of behavior.

Another distinctive property of play behavior is its low status in the hierarchy of behavior types. Animals play when they have nothing else to do. We are reminded of preening behavior in birds, which only continues as long as no other behavior is favored. If playful fighting turns into a real fight, which is not uncommon, the pattern undergoes a complete change. Playful prey catching changes to the normal behavior when the animal becomes hungry. Withdrawal behavior also normally takes precedence over play. In sexual behavior we commonly see signs of intermingling of the normal and playful versions of the same behavioral category.

The value of approaching play behavior through its temporal organization is difficult to assess because we have so few data to consider. Whether or not this discussion is well founded, it may at least serve to point up the need for precise descriptions of the temporal patterning of play behavior, as of natural behavior in general. Fruitful discussion of the factors which control play may follow a more satisfactory definition of what it actually comprises.

◆ *The Functions and Phylogeny of Play Behavior.* Armchair judgments are often unreliable guides to the function of behavior. Experimentation is called for, and play behavior has rarely been approached from this point of view.

Many authors feel that play, particularly in juveniles, provides a means of introducing animals to new physical or social environments. Proof is lacking of the efficacy of the experience thus gained in aiding adult survival. Animals raised in isolation from social companions, and thus deprived of the opportunity for social play, may show abnormal social behavior. This has been found to be true in dogs and rhesus monkeys (Thompson 1955, Harlow and Zimmerman 1959, see page 671). However, it is difficult to determine which of the many restrictions imposed by the isolation is responsible for the alteration. Is the elimination of social play more important than, say, the limitation of direct sensory experience?

Although play behavior has been recorded from all the vertebrate classes except fishes, it is more characteristic of certain mammals, especially the carnivores and the primates (Meyer-Holzapfel 1956, Rensch and Dücker 1959). It is typical of juveniles but is by no means rare in adults. The correlation with higher mental development and greater dependence on learning as a factor in behavioral development is obvious. Yet we must take care not to leave the issue there, for there are many ways in which such a correlation could arise. Play consists both of elements from other behavioral groupings and of components which are invented. Do these exert the same kind of influence upon subsequent development? It seems unlikely. The significance of play among conspecific social companions may differ from play with other species, which may differ again from play with inanimate objects. The roles of exogenous and endogenous factors in evoking play behavior may well vary with different types of play and from one species to another. More observation and experiment are necessary before we can begin to ask the proper questions, let alone answer them.

REFERENCES

Allee, W. C. 1938. *The Social Life of Animals.* W. W. Norton and Company, New York.

Altmann, S. 1962. A field study of the sociobiology of rhesus monkeys, *Macaca mulatta. Ann. N.Y. Acad. Sci.*, **102**:338–435.

Andrew, R. J. 1956a. Some remarks on behaviour in conflict situations, with special reference to *Emberiza* spp. *Brit. J. Anim. Behav.*, **4**:41–45.

———. 1956b. Normal and irrelevant toilet behaviour in *Emberiza* spp. *Brit. J. Anim. Behav.*, **4**:85–91.

———. 1957. Influence of hunger on aggressive behavior in certain buntings of the genus *Emberiza. Physiol. Zool.*, **30**:177–185.

Armstrong, E. A. 1947. *Bird Display and Behaviour.* Lindsey Press, London.

Baerends, G. P., R. Brouwer, and H. Tj. Waterbolk. 1955. Ethological studies on *Lebistes reticulatus* (Peters). I. An analysis of the male courtship pattern. *Behaviour.* **8**:249–334.

Barlow, G. W. 1962a. Ethology of the Asian teleost *Badis badis.* I. Locomotion, maintenance, aggregation and fright. *Trans. Ill. Acad. Sci.*, **54**:175–188.

———. 1962b. Ethology of the Asian teleost *Badis badis.* III. Aggressive behavior. *Z. Tierpsychol.*, **19**:29–55.

———. 1962c. Ethology of the Asian teleost *Badis badis.* IV. Sexual behavior. *Copeia.* **1962**: 346–360.

———. 1963. Ethology of the Asian teleost *Badis badis.* II. Motivation and signal value of the colour patterns. *Anim. Behav.*, **11**:97–105.

Barnett, S. A. 1955. "Displacement" behaviour and "psychosomatic" disorder. *Lancet.* **269**:1203–1208.

———. 1958. Exploratory behaviour. *Brit. J. Psychol.*, **49**:289–310.

———. 1963. *A Study in Behaviour.* Methuen and Company, London.

Bastock, M., D. Morris, and M. Moynihan. 1953. Some comments on conflict and thwarting in animals. *Behaviour*, **6**:66–84.

Beach, F. A. 1945. Current concepts of play in animals. *Amer. Nat.*, **79**:523–541.

———. 1948. *Hormones and Behavior.* Paul B. Hoeber, New York.

Bennet, M. A. 1940. The social hierarchy in ring doves. II. The effect of treatment with testosterone propionate. *Ecology*, 21:148–165.

Berlyne, D. E. 1955. The arousal and satiation of perceptual curiosity in the rat. *J. comp. physiol. Psychol.*, 48:238–246.

———. 1960. *Conflict, Arousal and Curiosity*. McGraw-Hill Book Company, New York.

——— and J. Slater. 1957. Perceptual curiosity, exploratory behavior, and maze learning. *J. comp. physiol. Psychol.*, 50:228–232.

Bindra, D. 1959. *Motivation. A Systematic Reinterpretation*. The Ronald Press Company, New York.

——— and N. Spinner. 1958. Response to different degrees of novelty: The incidence of various activities. *J. Exp. Anal. Behav.*, 1:341–350.

Bourlière, F. 1955. *The Natural History of Mammals*. Alfred A. Knopf, New York.

Boyd, H. 1953. On encounters between wild white-fronted geese in winter flocks. *Behaviour*, 5:85–129.

Brady, J. V. 1960. Emotional behavior. In *Handbook of Physiology*, ed. by J. Field, Sec. 1, Vol. 3:1529–1552. American Physiological Society, Washington, D.C.

Brown, J. L. 1963. Aggressiveness, dominance and social organization in the Steller jay. *Condor*, 65:460–484.

———. 1964. The evolution of diversity in avian territorial systems. *Wilson Bull.*, 76:160–169.

——— and R. W. Hunsperger. 1963. Neuroethology and the motivation of agonistic behaviour. *Anim. Behav.*, 11:439–448.

Bruce, R. H. 1941. An experimental analysis of social factors affecting the performance of white rats. *J. Comp. Psychol.*, 31:395–412.

Burckhardt, D. 1944. Möwenbeobachtungen in Basel. *Orn. Beo.*, 41:49–76.

Burt, W. H. 1943. Territoriality and home range concepts as applied to mammals. *J. Mammal.*, 24:346–352.

Butler, R. A. 1953. Discrimination learning by rhesus monkeys to visual-exploration motivation. *J. comp. physiol. Psychol.*, 46:95–98.

———. 1954. Incentive conditions which influence visual exploration. *J. Exp. Psychol.*, 48:19–23.

———. 1958. The differential effect of visual and auditory incentives on the performance of monkeys. *Amer. J. Psychol.*, 71:591–593.

———. 1960. Acquired drives and the curiosity-investigative motives. In *Principles of Comparative Psychology*, ed. by R. H. Waters, D. A. Rethlingshafer, and W. E. Caldwell: 144–176. McGraw-Hill Book Company, New York.

Carrick, R. 1963. Ecological significance of territory in the Australian magpie, *Gymnorhina tibicen*. *Proc. 13th Orn. Congr.*: 740–753.

Chance, M. R. A. 1962. An interpretation of some agonistic postures; the role of "cut-off" acts and postures. *Symp. Zool. Soc. Lond.*, 8:71–89.

Christian, J. J. 1959. The roles of endocrine and behavioral factors in the growth of mammalian populations. In *Comparative Endocrinology*, ed. by A. Gorbman: 71–97. John Wiley and Sons, New York.

Collias, N. E. 1944. Aggressive behavior among vertebrate animals. *Physiol. Zool.*, 17:83–123.

———. 1950. Hormones and behavior with special reference to birds and the mechanisms of hormone action. In *A Symposium on Steroid Hormones*, ed. by E. S. Gordon: 277–329. University of Wisconsin Press, Madison.

Colquhoun, M. K. 1942. Notes on the social behaviour of blue tits. *Brit. Birds*, 35:234–240.

Conder, P. J. 1949. Individual distance. *Ibis*, 91:649–655.

Craig, W. 1918. Appetites and aversions as constituents of instincts. *Biol. Bull.*, 34:91–107.

———. 1928. Why do animals fight? *Int. J. Ethics*, 31:264–278.

Crook, J. H. 1953. An observational study of the gulls of Southampton Water. *Brit. Birds*, 46:385–397.

――. 1961. The basis of flock organisation in birds. In *Current Problems in Animal Behaviour*, ed. by W. H. Thorpe and O. L. Zangwill: 125–149. Cambridge University Press, Cambridge.

Crowcroft, P. 1955. Territoriality in wild house mice, *Mus musculus* L. *J. Mammal.*, 36:299–301.

Darchen, R. 1952. Sur l'activité exploratrice de *Blattella germanica*. *Z. Tierpsychol.*, 9:362–372.

――. 1955. Stimuli nouveaux et tendance exploratrice chez *Blattella germanica*. *Z. Tierpsychol.*, 12:1–11.

·Darling, F. F. 1937. *A Herd of Red Deer*. Oxford University Press, London.

Darwin, C. 1872. *The Expression of the Emotions in Man and the Animals*. John Murray (Publishers), London.

Davis, D. E. 1957. Aggressive behavior in castrated starlings. *Science*, 126:253.

――. 1958. The role of density in aggressive behaviour of house mice. *Brit. J. Anim. Behav.*, 6:207–210.

――. 1959. Territorial rank in starlings. *Anim. Behav.*, 7:214–221.

DeVore, I. and S. L. Washburn. 1963. Baboon ecology and human evolution. In *African Ecology and Human Evolution*, ed. by F. C. Howell and F. Bourlière: 335–367. Aldine Publishing Company, Chicago.

Diebschlag, E. 1941. Psychologische Beobachtungen über die Rangordnung bei der Haustaube. *Z. Tierpsychol.*, 4:173–187.

Dollard, J., N. E. Miller, L. W. Doob, O. H. Mowrer, and R. R. Sears. 1939. *Frustration and Aggression*. Kegan Paul, Trench, Trubner and Company, London.

Eibl-Eibesfeldt, I. 1950. Über die Jugendentwicklung des Verhaltens eines männlichen Dachses (*Meles meles* L.) unter besonderer Berücksichtigung des Spieles. *Z. Tierpsychol.*, 7:327–355.

――. 1953. Zur Ethologie des Hamsters (*Cricetus cricetus* L.). *Z. Tierpsychol.*, 10:204–254.

――. 1956. Einige Bemerkungen über den Ursprung von Ausdrucksbewegungen bei Säugetieren. *Z. Säugetierk.*, 21:29–43.

――. 1958. Das Verhalten der Nagetiere. *Handb. Zool. Berlin*, 8(12):1–88.

Eisenberg, J. 1962. Studies on the behavior of *Peromyscus maniculatus gambelii* and *Peromyscus californicus parasiticus*. *Behaviour*, 19:177–207.

――. 1963. The behavior of heteromyid rodents. *Univ. Calif. Publ. Zool.*, 69:1–114.

Emlen, J. T. 1952a. Flocking behavior in birds. *Auk*, 69:160–170.

――. 1952b. Social behavior in nesting cliff swallows. *Condor*, 54:177–199.

Fabricius, E. and K.-J. Gustafson. 1954. Further aquarium observations on the spawning behaviour of the char, *Salmo alpinus* L. *Inst. Freshwater Res. Rep.*, No. 35:58–104.

Ginsburg, B. and W. C. Allee. 1942. Some effects of conditioning on social dominance and subordination in inbred strains of mice. *Physiol. Zool.*, 15:485–506.

Göz, H. 1954. Über den Art- und Individualgeruch bei Fischen. *Z. vergl. Physiol.*, 29:1–45.

Groos, K. 1898. *The Play of Animals* (trans. by E. A. Baldwin). D. Appleton and Company, New York.

Guhl, A. M. 1961. Gonadal hormones and social behavior in infrahuman vertebrates. In *Sex and Internal Secretions*, ed. by W. C. Young, Vol. 2:1240–1267. The Williams and Wilkins Company, Baltimore.

―― and L. L. Ortman. 1953. Visual patterns in the recognition of individuals among chickens. *Condor*, 55:287–298.

Hall, C. S. 1941. Temperament: a survey of animal studies. *Psychol. Bull.*, 38:909–943.

―― and S. J. Klein. 1942. Individual differences in aggressiveness in rats. *J. Comp. Psychol.*, 33:371–383.

Hall, K. R. L. and I. DeVore. 1965. Baboon social behavior. In *Primate Behavior,* ed. by I. DeVore: 53–110. Holt, Rinehart and Winston, New York.

Harlow, H. F. and G. E. McClearn. 1954. Object discrimination learned by monkeys on the basis of manipulation motives. *J. comp. physiol. Psychol.,* **47**:73–76.

———— and R. R. Zimmerman. 1959. Affectional responses in the infant monkey. *Science,* **130**:421–432.

Hediger, H. 1950. *Wild Animals in Captivity.* Butterworth and Company (Publishers), London.

Hinde, R. A. 1952. Behaviour of the great tit (*Parus major*) and some other related species. *Behaviour Suppl.,* **2**:1–201.

————. 1953. The conflict between drives in the courtship and copulation of the chaffinch. *Behaviour,* **5**:1–31.

————. 1954a. The courtship and copulation of the greenfinch (*Chloris chloris*). *Behaviour,* **7**:207–232.

————. 1954b. Factors governing the changes in strength of a partially inborn response, as shown by the mobbing behaviour of the chaffinch (*Fringilla coelebs*). I. The nature of the response, and an examination of its course. *Proc. Roy. Soc. Lond., B,* **142**:306–331.

————. 1955–1956a. A comparative study of the courtship of certain finches (Fringillidae). *Ibis,* **97**:706–745, **98**:1–23.

————. 1956b. The biological significance of the territories of birds. *Ibis,* **98**:340–369.

————. 1959. Behaviour and speciation in birds and lower vertebrates. *Biol. Rev.,* **34**:85–128.

Hutchinson, G. E. 1953. The concept of pattern in ecology. *Proc. Acad. Nat. Sci. Phila.,* **105**:1–12.

Huxley, J. S. 1923. Courtship activities in the red-throated diver (*Colymbus stellatus* Pontopp.); together with a discussion of the evolution of courtship in birds. *J. Linn. Soc. Lond.* (Zool.), **35**:253–292.

Iersel, J. J. A. van and A. C. A. Bol. 1958. Preening of two tern species. A study on displacement activities. *Behaviour,* **13**:1–88.

Imanishi, K. 1960. Social organization of subhuman primates in their natural habitat. *Curr. Anthrop.,* **1**:393–407.

Inhelder, E. 1955a. Zur Psychologie einiger Verhaltensweisen-besonders des Spiels-von Zootieren. *Z. Tierpsychol.,* **12**:88–144.

————. 1955b. Über das Spielen mit Gegenständen bei Huftieren. *Rev. Suisse Zool.,* **62**:240–250.

Jackson, L. 1954. *Aggression and Its Interpretation.* Methuen and Company, London.

Jenkins, D. W. 1944. Territory as a result of despotism and social organization in geese. *Auk,* **61**:30–47.

Kortlandt, A. 1940. Wechselwirkung zwischen Instinkten. *Arch. Néerl. Zool.,* **4**:442–520.

Lack, D. 1943. *The Life of the Robin.* H. F. and G. Witherby, London.

Leyhausen, P. 1956. Das Verhalten der Katzen (Felidae). *Handb. Zool. Berlin,* **8**(7):1–34.

Lind, H. 1959. The activation of an instinct caused by a "transitional action." *Behaviour,* **14**:123–135.

Lindsley, D. B. 1951. Emotion. In *Handbook of Experimental Psychology,* ed. by S. S. Stevens: 473–516. John Wiley and Sons, New York.

Loewenstein, W. R. 1956. Modulation of cutaneous mechanoreceptors by sympathetic stimulation. *J. Physiol.,* **132**:40–60.

Lorenz, K. Z. 1956. Plays and vacuum activities. In *L'Instinct dans le Comportement des Animaux et de l'Homme:* 633–638. Fondation Singer-Polignac. Masson et Cie Editeurs, Paris.

McBride, G., J. W. James, and R. N. Shoffner. 1963. Social forces determining spacing and head orientation in a flock of domestic hens. *Nature,* **197**:1272–1273.

McClearn, G. E. 1959. The genetics of mouse behavior in novel situations. *J. comp. physiol. Psychol.,* **52**:62–67.

Maier, N. R. F. and T. C. Schneirla. 1935. *Principles of Animal Psychology.* McGraw-Hill Book Company, New York.

Makkink, G. F. 1936. An attempt at an ethogram of the European avocet (*Recurvirostra avosetta* L.) with ethological and psychological remarks. *Ardea,* 25:1–62.

Marler, P. 1955a. Studies of fighting in chaffinches. (1) Behaviour in relation to the social hierarchy. *Brit. J. Anim. Behav.,* 3:111–117.

———. 1955b. Studies of fighting in chaffinches. (2) The effect on dominance relations of disguising females as males. *Brit. J. Anim. Behav.,* 3:137–146.

———. 1956a. Behaviour of the chaffinch, *Fringilla coelebs. Behaviour Suppl.,* 5:1–184.

———. 1956b. Studies of fighting in chaffinches. (3) Proximity as a cause of aggression. *Brit. J. Anim. Behav.,* 4:23–30.

———. 1957. Studies of fighting in chaffinches. (4) Appetitive and consummatory behaviour. *Brit. J. Anim. Behav.,* 5:29–37.

———. 1961. The evolution of visual communication. In *Vertebrate Speciation,* ed. by W. F. Blair: 96–121. University of Texas Press, Austin.

———. 1965. Communication in monkeys and apes. In *Primate Behavior,* ed. by I. DeVore: 544–584. Holt, Rinehart and Winston, New York.

Maslow, A. H. 1936. The role of dominance in the social and sexual behavior of infra-human primates: IV. The determination of hierarchy in pairs and in a group. *J. Genet. Psychol.,* 49:161–198.

Mayr, E. 1963. *Animal Species and Evolution.* Harvard University Press, Cambridge.

Meyer-Holzapfel, M. 1956. Das Spiel bei Säugetieren. *Handb. Zool. Berlin,* 8(2):1–36.

Miller, N. E. 1941. I. The frustration-aggression hypothesis. *Psychol. Rev.,* 48:337–342.

———. 1944. Experimental studies of conflict. In *Personality and the Behavior Disorders,* ed. by J. McV. Hunt, Vol. 1:431–465. The Ronald Press Company, New York.

Montgomery, K. C. 1953. Exploratory behavior as a function of "similarity" of stimulus situations. *J. comp. physiol. Psychol.,* 46:129–133.

———. 1954. The role of exploratory drive in learning. *J. comp. physiol. Psychol.,* 47:60–64.

———. 1955. The relation between fear induced by novel stimulation and exploratory behavior. *J. comp. physiol. Psychol.,* 48:254–260.

Morris, D. 1954. The reproductive behaviour of the zebra finch (*Poephila guttata*), with special reference to pseudofemale behaviour and displacement activities. *Behaviour,* 6:271–322.

———. 1956. The function and causation of courtship ceremonies. In *L'instinct dans le Comportement des Animaux et de L'homme:* 261–286. Fondation Singer-Polignac. Masson et Cie Editeurs, Paris.

———. 1958. The reproductive behaviour of the ten-spined stickleback (*Pygosteus pungitius* L.). *Behaviour Suppl.,* 6:1–154.

Moynihan, M. 1955. Some aspects of reproductive behavior in the black-headed gull (*Larus ridibundus ridibundus* L.) and related species. *Behaviour Suppl.,* 4:1–201.

Nice, M. M. 1941. The role of territory in bird life. *Amer. Midl. Nat.,* 26:441–487.

Nissen, H. W. 1951. Phylogenetic comparison. In *Handbook of Experimental Psychology,* ed. by S. S. Stevens: 347–386. John Wiley and Sons, New York.

———. 1954. The nature of the drive as innate determinant of behavioral organization. *Neb. Symp. Motiv.,* 2:281–321.

Nowlis, V. 1941. The relation of degree of hunger to competitive interaction in chimpanzee. *J. Comp. Psychol.,* 32:91–115.

Orians, G. and M. F. Willson. 1964. Interspecific territoriality of birds. *Ecology,* 45:736–745.

Pitelka, F. A. 1942. Territoriality and related problems in North American hummingbirds. *Condor,* 44:189–204.

————. 1951. Ecologic overlap and interspecific strife in breeding populations of Anna and Allen hummingbirds. *Ecology,* **32:**641–661.

————. 1959. Numbers, breeding schedule, and territoriality in pectoral sandpipers of northern Alaska. *Condor,* **61:**233–264.

Rand, A. L. 1941. Development and enemy recognition of the curve-billed thrasher *Toxostoma curvirostre. Bull. Amer. Mus. Nat. Hist.,* **78:**213–242.

Rensch, B. and G. Dücker. 1959. Die Spiele von Mungo und Ichneumon. *Behaviour,* **14:**185–213.

Ritchey, F. 1951. Dominance-subordination and territorial relationships in the common pigeon. *Physiol. Zool.,* **24:**167–176.

Rowell, C. H. F. 1961. Displacement grooming in the chaffinch. *Anim. Behav.,* **9:**38–63.

Sabine, W. S. 1959. The winter society of the Oregon junco: intolerance, dominance, and the pecking order. *Condor,* **61:**110–135.

Schjelderup-Ebbe, T. 1922. Beiträge zur Sozialpsychologie des Haushuhns. *Z. Psychol.,* **88:**225–252.

————. 1935. Social behavior of birds. In *A Handbook of Social Psychology,* ed. by C. Murchison: 947–972. Clark University Press, Worcester, Massachusetts.

Schleidt, W. M. 1961a. Über die Auslösung der Flucht vor Raubvögeln bei Truthühnern. *Naturwissenschaften,* **48:**141–142.

————. 1961b. Reaktionen von Truthühnern auf fliegende Raubvögel und Versuche zur Analyse ihrer AAM's. *Z. Tierpsychol.,* **18:**534–560.

Schmid, B. 1935. Über die Ermittelung des menschlichen und tierischen Individualgeruches durch den Hund. *Z. vergl. Physiol.,* **22:**524–538.

Schneirla, T. C. 1959. An evolutionary and developmental theory of biphasic processes underlying approach and withdrawal. *Neb. Symp. Motiv.:* 1–42.

Scott, J. P. 1958. *Aggression.* University of Chicago Press, Chicago.

———— and E. Fredericson. 1951. The causes of fighting in mice and rats. *Physiol. Zool.,* **24:**273–309.

Sevenster, P. 1961. A causal analysis of a displacement activity (fanning in *Gasterosteus aculeatus* L.). *Behaviour Suppl.,* **9:**1–170.

Seward, J. P. 1945–1946. Aggressive behaviour in the rat, I–IV. *J. Comp. Psychol.,* **38:**175–197, 213–224, 225–238; **39:**51–76.

Solomon, P., P. E. Kubzansky, P. H. Leiderman, J. H. Mendelson, R. Trumbull, and D. Wexler. 1961. *Sensory Deprivation.* Harvard University Press, Cambridge.

Tembrock, G. 1957. Zur Ethologie des Rotfuchses (*Vulpes vulpes* L.), unter besonderer Berucksichtigung der Fortpflanzung. *Zoolog. Gart.* (N.F.), **23:**289–532.

Thiessen, D. D. and D. A. Rodgers. 1961. Population density and endocrine function. *Psychol. Bull.,* **58:**441–451.

Thompson, W. L. 1960. Agonistic behavior in the house finch. Part II: Factors in aggressiveness and sociality. *Condor,* **62:**378–402.

Thompson, W. R. 1953. The inheritance of behaviour: behavioural differences in fifteen mouse strains. *Canad. J. Psychol.,* **7:**145–155.

————. 1955. Early environment—its importance for later behavior. In *Psychopathology of Childhood,* ed. by P. H. Hoch and J. Zubin: 120–139. Grune and Stratton, New York.

Thorpe, W. H. 1944. Some problems of animal learning. *Proc. Linn. Soc. Lond.* (Zool.), **156:**70–83.

————. 1950. The concepts of learning and their relation to those of instinct. *Symp. Soc. Exp. Biol.,* **4:**387–408.

————. 1963. *Learning and Instinct in Animals.* Harvard University Press, Cambridge.

Tinbergen, N. 1940. Die Übersprungbewegung. *Z. Tierpsychol.*, **4**:1–40.

———. 1951. *The Study of Instinct.* Oxford University Press, London.

———. 1952. "Derived" activities; their causation, biological significance, origin, and emancipation during evolution. *Quart. Rev. Biol.*, **27**:1–32.

———. 1954. The origin and evolution of courtship and threat display. In *Evolution as a Process,* ed. by J. S. Huxley, A. C. Hardy, and E. B. Ford: 233–250. Allen and Unwin, London.

———. 1959. Comparative studies of the behaviour of gulls (Laridae): a progress report. *Behaviour,* **15**:1–70.

——— and M. Moynihan. 1952. Head flagging in the black-headed gull; its function and origin. *Brit. Birds,* **45**:19–22.

Tompkins, G. 1933. Individuality and territoriality as displayed in winter by three passerine species. *Condor,* **35**:98–106.

Uhrich, J. 1938. The social hierarchy in albino mice. *J. Comp. Psychol.,* **25**:373–413.

Washburn, S. L. and I. DeVore. 1961. The social life of baboons. *Sci. Amer.,* **204**(6):62–71.

Weeden, J. S. and J. B. Falls. 1959. Differential responses of male ovenbirds to recorded songs of neighboring and more distant individuals. *Auk,* **76**:343–351.

Welker, W. I. 1956. Some determinants of play and exploration in chimpanzees. *J. comp. psysiol. Psychol.,* **49**:84–89.

———. 1959. Escape, exploratory, and food-seeking responses of rats in a novel situation. *J. comp. physiol. Psychol.,* **52**:106–111.

Wickler, W. 1957. Das Verhalten von *Xiphophorus maculatus* var. Wagtail und verwandten Arten. *Z. Tierpsychol.,* **14**:324–346.

Wiepkema, P. R. 1961. An ethological analysis of the reproductive behaviour of the bitterling (*Rhodeus amarus* Bloch). *Arch. Néerl. Zool.,* **14**:103–199.

Woodworth, R. S. 1947. Reinforcement of perception. *Amer. J. Psychol.,* **60**:119–124.

Wundt, W. 1874. Quoted in Berlyne (1960).

Wynne-Edwards, V. C. 1962. *Animal Dispersion in Relation to Social Behaviour.* Oliver and Boyd, Edinburgh and London.

Yerkes, R. M. 1940. Social behavior of chimpanzees: dominance between mates, in relation to sexual status. *J. Comp. Psychol.,* **30**:147–186.

Young, P. T. 1961. *Motivation and Emotion.* John Wiley and Sons, New York.

six

LOCOMOTION: CHAIN REFLEXES
OR ENDOGENOUS CONTROL?

The work to be done in locomotion • Patterns of gait in vertebrates and insects • Neural mechanisms underlying locomotion • The role of proprioception and endogenous neural rhythms • Swimming in fish • Hierarchical levels of organization.

The ease with which normal locomotion can be elicited under laboratory conditions makes it an ideal subject for descriptive study and experimental analysis. The repetition of relatively stereotyped motor patterns permits extended observation of long sequences of actions and an accuracy of statistical description that is seldom possible with other types of behavior. By the same token, the maintenance of locomotion by animals that have been subjected to more or less chronic surgery or electrode implantation allows thorough physiological exploration. The convenience of locomotion for this type of analysis is matched only by other repetitive patterns, such as the crustacean heartbeat (Maynard 1960) or the song-producing tymbal movements of cicadas (Hagiwara and Watanabe 1956).

Studies of the physiological control of such activities have repeatedly raised an issue which is very reminiscent of the exogenous-endogenous controversy about the control of circadian rhythms. It concerns the role of endogenous neural rhythms in controlling these repetitive patterns of activity. The discovery of proprioceptive receptors that were stimulated by movements of the muscles of the body inspired the notion that many patterns of activity arise as chain reflexes. According to this idea each phase of the locomotory cycle is followed by proprioceptive feedback stimuli that then elicit the next phase, and so on. Only in recent years has the important contribution of patterned motor output from the central nervous system been properly appreciated (see Horridge 1963). We shall try to show that the conflicting views are strongly reminiscent of theories about the control of slower rhythms with a daily or seasonal basis. The subject of locomotion is best broached from the point of view of the structure of the motor equipment and the work that it has to perform in carrying the animal from one place to another.

THE MECHANICAL WORK TO BE DONE

As with any behavior pattern, the details of locomotory behavior are dictated in part by the mechanical properties of the motor equipment of the animal and the loads it is called upon to carry. One productive way of investigating locomotory patterns is to describe them and relate their forms to the mechanical problems which the animal faces. The particular behavioral outcome of the cooperation between two sets of factors will relate in turn to the functional requirements which the behavior satisfies.

The machinery for locomotion varies from species to species, and differences can be related to requirements for persistent speed, endurance, and acceleration (Figure 6-1a). Body size places severe restrictions upon the organization of the locomotory apparatus. The weight of an animal increases as the cube of its length, the power of muscles with the square of their cross section. The power of muscles can be increased by more rapid contraction—but there are physical limits which restrict the extent of this gain. Thus the largest animals can neither run nor trot, and small mammals such as a rabbit or a fox may at top speeds match or exceed the maxima of larger animals. Maximal speeds are attained by most four-footed animals by changing the gait to a series of jumps (Hildebrand 1959, 1960, 1961).

◆ *Quadrupedal Locomotion.* Gray (e.g. 1950, 1953) has shown that the pattern of walking in terrestrial animals can be related to the functional requirements of the situation:

If you watch any four-legged animal walking very slowly but steadily, no matter whether it be a newt, a toad, a tortoise, a chameleon, a sheep or an elephant—or even a young child on all fours—you will find that the pattern of limb movements is always the same [Figure 6-1]. . . . In every case the four legs are lifted from the ground (or replaced on the ground) in a definite order; if we begin to watch when the right forefoot lifts [Figure 6-1, 1-7], the next leg to lift is always the hind foot on the left side (8-14); this is followed by the left forefoot (15-21), and this in turn by the right hindfoot (22-28); after this the right forefoot lifts again and the order is repeated.

When we work out the geometry of this diagonal pattern, we find that it is the only order of stepping which conforms to the requirement that no foot should ever be lifted unless the center of gravity of the body lies over the triangle marked out by the other three. . . . As each foot comes down it forms the corner of a new triangle of support, and as soon as the centre of gravity comes to lie within this triangle the fourth foot, the one not involved in this triangle, can move. In other words, four-legged animals, when moving slowly, move their legs in such a way that it is possible for the body to stop at any instant without falling over (Gray 1953, p. 55).

Such locomotion is necessarily slow, and as Gray points out few animals are content to move at this rate all the time. The pace is quickened "by sacrificing the ability to stop at any instant without loss of balance. As the rate of walking gets faster each foot is lifted off the ground *before* the one next ahead of it in the diagonal series reaches the ground—so that there is now a short period during which only two feet are on the ground," as in a walking horse. The process proceeds further in a trotting horse and reaches an extreme condition in galloping, a gait which is actually a series of jumps. Thus in terrestrial locomotion of quadrupeds we see a series of basic action patterns which recur widely in the animal kingdom and whose form is apparently dictated by the functional requirements of the situation.

◆ *Insect Locomotion.* Insects that habitually walk on four legs, such as the praying mantis, use the typical quadrupedal gait; those that use all six legs have different patterns which are also predictable (Hughes 1952, Wilson 1966). No foreleg or middle leg is protracted until the leg behind has taken up its supporting position; each leg alternates with the contralateral one of the same segment. An increase in speed is achieved by a continuously varying adjustment of such factors as stride length, stepping frequency, relative phasing of the limbs, and the times of protraction and retraction. But insects, unlike quadrupeds, are able to make these adjustments with no loss of stability, so that motion can be arrested at any point of the cycle, even in fast running (Hughes 1952).

Within these relatively stereotyped patterns a certain degree of variation is permitted. Variation is necessary if the animal is to walk sideways and backward as well as forward, or to compensate for irregularities in the terrain.

Experiments on the effects of amputation of legs on locomotion rhythms demonstrate that the animal is by no means to be regarded as an automaton. The most thorough studies are of insects (Bethe 1931, ten Cate

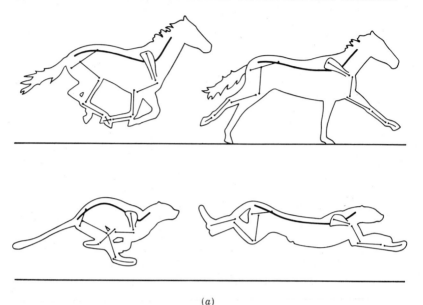

(a)

Figure 6-1   (a) The locomotor equipment of two plains-living animals, one a predator, the cheetah, and one a prey species, the horse. Each attains maximal speed within the limits of its phyletic group. Swiveling shoulder blades add several inches to their stride length. The cheetah gains 6 miles per hour from its flexible spine. A further increase in body length would mean a prohibitive increase in weight. The horse's relatively longer legs compensate for its rigid spine. After Hildebrand 1960. (b) The generalized pattern of locomotion of a four-legged animal is typified by a salamander. After Gray 1953.

1941, Hughes 1957, Wendler 1964, Wilson 1966). Drastic changes occur in the gait, the nature of which depends on which limb is amputated. The adjustments are immediate, and "are such that the support usually provided by the missing leg is taken over by the other two legs on that side. Compensating movements are also found in the contralateral legs" (Hughes 1957). After removal of a leg on each side, a cockroach walks with much the same basic gait as a quadruped.

The plasticity of walking patterns of invertebrates with more numerous legs is equally striking after amputation. The decapod crab, *Carcinus,* responds to each amputation with a new pattern of locomotion as long as at least one leg remains (Bethe 1931). There are 256 possible combinations of amputation. New phase relationships of limb movement have been noted in the crab, *Astacus,* and in centipedes in response to limb amputation and irregularities in the terrain (von Holst 1943, 1948).

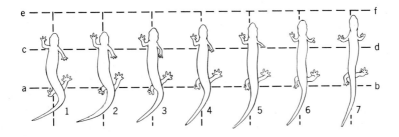

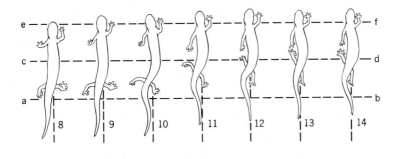

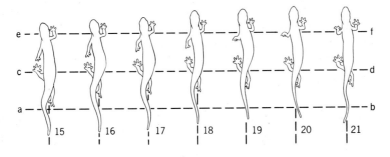

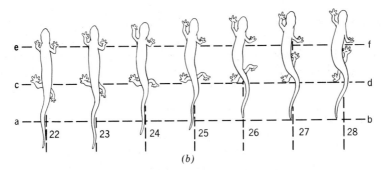

(b)

MECHANISMS OF LOCOMOTION
AND OTHER MOTOR PATTERNS IN ARTHROPODS

Demonstrations of the rapid and functionally effective adjustments following amputation lead to questions about the plasticity of the underlying mechanism (Huber 1963). The range of adjustments to amputation is complex and varied, and the physiological mechanisms have been little explored. It seems clear that altered sensory connections between limbs and the central nervous system and interconnections between segments play a major role. In the stick insect, *Carausius morosus*, the proprioceptive hair plates in the joints are involved in the adjustments (Wendler 1964, Figure 6-2); elimination of some of them changes the patterns of coordination. They participate in a system of feedback control.

The legs on an isolated segment respond to stimulation with actions of righting and cleaning, as well as stepping movements. These movements may be rhythmical if the legs are placed in contact with a rough surface (ten Cate 1928). Electrophysiological studies suggest that each thoracic segment is a potentially self-contained unit for rhythmical stepping. Stimuli generated at one phase, from either sensory hairs or campaniform sensillae, seem to elicit the next, showing that a feedback relationship exists between stages of the complete cycle. Nervous connections between segments serve in turn to coordinate the cycles of activity in the three pairs of legs (Pringle 1940, Roeder 1953). The role of endogenous factors in this case is not clear, although the ganglion in the first thoracic segment seems to play a special role in generating the locomotory rhythm.

◆ *Praying Mantis Locomotion and Sexual Behavior.* The suboesophageal ganglion of the praying mantis appears to exert an excitatory influence upon the thoracic ganglia, for when it is removed locomotion can be elicited only by the strongest stimulation. It in turn is subject to inhibitory control by the protocerebral ganglia. When they are removed, there is continuous locomotor activity. In the intact mantis locomotor activity thus seems to be controlled by an interplay of exciting and inhibiting influences of the central nervous system acting upon the thoracic ganglia. These ganglia in turn coordinate the temporal patterning of the motor activity (Roeder 1937, 1963).

The suboesophageal ganglion also controls sexual behavior of the male, but in a rather different way. Removal of the suboesophageal ganglion of a male mantis greatly reduces the frequency of ordinary locomotion while facilitating the occurrence of sexual behavior (Roeder, Tozian, and Weiant 1960, Roeder 1963).

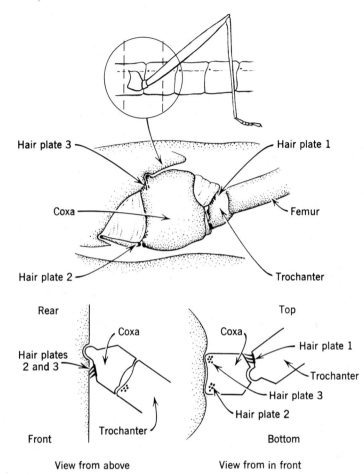

Figure 6-2   Diagram of the distribution of hair plates in the left hindleg of the stick insect, *Carausius morosus*. After Wendler 1964.

A female mantis may respond to the overtures of a courting male by attacking and eating him.

The head and prothorax of an approaching male are naturally most exposed to the female's attack, and are therefore eaten first. This is followed within a few minutes by intense and continuous sexual movements (S-bending) of the male abdomen accompanied by curious locomotor movements that have never been observed in the intact male mantis. These are lateral or rotary walking movements that tend to carry the body of the male from the head-to-head position at the time of the attack to a position parallel to the female, and eventually onto her back. The movements are sufficiently powerful that the remains of the male's body are pulled out of reach of the female mandibles, and she is rarely able to eat more than part of the male thorax. The sexual movements of the male abdomen continue with vigor, and coupling takes place shortly after mounting. Copulation continues for several hours and a normal spermatophore is formed (Roeder 1963, p. 136).

Experiments show that removal of the suboesophageal ganglion is critical in eliciting this behavior. It continues without any of the distance receptors and seems to originate largely from endogenous motor activity in the ventral nerve cord that is triggered by the removal of the inhibiting influence of the suboesophageal ganglion.

◆ *Prey Capture in Mantids.* The strike of the forelegs of a mantis at a fly is very rapid, taking from 10 to 30 milliseconds, triggered by movement of the prey (Rilling, Mittelstaedt, and Roeder 1959). It is too fast for adjustments of direction during the strike. Although the head and prothorax tend to come into line with the prey, the mantis can strike accurately to the right or left of the midline. How does it manage this? The movement is obviously guided by vision. But the mantis also needs to know the orientation of the head relative to the prothorax with which the forelegs are articulated. The compound eyes are of course fixed in the head. Proprioceptive hair plates in the neck region are placed to register movements of the head relative to the prothorax. In a series of ingenious experiments Mittelstaedt (1957, 1962) established the role of these two sensory systems in control of the prey-catching behavior.

If the afferent nerves from the hair plates had been cut on both sides, there was a great increase in the number of strikes that missed the target. The mantis could only catch flies directly ahead. Transection of the nerve on one side, say the left, resulted in a preponderance of misses to the right of the target, and vice versa. Another approach was to fix the head relative to the thorax by cementing it with a small bridge of balsa wood. With the head fixed to look directly ahead, the accuracy was good. Fixed to one side, errors were made in the opposite direction. Thus with a head fixed 30 degrees to the left of the midline, strikes erred to the right of the target. Evidently both proprioception and vision are required. This is confirmed by a further change in behavior if the afferent nerves from the hair plates are cut in an animal with a fixed head, the effects being additive. On the basis of such data Mittelstaedt devised a model derived from control system theory (Figure 6-3). According to this hypothesis the direction of the strike depends on both visual and proprioceptive feedback. Comparison of these two sources of information enables the mantis to allow for deviation of the head from the prothorax in directing the strike.

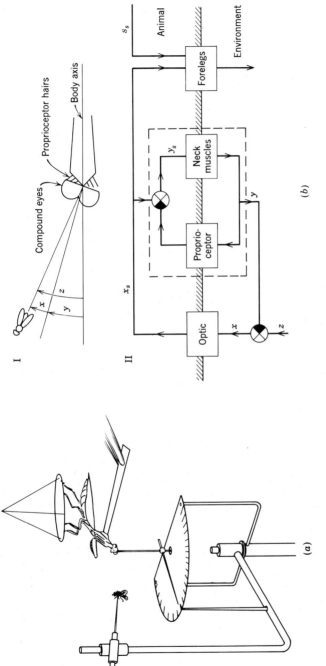

Figure 6-3 Prey capture in mantids. (a) The experimental arrangement for accurate recording of orientation of the strike with the forelegs. After Mittelstaedt 1957. (b) I. Head and prothorax of a mantis fixating on a fly: x, fixation deficit; y, deviation of head from body axis when prey is fixated; z, deviation of prey from body axis. II. Control pattern for prey localization. Boxes represent nervous and muscular elements of each subsystem. The optic feedback loop contains within it the proprioceptor loop (dashed box) that runs counter to it. The optic output x_s contains the correct aiming signal which takes effect upon arrival of the strike signal s_s. White segments within circles indicate addition, black segments subtraction. From Roeder 1963 after Mittelstaedt 1957.

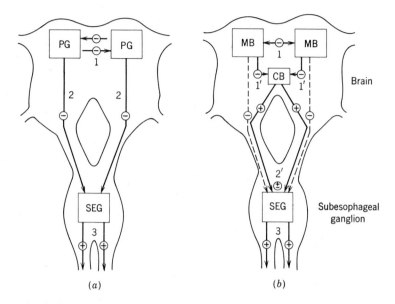

(a)   (b)

Figure 6-4 Huber's scheme of the interaction between the brain and suboesophageal ganglion of (a) a mantis and (b) a cricket. The mushroom bodies (MB) and
protocerebral ganglia (PG) mutually inhibit (1) one another. The mushroom bodies
inhibit (1') the central body (CB), the protocerebral ganglia and mushroom bodies
inhibit (2) the suboesophageal ganglion (SEG), and the steering component of the
activity of the suboesophageal ganglion is controlled by excitatory and inhibitory
action (2,2') from the central body and mushroom bodies. The suboesophageal
ganglion in turn controls (3) the motor centers in the thorax. After Huber 1960.

◆ *Role of the Brain in Cricket Locomotion.* With the aid of delicate techniques
for electrical stimulation of the central nervous system of crickets, Huber
(1960, 1963) was able to confirm and extend Roeder's observations upon
the physiological control of insect locomotion. The brain not only exerts
inhibiting influences on the thoracic ganglia but also indirectly affects
flight and jumping behavior as well as walking. The brain "gives rise
to diffusely-arranged neurons which contribute to the onset, the duration and the intensity of locomotory movements, as well as coordinating
them with movements of the antennae and palps." The inhibiting effects
arise in the mushroom bodies of the brain; their destruction leads to incessant movement. Facilitation arises in the central body and destruction
leads to the cessation of locomotion, through effects on the suboesophageal
ganglion (Figure 6-4).

Rowell (1963, 1964) has shown that stimulation of parts of the locust
brain permits the experimenter to control whether or not a given external

stimulus will elicit a response—whether a touch elicits movement of an antenna or leg, whether or not food elicits feeding. Recognition of the fact that stimuli for such responses are present much of the time in the locust's sensory world leads to fuller appreciation of the importance of central nervous inhibition.

Most forms of behaviour in animals are in response to stimuli which are continually present at greater or lesser intensity. An animal is almost always to some extent hungry, sexually motivated, frightened, itchy and sleepy. The input to which it actually responds (subjectively the 'strongest') is determined by factors including both the absolute intensity of the stimulus and variation in the physiological state of the animal; the last category includes the results of learning processes as well as more transitory changes. This picture of an animal containing many different action-systems, each already 'ticking over' to some extent, implies inhibitory relations between them if single coherent actions are ever to emerge; it is important not to try to do everything at once (Rowell 1964, p. 570).

Central nervous factors make a major contribution to the instigation, coordination, and maintenance of the action patterns of locomotion in insects. How is a particular temporal pattern of coordination achieved? Is it the result of an endogenous pattern of activation arising in the central nervous system? Or can the pattern be completely explained by sensory feedback mechanisms, with stimuli generated by each movement in a sequence eliciting the next?

◆ *Flight Mechanisms in Locusts.* An elegant analysis of the physiological mechanism underlying flight in locusts has shown that the truth lies somewhere between these extremes (Wilson 1961, Wilson and Weis-Fogh 1962, Wilson and Gettrup 1963). Sustained flight can readily be elicited in the laboratory. With appropriate instrumentation the properties of the action pattern can be accurately described. Surgical elimination of various sources of sensory feedback from the wings shows that "the basic coordination of flight is an inherent function of the central nervous system." No patterned input of sensory feedback is needed to produce a patterned motor output.

But the rhythm of flight cannot arise without some sensory input. The nervous system must be aroused. This can be done in a number of ways, such as by blowing air on the antennae (Weis-Fogh 1956) or by electrically stimulating the nerve cord. The effects of such input are tonic rather than phasic, however. Stimulation triggers the activity and may affect its rate, but there is no detailed relationship between the patterns of input and output.

Yet in the intact animal there is much sensory feedback activity synchronized with the wingbeat frequency. The stretch receptors of the wing hinge, for example, fire once or twice at the top of each wingstroke. Removal of these receptors so that they no longer participate in control halves the wingbeat frequency. Nonetheless, interference with the normal timing of their input does not affect the wingbeat frequency. This particular feedback pathway causes an increase in the rate of wing movement without having any specific cycle-to-cycle influence (Wilson and Gettrup 1963).

The mechanisms that control the flight movements of insects are reminiscent in many ways of circadian rhythms (see page 68), and it is necessary to use the term endogenous with caution for similar reasons. The central nervous system is clearly capable of rhythmical motor output. Endogenous neural rhythms have been described in the control of spiracle movements in locusts (Hoyle 1959, Miller 1960) and shell movements of clams (Horridge 1961). But certain conditions outside the nervous system are necessary for rhythmical activity to occur. Moreover, the rate of rhythmical output is affected by the particular set of prevailing external conditions. Once more there is intimate exogenous-endogenous interaction, even in a case such as this in which endogenous effects are so prominent.

◆ *Crayfish Locomotion.* The metachronal rhythm of swimmeret movements in crayfish is associated with a rhythm of neural activity. But with a totally isolated nerve cord the motor roots which innervate the swimmerets still show some rhythmical activity. "Since such discharges are absent from the other roots, which do not innervate the swimmerets, and since the discharges in the first roots, though greatly changed from those during regular beating, are still like those which can normally occur when the swimmerets are not well co-ordinated, it appears that they do represent abortive attempts at rhythmic swimmeret movements" (Hughes and Wiersma 1960).

If the sensory root of one swimmeret is left intact, all swimmerets beat in the normal pattern. But this sensory inflow seems to be more important in eliciting locomotion than in providing patterned stimulation for the timing of movements of the swimmerets. Moreover, electrical stimulation of anterior parts of the central nervous system could elicit more normal beating without providing any local patterned stimulation.

The central nervous system can evidently maintain the normal temporal pattern, provided that it receives tonic external stimulation. Nevertheless, in the intact animal local external stimuli must often assume a dominant role in timing and orientation of the sequence of acts. The locomotion of a normal animal is the result of a combination of influences, arising both within and outside the central nervous system.

MECHANISMS OF LOCOMOTION IN VERTEBRATES

◆ *Methods of Analysis.* Examination of the basic patterns of locomotion in many vertebrates reveals relatively fixed modes around which the patterns of locomotion are grouped. Once more there is the problem of defining the physiological basis of the action patterns. As with invertebrates, there have been two main approaches. One is to intervene directly in the locomotor apparatus of the animal, attempting to discover the source of the pattern of overt behavior. The other is to observe the behavior itself in detail, documenting the forms and degrees of variation of the behavior, and then to infer the properties of the underlying physiological mechanism. There are excellent examples of both approaches, directed mainly toward analysis of the swimming movements of fish.

◆ *Von Holst's Studies of Fish Locomotion.* In a long series of brilliant and penetrating papers, largely summarized in a review in 1939 (a), von Holst used various descriptive approaches to the principles underlying the locomotory movements of fishes. He cut the brain stem just anterior to the medulla oblongata in various species of fish. After recovering from the operation, these fish continued to perform frequent complex swimming activities for long periods, even while the body was restrained in a harness (Figure 6-5). By attaching kymograph levers to the fins, or to different rays on the same fin, he constructed a detailed picture of their temporal patterns of activity. He was primarily concerned with the temporal coordination of movements of the pectoral, dorsal, and caudal fins, and their rays (von Holst 1935a, b, 1939a, b).

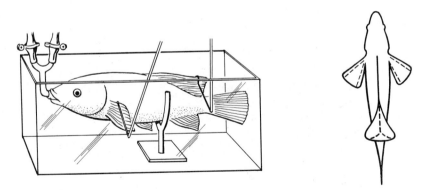

Figure 6-5 Von Holst determined the rhythm of fin movement in spinal fish by restraining them in a harness. Levers were attached to fins to register the rhythm of their beating. Movements of the pectoral and dorsal fins of *Labrus* are shown on the right. After von Holst 1935a.

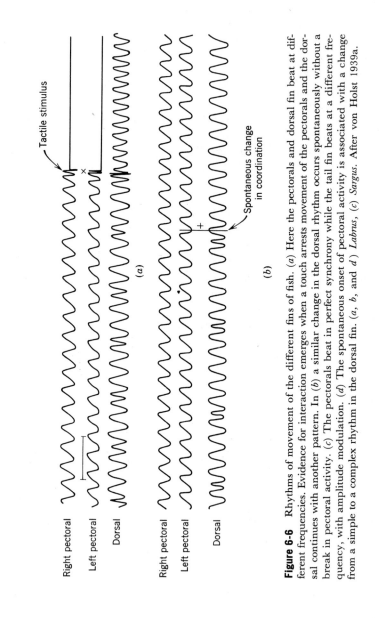

Figure 6-6 Rhythms of movement of the different fins of fish. (*a*) Here the pectorals and dorsal fin beat at different frequencies. Evidence for interaction emerges when a touch arrests movement of the pectorals and the dorsal continues with another pattern. In (*b*) a similar change in the dorsal rhythm occurs spontaneously without a break in pectoral activity. (*c*) The pectorals beat in perfect synchrony while the tail fin beats at a different frequency, with amplitude modulation. (*d*) The spontaneous onset of pectoral activity is associated with a change from a simple to a complex rhythm in the dorsal fin. (*a, b,* and *d*) *Labrus,* (*c*) *Sargus.* After von Holst 1939a.

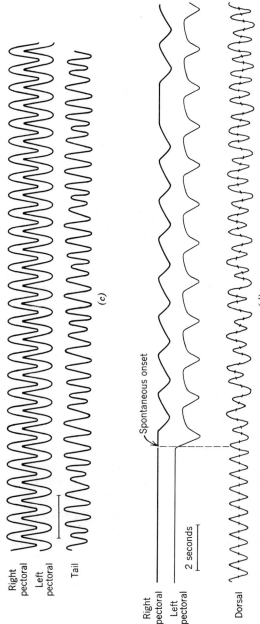

Right
pectoral

Left
pectoral

Tail

(c)

Spontaneous onset

Right
pectoral

Left
pectoral

2 seconds

Dorsal

(d)

The fin movements were clearly rhythmical; over long periods of time each fin maintained a regular rhythm of activity. At the same time other fins often maintained an equally regular rhythm, but with a different frequency. These sustained rhythms seemed to occur without any obvious rhythmical external input; they were in some sense endogenous to the organism. Nonetheless, the frequency of the rhythm depended on, among other things, such external conditions as temperature and oxygen concentration. Von Holst concluded that this rhythmical activity is a property of a group of neurons in the spinal cord. These hypothetical neurons in turn control the motor neurons which innervate the muscles of the fin rays, rhythmically contracting and relaxing antagonistic muscles.

The individual rays within each fin also have a pattern of temporal activity. All rays within a fin generally move with the same frequency. But each is slightly out of phase with its neighbors, so that contraction passes across the entire fin in a very regular manner. The amplitude of the movement may differ strikingly in different rays, depending on the type of movement being executed. Although the group normally behaves as a unit, there are circumstances in which unity breaks down. Under the influence of drugs or other chemicals, the individual rays in a fin can beat at independent frequencies. In more normal circumstances change may also occur when external stimuli impinge upon the fin, or when there is a change of direction of movement. Here, too, von Holst postulates groups of neurons which can operate somewhat independently of one another. Much of the time, however, they operate with a particular phase relationship to each other, resulting in the orderly movement of the entire fin. The normal behavior is the result of a combination of factors both exogenous and endogenous relative to the postulated groups of control neurons.

Although individual fins beat with independent rhythms much of the time, they can influence one another. One example is what von Holst calls a 'magnet effect.' Sometimes the temporal rhythm of one fin becomes completely entrained to that of another, so that they beat in the same phase relationship with the same frequency. Alternatively, the dependent rhythm may be a fraction or multiple of the dominant one (Figure 6-7). This is rare. More often the magnet effect is manifest as a shift in the frequency of the dependent fin, either slower or faster, toward that of the dominant fin (Figure 6-7). In other cases both may change, converging toward the same intermediate frequency.

A further complication sometimes arises when a fin becomes entrained to a dominant rhythm, yet retains its own rhythm, moving with two or more frequencies at the same time. Depending on the species, certain

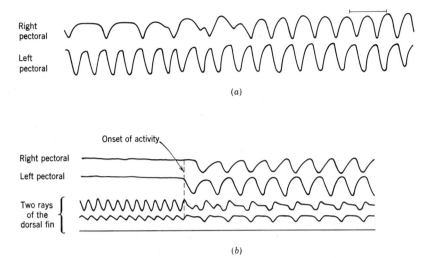

(a)

(b)

Figure 6-7   The 'magnet' effect in the relative coordination of fin movements. (*a*) After a period of inhibition the right pectoral becomes active and gradually enters complete coordination with the left pectoral. (*b*) With the onset of activity in the two pectorals the faster rhythms of two rays of the dorsal fin are slowed down to the same frequency. (*a* and *b*) *Labrus*. After von Holst 1939a.

pairs of fins or fin groups are particularly prone to show these kinds of mutual interaction. Others, such as the dorsal fin of *Labrus,* are resistant to influence by the rhythms of other fins and are difficult to inhibit.

There are many other details of interaction between the movements of different fins revealed by von Holst's descriptive studies. Those we have considered suffice to support his contention that the neural systems controlling the movements of fins and their rays are capable of many different kinds of mutual interaction, overriding in varying degrees their own autonomous rhythms.

◆ *Locomotion in Domestic Chicks.* The principles of organization revealed by von Holst's studies are not confined to fish swimming. Bangert (1960) studied walking in domestic chicks. Analysis of the movements of the head and legs during walking revealed an interaction between the mechanisms for controlling different parts of the body. As the chick walks, the head nods so that the eye remains stationary for a moment. The rhythms of head and leg movement may fall into complete coordination, so that the rhythm of one drives the other. The pattern of leg movement is usually dominant (Figure 6-8).

Relative coordination may also occur, so that change in one rhythm

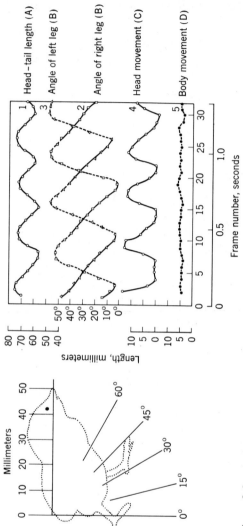

Figure 6-8 A cinematographic analysis of the phase relationships of the movements of a 3-hour-old chick. Head movements are recorded as changes in the distance from tail to tip of the bill (A) and also as the distance covered by the bill in relation to the background from one frame to the next (C). Body movement against the background was measured in the same way, using the base of the tail as a reference point (D). Angles of the legs were also measured (B). After Bangert 1960.

may influence the other, even though they are not identical in frequency. For example, a chick that is passively moved through a visual field usually nods its head to and fro with a frequency of about 3 cycles/sec. It sometimes moves its legs in a rhythmical fashion as well. Here the most common frequency is about 2.2 cycles/sec. Because it is the dominant rhythm, the onset of leg movement often results in a lowering of the frequency of head movements, and the two may become perfectly synchronized. Movement of the retinal image must play a role in eliciting the nodding of the head, but this image is not indispensable. A chick with frosted translucent spectacles over its eyes nods when it walks. Several physiological systems are evidently involved, interacting with one another in a complex manner to produce the natural behavior.

◆ *Role of Proprioceptive Feedback.* The effects of progressive elimination of proprioceptive feedback upon the locomotory patterns of vertebrates are strikingly similar to those in invertebrates. Graham-Brown (1914) showed in dogs that "the self-generated proprioceptive stimuli of the muscles which take part in progression can regulate the act but are not essential to its rhythm." The same is true of the scratch reflexes of dogs. "The phasing of these alternating reflexes can be affected by the proprioceptive and other stimuli which they generate—as well as of course by many other extrinsic stimuli—but their phasing is not *caused* by peripheral stimuli" (Creed et al. 1932).

In amphibians and fishes as well, deafferentation of the limbs or fins does not inhibit more or less normal locomotory rhythms (von Holst 1935b, Gray and Lissmann 1946, Weiss 1941, Gray 1950). Careful experimentation, however, shows that complete deafferentation, involving the cutting of all the dorsal spinal roots instead of just those going to the limbs, results in immobility. Locomotory rhythms depend on at least one intact dorsal root. Similarly, in crayfish the sensory root of one swimmeret must remain if a normal locomotory rhythm is to occur (Hughes and Wiersma 1960). It seems most reasonable to infer that this one sensory pathway is required not to provide patterned stimulation but to trigger the endogenous pattern.

The evidence led Gray (1950) to postulate some of the properties that neurons of the spinal cord must possess, just as von Holst had done on a different level. In a quadruped, for example, he suggests that there may be two mutually inhibiting centers for each limb. In the intact animal these are driven by rhythmic proprioceptive impulses to each in turn. But they have the capability of behaving rhythmically if the normal input is replaced by a nonrhythmical input from elsewhere. There are parallels between such a hypothetical system and the mechanisms which are known to play a part in controlling respiration and feeding behavior (see page 150).

CONCLUSIONS ON THE ORGANIZATION OF LOCOMOTORY BEHAVIOR

◆ *Role of Description.* This review of studies of the locomotor activities of animals conducted from different points of view has illustrated several principles of behavioral analysis. Perhaps most important is the fundamental role of description. It is relatively easy to delineate the basic action patterns of locomotion. The behavior is by no means completely stereotyped. Nevertheless, the variations are grouped around one or more modes, thus providing a solid basis for analysis. One may go on to explore the neurophysiological mechanisms underlying these rhythms, as Gray, Wilson, and others have done. Or one may study the variations in actual behavior more closely, and draw logical inferences about some of the necessary properties of the mechanisms which underlie them, in the manner of von Holst. Alternatively, the behavior can be approached from the point of view of the mechanical work to be accomplished. It may be shown, as Gray and Hughes have done, that the basic action patterns seem to be largely dictated by the physical function which the behavior must serve. Function is seldom as easy to determine as it is in locomotion, but we see that the approach can be productive when applied in the right context.

◆ *Hierarchical Levels of Organization.* In discussing the physiological mechanism underlying locomotory activities, it is necessary to specify the level of organization being considered. To take an extreme case, seasonal variations in the readiness of a fish to swim upstream call for different treatment than changes in the pattern of movement of fin rays. The levels of organization can be arranged in several different types of logical hierarchy.

If we consider, for example, temporal organization, we see that the levels may range from the overall pattern of occurrence of an activity through the life cycle of the individual, through variations with the season or the reproductive and nonreproductive phases, through shorter-term cycles down to the circadian level. Still lower levels occur in the sequences in the course of a day's activity, in the timing within sequences, in the action patterns from which the sequences are constructed, and finally in the timing of the smallest elements within the acts. This temporal hierarchy is one of the phenomena that must eventually be explained in physiological terms.

An alternative is an effector hierarchy that takes account of the organization of the smallest motor acts into many different behavioral activities. The 'final common path' may be used as the logical point of departure. The motor nerve that evokes retraction of a leg is an example. This leg movement is incorporated in various action patterns. The next level in the hierarchy is made up of the different general types of behavior in which the action patterns occur and any longer-term patterns, seasonal, reproductive, and so on, that these patterns may show, thus bringing us once more to the level of the individual life cycle.

In this effector hierarchy a parallel hierarchical organization of the underlying physiological mechanisms is again implied, as Tinbergen (1950, 1951) has shown. Some levels of the hierarchy may be mainly hormonally controlled, and somatic factors or the nervous system may be more responsible for others. Thus the hierarchy is committed not to actual structures but only to the principles of behavioral organization.

In certain animals the structural basis of hierarchical systems of organization has been described. Roeder and Huber have demonstrated that such a system controls the locomotory activity of certain insects. The basic movements, resulting from the structural arrangement of the legs and their musculature, are controlled by mutually antagonistic systems at the segmental level. Intersegmental connections organize the basic movements into the temporal sequences which constitute the action patterns. These in turn are controlled by facilitating and inhibiting centers in the brain, through the suboesophageal ganglion (Rowell 1963, 1964). This whole system must be further subject to various types of other influences that permit both gross temporal organization into sequences (see page 718) and also fine adjustments of the motor patterns.

The vertebrate nervous system also exhibits a hierarchical pattern of organization. The classical researches of Sherrington and his colleagues established the existence of the basic mechanisms for mammalian locomotion in the spinal cord. Pairs of mutually antagonistic 'half centers' govern the retraction and protraction of each limb, with interconnections between them serving to coordinate the overall pattern (see Eldred 1960). At higher levels these elementary patterns are integrated into broader patterns of complex motor activity and are related to an increasing variety of external influences (Jackson 1898, Weiss 1950, others). The details of the relationship between the different levels of the nervous system are beyond our present scope (see Field 1960). Wiersma (1962) suggests that certain general principles are beginning to emerge. In particular, he notes that "the function of higher centers consists essentially of activating excitatory and inhibitory command fibers controlling the reflex pathways." Notwithstanding the differences in structure and complexity between vertebrates and invertebrates (Vnwles 1961), Wiersma feels that the same principles are likely to hold. In both groups there are lower motor centers with a considerable degree of autonomy, often subject to several kinds of direct sensory control, in which the higher centers may or may not participate (Rowell 1963, 1964).

➤ *Exogenous and Endogenous Factors.* The rhythmical characteristics of locomotion in several animals can be generated endogenously by the central nervous system. The pattern is modulated in the intact animal by proprioceptive and other kinds of sensory input to make normal locomotion possible. We are reminded of the properties of circadian rhythms. It is important to recall from earlier discussion the limitations on use of the term endogeneity (see page 41). In both cases the endogenous rhythm is not independent of external conditions. An appropriate stimulus situation in the form of a tonic input is often necessary for a locomotor rhythm to appear. The frequency of the rhythm is also affected by the external conditions, such as temperature and, in von Holst's fishes, oxygen concentration. The endogenous rhythmicity is a result of interaction between the nervous system and its environment both within and outside the organism. The potentiality for endogenous rhythmicity is present, but the precise rhythm with which it will appear can only be predicted if the conditions external to the nervous system, constant or not, are considered. It can be misleading to speak simply of an endogenous rhythm without specifying these conditions.

Endogenous neural rhythms have a special interest for physiologists (Roeder 1955, 1962, 1963, Bullock 1961, 1962). In a penetrating discussion of the relationship between temporal patterning of behavior and nervous activity on the one hand, and the external stimulus situation on the other, Bullock (1961) goes still further. He suggests that precise correspondence between the patterns of input and output is probably rare. It is true that the timing of some nonrhythmical responses may be dictated by external stimuli, as with the elementary reflexes such as an eye blink. Even here the internal timing of the act is independent. With rhythmical responses, such as the scratch reflex of a dog, a tactile stimulus on the flank determines the time of onset of the first scratch. But it does not control the rhythm of the subsequent movements.

It is often useful to think of an external eliciting stimulus as a trigger. As such it evokes a course of action which is itself largely determined by other factors, both spatially and temporally (Bullock 1956). These other factors may be different external stimuli (see page 251), sources of proprioceptive feedback generated by different phases of the response (e.g. Mittelstaedt 1957), or they may arise endogenously from pacemakers in the central nervous system. Certainly in some cases, "it seems at present likely that for many relatively complex behavioral actions, the nervous system contains not only genetically determined circuits but also genetically determined physiological properties of their components so that the complete act is represented in coded form and awaits only an adequate trigger, either internal or external" (Bullock 1961).

Here is a familiar theme. The animal cannot behave completely independently of its external conditions. At the same time it is seldom the complete victim of external conditions. It can be as deceptive to overestimate the contribution of the external environment and proprioceptive feedback to the control of locomotion as to underestimate it.

REFERENCES

Bangert, H. 1960. Untersuchungen zur Koordination der Kopf- und Beinbewegungen beim Haushuhn. *Z. Tierpsychol.*, **17**:143–164.

Bethe, A. 1931. Plastizität und Zentrenlehre. *Handb. Norm. Path. Physiol.*, **15**:1175–1220.

Bullock, T. H. 1956. The trigger concept in biology. In *Physiological Triggers and Discontinuous Rate Processes*, ed. by T. H. Bullock: 1–7. American Physiological Society, Washington, D.C.

————. 1961. The origins of patterned nervous discharge. *Behaviour*, **17**:48–59.

————. 1962. Integration and rhythmicity in neural systems. *Amer. Zoologist*, **2**:97–104.

Cate, J. ten. 1928. Contribution à la physiologie des ganglions thoraciques des insectes. *Arch. Néerl. Physiol.*, **12**:327–335.

————. 1941. Quelques remarques à propos de l'innervation des movements locomotoires de la Blatte (*Periplaneta americana*). *Arch. Néerl. Physiol.*, **25**:401–409.

Creed, R. S., D. Denny-Brown, J. C. Eccles, E. G. T. Liddell, and C. S. Sherrington. 1932. *Reflex Activity of the Spinal Cord*. Oxford University Press, London.

Eldred, E. 1960. Posture and locomotion. In *Handbook of Physiology*, ed. by J. Field, Sec. 1, Vol. 2:1067–1088. American Physiological Society, Washington, D.C.

Field, J. (Ed.). 1960. *Handbook of Physiology*. American Physiological Society, Washington, D.C.

Graham-Brown, T. 1914. On the nature of the fundamental activity of the nervous centres; together with an analysis of the conditioning of rhythmic activity in progression, and a theory of the evolution of function in the nervous system. *J. Physiol.*, **48**:18–46.

Gray, J. 1950. The role of peripheral sense organs during locomotion in the vertebrates. *Symp. Soc. Exp. Biol.*, **4**:112–126.

————. 1953. *How Animals Move*. Cambridge University Press, Cambridge.

———— and H. W. Lissmann. 1946. Further observations on the effect of de-afferentation on the locomotory activity of amphibian limbs. *J. Exp. Biol.*, **23**:121–132.

Hagiwara, S. and A. Watanabe. 1956. Discharges in motoneurons of cicada. *J. Cell. Comp. Physiol.*, **47**:415–428.

Hildebrand, M. 1959. Motions of the running cheetah and horse. *J. Mammal.*, **40**:481–495.

————. 1960. How animals run. *Sci. Amer.*, **202**:148–157.

————. 1961. Further studies on locomotion of the cheetah. *J. Mammal.*, **42**:84–91.

Holst, E. von. 1935a. Über den Prozess der zentralnervösen Koordination. *Pflüg. Arch. ges. Physiol.*, **236**:149–158.

————. 1935b. Weitere Reflexstudien an spinalen Fischen. *Z. vergl. Physiol.*, 21:658–665.

————. 1939a. Die relative Koordination als Phänomen und als Methode zentralnervöser Funktionsanalyse. *Ergebn. Physiol.*, 42:228–306.

————. 1939b. Über die nervöse Funktionsstruktur des rhythmisch tätigen Fischrückenmarks. *Pflüg. Arch. ges. Physiol.*, 241:569–611.

————. 1943. Über relative Koordination bei Arthropoden. *Pflüg. Arch. ges. Physiol.*, 246:847–865.

————. 1948. Von der Mathematik der nervösen Ordnungsleitung. *Experientia*, 4:374–381.

Horridge, G. A. 1961. The centrally determined sequence of impulses initiated from a ganglion of the clam *Mya. J. Physiol.*, 155:320–336.

————. 1963. Comparative physiology: integrative action of the nervous system. *Ann. Rev. Physiol.*, 25:523–544.

Hoyle, G. 1959. The neuromuscular mechanism of an insect spiracular muscle. *J. Insect Physiol.*, 3:378–394.

Huber, F. 1960. Untersuchungen über die Funktion des Zentralnervensystems und insbesondere des Gehirnes bei der Fortbewegung und der Lauterzeugung der Grillen. *Z. vergl. Physiol.*, 44:60–132.

————. 1963. Lokalisation und Plastizität im Zentralnervensystem der Tiere. *Zool. Anz., Suppl.*, 26:200–267.

Hughes, G. M. 1952. The co-ordination of insect movements. I. The walking movements of insects. *J. Exp. Biol.*, 29:267–284.

————. 1957. The co-ordination of insect movements. II. The effect of limb amputation and the cutting of commissures in the cockroach (*Blatta orientalis*). *J. Exp. Biol.*, 34:306–333.

———— and C. A. G. Wiersma. 1960. The co-ordination of swimmeret movements in the crayfish, *Procambarus clarkii* (Girard). *J. Exp. Biol.*, 37:657–670.

Jackson, J. 1898. Relation of different divisions of the central nervous system to one another and to parts of the body. In *Selected Writings of John Hughlings Jackson*, ed. by J. Taylor. Vol. II. Basic Books, Publishers, New York.

Maynard, D. M. 1960. Circulation and heart function. In *The Physiology of Crustacea*, ed. by T. H. Waterman, Vol. 1:161–226. The Academic Press, New York.

Miller, P. L. 1960. Respiration in the desert locust. I and II. *J. Exp. Biol.*, 37:224–236, 237–263.

Mittelstaedt, H. 1957. Prey capture in mantids. In *Recent Advances in Invertebrate Physiology*, ed. by B. T. Scheer: 51–71. University of Oregon Publications, Oregon.

————. 1962. Control systems of orientation in insects. *Ann. Rev. Ent.*, 7:177–198.

Pringle, J. W. S. 1940. The reflex mechanism of the insect leg. *J. Exp. Biol.*, 17:8–17.

Rilling, S., H. Mittelstaedt, and K. D. Roeder. 1959. Prey recognition in the praying mantis. *Behaviour*, 14:164–184.

Roeder, K. D. 1937. The control of tonus and locomotor activity in the praying mantis (*Mantis religiosa* L.). *J. Exp. Zool.*, 76:353–374.

————. 1953. *Insect Physiology*. John Wiley and Sons, New York.

————. 1955. Spontaneous activity and behavior. *Scient. Monthly*, 80:361–370.

————. 1962. Neural mechanisms of animal behavior. *Amer. Zoologist*, 2:105–115.

————. 1963. *Nerve Cells and Insect Behavior*. Harvard University Press, Cambridge.

————, L. Tozian, and E. A. Weiant. 1960. Endogenous nerve activity and behaviour in the mantis and cockroach. *J. Insect Physiol.*, 4:45–62.

Rowell, C. H. F. 1963. A method for chronically implanting stimulating electrodes into the brains of locusts, and some results of stimulation. *J. Exp. Biol.*, 40:271–284.

————. 1964. Central control of an insect segmental reflex. I. Inhibition by different parts of the central nervous system. *J. Exp. Biol.*, 41:559–572.

Tinbergen, N. 1950. The hierarchical organization of nervous mechanisms underlying instinctive behaviour. *Symp. Soc. Exp. Biol.*, 4:305–312.

———. 1951. *The Study of Instinct*. Oxford University Press, London.

Vowles, D. M. 1961. Neural mechanisms in insect behaviour. In *Current Problems in Animal Behaviour*, ed. by W. H. Thorpe, and O. L. Zangwill: 5–29. Cambridge University Press, Cambridge.

Weis-Fogh, T. 1956. Biology and physics of locust flight. IV. Notes on sensory mechanisms in locust flight. *Phil. Trans. Roy. Soc. Lond., B,* **239:**553–584.

Weiss, P. 1941. Self-differentiation of the basic patterns of coordination. *Comp. Psychol. Monogr.,* **17**(4):1–96.

———. 1950. Experimental analysis of co-ordination by the disarrangement of central-peripheral relations. *Symp. Soc. Exp. Biol.,* **4:**92–111.

Wendler, G. 1964. Laufen und Stehen der Stabheuschrecke *Carausius morosus:* Sinnesborsten-felder in den Beingelenken als Glieder von Regelkreisen. *Z. vergl. Physiol.,* **48:**198–250.

Wiersma, C. A. G. 1962. The organization of the arthropod central nervous system. *Amer. Zoologist,* **2:**67–78.

Wilson, D. M. 1961. The central nervous control of flight in a locust. *J. Exp. Biol.,* **38:**471–490.

——— and T. Weis-Fogh. 1962. Patterned activity of co-ordinated motor units, studied in flying locusts. *J. Exp. Biol.,* **39:**643–667.

——— and E. Gettrup. 1963. A stretch reflex controlling wingbeat frequency in grasshoppers. *J. Exp. Biol.,* **40:**171–185.

———. 1966. Insect walking. *Ann. Rev. Ent.,* **11:**103–122.

seven

EXTERNAL STIMULI, ADAPTIVENESS, AND STIMULUS SPECIFICITY

Types of stimulus control • Feeding in phytophagous insects • The adaptiveness of stimulus filtering • Prey-catching behavior • Experiments with models • Courtship of butterflies • Escape behavior • Owl mobbing • Stimulus-response chains • Examples of unspecific responsiveness • Ensurance of specificity by prior events.

The functions that much behavior serves might be reduced to two simple categories: (1) exchanging something between the body and the environment, either taking it in or giving it out, and (2) modifying the external environment, either directly by imposing some change on it or indirectly by moving to another environment. The importance of the relationship between the animal and its environment in the control of behavior is immediately apparent. The ultimate criterion for effectiveness of much behavior must be sought in the efficiency of interaction between the organism and its environment. At one level the exploration of the ultimate nature and consequences of the relationship lies within the domain of the ecologist and population geneticist. Behaviorists are more concerned with the proximal role of environmental factors in the control of behavior.

KINDS OF STIMULUS CONTROL

A given external stimulus may increase or reduce the probability of the occurrence of behavior. The same stimulus may facilitate some actions and inhibit others. Behavior patterns so affected may be many, so that whole classes of action patterns are involved. Such is the case with stimuli favoring sleeping or awakening. At other times the effects may be highly specific, encouraging or inhibiting one particular action over all others.

A facilitating stimulus can affect behavior in one or more of three ways: by sensitizing it to other stimuli, by triggering certain actions, or by orienting the behavior with respect to the source of the stimulus. Inhibiting stimuli can have the opposite effects: by desensitizing the animal to certain stimuli, by arresting behavior that is already in progress, or by disorienting the animal (Table 7-1).

Consider the effect of the visual stimuli from a hawk flying overhead on the behavior of a group of chaffinches. When the birds are feeding in the open, away from trees, the eliciting effect of the hawk stimulus is clear. There is immediate triggering of precipitant flight to the nearest cover. Other stimuli may contribute to the response that the hawk evokes. An alarm cry from another species or individual may alert the birds to the impending danger, making their flight more immediate when the hawk suddenly appears. Sensitization can appear in a variety of other ways. Merely being away from cover makes the birds more alert. The sudden quieting of song in the woods that tracks the movement of a hawk above has a similar effect. Prior experience with a hawk may further prepare them. This longer-term sensitization contrasts with the immediate sensitization by stimuli which are present at the time. External stimuli contribute to the orientation of the flight. In this case the orienting stimuli emanate not from the hawk but from the nearest cover.

What of inhibitory effects? Suppose that instead of being in the open the birds are perched in a bush when they see the hawk overhead. Now they are unlikely to flee. Instead they freeze, crouch against the perch,

Table 7-1 Some Effects of External Stimuli on Behavior

Facilitating effects	Inhibiting effects
Eliciting or triggering	Arresting or checking
Sensitizing, alerting or predisposing	Desensitizing or depressing
Orienting	Disorienting or failing to orient

and follow the movement overhead with their eyes. This stimulus configuration inhibits movement rather than facilitating it, though the bird is fully alert and tense. In different circumstances, a fully aroused bird may be relatively unresponsive to a hawk when it is intensely involved in some other activity, such as sexual behavior or fighting. The stimuli eliciting these activities also desensitize the bird to the sight of the hawk. Desensitization to external stimulation also accompanies a loss of general alertness. Warmth and a full stomach may make the bird sleepy, imposing a degree of desensitization upon responsiveness to a wide range of external stimuli including the hawk.

Disorientation and failure to orient are other negative or inhibitory effects. They may occur either by the elimination of stimuli which provide orienting cues or by the presence of false cues. The cryptic behavior of the crouching chaffinch minimizes the transmission of visual stimuli to the hawk. In addition, such a bird may give a special alarm call which is difficult for vertebrates to locate (see page 464). This ventriloquial signal serves to disseminate the alarm without fully revealing the position of the calling bird and may actually confuse the hawk to some extent (Marler 1955b). The 'flash colors' on the underwings of some grasshoppers that disappear when they alight may function to distract predators. Cott (1957) has made a special study of structures and behavior patterns that have such 'disorienting' effects.

Facilitation and inhibition are intimately related, and many stimuli must perform both functions simultaneously. The promotion of one activity must carry with it an inevitable reduction in the likelihood of others occurring. Conversely, the arresting of one activity always involves the elicitation of another, even if this is only the act of standing still. Furthermore, the discontinuation of an activity may result from the discontinuation of facilitating stimuli rather than contact with new inhibitory stimuli. It is often difficult to separate these alternatives, especially when preceding behavior of the animal is responsible for the change in the stimulus situation. But these complications do not negate the usefulness of a simple classification for characterizing the effects of external stimuli on particular behavior patterns.

◆ *Feeding Stimuli in Plant-Eating Insects.* Tinbergen (1951) points out that selective sensitivity of feeding behavior is encountered in every species. No animal eats everything it finds; each exerts a definite choice. Perhaps the widest spectrum of variability in any animal group is seen in phytophagous insects which may forage on a single plant species or may eat several plants and prey upon other insects as well. The widespread economic importance of plant-eating insects has encouraged work on the role of external stimuli in evoking feeding. These studies have become a major source of empirical information and have also stimulated new theoretical points of view (e.g. Dethier 1947, 1951, Kennedy 1958, Thorsteinson 1958, 1960).

No plant species is attacked by all the insect species in its environment. Nor is it common, if it occurs at all, that an insect species devours indiscriminately all the plants in its geographic range. Many insect species are conspicuously associated with particular plant species as is evident from the common names of many insects (potato beetle, corn borer, etc.). Furthermore, each insect species is associated with a group of plants, large or small in number, which we designate as its food-plant range. The food-plant range of some insects is curiously correlated with natural taxonomic plant groupings (genera or families, etc.), but the food plants of many insects are distributed in an apparently random pattern among plants without special regard to botanical affinities (Thorsteinson 1960, p. 193).

What is the role of external stimuli in the control of this varying pattern of food selection? In some plant-feeding insects the situation appears rather simple. The weevil, *Sitona cylindricollis,* is attracted to its host plant, sweet clover, by the substance coumarin, which is the source of the characteristic odor of these plants (Thorsteinson 1960, Hans and Thorsteinson 1961). This substance elicits approach and arrests flying. Larvae of various species of the swallowtail butterflies, *Papilio,* which feed on umbelliferous plants, are attracted by the essential oils of these plants which give them their characteristic odors (Dethier 1941). The same compounds occur in certain other plant families such as the Rutaceae, and these plants are also accepted by the larvae as food.

Other insects are less specific. The diamondback moth, *Plutella maculipennis,* feeds on a wide variety of plants; Thorsteinson (1953) demonstrated the acceptability of 39 species belonging to five families. All had in common the presence of mustard oils and their glucosides. Only one species known to have mustard oils present was rejected. Of fourteen plant species tested which were lacking in mustard oils, only two were accepted as food. By coating their leaves with a 3 percent solution of two mustard oil constituents (sinigrin and sinalbin), five more were made acceptable. The larvae also fed much more readily on nutrient media if a trace of one of nine different mustard oil glucosides was added (Nayar and Thorsteinson 1963).

Although the diamondback moth accepts a wider range of plants as food, as compared with the sweet clover weevil, responsiveness is still focused upon a stimulus property which they all have in common. However, the mustard oil glucosides are a less specific stimulus than coumarin in the sense that they are more generally present in plant species. Further studies revealed some complications. Certain plant species rejected by the moth larvae contain constituents that inhibit feeding (Gupta and Thorsteinson 1960a). This is another mechanism restricting the choice of food plants. Egg-laying activities of the female diamondback moth are more strongly favored by the presence of the free mustard oils than by the glucosides. Allyl isothiocyanate on the right kind of textured surface is a particularly effective stimulus. This behavior ensures that the larvae will hatch in an appropriate environment for feeding. Like feeding, oviposition may also be inhibited by stimuli from certain plant species (Gupta and Thorsteinson 1960b).

In truly polyphagous species such as grasshoppers still less specific stimuli are effective. Feeding is evoked by plant substances which are widespread, such as sucrose (Thorsteinson 1960, Dadd 1963) and phospholipids (Thorsteinson and Nayar 1963). Wireworms orient directly to plant roots by perception of such common substances as asparagin and sugars, and biting is evoked by a wide variety of substances (Thorpe et al. 1947). Observations of this kind give rise to the notion that some insects can assess the presence of nutritive substances directly without relying on the triggering of feeding by substances like mustard oils, which have no food value themselves. This has led to the suspicion that the role of token stimuli in food selection has been overemphasized. There is no reason, however, why nutritive substances should not serve as eliciting stimuli (Thorsteinson 1960). In the blowfly, *Phormia regina,* Evans and Dethier (1957) have shown that feeding is evoked in a specific manner by sugars. But there does not seem to be any assessment of the nutritive value of the sugar, for feeding is elicited by fucose, a sugar which is nutritionally valueless to the blowfly.

Several stimuli often collaborate in the control of feeding. For example, different stimuli may be required to elicit the first biting and to maintain further feeding. While the eliciting stimuli vary widely from species to species among insects, sugars are effective in maintaining feeding in several species. The sugars may operate alone or only after sensitization by other stimuli. To the larva of the diamondback moth mustard oils, glucosides, and sucrose have such a synergistic effect. They elicit little feeding when presented alone.

The process of food selection in the potato beetle larva, *Leptinotarsa decemlineata,* illustrates some of the complexities that can arise (de Wilde 1958). The main responsibility for food selection lies with the mother and her choice of a site for egg laying. Feeding does not usually start near the place of hatching. The larvae begin to move around, guided mainly by vision. Olfactory stimuli from potato plants are also attractive, but only at close range. Thus the first discovery of a potato plant is largely accidental. Next comes a phase of random biting, by which the larva samples the substrate over which it is walking. The time elapsing before this phase begins is a function of the attractiveness of the substrate, determined in part at least by the olfactory stimulus. While the substance involved has not been isolated or identified, removal of the palps and antennae, which carry the olfactory receptors, encourages the biting of neutral substrates such as glass or filter paper, which would otherwise be rejected.

The consequences of random biting depend on the stimuli provided by contact with the substrate. With a proper host plant, any hairs present are shaved off, and then the epidermis is pierced. Again a specific compound, provisionally identified as a flavoglucoside, is particularly effective in maintaining continued feeding (Chauvin 1952). The response to plants which are closely related to the potato is governed by the presence of a variety of alkaloids that inhibit the feeding response of *Leptinotarsa*. Once again, removal of the palps will eliminate the inhibition, so that the larva will then eat substances which are positively harmful to it. The corresponding alkaloid present in the normal food plant, the potato, appears to be neutral in effect. It seems that the same positive stimulus for feeding is present throughout the *Solanum* group studied.

The final choice of food by the potato beetle larva is thus determined by a complex combination of facilitation and inhibition. This relates in turn to the ability of larvae to survive on certain members of the genus *Solanum* and not on others. The substance that encourages sustained feeding is apparently widespread or universal in the family Solanaceae. Restriction of feeding to certain members of the genus is achieved by the existence in most species of various inhibitory alkaloids, many of them toxic to *Leptinotarsa*. It is difficult to avoid the conclusion that the normal host species has been least successful in evolving alkaloids with an inhibitory or repellent effect (Fraenkel 1959).

There can be little doubt that the relationship between the food preferences of insects and the presence of secondary plant substances with repellent and toxic effects is constantly changing in response to natural selection. It is against this background that the responsiveness of the insects to stimuli of varying degrees of specificity must be observed. Monophagous insects seem to respond to a stimulus that is species specific to their hosts. The stimulus they select might even be a substance that the plant had originally evolved to repel herbivores. Polyphagous insects, on the other hand, have a broader responsiveness. In the extreme case this allows them to respond directly to nutrients present in the plants without the intervention of a secondary stimulus. Here any choice must depend primarily on rejection of plants carrying repellent substances. We may assume that polyphagous species are less dependent on a par-

Table 7-2   Thorsteinson's Chemotactic Classification of Preferences of Insects for Food Plants for Feeding and Oviposition

Insect	Plant	
	Facilitating chemicals	Inhibiting chemicals
Type I		
A Grasshoppers, cutworms	All plants	Randomly distributed
B *Leptinotarsa, Bombyx mori*	All plants	One or more in all plants, except group eaten
Type II		
A *Pieris rapae, P. brassicae, Plutella*	Unusual, correlated with plant taxa	—
B (theoretically possible) No known examples	Unusual, random according to taxa	—

After Thorsteinson 1960.

ticular plant for growth and development than monophagous species, many of which are physiologically unable to survive away from the usual host. Plants are evidently more successful in evading the attacks of some insects than others and are least successful with polyphagous insects (Table 7-2).

Studies of plant-feeding insects have illuminated the orienting function of stimuli (e.g. Dethier, Barton Browne, and Smith 1960). If locusts are placed in moving air that carries no food plant odor, they move downwind. If odors are present, however, starved locusts reorient upwind and seek out the food source, apparently orienting by the concentration gradient of the odor. Once satiated they move downwind again (Haskell, Paskin, and Moorhouse 1962). When hungry locusts find food, locomotion stops and they start feeding. This simple inhibitory effect of food stimuli on movement can result in aggregation. Conversely an apparent repellence from a source can be evoked by a chemical stimulus which causes an increase in locomotion rate without affecting the orientation of movement. Pyrethrum and DDT have such effects. But another repellent, indalone, actually orients movement away from the source (Dethier et al. 1960).

◆ *Host Selection by Parasitic Insects.* Most parasitic insects are highly specific in their responsiveness to a host, generally by reference to olfactory stimuli. The parasitic wasp, *Nemeritis canescens,* is responsive to the specific smell of its main natural host, the moth, *Ephestia kuhniella,* even when raised in the laboratory on an abnormal host species (Thorpe and Jones 1937). Another specific parasite, the chalcid wasp, *Microplecton fascipennis,* parasitizes members of the genus *Diprion.* In addition to the stimuli of shape, size, visibility, and movement of the larvae within the cocoon, the specific smell of the host is a major stimulus (Ullyett 1936).

Other parasites are more catholic in their choice of hosts. The chalcid wasp, *Melittobia acasta,* lays eggs in a wide range of insects. The main criteria seem to be that the host must be at least twice as large as the parasite and be surrounded by an envelope of some sort (Thompson and Parker 1927).

In *Trichogramma evanescens,* another uncritical chalcid wasp which parasitizes the eggs of more than 180 species, the relevant stimuli are known in more detail. The conditions evoking attempts at oviposition are simply that the object must protrude from the ground surface, be firm enough to walk upon, fall within certain size limits, and have no dimension greater than four times any other. Odor, color, and surface texture are irrelevant as long as the object is neither wet nor sticky. As a result of this wide sensitivity, this wasp will attempt to lay eggs in such improbable objects as a chip of glass or a drop of mercury, and may even select these in preference to eggs of the normal host (Salt 1935). Yet *Trichogramma* does make specific responses; it will not lay in eggs that have previously been parasitized. This avoidance is caused by the smell which the previous female has left behind and can be eliminated by washing the egg (Salt 1937). Additional specificity in *Trichogramma* stems from its more specific responsiveness to the olfactory stimuli of the host's food plant (Laing 1938).

Variations in the specificity of stimuli evoking host selection in parasites are well correlated with the appropriate conditions for survival. Potential host species have many means of defending themselves against attack (see Salt 1941, 1961). Their efforts are more effective against some parasites than they are against others. Those parasites specialized to survive only on certain hosts are responsive to highly specific stimuli in oviposition.

THE ADAPTIVENESS OF STIMULUS FILTERING

◆ *Problem of Interpreting 'Adaptiveness.'* The relationship between animals and their environment implies a process of filtering to insure that only a part of the environmental stimulus situation affects behavior. This system is effective and economical; many of the events in the animal's sensory world are not relevant to its survival.

This line of argument is convincing, but it can be dangerous. It implies a judgment about what is relevant to survival and what is not. Conclusions concerning the adaptiveness of behavior are all to easy to derive and all too convincing. But we should not forget how few of them are supported by scientific proof. Such proof requires empirical demonstration that a particular characteristic enhances the reproductive success of the animal.

The danger inherent in such judgments about behavior arises from the difficulty of assembling all the information about its precise nature and about all aspects of its function in the natural state that is necessary to give it a sound basis. Just as in comparative anatomy, these judgments must be made. Moreover, they provide a valuable source of hypotheses for further work. We assume a responsibility, then, to collect and assess as much of the relevant information as possible. It is toward this end that Lorenz (1950), Tinbergen (1951), and others emphasize the need to see the animal's whole behavior, in its natural context if possible, before forming hypotheses about functional significance.

Specificity of external stimuli that elicit behavior ranges from extreme specificity to an almost complete lack of specificity. These wide variations may be regarded as adaptive, directly related to the conditions that have affected the survival of the species.

◆ *Prey Catching.* No predator is entirely indiscriminate in selecting food, but the range of acceptable prey nevertheless varies widely. Among predatory insects, for example, some are very specific in their choice of prey. Dacetine ants feed only on a few species of Collembola, which they apparently recognize by smell (Brown 1953, Wilson 1953). The range of prey organisms in most predators is wider. Ants such as *Eciton* are attracted to the odor of almost any animal tissue and are particularly stimulated to bite by movement (Vowles 1955).

Movement is the most widely shared characteristic of prey animals, and unspecific predators make use of this, often ignoring the color, shape, or pattern of the prey. Movement evokes feeding behavior in a great variety of predators, provided that the object falls within certain size limits.

Dragonfly larvae snap at any near moving object within certain size limits (Baldus 1926, Sälzle 1932). The optimal velocity of a prey object for eliciting a strike can be precisely determined (Etienne and Howland 1964). The bee wasp, *Philanthus trigranulatum,* makes its first response in the feeding sequence to any moving, airborne object of approximately the right size (Tinbergen 1935). Many spider species attack any moving objects of a certain size (Bristowe 1941). Frogs show the same response (Russell 1943) and may fail to feed on dead mealworms, even after months of training. So strongly is the frog compelled to snap at small moving objects that one individual severely injured itself by repeatedly lunging and snapping at a fly pinned in the center of a ring of needles (Maier and Schneirla 1964). The common toad, *Bufo bufo*, strikes at all moving objects of a certain size, though it is able to learn to respond to shape, color, and mode of movement (Eibl-Eibesfeldt 1952). Certain snakes that rely heavily on vision in predation behave similarly (Maier and Schneirla 1935, Russell 1943). Fighting fish, *Betta splendens*, snap at all small moving objects, irrespective of their form and color (Lissmann 1932), although they also can learn to be more discriminating (Beniuc 1933). The ubiquity of this response has been exploited by the predatory angler fish, *Lophius piscatorius*, whose moving lure attracts a variety of victims (Wilson 1937 in Russell 1943). Birds such as shrikes and young owls, and even cats, may treat any small moving object as prey (Miller 1931, Sumner 1934, Räber 1950).

For relatively omnivorous predators, the comparatively unspecific sensitivity to moving objects during prey-catching behavior is adaptive. To catch prey they must make a quick decision. Size relative to the predator and movement are the most conspicuous features likely to be shared by all prey animals. Once captured more specific discrimination becomes possible by chemical or other means. *Philanthus*, the bee wasp, first moves downwind, and only the scent of bees evokes the next stage in prey catching (Tinbergen 1935). Thus the initially broad sensitivity can be narrowed by subsequent steps in the behavior sequence.

Specificity of responsiveness may be drastically sharpened by learning. This is probably how normal feeding patterns develop in many predators, enabling them to exploit available prey without sacrificing adaptability. In some cases the learning of parental traditions may be as important as direct experience with prey (Cushing 1944).

THE USE OF MODELS OF COMPLEX VISUAL STIMULI

In most of the examples we have considered so far, experimenters have obtained their results by the manipulation of relatively few stimulus variables, such as the chemical characteristics of a foodstuff or the presence or absence of movement. Stimuli of this type can readily be controlled in the laboratory, and physiologists generally prefer to use such elementary stimulus variables. Many behavior patterns can be elicited only by more complex stimulus patterns. One achievement of pioneer ethologists was the development of means by which complex patterns can be experimentally generated.

◆ *Early Experiments with Models.* The method of using biologically meaningful models as stimulus objects gained particular impetus in Germany from Jacob von Uexküll (e.g. 1921, see Schiller 1957), who had a strong influence on such workers as Baldus, Lissmann, and Beniuc, as well as Lorenz and Tinbergen. Hertz (1929–1931) constructed artificial flower patterns and demonstrated the significance of color and degree of brokenness of the model in attracting honeybees. Lissmann (1932, Hess 1952) used models to analyze the visual stimuli evoking feeding and attack by male fighting fish, *Betta splendens* (Figure 7-1). Meanwhile, at the American Museum of Natural History in New York, Noble and Bradley (1933) showed that male fence lizards will attack plasticene models of their own species, provided that they carry the blue throat of the male.

In Holland, ter Pelkwijk and Tinbergen (1937) designed model fish which a male three-spined stickleback would attack within his territory. The most effective models were those with red bellies, a distinctive characteristic of a male in breeding condition. The shape of the model was relatively unimportant as long as the red was on the ventral side (Figure 7-2). A vertical posture, similar to that assumed by a male in defending his territory, was also significant. A male in a glass tube was attacked more strongly in a vertical, head-down position than in a horizontal one (Figure 7-2a). Courtship responses from the male could be elicited by a model with a swollen silver underside as in a gravid female (Figure 7-2c). In this case it was most effective in a head-up position.

◆ *Begging in Nestling Birds.* Of these pioneer workers, N. Tinbergen continued to develop the method and apply it to a variety of animals. In 1939 he published, with D. J. Kuenen, an analysis of the stimuli evoking begging in nestling blackbirds and thrushes. They found that at first, before the eyes of the nestlings open, mechanical stimuli are effective. After the eyes open a visual component is added; to be effective a model must move, be above eye level, and be larger than three millimeters in diameter. Other than this, changes in the form of the model have no effect on the evoking property of the model, although they do control the orientation of the begging response. In the youngest nestlings, orientation is to gravity; they simply beg upward. Later they lean toward the model, selecting the part that corresponds to its 'head.' This head elicits the strongest orientation if it is separated from the main body of the model by an indentation, representing a convex break in its outline. It is most

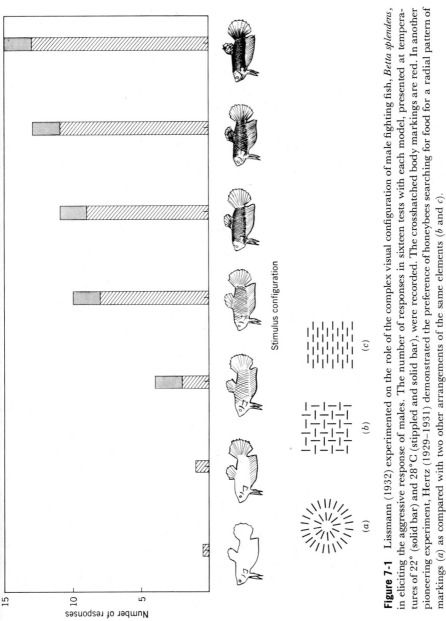

Figure 7-1 Lissmann (1932) experimented on the role of the complex visual configuration of male fighting fish, *Betta splendens*, in eliciting the aggressive response of males. The number of responses in sixteen tests with each model, presented at temperatures of 22° (solid bar) and 28°C (stippled and solid bar), were recorded. The crosshatched body markings are red. In another pioneering experiment, Hertz (1929–1931) demonstrated the preference of honeybees searching for food for a radial pattern of markings (*a*) as compared with two other arrangements of the same elements (*b* and *c*).

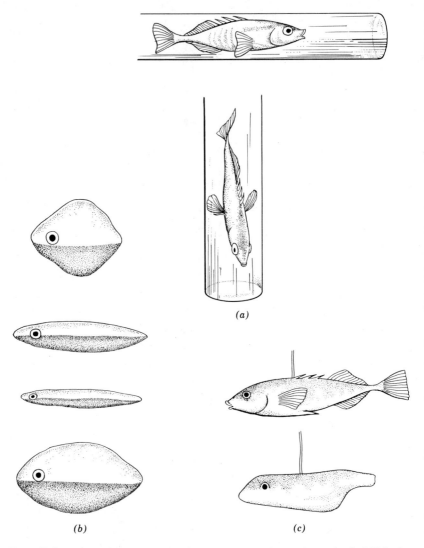

Figure 7-2 Models elicit courtship and threat behavior of male three-spined sticklebacks, *Gasterosteus aculeatus*. (*a*) A stimulus male is restrained in a tube so that he can be presented in a horizontal position or a vertical threat posture. (*b*) A series of red-bellied male models is shown, all effective. (*c*) A detailed model of the female and a simplified version with the swollen abdomen of a ripe female are both effective in eliciting male courtship. After Tinbergen 1951.

effective if the break is at the top of the model, and if it is nearer than the main body. Other variations in shape have no effect. Perhaps the most striking discovery was that wide variation in the form of the model had no effect.

◆ *Courtship of Butterflies.* Studies of the social behavior of butterflies made use of the fact that they will court paper models dangled on a string at the end of a wand (Tinbergen, Meeuse, Boerema, and Varossieau 1942). We shall discuss the results a little later. Perhaps the most elaborate model experiment inspired directly by Tinbergen's work is that of Magnus (1958), on the silver-washed fritillary, *Argynnis paphia.* He presented stimulus objects on the tips of the arms of a carousel. By this means he was able to control the manner of movement. At first a model with flapping wings was used (Figure 7-3). Subsequently the particular type of motion was found to be less important than the rate of flickering presented to the eye of the male butterfly.

In later experiments the models were pasted on the surface of a revolving drum. By counting the choices made by the male between models moving at different rates on each arm of the carousel, Magnus was able to compare the effectiveness of different models. He found that increasing the rate of flicker made the model more attractive. This improvement continued to rates that were far greater than that presented by a flying butterfly, only falling off above about 140 stimulus changes per second. In this way a 'supernormal' stimulus complex could be created that was more effective in evoking male approach than the natural stimulus. This phenomenon of the supernormal stimulus object has been demonstrated many times, and can be helpful in interpreting the physiological mechanisms which underlie the process of stimulus filtering.

◆ *Disguising Animals.* Not all responses can be evoked by simplified models. Often the necessary configurations of stimuli, perhaps involving more than one sensory mode, are too difficult for the experimenter to imitate effectively. This is especially true of social responses, which can seldom be evoked by models in birds and mammals, though there are some exceptions. The main difficulty seems to lie in designing a model that looks and moves like a live animal. This can sometimes be circumvented by disguising live animals, a method that has been used to demonstrate social responses to body colors and patterns in lizards and birds (e.g. Noble and Bradley 1933, Noble 1936, Kramer 1937, Kitzler 1941). The male chaffinch, *Fringilla coelebs,* differs from the gray-brown female in its red- or orange-brown underparts. In the fighting behavior which takes place between the sexes in the winter flock, males normally win over females. It can be shown that this is partly a result of the red breast. Females disguised with red ink in imitation of the male win more fre-

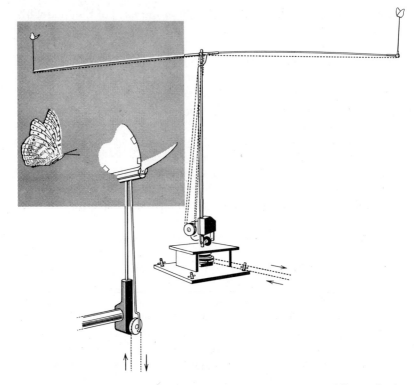

Figure 7-3 Two versions of the carousel used by Magnus to present different stimulus patterns to wild male silver-washed fritillary butterflies, *Argynnis paphia*. The ends of the carousel arms carried either a flapping butterfly model or revolving cylinders with colored patterns and pieces of butterfly wing pasted on them. After Magnus 1958.

quently in encounters with other females and males (Marler 1955a, Table 7-3).

G. K. Noble and B. Curtis (1939) used a particularly elegant version of this method. They were interested in the significance of the red coloration of the male jewel fish, *Hemichromis bimaculatus*, in the control of the mating behavior of the female. Several individual males were placed in tanks adjacent to females to see which they would spawn in front of. If a male's red coloration was intensified by the injection of a drug which expanded his melanophores and erythrophores, the female chose him in preference to his duller rivals (Figure 7-4). Movement is also important; when a bright male was blindfolded so that he was inactive, the female chose a site before a pale but active male for spawning.

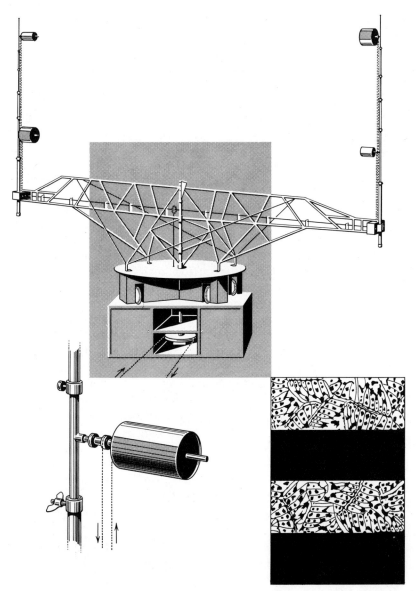

◆ *Responses of Zebra Finches to Models.* One of the few studies of birds in which inanimate models have been successfully used to test the visual stimuli evoking social responses was conducted by Immelmann (1959) with a common cage bird, the zebra finch, *Taeniopygia castanotis.* The

Table 7-3 Effects of Male Disguise on Dominance Relations of Female Chaffinches

	Experiment number					
	1	2	3	4	5	Total
Red breast ♀ wins	75	71	42	92	71	351
Normal ♀ wins	29	11	25	5	0	70
Red breast wins, percent	72	87	63	95	100	84

When the breast of a female chaffinch, *Fringilla coelebs,* is painted red to simulate male coloration, there is an increase in the probability that she will win in aggressive encounters with other females. In each experiment there were two 'red' females and two normal females, the latter painted with soap solution to serve as controls. From Marler 1955a.

courtship and fighting behavior of zebra finches can readily be distinguished. Females evoke courtship from males, males elicit fighting. Immelmann discovered that males responded to models, and he was able to determine which of the elements in the rather distinctive plumage pattern were required.

In order to evoke any social responses from a male it was necessary for the model to carry the characteristic red bill. A crude cylindrical model with no other adornment would evoke courtship if the red bill was present. The addition of other male markings to the model led to aggressive responses by the male. The most potent markings were those on the flanks, the breast, and the cheeks, in that order.

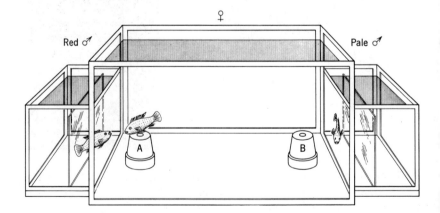

Figure 7-4 Female jewel fish, *Hemichromis bimaculatus,* spawned in flowerpot A in front of the reddened male in 22 consecutive experiments. After Noble and Curtis 1939.

White zebra finches, the product of artificial selection by aviculturists, lack the normal plumage colors but retain the red bill. They show none of the responses to wild-type parents but court and fight with white models instead, apparently relying on slight differences in the intensity of the red color of the bill to distinguish males from females.

In studies of this type it is important not to overlook the possible influence of stimuli perceived through more than one sensory mode. Visual stimuli, including both shape and color, are significant in evoking the social behavior of many fish. But chemical stimuli can also be important, as in courtship of the fish, *Bathygobius soporator*. Tavolga (1954, 1956, 1958) showed that the male responds to the sight of the female and chemical stimuli from her ovarian fluid. The female responds to the visual characteristics of the male and to his peculiar grunting sounds.

◆ *Escape Behavior.* Most animals have to avoid a wide variety of dangers during the course of their lives if they are to survive. Many of them flee from a range of unspecific stimuli which can be summarized as "a sudden change in intensity or kind of stimulation of any of the sensory modes" (Thorpe 1944). Dogs and horses, for example, may be terrified by loud noises, rodents by sounds of high pitch, and most visual animals are startled by sudden movement or strange surroundings. Sometimes the range of circumstances which will elicit alarm behavior or flight extends further, to include social isolation—the absence of parents or companions. Distress calling in small domestic chicks is evoked by isolation, cold, hunger, thirst, pain, restraint, and large objects (Collias 1952, Kaufman and Hinde 1961, Bermant 1963).

In some animals, however, the variety of hazards is dwarfed by one particular danger. Here highly specific responsiveness can play a part. Night-flying moths react with evasive maneuvers to a wide variety of stimuli but they also respond to the high-pitched sounds of the bats which hunt them, either by fleeing or by going into catalepsy. Although they respond to sounds from 10 to 200 kc in frequency, they are most sensitive between 40 and 80 kc (Schaller and Timm 1950, Treat 1955, Roeder 1963), a frequency range which corresponds to the echolocating calls of many bat species (see page 482). The sounds not only elicit avoidance behavior in the moths but also orient them under certain conditions (Figure 7-5).

The escape responses of intertidal gastropod molluscs and the habits of predatory echinoderms are closely interrelated. Some mollusc species which live in the mid- and low-tide regions have a strong response to chemical stimuli from the tube feet of starfish. Limpets living in more exposed places seldom invaded by starfish have no response to these

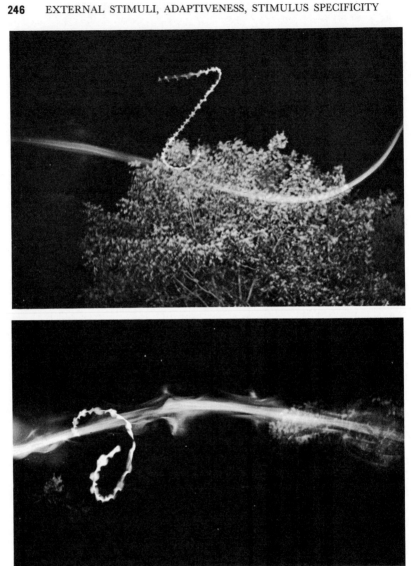

Figure 7-5 The looping trail of a bat attacking a moth. The moth is warned by the high-frequency cries of the bat, takes evasive action, and so avoids capture. Photograph by Frederic A. Webster. From Roeder 1963.

chemical stimuli (Bullock 1953). Echinoderms which are herbivorous or omnivorous evoke no response.

The escape behavior of birds shows a striking parallel. Many birds flee at the sight of a hawk flying overhead. Tests with several species of birds show that a model will evoke the same escape behavior if it has a certain shape (Goethe 1940, Lorenz 1939, Krätzig 1940). The key properties are wings, a short neck, and a long tail. The importance of a short neck and a long tail is confirmed by the loss of effectiveness of the model when the direction of movement is reversed (Figure 7-6).

In these and other experiments that deal with complex visual configurations it is remarkable that they succeed at all in eliciting responses. The response levels are seldom complete in comparison with the natural behavior. The extent of the difference has been determined by Martin and Melvin (1964) who compared responses of bobwhite quail, *Colinus virginianus,* to a natural predator of the species, the red-tailed hawk, *Buteo jamaicensis,* and to a model of the same species. Their experiments show that the model is, at best, a poor substitute and, significantly, habituation

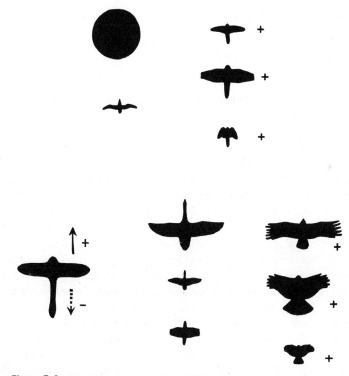

Figure 7-6 Models can be passed over birds subject to hawk predation in nature. Silhouettes that resemble hawks elicit escape responses (+). The direction of movement may also be critical in evoking escape. After Tinbergen 1951.

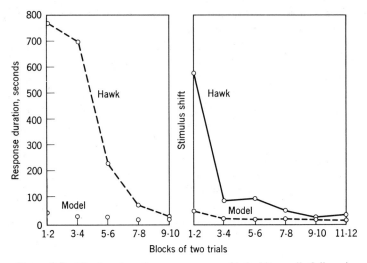

Figure 7-7   The duration of escape responses of bobwhite quail, *Colinus virginianus*, to a model of a red-tailed hawk, *Buteo jamaicensis*, and a live hawk. The stimulus shift involved a change from model to hawk and hawk to model. After Martin and Melvin 1964.

to the model was followed by strong responses when the live hawk was substituted (Figure 7-7).

◆ *'Mobbing' Responses*. Closely related to escape behavior is the response known as mobbing, which birds give to novel objects, owls, and other predators. At low intensity it merges with certain kinds of exploratory behavior in which the animal approaches and investigates the object from a distance, often with a special display. In some small birds these two types of behavior can probably be considered in the same terms (Hinde 1954). In general, they are evoked by a wide range of unfamiliar stimuli which are not strong enough to evoke full escape—a strange object, a familiar object in a strange place, an unusual sound, and so on (see page 162). Presumably the main survival value of approach and investigation is the opportunity to reduce the chance of being caught unawares and the chance to learn the characteristics of potential dangers.

In nature owls are a special object of this behavior. Experiments on captive song sparrows (Nice and ter Pelkwijk 1941), captive chaffinches (Hinde 1954), and several other species in the wild state (Hartley 1950) suggest that the following properties are the key elements which elicit owl mobbing (Hinde 1954):

1. Owl-like outline, big-headed, short-necked, and short-tailed.

2. Solid in contour.
3. Colored in browns and/or grays, or in tone contrasts of these colors.
4. Patterned in a system of spots, streaks, or bars.
5. Presence of a beak and a pair of frontal eyes.

Even the calls of owls evoke mobbing by some passerine birds in the wild (Miller 1952). The degree of vulnerability to a particular predator will vary greatly from bird to bird, and we might expect differences in the responsiveness to owls. A wide range of stimuli evokes mobbing in the curve-billed thrasher, with no special response to owls (Rand 1941b). The European bullfinch, *Pyrrhula pyrrhula,* lives in dense thickets and is probably exposed to little owl predation. Unlike its close relative the chaffinch, it is not very responsive to owls or other birds of prey. The stimuli evoking exploration and mobbing in bullfinches can be summarized only in the broadest terms: hairy or feathery texture, convex shape and colored surface (Kramer and von St. Paul 1951). Although hand-raised magpies, *Pica pica,* mob predators, hand-raised jackdaws, *Corvus monedula,* do not (Lorenz 1935). Curio (1961) has shown that the flycatcher, *Muscicapa h. hypoleuca,* living within the range of the predatory red-backed shrike, *Lanius collurio,* in Germany, will mob shrike models, but the Spanish subspecies living beyond the shrike's geographical range does not. As with the escape responses of gastropods to starfish, the stimuli inducing birds to mob varies even in close relatives, presumably in harmony with differences in predator-prey relationships (review in Curio 1963). Again we should recall that the survival value of such behavior has never been demonstrated directly and that there is considerable argument about what the function of mobbing actually is.

CONCLUSIONS ON THE SPECIFICITY OF STIMULUS FILTERING

In emphasizing the extreme specificity of the filtering of external stimuli in some behavior, there is a tendency to forget that this specificity is by no means universal. Oversight on the part of some workers has earned some justifiable criticism (e.g. Lack 1941, Rand 1941a). On the other hand, one should not conclude that a high degree of specificity is an exceptional or atypical condition. There is surely no such thing as completely unspecific responsiveness. Even the examples of broadest sensitivity just described above are specific when considered in terms of the physical environment as a whole. For example, sudden and unfamiliar change, which evokes escape behavior, is by definition a relatively improbable event in the individual animal's particular environment. From newborn vertebrates to unicellular Protozoa there are different responses to different stimuli, even if only at the simplest level; there is approach or feeding in response to weak stimuli and avoidance in response to stronger ones (Maier and Schneirla 1964).

The filtering of external stimuli ranges from the selection of a sensory mode and the strength of its stimulation to precise responsiveness to elaborate configurations of patterns, colors, sounds, flavors, and odors. The usual situation is neither complete unspecificity nor extreme specificity,

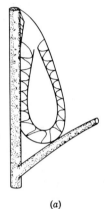

(a)

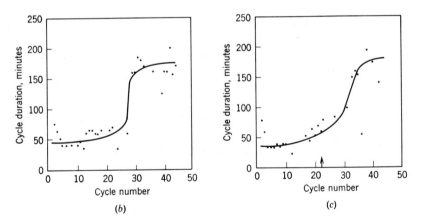

(b)   (c)

Figure 7-8 When the silkworm moth, *Platysamia cecropia,* spins a cocoon (*a*) it works from the outside in. The rate of turning slows down (*b*) when the inner envelope is begun. The slowing down is indicated on the graphs as an increase in the cycle duration. When the worm is removed from its cocoon (arrow in *c*) and allowed to resume spinning, the change to slow spinning and inner envelope construction proceeds on the original schedule. When a flat web is spun inside an inflated balloon and the worm is then removed, the features of the cocoon which is subsequently constructed depend on the amount of silk already spun, not on elapsed time or on sensory feedback from the cocoon (*d*). After Van der Kloot and Williams 1953a, b.

but something between, leaning one way or the other according to what we assume to be the dictates of survival value and reproductive advantage.

STIMULUS-RESPONSE CHAINS

Many behavior patterns form part of a more or less regular or obligatory sequence when performed under natural conditions. There is thus a sense in which we can speak of a series of stimulus-response relationships linked together in a chain.

◆ *Stickleback Courtship.* The courtship of the three-spined stickleback, *Gasterosteus aculeatus,* is a celebrated example (Tinbergen 1951). The male's courtship dance is elicited by the sight of a gravid female (see page 238). His movements induce her to follow him to the nest where she is shown the nest entrance. She responds by pushing through the nest and laying eggs which the male then fertilizes. Thus "each reaction of either male or female is released by the preceding reaction of the partner" (Tinbergen 1951).

◆ *Web Spinning in Silkworms.* An individual may generate a sequence by its own behavior without the intervention of another animal, for example, the cocoon spinning of the Cecropia silkworm, *Platysamia cecropia* (Van der Kloot and Williams 1953a, b). Several of the actions used seem to be

Animal number	Time in balloon, hours	Percent silk spun in balloon	Architecture of subsequent balloon		
			Outer envelope	Intermediate layer	Inner envelope
1	25	0	+ +	+ +	+ +
2	16	14	+ +	+ +	+ +
3	27	28	+	+ +	+ +
4	17	33	+	+ +	+ +
5	19	36	+	+ +	+ +
6	24	63	0	0	+ +
7	33	66	0	0	+ +
8	19	66	0	0	+ +
9	16	78	0	0	+
10	25	100	0	0	0
11	48	100	0	0	0
12	43	100	0	0	0

(*d*)

generated as chain reflexes; completion of one movement triggers the next. But the results of this study show the caution needed in interpreting sequences of different behavior patterns. External stimuli sometimes play only a permissive role, with endogenous mechanisms contributing to the chain. First the silkworm builds an outer shell, then a spongy layer, and finally an inner lining. As it starts on the inner envelope there is a characteristic decrease in the frequency of turning movements of the whole body during spinning. Do stimuli provided at the completion of each stage of the cocoon trigger the next phase of construction? Van der Kloot and Williams demonstrated that depletion of the supply of silk from the silk glands, to about 60 percent of the supply, is a major factor in determining when construction of the inner layer shall begin. Depletion is also responsible for the changed frequency of the turning movements (Figure 7-8b, c). Silkworms which have been experimentally induced to spin 60 percent of their silk as a flat sheet and are then placed in a normal environment will immediately spin just an inner envelope (Figure 7-8). Similarly, a worm taken from a half-finished cocoon and allowed to start again increased its turning rate on the original time schedule.

◆ *Nest Building in Canaries.* Often a chain or sequence of behavior results from a combination of exogenous and endogenous factors. Such is the case when a canary makes a nest (Hinde 1958). Usually the body of the nest is made of grass, then lined with feathers. If the experimenter adds to the nest, reducing the size of the cup, feathers are brought in earlier. Stimuli from the nest thus influence subsequent nest-building behavior. If a complete artificial nest is provided as a starting point, however, the number of feathers brought to the nest still increases as the time for egg laying approaches, even though the material added to the nest cup is removed by the experimenter each day so that it remains unchanged in size. Endogenous factors seem implicated. There is yet another complication (Warren and Hinde 1959, Steel and Hinde 1963). Hormonal factors participate in the endogenous changes, and we have already noted that hormones may achieve their effects by sensitizing receptors to external stimuli (see page 105). This is probably the case in canary nest building. The incubation patch on the belly of the female becomes bare and vascular as the breeding season proceeds. Experiments show that it becomes more sensitive as the time for egg laying approaches. Thus the increasing preference for feathers as nest material at this time may result from a rise in tactile sensitivity of the brood patch (Hinde, Bell, and Steel 1963).

Whatever the mechanism underlying such sequences of behavior, a chain of stimulus-response relationships, a series of endogenous changes, or a combination of both, the serial order of the actions influences the specificity of response to external stimuli (see page 261).

UNSPECIFIC RESPONSIVENESS
DUE TO RECEPTOR DEFICIENCIES

We have argued that the specificity of responsiveness to external stimuli is closely adjusted to the functional requirements of the situation. But in some cases this is not so; specificity of responsiveness may be limited by the properties of the receptors. Unspecific responsiveness sometimes seems to occur because the sense organs are not efficient enough to permit greater specificity. The best examples of the latter condition come from arthropods.

Invertebrates generally respond mainly to chemical stimuli when highly specific responsiveness to the environment is required. Many invertebrates are unable to see details, and vision is confined largely to perception of movement, detection of light and dark, and discrimination of broad outlines. But some arthropods, active predators for the most part, have large and highly developed eyes which are capable of more detailed perception. They also react to more specific visual stimuli in breeding behavior. This is particularly evident in responses given at a distance, where olfactory control is in many ways less certain. Animals with poor vision must respond to relatively unspecific visual stimuli and rely upon chemoreception at later stages in a sequence to increase the specificity.

◆ *Spider Hunting and Courtship.* Spiders illustrate well both types of specificity. They have simple rather than compound eyes, and most of them have poor vision. Spiders that capture prey with a snare or web cannot distinguish between prey items until they approach and measure them with their forelegs and smell or taste them (Bristowe 1941). In courtship as well, the spiders with poor vision rely largely on chemical and tactile stimuli during courtship to find mates (Crane 1949). The male cannot effectively signal his approach to the female from a distance, yet he must avoid being treated as prey. This he achieves by rushing the female, locking jaws with her and, in some species, tying her down with a web. The male of some species takes possession of a female while she is still young, encloses her in a cell, and mates with her soon after the final moult, before she has reached full strength (Bristowe 1941).

Some of the salticid jumping spiders have much better vision, reflected in their behavior in many ways. Unlike the web spinners they actively search for their prey and their hunting behavior depends on vision. Slow movement evokes stalking, fast movement a quick run to within jumping distance. They are capable of better visual discrimination than the short-sighted species and can be seen scanning potential prey objects. The visual stimuli involved in courtship are quite specific (Crane 1949, Drees 1952).

In work with a variety of jumping spider species, Crane (1949) found that movement and appropriate model size were important in evoking courtship by the male. The male spiders respond to the shape of the model, especially to the presence of legs. In one black and yellow species the presence of these colors was necessary on the model to evoke maximum response. The detailed structure of the color patterns, however, seemed to have little significance, except in certain cases of recognition between males. In the species that Drees (1952) studied, *Epiblemum scenicum,* the situation proved to be more complex (Figure 7-9). The males were responsive not only to the presence of legs, but also to the pattern of black and white stripes on the female's abdomen and to the relative proportions of thorax and abdomen.

The lack of specificity in the visual stimuli evoking the courtship responses of spiders with small eyes seems to be a compromise with their somewhat inefficient distance vision.

◆ *Insect Eyes.* The compound eyes of insects vary greatly in size from the 500 or so facets in the eye of some ants to more than 28,000 in the eye of a dragonfly. There is a corresponding variation in capacity for detailed vision (Imms 1957, Wigglesworth 1953). Nevertheless, the compound eye gives at best only moderate form vision, being more suited to the perception of movement. The flicker fusion frequency is much higher than in the vertebrate eye. And there is evidence that form vision consists largely of the perception of different degrees of flicker (Autrum 1949, Wigglesworth 1953) (see page 338).

Most insects probably rely upon olfaction to find mates. In some small insects such as the bug, *Pyrrhocoris apterus,* and the pond skater, *Gerris lacustris,* the species form, color, and markings are not perceived at a distance and the visual stimuli that elicit the first response are quite unspecific. The first response, approach, is made simply to jerky movement. Only at close ranges are more specific responses made, apparently to odor (Hellwig and Ludwig 1951).

Lepidoptera have been divided roughly into two groups, those whose distance responses in feeding and courtship are mainly evoked by airborne chemical stimuli, and those responding mainly to visual stimuli, with many intermediates of course (Ilse 1928). Males of the 'chemical' type have to follow the scent upwind in a gradual zigzag flight to find the female. Males of the 'visual' type can see females and approach quickly and directly (see Petersen et al. 1952).

The visual stimuli that evoke the initial phase of the mating sequence have been analyzed in four species. The experiments all stem from a study made by Tinbergen, Meeuse, Boerema, and Varossieau in 1942 on the grayling butterfly, *Eumenis semele*. The males of this species station

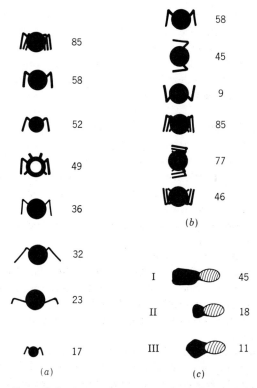

Figure 7-9 Courtship responses of male hunting spiders, *Epiblemum scenicum*, to models. (*a*) The percentage of trials in which these various silhouettes evoked the courtship actions of foreleg waving. (*b*) By the same measure variation in orientation of a model changes its effectiveness in eliciting male courtship. (*c*) Using the frequency of the male's courtship dance as a measure, we see that the proportions of the female cephalothorax to abdomen are significant to the male. I, normal proportions; II and III, models with a small cephalothorax. After Drees 1952.

themselves on the ground or on the bole of a tree, and pursue other butterflies that pass by. When a female grayling ready to mate is approached,
she alights, the male follows, and after various preliminaries he mates
with her. The initial phases of pursuit can be readily evoked by a paper
model dangled from a string on the end of a wand. The effectiveness of
various characteristics was determined by substituting different models
and counting the number of male approaches each elicited.

Many of the results of this study were negative. Variations in the color,
size, and shape of the model had little influence. The brightness of the
model, however, as well as the way in which it was moved and its distance,
all had a marked influence on the male. The strongest responses were
evoked by a close, fluttering, dark model. In a similar study of pierid
butterflies Petersen, Törnblom, and Bodin (1952) concentrated on the
effects of color. White models, colored like females, evoked the strongest
responses. The dark veins and streaks of the wings seemed to have no
effect.

The work of Magnus on the silver-washed fritillary, *Argynnis paphia*,
has already been reviewed (see page 241). Movement is especially important in eliciting courtship approaches of males. The form of the model and
the black markings on the wings appeared to have no significance. But
color had a strong effect, a maximum number of responses being given
to an orange-yellow model matching closely the normal color of the female. Size was also important: larger models evoked more responses,
within the limits explored.

The tropical butterfly, *Heliconius erato*, is black with a broad band of
red across the forewing. Crane (1955) studied the role of this pattern in
evoking male courtship. She found that the strongest responses were made
to orange-red models resembling the female, and that a model colored
orange-red all over was more effective than a normal female. Movement
was also important.

The most thorough study of the effect of detailed variations of pattern
on butterfly courtship was made by G. O. Stride (1956, 1957, 1958) on
the African species, *Hypolimnas misippus*. He used essentially the same
method as previous workers. But he concentrated less on stimuli evoking
the first approach of the male and more on the amount of time the male
would follow the model after approaching it, and on the incidence of
later phases of male courtship.

The males of this species are black with a large white patch in the
center of each wing. The females are typically orange-brown with black
tips and edges marked with white. Tests of models with different wings
and bodies showed that the female wings are necessary for a strong response. The coloration of the hindwing proved to have special significance

to the male. A model with male forewing and female hindwing evoked stronger responses than one with female forewing and male hindwing (Table 7-4). A large white patch on the hindwing inhibits the male, and this is evidently a major factor in reducing the male's responsiveness to other males and perhaps to other species of butterflies with white wings.

Stride had difficulty creating an artificial model that was as effective as the mounted wings of a female (Table 7-4). Removal of the scales reduced their effectiveness. Red and yellow models evoked the most responses. The brighter the color, the more effective they were. Strangely enough, the strongest responses were evoked by an orange forewing and a black hindwing. But normal female wings had more effect. The black and white markings on the wing tips and edges were not significant. After eliminating olfactory clues, Stride concluded that subtle visual properties associated with the brown areas of the normal female wing, difficult to imitate, evoke the maximal response from a male. Size had only general significance; models too large or too small had little effect.

Hypolimnas and *Argynnis* males seem to be more responsive to detailed visual stimuli than the grayling studied by Tinbergen and his associates (1942). A difference in methods in these studies may be involved, however. The studies of graylings concentrated on stimuli evoking the male's first approach. Magnus and Stride were more concerned with stimuli evoking persistent following. They could be sure that the model had been perceived in every case because an initial response had already been given. There is no doubt that they were investigating variations in the duration of response induced by the models. The grayling data, however, may

Table 7-4 The Responses of the Male Butterfly, *Hypolimnas misippus,* to Female Models

Female model color	Duration of male following, seconds										
	2	4	6	8	10	12	14	16	18	20	20+
White	12	–	–	–	–	–	–	–	–	–	–
Light gray	13	–	–	–	–	–	–	–	–	–	–
Dark gray	12	–	–	–	–	–	–	–	–	–	–
Black	12	–	–	–	–	–	–	–	–	–	–
Gray	11	1	–	–	–	–	–	–	–	–	–
Red	3	3	3	1	–	–	–	–	1	–	1
Orange forewings, black hindwings	2	1	5	1	2	1	–	–	1	1	4
Dried female	–	2	1	–	1	–	1	–	–	–	13

The most effective 'model' is a preserved specimen of the female. After Stride 1958.

include variations in initial perception of the models. It is conceivable that in later stages of the courtship flight more specific visual stimuli might prove to be significant in the grayling as well.

In summary, the quality which seems to be universally necessary to elicit the courtship approach of male butterflies is movement, to which the compound eye is particularly sensitive. A common means of increasing specificity is by limiting the response to objects of approximately the right size. Further specificity is achieved by relying on the light intensity reflected from the object. Pale butterflies, like the cabbage and green-veined whites, *Pieris brassicae* and *P. napi*, respond more to light objects, darker species like the grayling and *Heliconius* more to dark models. Butterflies can also see colors, and with the exception of the grayling all species that have been studied tend to be most responsive to the general color of their females' wings. Thus a broadly specific response is possible. However, the range of objects that will evoke approach is wide, as perusal of any of the papers mentioned will show. The markings on the female wings of the green-veined white butterfly, silver-washed fritillary, and *Heliconius* seem to evoke no response from males, even at close range. It would seem that these butterflies have reached a compromise, responding as specifically as their eyes will permit at a distance. At closer range a more specific response is possible. This may be based on a change to olfaction, as apparently occurs in the grayling (Tinbergen et al. 1942), and sometimes vision is again used, as in *Hypolimnas*. But often details of pattern striking to the human eye are ineffective in influencing male responsiveness.

◆ *Dragonfly Aggression and Mating Behavior.* Dragonflies have larger eyes than any other insect and are capable of more specific visual responsiveness at a distance than butterflies. They discriminate specific differences in wing transparency with great accuracy, as well as size, movement, and color. Nevertheless, dragonflies often do not respond to differences in other characteristics of wing structure and marking (Buchholtz 1951, 1955).

The need to distinguish stimuli evoking different phases of a response is well illustrated by several experiments. Moore (1952) tethered individuals of several British species on a cotton thread and released them near wild males, where they evoked a variety of responses. Table 7-5 shows the differences in the courtship posture achieved with different subjects, ranging through approach, a clash, grasping the partner's thorax, and tandem, with the male clasping the other's thorax in its anal pincers. Males approach females of the same species and usually continue to a tandem position; males clash with males of the same species and occasionally grasp them and reach the tandem position. Males and females of other species are merely approached. Evidently males are able to distinguish conspecific males from those of other species, but this discrimination occurs after the initial approach. The first phase of the response is evoked by unspecific stimuli, later phases by more specific stimuli.

Buchholtz (1951, 1956), Loibl (1958), and Krieger and Krieger-Loibl (1958) have analyzed the effective visual stimuli by the use of models. Movement is a critical factor in evoking the first male approach. A good imitation of dragonfly flight is the most effective. In *Calopteryx*, size seems to play a role, since there are upper and lower limits beyond which there is no response. Wide variations in wing shape have no effect. The most critical factors are the color and transparency of the wings.

Investigations of two species of *Platycnemis* (Buchholtz 1956) revealed more of the significance of color patterns. In *P. pennipes,* young females not yet ready for mating are colored yellowish-brown on the head, thorax, and abdomen. Older females are greenish-brown. Males approach older females, but not younger ones, apparently as a result of differential responsiveness to their color. The detailed markings were not important at this stage, but when the male approached the grasping position the specific markings on the dorsal side of the thorax became important,

Table 7-5 Responses of Free-Flying Dragonflies to Tethered Individuals

Species		Nil	Approach	Clash	Pretandem	Tandem
Free	Tethered					
LQ ♂	LQ ♀	–	–	1	–	3
LQ ♂	LQ ♂	–	2	22	9	3
LQ ♂	(OS) ♀	–	2	3	–	–
LQ ♂	(OS) ♂	6	21	3	–	–
SS ♂	SS ♀	6	1	5	2	23
SS ♂	SS ♂	–	–	21	8	2
SS ♂	(OS) ♀	–	2	–	–	–
SS ♂	(OS) ♂	–	8	1	–	–
OC ♂	OC ♀	–	–	–	–	2
OC ♂	OC ♂	–	4	19	9	2
OC ♂	(OS) ♀	1	8	–	–	–
OC ♂	(OS) ♂	1	3	–	–	–

The species are *Libellula quadrimaculata, Sympetrum striolatem* and *Orthetrum cancellatum.* OS is another species. After Moore 1952.

providing the basis for his selection of a conspecific mate. In *Plathemis lydia,* a species with prominent white markings on the male wings and upper abdomen, males with darkened abdomens are unable to defend territories effectively and are less successful in mating (Jacobs 1955). The same is true of *Peritremis tenera* if the amber wing markings are obscured. But *Plathemis* females painted white, while they are attacked initially, are eventually mated with; evidently new stimuli block aggression once contact has been made.

Studies of two species of *Ischnura* revealed a rather similar situation (Krieger and Krieger-Loibl 1958). Although males would respond to females of other species, they reacted most strongly to conspecifics. Again wing color and transparency were important. A bright yellow ring on the abdomen of one species was critical in recognition at close range. In species of *Sympecma* and *Lastes* the situation was somewhat different (Loibl 1958), for males approached and tried to mate with females of several species. In this case responsibility for specific discrimination seemed to be the prerogative of the female; she rejected males of other species by a special posture. The structure of the anal forceps may play a significant role in her recognition of an appropriate mate.

These studies of the Odonata illustrate a number of principles. The earliest phase of a sexual encounter in several groups of dragonflies is evoked by relatively unspecific stimuli. At closer range more specific stimuli come into play, enabling either the male or the female to make a species-specific discrimination. In at least one case, *Platycnemis,* a phase of specific responsiveness is followed by a phase of highly unspecific responsiveness. Once in the tandem position, the culminating stages of the male's copulatory sequence are unaffected by the specific stimuli of the earlier phases. Instead they are elicited by the self-stimulation achieved by the male in touching the female's head with his copulatory organs. Using the tip of a needle to artificially stimulate a male who is in tandem with a dead female model can serve equally well to elicit the next phase of the response. Yet in nature, of course, a specific response is ensured by what has gone before.

In conclusion, we find that even in reproductive behavior, where responsiveness to highly specific stimuli will presumably be favored by natural selection, some arthropods show unspecific responsiveness to visual stimuli *at a distance.* The reason must be their incapacity to see clearly under these conditions. Even with the compound eye at its best, as in the Odonata, the more specific details of the object often fail to evoke responses. It seems probable that this is simply because they cannot see them very well. Greater specificity is either ensured by subsequent behavior at closer range or may already have been guaranteed by some previous event.

UNSPECIFIC RESPONSIVENESS; SPECIFICITY ENSURED BY PRIOR EVENTS

Sensitivity to influence by a broad range of external stimuli can be demonstrated experimentally with many responses that, in nature, are nonetheless restricted to highly specific situations. This often occurs when some combination of previous events makes it highly probable that the only object providing these unspecific stimuli will be the biologically appropriate one. If, for example, a black-headed gull, *Larus ridibundus*, sits on its nest and feels too few eggs against its brood patch, it will roll into the nest any nearby object of approximately the right size and texture. In nature there is a high probability that this object will be her missing egg. But the experimenter can substitute white or colored pottery eggs, red and blue wooden eggs, balls, cubes, cylinders, and even a flat wooden box, and they will be retrieved.

Many animals increase the chance of specific responsiveness simply by seeking a particular environment, as various nematoceran flies do when looking for a mate (Downes 1958). Even a polyphagous insect parasite such as *Trichogramma evanescens*, whose egg-laying behavior is evoked by a wide range of stimuli (see page 235), is guaranteed some degree of specificity by seeking its host in a certain habitat or by locating it roughly through olfactory stimuli (Laing 1938). The same principle may apply to breeding behavior. One of the functions of certain taxic responses of lower invertebrates, besides keeping the animal in a suitable environment, may be to ensure that other members of the species do the same and so improve their chances of meeting (Fraenkel and Gunn 1940).

In species that practice parental care the bond between parents and young is often highly specific, extending beyond species specificity to a relationship between particular individuals. Yet the stimuli by which an experimenter can evoke both parental behavior and the appropriate response from the young are often quite unspecific. Overall specificity is ensured in nature by the strong attachment of the parent to the nest site; the only effective stimuli the young are likely to perceive under natural conditions come from the parent (Lorenz 1935, Cushing and Ramsay 1949).

◆ *Begging in Nestling Birds.* Birds provide clear examples of the way in which this general situation may serve particular needs. The requirements differ in 'altricial' and 'precocial' species. Altricial nestlings remain in a nest. It suffices for the parents to give food to anything in their nest that resembles a nestling. Many altricial passerine birds do not seem to recognize their own young (Nice 1943), setting the stage for exploitation by parasitic birds. Many passerines will accept and rear the young of other species. The responses of some parents are confined to stimuli from the nest to an extraordinary degree. They will ignore their own nestlings just outside it and may even eat them (review in Nice 1943). Once out of the nest, mixing of different broods is frequent (e.g. in titmice, Hinde 1952), again suggesting that there is little individual recognition.

The stimuli evoking the begging behavior of altricial young are unspecific. They will beg not only to foster parents quite unlike their actual parents but also to much more dissimilar stimuli. Very young starlings, *Sturnus vulgaris,* will beg to moderate vibration, sounds of various kinds, and contact on the bill (Meyer–Holzapfel 1939). This breadth of effective stimuli is familiar to anyone who has reared young birds by hand. Later, visual stimuli become more important, and here there may be a certain specificity. Young blackbirds and thrushes, *Turdus merula* and *T. ericetorum,* respond most readily to objects which are moving, are of a certain size, and appear in the upper half of their visual field (Tinbergen 1951). Nevertheless, the range of effective stimuli, both visual and auditory, which elicit begging by altricial birds is enormous (Nice 1943). As a result of experience hand-reared birds can come to respond strongly to quite artificial stimuli, such as forceps and human beings (Meyer–Holzapfel 1939, Nice 1943).

◆ *Mating Behavior of Birds.* Interspecific mating is rare in nature. Yet in captivity many birds will regularly copulate with species other than their own if deprived of a normal mate. The productivity of such unions in terms of numbers of viable eggs laid may be as high as from conspecific pairs (Hinde 1956). The stimuli evoking copulation are less specific than those involved in natural pair formation, so that interspecific pairs formed artificially may mate and successfully rear young. In nature overall specificity is nevertheless ensured by previous behavior. In finches, for example, responses during pair formation to highly specific songs, displays, and plumage colors would have gone before (Hinde 1956).

Copulation may be evoked by stuffed birds, or even by a corpse (review in Nice 1943). Male ruffed grouse, *Bonasa umbellus,* will copulate with a stuffed female laid on the ground (Allen 1934). As in many species the most important stimulus seems to be a still female, provided by model and corpse alike. The precise posture may be less important than stillness

(Lack 1940). Sometimes there is still less selectivity, and male models, even those of other species, may be mounted as well. A male cowbird, *Molothrus ater,* copulated with a stuffed house wren, *Troglodytes aedon* (Friedmann, quoted by Allen 1934). House wrens will mate with a stuffed winter wren, *Telmatodytes palustris* (Noble and Vogt 1935). The most careful study was made on redwing blackbirds, *Agelaius phoeniceus.* First-year males would mate with a cardinal, *Richmondena cardinalis;* a blue jay, *Cyanocitta cristata;* a meadowlark; male and female towhees, *Pipilo erythropthalmus;* a budgerigar; a wood thrush, *Hyocichla mustelina;* a fox sparrow, *Passerella iliaca;* a northern shrike, *Lanius borealis;* a rusty blackbird, *Euphagus carolinus;* and a cowbird. However, the specificity of responsiveness was greater in older males, which mated only with models of females of their own species. The same was true of northern yellowthroats, *Geothlypis trichas* (Noble and Vogt 1935).

There are occasional records of birds that have mated with inanimate objects. An avocet, *Recurvirostra avocetta,* copulated with the water surface (Makkink 1936), and an unmated male gentoo penguin, *Pygoscelis papua,* courted and mounted a grass tussock (Roberts 1940). Sage grouse and an American robin have been seen behaving similarly (Simon 1940, Young 1949). A young male house sparrow, *Passer domesticus,* just coming into full breeding plumage, copulated with a dandelion seed head (Barraud 1953). Ficken and Dilger (1960) record captive male lovebirds, *Agapornis fischeri,* a wood thrush, *Hylocichla mustelina,* and the American redstart, *Setophaga ruticilla,* all mounting protuberances on a perch, or a stone, or a pile of droppings. A wild chaffinch mounted the upwardly directed tip of a dead branch, and a captive male without a mate repeatedly mounted a compact heap of dried grass. Two captive male bramblings, *Fringilla montifringilla,* went through motions of copulating with protuberances on a branch many times a day during one breeding season, even though they were provided with mates.

The mating behavior of birds thus provides a complete series from responsiveness to highly specific stimuli to relatively unspecific stimuli. But in the latter case, specificity is normally ensured in nature by previous events, ranging from youthful experience of stimuli from the parent to the establishment of the pair bond.

CONCLUSIONS ON RESPONSIVENESS TO EXTERNAL STIMULI

What conclusions can be drawn from this review of behavioral evidence for stimulus filtering? Confronted with a critical situation to which a response must be given, animals evolve mechanisms for responsiveness to some abstracted property of that situation. The essential quality of this sign stimulus or stimulus complex is that it is shared by all situations in which the response is appropriate. The representative stimulus itself may be without any inherent relevance to survival. There is no reason, however, why a biologically significant property of the situation—a nutritive substance to trigger feeding, for example—should not assume the same role, provided that it satisfies the necessary conditions.

The degree of specificity of an effective stimulus will vary widely in relation to several factors. If a narrow range is appropriate, responsiveness will be restricted to highly specific stimuli, insofar as the capacity of the receptors permits this. If the receptors are inadequate, particularly at a distance, there is likely to be a sequence of stimulus-response relationships, unspecific at first but becoming more specific in subsequent steps. In other circumstances there may be a chain of stimuli and responses with a specific stimulus early in the sequence. Here intermediate responses in the chain may be evoked by unspecific stimuli, even though the ultimate biological situation is a specific one. Specificity will nevertheless be ensured by events earlier in the overall process if the sequence is a more or less obligatory one. A degree of filtering of the incoming stimuli is thus universal, varying in its refinement according to what we presume to be the dictates of natural selection.

REFERENCES

Allen, A. A. 1934. Sex rhythm in the ruffed grouse (*Bonasa umbellus* Linn.) and other birds. *Auk*, **51**:180–199.

Autrum, H. 1949. Neue Versuche zum optischen Ausflösungsvermögen fliegender Insekten. *Experientia*, **5**:271–277.

Baldus, K. 1926. Experimentelle Untersuchungen über die Entfernungslokalisation der Libellen (*Aeschna cyanea*). *Z. vergl. Physiol.*, **3**:475–505.

Barraud, E. M. 1953. Sexual behaviour occurring as overflow activity in juvenile house sparrow. *Brit. Birds*, **46**:382.

Beniuc, M. 1933. Bedeutungswechsel der Dinge in der Umwelt des Kampffisches *Betta splendens* Regan. *Z. vergl. Physiol.*, **18**:437–458.

Bermant, G. 1963. Intensity and rate of distress calling in chicks as a function of social contact. *Anim. Behav.*, **11**:514–517.

Bristowe, W. S. 1941. *The Comity of Spiders*. Vol. II. Adlard and Sons, London.

Brown, W. L., Jr. 1953. A preliminary report on dacetine ant studies in Australia. *Ann. Ent. Soc. Amer.*, **46**:465–471.

Buchholtz, C. 1951. Untersuchungen an der Libellen-Gattung *Calopteryx*-Leach unter besonderer Berücksichtigung ethologischer Fragen. *Z. Tierpsychol.*, **8**:273–293.

———. 1955. Eine vergleichende Ethologie der orientalischen Calopterygiden (Odonata) als Beitrag zu ihrer systematischen Deutung. *Z. Tierpsychol.*, **12**:364–386.

———. 1956. Eine Analyse des Paarungsverhaltens und der dabei wirkenden Auslöser bei den Libellen *Platycnemis pennipes* Pall. und *Pl. dealbata* Klug. *Z. Tierpsychol.*, **13**:13–25.

Bullock, T. H. 1953. Predator recognition and escape responses of some intertidal gastropods in presence of starfish. *Behaviour,* 5:130–140.

Chauvin, R. 1952. Nouvelles recherches sur les substances qui attirent le Doryphore (*L. decemlineator* Say) vers la pomme de terre. *Ann. Inst. Nat. Rech. Agron.,* 3:303–308.

Collias, N. E. 1952. The development of social behavior in birds. *Auk,* 69:127–159.

Cott, H. B. 1957. *Adaptive Coloration in Animals.* Methuen and Company, London.

Crane, J. 1949. Comparative biology of salticid spiders at Rancho Grande, Venezuela. Part IV. An analysis of display. *Zoologica,* 34:159–214.

————. 1955. Imaginal behavior of a Trinidad butterfly, *Heliconius erato hydara* Hewitson, with special reference to the social use of color. *Zoologica,* 40:167–196.

Curio, E. 1961. Rassenspezifisches Verhalten gegen einen Raubfeind. *Experientia,* 17:188–189.

————. 1963. Probleme des Feinderkennens bei Vögeln. *Proc. 13th Int. Orn Congr.,* Vol. 1: 206–239.

Cushing, J. E., Jr. 1944. The relation of non-heritable food habits to evolution. *Condor,* 46: 265–271.

———— and A. O. Ramsay. 1949. The non-heritable aspects of family unity in birds. *Condor,* 51:82–87.

Dadd, R. H. 1963. Feeding behaviour and nutrition in grasshoppers and locusts. *Adv. Insect Physiol.,* 1:47–109.

Dethier, V. G. 1941. Chemical factors determining the choice of food plants by *Papilio* larvae. *Amer. Nat.,* 75:61–73.

————. 1947. *Chemical Insect Attractants and Repellents.* Blakiston, Philadelphia.

————. 1951. Host plant perception in phytophagous insects. *Trans. 9th Int. Congr. Ent.,* Vol. 2:81–89.

————, L. Barton Browne, and C. N. Smith. 1960. The designation of chemicals in terms of the responses they elicit from insects. *J. Econ. Ent.,* 53:134–136.

Downes, J. A. 1958. Assembly and mating in the biting Nematocera. *Proc. 10th Int. Congr. Ent.* (1956), Vol. 2:425–434.

Drees, O. 1952. Untersuchungen über die angeborenen Verhaltensweisen bei Springspinnen (*Salticidae*). *Z. Tierpsychol.,* 9:169–207.

Eibl-Eibesfeldt, I. 1952. Nahrungserwerb und Beuteschema der Erdkröte (*Bufo bufo* L.). *Behaviour,* 4:1–35.

Etienne, A. and H. Howland. 1964. Elicitation of strikes of predatory insects by projected images and light spots. *Experientia,* 20:152.

Evans, D. R. and V. G. Dethier. 1957. The regulation of taste thresholds for sugars in the blowfly. *J. Insect Physiol.,* 1:3–17.

Ficken, M. S. and W. C. Dilger. 1960. Comments on redirection with examples of avian copulations with substitute objects. *Anim. Behav.,* 8:219–222.

Fraenkel, G. S. 1959. The raison d'être of secondary plant substances. *Science,* 129:1466–1470.

———— and D. L. Gunn. 1940. *The Orientation of Animals.* Oxford University Press, London.

Friedmann, H. 1929. Quoted in Allen (1934).

Goethe, F. 1940. Beobachtungen und Versuche über angeborene Schreckreaktionen junger Auerhühner (*Tetrao u. urogallus* L.). *Z. Tierpsychol.,* 4:165–167.

Gupta, P. D. and A. J. Thorsteinson. 1960a. Food plant relationships of the diamond-back moth (*Plutella maculipennis* (Curt.)). I. Gustation and olfaction in relation to botanical specificity of the larva. *Ent. Exp. Appl.,* 3:241–250.

———— and ————. 1960b. Food plant relationships of the diamond-back moth (*Plutella maculipennis* (Curt.)). II. Sensory regulation of oviposition of the adult female. *Ent. Exp. Appl.,* 3:305–314.

Hans, H. and A. J. Thorsteinson. 1961. The influence of physical factors and host plant odour on the induction and termination of dispersal flights in *Sitona cylindricollis* Fahr. *Ent. Exp. Appl.*, **4**:165–177.

Hartley, P. H. T. 1950. An experimental analysis of interspecific recognition. *Symp. Soc. Exp. Biol.*, **4**:313–336.

Haskell, P. T., M. W. J. Paskin, and J. E. Moorhouse. 1962. Laboratory observations on factors affecting the movements of hoppers of the desert locust. *J. Insect Physiol.*, **8**:53–78.

Hellwig, H. and W. Ludwig. 1951. Versuche zur Frage der Arterkennung bei Insekten. *Z. Tierpsychol.*, **8**:456–462.

Hertz, M. 1929–1931. Die Organisation des optischen Feldes bei der Biene. I–III. *Z. vergl. Physiol.*, **8**:693–748, **11**:107–145, **14**:629–674.

Hess, E. H. 1952. Temperature as a regulator of the attack-response of *Betta splendens. Z. Tierpsychol.*, **9**:379–382.

Hinde, R. A. 1952. Behaviour of the great tit (*Parus major*) and some other related species. *Behaviour Suppl.*, **2**:1–201.

——. 1954. Factors governing the changes in strength of a partially inborn response, as shown by the mobbing behaviour of the chaffinch (*Fringilla coelebs*). I. The nature of the response, and an examination of its course. *Proc. Roy. Soc. Lond., B*, **142**:306–331.

——. 1956. Breeding success in cardueline interspecies pairs, and an examination of the hybrids' plumage. *J. Genet.*, **54**:304–310.

——. 1958. The nest-building behaviour of domesticated canaries. *Proc. Zool. Soc. Lond.*, **131**:1–48.

——, R. Q. Bell, and E. Steel. 1963. Changes in sensitivity of the canary brood patch during the natural breeding season. *Anim. Behav.*, **11**:553–560.

Ilse, D. 1928. Über den Farbensinn der Tagfalter. *Z. vergl. Physiol.*, **8**:658–692.

Immelmann, K. 1959. Experimentelle Untersuchungen über die biologische Bedeutung artspezifischer Merkmale beim Zebrafinken (*Taeniopygia castanotis* Gould). *Zool. Jahrb., Abt. Syst. Ökol. Geogr.*, **86**:437–592.

Imms, A. D. 1957. *A General Textbook of Entomology* (9th edition). Methuen and Company, London.

Jacobs, M. E. 1955. Studies on territorialism and sexual selection in dragonflies. *Ecology*, **36**:566–586.

Kaufman, I. C. and R. A. Hinde. 1961. Factors influencing distress calling in chicks, with special reference to temperature changes and social isolation. *Anim. Behav.*, **9**:197–204.

Kennedy, J. S. 1958. The experimental analysis of aphid behavior and its bearing on current theories of instinct. *Proc. 10th Int. Congr. Ent.* (1956), Vol. 2:397–404.

Kitzler, G. 1941. Die Paarungsbiologie einiger Eidechsen. *Z. Tierpsychol.*, **4**:353–402.

Kramer, G. 1937. Beobachtungen über Paarungsbiologie und soziales Verhalten von Mauereidechsen. *Z. Morphol. Ökol. Tiere*, **32**:752–783.

—— and U. von St. Paul. 1951. Über angeborenes und erworbenes Feinderkennen beim Gimpel (*Pyrrhula pyrrhula* L.). *Behaviour*, **3**:243–255.

Krätzig, H. 1940. Untersuchungen zur Lebensweise des Moorschneehuhns (*Lagopus l. lagopus* L.) während der Jugendentwicklung. *J. Orn.*, **88**:139–165.

Krieger, F. and E. Krieger-Loibl. 1958. Beiträge zum Verhalten von *Ischnura elegans* und *Ischnura pumilio* (Odonata). *Z. Tierpsychol.*, **15**:82–93.

Lack, D. 1940. The releaser concept in bird behaviour. *Nature*, **145**:107–108.

——. 1941. Some aspects of instinctive behaviour and display in birds. *Ibis*, Ser. 14, **5**:407–441.

Laing, J. 1937. Host-finding by insect parasites. I. Observations on the finding of hosts by *Alysia manducator, Mormoniella vitripennis* and *Trichogramma evanescens. J. Anim. Ecol.*, **6**:298–317.

————. 1938. Host-finding by insect parasites. II. The chance of *Trichogramma evanescens* finding its hosts. *J. Exp. Biol.*, **15**:281–302.

Lismann, H. W. 1932. Die Umwelt des Kampffisches (*Betta splendens* Regan). *Z. vergl. Physiol.*, **18**:65–111.

Loibl, E. 1958. Zur Ethologie und Biologie der deutschen Lestiden (Odonata). *Z. Tierpsychol.*, **15**:54–81.

Lorenz, K. Z. 1935. Der Kumpan in der Umwelt des Vogels. *J. Orn.*, **83**:37–213, 289–413.

————. 1939. Vergleichende Verhaltensforschung. *Zool. Anz. Suppl.*, **12**:69–102.

————. 1950. The comparative method in studying innate behaviour patterns. *Symp. Soc. Exp. Biol.*, **4**:221–268.

Magnus, D. 1958. Experimentelle Untersuchungen zur Bionomie und Ethologie des Kaisermantels *Argynnis paphia* L. (Lep. Nymph.) *Z. Tierpsychol.*, **15**:397–426.

Maier, N. R. F. and T. C. Schneirla. 1964. *Principles of Animal Psychology.* Dover Publications, New York.

Makkink, G. F. 1936. An attempt at an ethogram of the European avocet (*Recurvirostra avosetta* L.) with ethological and psychological remarks. *Ardea*, **25**:1–62.

Marler, P. 1955a. Studies of fighting in chaffinches. (2) The effect on dominance relations of disguising females as males. *Brit. J. Anim. Behav.*, **3**:137–146.

————. 1955b. Characteristics of some animal calls. *Nature*, **176**:6–8.

Martin, R. C. and K. B. Melvin. 1964. Fear responses of bobwhite quail (*Colinus virginianus*) to a model and a live red-tailed hawk (*Buteo jamaicensis*). *Psychol. Forschung*, **27**:323–336.

Meyer-Holzapfel, M. 1939. Analyse des Sperrens und Pickens in der Entwicklung des Stars. *J. Orn.*, **87**:525–553.

Miller, A. H. 1931. Systematic revision and natural history of the American shrikes (*Lanius*). *Univ. Calif. Publ. Zool.*, **38**:11–242.

Miller, L. 1952. Auditory recognition of predators. *Condor*, **54**:89–92.

Moore, N. W. 1952. On the so-called "territories" of dragonflies (Odonata-Anisoptera). *Behaviour*, **4**:85–100.

Nayar, J. K. and A. J. Thorsteinson. 1963. Further investigations into the chemical basis of insect-host plant relationships in an oligophagous insect, *Plutella maculipennis* (Curt) (Lepidoptera: Plutellidae). *Can. J. Zool.*, **41**:923–929.

Nice, M. M. 1943. Studies in the life history of the song sparrow. II. The behavior of the song sparrow and other passerines. *Trans. Linn. Soc. N.Y.*, **6**:1–328.

———— and J. ter Pelkwijk. 1941. Enemy recognition by the song sparrow. *Auk*, **58**:195–214.

Noble, G. K. 1936. Courtship and sexual selection of the flicker (*Colaptes auratus luteus*). *Auk*, **53**:269–282.

———— and H. T. Bradley. 1933. The mating behavior of lizards; its bearing on the theory of sexual selection. *Ann. N.Y. Acad. Sci.*, **35**:25–100.

———— and B. Curtis. 1939. The social behavior of the jewel fish, *Hemichromis bimaculatus* Gill. *Bull. Amer. Mus. Nat. Hist.*, **76**:1–46.

———— and W. Vogt. 1935. An experimental study of sex recognition in birds. *Auk*, **52**:278–286.

Pelkwijk, J. J. ter and N. Tinbergen. 1937. Eine reizbiologische Analyse einiger Verhaltensweisen von *Gasterosteus aculeatus* L. *Z. Tierpsychol.*, **1**:193–200.

Petersen, B., O. Törnblom, and N.-O. Bodin. 1952. Verhaltensstudien am Rapsweissling und Berkweissling (*Pieris napi* L. und *Pieris bryoniae* Ochs.). *Behaviour*, **4**:67–84.

Räber, H. 1950. Das Verhalten gefangener Waldohreulen (*Asio otus otus*) und Waldkäuze (*Strix aluco aluco*) zur Beute. *Behaviour*, **2**:1–95.

Rand, A. L. 1941a. Lorenz's objective method of interpreting bird behavior. *Auk*, **58**:289–291.

————. 1941b. Development and enemy recognition of the curve-billed thrasher, *Toxostoma curvirostre*. *Bull Amer. Mus. Nat. Hist.,* **78**:213–242.

Roberts, B. 1940. The breeding behaviour of penguins with special reference to *Pygoscelis papua* (Forster). *Brit. Graham Land Exped. 1934–1937 Sci. Rep.,* **1**:195–254.

Roeder, K. D. 1963. *Nerve Cells and Insect Behavior.* Harvard University Press, Cambridge.

Russell, E. S. 1943. Perceptual and sensory signs in instinctive behaviour. *Proc. Linn. Soc. Lond.* (Zool.), **154**:195–216.

Salt, G. 1935. Experimental studies in insect parasitism. III. Host selection. *Proc. Roy. Soc. Lond., B,* **117**:413–435.

————. 1937. The sense used by *Trichogramma* to distinguish between parasitized and unparasitized hosts. *Proc. Roy. Soc. Lond., B,* **122**:57–75.

————. 1941. Effects of hosts upon their insect parasites. *Biol. Rev.,* **16**:239–264.

————. 1961. The haemocytic reaction of insects to foreign bodies. In *The Cell and the Organism,* ed. by J. A. Ramsay and V. B. Wigglesworth: 175–192. Cambridge University Press, London.

Sälzle, K. 1932. Untersuchungen an Libellenlarven über das Sehen bewegter Objekte. *Z. vergl. Physiol.,* **18**:347–368.

Schaller, F. and C. Timm. 1950. Das Hörvermögen der Nachtschmetterlinge. *Z. vergl. Physiol.,* **32**:468–481.

Schiller, C. H. (Ed.). 1957. *Instinctive Behavior.* International Universities Press, New York.

Simon, J. R. 1940. Mating performance of the sage grouse. *Auk,* **57**:467–471.

Steel, E. A. and R. A. Hinde. 1963. Hormonal control of brood patch and oviduct development in domesticated canaries. *J. Endocrin.,* **26**:11–24.

Stride, G. O. 1956. On the courtship behaviour of *Hypolimnas misippus* L., (Lepidoptera, Nymphalidae), with notes on the mimetic association with *Danaus chrysippus* L., (Lepidoptera, Danaidae). *Brit. J. Anim. Behav.,* **4**:52–68.

————. 1957. Investigations into the courtship behaviour of the male of *Hypolimnas misippus* L. (Lepidoptera, Nymphalidae), with special reference to the role of visual stimuli. *Brit. J. Anim. Behav.,* **5**:153–167.

————. 1958. Further studies on the courtship behaviour of African mimetic butterflies. *Anim. Behav.,* **6**:224–230.

Sumner, E. L. 1934. The behavior of some young raptorial birds. *Univ. Calif. Publ. Zool.,* **40**:331–361.

Tavolga, W. N. 1954. Reproductive behavior in the gobiid fish, *Bathygobius soporator. Bull. Amer. Mus. Nat. Hist.,* **104**:427–460.

————. 1956. Visual, chemical and sound stimuli as cues in the sex discriminatory behavior of gobiid fish, *Bathygobius soporator. Zoologica,* **41**:49–64.

————. 1958. The significance of underwater sounds produced by males of the gobiid fish, *Bathygobius soporator. Physiol. Zool.,* **31**:259–271.

Thompson, W. R. and H. L. Parker. 1927. The problem of host relations with special reference to entomophagous parasites. *Parasitology,* **19**:1–34.

Thorpe, W. H. 1944. Some problems of animal learning. *Proc. Linn. Soc. Lond.* (Zool.), **156**:70–83.

————, A. C. Crombie, R. Hill, and J. H. Darrah. 1947. The behaviour of wireworms in response to chemical stimulation. *J. Exp. Biol.,* **23**:234–266.

———— and F. G. W. Jones. 1937. Olfactory conditioning in a parasitic insect and its relation to the problem of host selection. *Proc. Roy. Soc. Lond., B,* **124**:56–81.

Thorsteinson, A. J. 1953. The chemotactic responses that determine host specificity in an oligophagous insect (*Plutella maculipennis* (Curt.) Lepidoptera). *Can. J. Zool.,* **31**:52–72.

————. 1958. Acceptability of plants for phytophagous insects. *Proc. 10th Int. Congr. Ent.* (1956), Vol. 2:599–602.

————. 1960. Host selection in phytophagous insects. *Ann. Rev. Ent.,* 5:193–218.

———— and J. K. Nayar. 1963. Plant phospholipids as feeding stimulants for grasshoppers. *Can. J. Zool.,* 41:931–935.

Tinbergen, N. 1935. Über die Orientierung des Bienenwolfes (*Philanthus triangulum* Fabr.) II. Die Bienenjagd. *Z. vergl. Physiol.,* 21:699–716.

————. 1951. *The Study of Instinct.* Oxford University Press, London.

———— and D. J. Kuenen. 1939. Über die auslösenden und die richtunggebenden Reizsituationen der Sperrbewegung von jungen Drosseln (*Turdus m. merula* L. und *T. e. ericetorum* Turton). *Z. Tierpsychol.,* 3:37–60.

————, B. J. D. Meeuse, L. K. Boerema, and W. W. Varossieau. 1942. Die Balz des Samtfalters, *Eumenis* (= *Satyrus*) *semele* (L.). *Z. Tierpsychol.,* 5:182–226.

Treat, A. E. 1955. The response to sound in certain Lepidoptera. *Ann. Ent. Soc. Amer.,* 48:272–284.

Uexküll, J. von. 1921. *Umwelt und Innenwelt der Tiere* (2nd edition). Springer–Verlag, Berlin.

Ullyett, G. C. 1936. Host selection by *Microplectron fuscipennis,* Zett. (Chalcididae, Hymenoptera). *Proc. Roy. Soc. Lond., B,* 120:253–291.

Van der Kloot, W. G. and C. M. Williams. 1953a. Cocoon construction by the Cecropia silkworm. I. The role of the external environment. *Behaviour,* 5:141–156.

———— and ————. 1953b. Cocoon construction by the Cecropia silkworm. II. The role of the internal environment. *Behaviour,* 5:157–174.

Vowles, D. M. 1955. The foraging of ants. *Brit. J. Anim. Behav.,* 3:1–13.

Warren, R. P. and R. A. Hinde. 1959. The effect of oestrogen and progesterone on the nest-building of domesticated canaries. *Anim. Behav.,* 7:209–213.

Wigglesworth, V. B. 1953. *The Principles of Insect Physiology* (5th edition). Methuen and Company, London, and E. P. Dutton and Company, New York.

Wilde, J. de. 1958. Host plant selection in the Colorado beetle larva (*Leptinotarsa decemlineata* Say.). *Entomol. Exptl. Appl.,* 1:14–22.

Wilson, D. P. 1937. Quoted in Russell (1943).

Wilson, E. O. 1953. The ecology of some North American dacetine ants. *Ann. Ent. Soc. Amer.,* 46:479–495.

Young, H. 1949. Atypical copulatory behavior of a robin. *Auk,* 66:94.

eight

STIMULUS FILTERING: CHEMORECEPTION

Filtering of incoming stimuli • Types of chemoreception • Mechanisms of olfaction and taste • Role of chemoreception in selection of environments, predator-prey relationships, and commensalism • Pheromones, functioning in dispersal and aggregation • Individual and group recognition • Alarm substances, sex pheromones, and trail substances • Properties of chemical communication systems.

The sense organs are mediators between the organism and its environment. Their role is by no means a passive one. They are highly selective, transmitting only a part of the information from the environment that impinges on the organism. It is reasonable to assume that the sense organs mediate primarily with those classes of stimuli which have exerted some clear influence on each animal's phylogenetic history.

The range of external factors that bear on an organism's survival varies with its way of life, and correlates in turn with the range of stimuli to which its receptors will respond. When a limited number of simple, predictable influences dominate survival and reproduction, highly specialized receptors may evolve, responding to stimuli associated with these factors alone. A more complex way of life in which a wide array of environmental events can have potential significance for survival requires more versatile sense organs. They must respond to a wide array of stimuli in order to convey information about the few that have significance at any one time.

The distinction is well illustrated by comparing the olfactory receptors of a male silkworm moth and a dog. A dog can smell a huge array of chemical stimuli, identifying many different compounds by odor and distinguishing between mixtures of the same substances in slightly different proportions. Such versatility is appropriate in an animal that relies so strongly on its sense of smell in exploring its environment, detecting enemies and food, and recognizing a mate. By contrast, the male silkworm moth is apparently able to smell only one thing, a substance emitted by females of his species.

A remarkable series of experiments, approaching the problem with both behavioral and electrophysiological methods, have shown that the olfactory receptors in the male silkworm moth's antennae respond little or not at all to compounds other than the secretion of the female and a few closely related substances (Butenandt 1955, Schneider 1957). The narrowing of the responsiveness of receptors to highly specific stimuli is extreme. The correlation with the silkworm moth's way of life is clear. When the male silkworm moth emerges from the pupa, he has only one function in life—to find and mate with a conspecific female. The male neither feeds nor seeks a special environment. The service required of his olfactory receptors is to detect but one scent, and this they achieve with great efficiency. A female may be located more than a mile away. This feat seems especially remarkable to us when we consider the many other environmental odors from which the female scent must be distinguished. The specificity of the male's responsiveness aids him here, for if he does not smell other odors they cannot hinder his detection of the female.

◆ *The Problem of Stimulus Filtering.* Certain responses are evoked only by highly specific stimuli, others by less specific stimuli. In either case some degree of stimulus filtering is implied. The problem arises in its most acute form when responsiveness is highly specific. By what physiological mechanisms is this filtering achieved? What role do the receptors play? This depends, as we have noted, on how many other functions the receptors serve.

The properties of external stimuli can be classified into four groups, the perception of each creating its own special problems in receptor design: (1) qualitative properties such as color of light or pitch of sound, (2) quantitative properties of intensity, the brightness of a light or the loudness of a sound, (3) temporal properties, involving a changing pattern such as a melody or a moving visual field, and (4) spatial properties relating to the position in space where the stimulus is generated. These four categories overlap. Thus qualitative properties may be a function of temporal characteristics in the strictest sense, such as wavelength. No one receptor can register all these stimulus properties with equal efficiency by itself. Specialization for one function requires sacrifice elsewhere.

◆ *Qualitative Stimulus Properties.* There is enormous variation in the ranges and classes of stimuli to which different receptors respond. Some are highly specific, responding to one qualitative stimulus type within a single sensory modality. Certain chemoreceptors can be activated by only one particular type of molecule. At a somewhat lower degree of specificity there are receptors for a particular wavelength of light. In color-blind animals the visual receptors respond to a wider range of wavelengths.

A further specialization for the perception of qualitative stimulus properties is found where receptors are incorporated into cooperative systems which function together. The vertebrate cochlea is an example of such a receptor organ, registering the frequency and spectral composition of sounds. The taste receptors on the mammalian tongue also function as a compound system. Nowhere is the correlation between the way of life of an animal and the properties of its receptors more evident than in their responsiveness to qualitative stimulus properties.

◆ *Stimulus Intensity and Temporal Change.* The receptors of metazoan animals all signal information to the central nervous system in essentially the same way, by means of trains of action potentials passing along nerve fibers. The distinctive properties of each receptor are defined by the circumstances in which this firing takes place. Olfactory receptors are triggered by a chemical stimulus, photoreceptors are discharged by a light stimulus, and so on. Irrespective of these qualitative differences in responsiveness, all receptors respond to *change* in the stimulus situation and to stimulus *intensity*. The problems of perceiving change and intensity are so closely related that they are best considered together.

E. D. Adrian (1928) pointed out in his classic book, *The Basis of Sensation*, that there is a reciprocal relationship between the perception of stimulus change and stimulus intensity that is in turn related to the adaptation rates of the particular receptors. When a receptor is exposed to a sustained stimulus the rate of discharge quickly reaches a maximum, then declines. In a rapidly adapting receptor, activity is restricted to a short burst of action potentials at the onset of the stimulus. In receptors that adapt slowly the decline is slower and may be undetectable for a long time. Receptors that adapt rapidly are thus more effective in perceiving stimulus change.

Receptors may be specialized for fast or slow adaptation according to the premium placed on the perception of intensity and change. Proprioceptors such as the muscle spindles of mammals adapt slowly and are thus not suited to registering a sudden stimulus change. However, they are able to give an accurate measure of stimulus intensity, which is reflected in the rate of production of action potentials (Figure 8-1). This is consistent with the function they perform of transmitting information about the state of muscles, which may be contracted for long periods of time. Touch receptors provide a complete contrast. Their adaptation rate is usually rapid. Thus they provide less accurate information about differences in stimulus intensity, but they are well suited to register stimu-

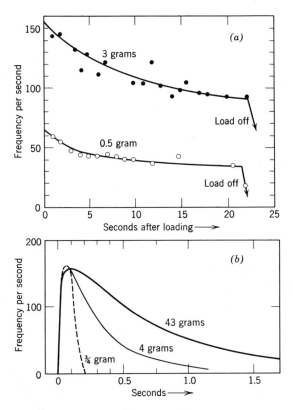

Figure 8-1 (*a*) The frequency of discharge of tension receptors caused by stretching a frog's sternocutaneous muscle varies with different weights. Discharge frequency in such a slowly adapting receptor system depends on stimulus intensity. (*b*) Discharge frequency in tactile receptors of a frog's skin in response to a needle point. The initial frequency of discharge of such a rapidly adapting system is independent of stimulus intensity, though discharge duration does vary with intensity. After Adrian 1928.

lus change and therefore to record temporal patterns of stimulation (Figure 8-1).

Many receptors fall clearly into one category or the other; others are intermediate. Chemoreceptors (e.g. Hodgson and Roeder 1956) generally adapt slowly and are highly responsive to variations in concentrations of chemicals. Temperature receptors also adapt slowly (Zotterman 1959). Visual receptors, on the other hand, often adapt rapidly. The ommatidia in the compound eye of fast flying insects are so responsive to a changing stimulus, such as a flickering light, that they are able to resolve a flicker rate as high as 300 changes per second (Autrum 1950). There are some visual receptors, however, such as those of the horseshoe crab, *Limulus,* that show a burst of activity at the onset of a light stimulus and then maintain a lower level of activity as long as the stimulus persists (e.g. Ratliff and Mueller 1957). Even temperature receptors may show an initial burst of activity before settling to a steady rate of discharge. It is thus possible to achieve a compromise, with moderate degrees of sensitivity both to the intensity of stimulation and to its temporal pattern. Further specialization can be achieved only by sacrificing the efficiency of one function.

◆ *Spatial Properties of Stimuli.* To complete the picture of the environment that external stimuli can convey to an organism we must consider the spatial position of a stimulus. How can the spatial properties of a stimulus be perceived? The answer depends in part on the other characteristics of the receptor system, especially its sensitivity. For example, relatively insensitive mechanoreceptors such as some organs of touch respond only when an object contacts the body surface. The position of the point of contact can readily be determined. More sensitive mechanoreceptors, such as the organs of hearing or the lateral line system of fishes, are able to detect disturbances in the surrounding medium some distance from the body. The problem of determining the direction and distance of a distant stimulus source is much greater.

The qualitative nature of the stimuli to which a receptor responds must also be considered. The source of a diffusing chemical is difficult for any organism to locate. The source of a light stimulus is more easily ascertained. A sound may be easy or difficult to locate, depending on the property of the sound wave that stimulates the receptor. Particle displacement has an inherent directional quality but sound pressure has not (see page 406).

Spatial patterns may be created by several stimuli impinging simultaneously on the body surface. The perception of spatial patterns of light rays constitutes form vision. What are its prerequisites? Assuming a spatial

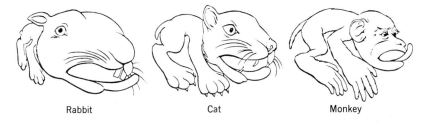

Rabbit   Cat   Monkey

Figure 8-2   Schematic outlines of body representation in parts of the thalamus showing species differences in the areas devoted to the feet. After Rose and Mountcastle 1959.

stimulus pattern with dimensions on the scale of the organism's sense organs, the receptors must resolve the components of the pattern. More closely packed receptors can discern finer patterns as long as the spatial information derived from the stimulation of separate receptors is not sacrificed for other purposes. In the rod-rich retinas of nocturnal animals such a sacrifice is made for increased sensitivity, with many receptor cells converging on the same ganglion. In a cone-rich retina there is much less convergence and, accordingly, form vision is better. The great density of cones in the region of the fovea of man, for example, guarantees maximal efficiency in resolution of the spatial properties of light rays in the direct line of vision. In the peripheral field there is poorer acuity and greater sensitivity.

The same principles apply to the sense of touch in which spatial organization is again crucial. The receptors are most densely distributed over those parts of the body where patterned stimulation is likely to be most significant for the animal's survival—on the hands and feet of a primate, for example, or on the snout of a pig. In mammals the significance of the tactile sense in different parts of the body is reflected in the areas of the brain devoted to them (Figure 8-2).

◆ *General Properties of Receptor Systems.* These are the characteristics of sensory receptors that must be considered if we are to understand the picture of the environment they present to the organism. Each one has certain qualitative properties defining the modality of stimuli to which it will respond, visual, auditory, chemical, and so on. Receptors also have certain thresholds of responsiveness specifying their sensitivity to varying intensities of stimulation. The actual intensity of stimulation can be recorded with varying accuracy, in part as a function of the rate of adaptation to a constant stimulus. Where adaptation is rapid the accuracy of the record of stimulus intensity will suffer. But the perception of temporal patterns, another significant property of external stimuli, is thereby improved. A mosaic of receptors with different thresholds and adaptation rates provides a good compromise. Resolution of the spatial properties of stimuli may also have crucial importance for the animal's survival.

CHEMORECEPTION

The capacity to perceive chemical characteristics of the environment is one of the most elementary and widespread attributes of living things. The chemical senses are involved in almost all kinds of behavioral responses. Animals depend on chemoreception to find food, a mate, a home, or to detect enemies. Specificity of responsiveness to chemical stimuli varies widely. What are the physiological mechanisms for achieving these varying degrees of specificity of responsiveness and, in particular, what role do the actual receptors play?

There are three main types of chemoreception, distinguished by the location of the receptors on the body surface and by their relative sensitivity. The least sensitive is the rather poorly defined 'general chemical sense,' mediated by free nerve endings and unspecialized receptors present on many parts of the body of organisms as various as vertebrates and protozoans. Their stimulation usually evokes simple avoidance reactions. More varied responses can be evoked through the other types of chemoreception, taste and smell. Taste, the 'chemotactic' sense, is intermediate in sensitivity and usually requires direct contact between the receptor surface and the stimulus source. The sense of smell, olfaction, is the most sensitive, responding to low concentrations of chemicals in the medium. The same principles apply whether the diffusion medium is air or water, so it is proper to speak of a sense of smell in fish as well as in mammals and insects. Usually the stimulus originates some distance from the animal. The anatomy and physiology of chemoreceptors have been thoroughly reviewed (e.g. Prosser and Brown 1961, Dethier 1953a, 1956, 1963, Pfaffmann 1959a, Adey 1959), and we need consider only the limited aspects of structure that bear directly on the problem of stimulus filtering.

Chemoreceptors are remarkable for their sensitivity, which is defined for some olfactory receptors in terms of numbers of molecules. Once stimulated, chemoreceptors usually continue to discharge as long as the stimulus persists, a characteristic which makes possible perception of the concentration of stimulating substances. Accordingly, there must be limitations upon the perception of stimulus change, restricting the use of temporal patterning of chemical stimuli in animal communication, as compared with vision and audition.

OLFACTION

◆ *Qualitative Stimulus Properties.* The qualitative characteristics of the responsiveness of smell receptors vary widely from species to species. One of the most specific receptor systems known occurs in the male silkworm moth, *Bombyx mori.* Tests of the behavioral responses of thousands of moths to many different chemicals suggested that their olfactory receptors, mounted on the very large antennae, were responsive only to the odor of the female and a few closely related chemicals (Butenandt 1955). The index of responsiveness was the frequency of the male's courtship responses when exposed to air carrying the test compound. The conclusions were dramatically confirmed by electrophysiological tests (Schneider 1957). After a number of abortive attempts to measure electrical activity in the antennae, in which the antennal responses were drowned by muscle potentials arising in the head, clear results were obtained by cutting off the antennae. Just as in the behavioral experiments, the only substances evoking strong electrical activity were the female secretion and the two closely related substances, cycloheptanone and sorbinol.

The method used by Butenandt involved tests of various substances in evoking pre-existing behavioral responses. It can be misleading to draw inferences about the properties of the actual receptors from this kind of experiment without confirmation by another method, such as electrophysiological analysis, or conditioning. In a classic controversy between von Frisch and Hess concerning the color vision of animals, Hess found that certain animals avoided some colors and not others. He concluded that colors evoking the same response were not distinguished and that the ability for color vision was thus limited. By other methods von Frisch demonstrated a greater ability to distinguish colors. Instead of relying on avoidance responses he used a training or conditioning procedure (Walls 1942).

The honeybee depends on antennal receptors for olfaction just as the male silkworm moth does, but the honeybee can distinguish many different chemical stimuli. To establish this von Frisch (1919, 1950) rewarded honeybees for responding to a certain chemical, for example, oil of lemon. He placed vials of sugar solution inside boxes containing filter paper impregnated with oils. Other boxes were left empty. At intervals during the experiment the arrangement of boxes was changed to discourage choices based upon position, so that the oil of lemon was the only clue to the location of the sugar water. Once the bees were regularly choosing the scented boxes, critical tests were made. The boxes were replaced by a new set, this time without any sugar water. All the boxes were scented, some with oil of lemon, others with different scents, and the ability of the bees to distinguish the oil of lemon from the other odors was observed.

By this method von Frisch found 43 different oils which the bees could distinguish. There were a few cases of confusion between two substances, which also smell alike to us. Even some of these pairs, such as benzaldehyde and nitrobenzene, were distinguished by the honeybees, though there was some confusion. So honeybee antennal receptors respond to a wide array of stimuli, providing a much richer picture of the chemical environment than the highly specific receptors of the silkworm moth. Other insects have versatile chemical receptors, and a number of insects even seem to be able to smell water vapor (e.g. Slifer 1955).

In fish (e.g. Teichmann 1959) and mammals, rats for example, many odors are distinguished, some probably rare in their natural environment (Le Magnen 1953). The mammalian olfactory receptor system is highly versatile. Domestic dogs have been intensively studied. Not only are they able to differentiate a great many chemical stimuli, but they can also distinguish between mixtures of odors, differing only slightly in the proportion of the constituents (Neuhaus 1956a, b). This ability is important in its bearing on such subtle problems as individual identification of other animals by olfaction, probably based on the ability to distinguish variations in the proportions of the constituents of complex mixtures of compounds rather than on qualitative differences between individuals (Neuhaus 1956b, Ruzica, quoted by Le Magnen 1953). There is evidently an acute perception of stimulus intensity, correlated with the slow adaptation rate of the receptors.

In man a wide range of qualitatively different classes of olfactory stimuli are perceived. The physiological mechanism underlying the perception of these qualitative differences is not understood. Many correlations have been drawn between the responses to chemical stimuli and their molecular properties such as boiling points, thermodynamic activity, and the number and arrangement of carbon atoms (Dethier 1956, Mullins 1955, Moncrieff 1944). These correlations show many parallels between mammals and insects (Dethier 1956). There are exceptions to all the rules. Quite different molecules may smell the same; stereoisomers may be different. Some compounds have different odors at high and low concentrations. The idea that there are many types of specific receptors, each responding only to one qualitative class of stimuli, is no longer supportable. Rather, each identifiable stimulus evokes a particular spatio-temporal pattern of activity on the olfactory epithelium (Le Magnen 1953, Hainer, Emslie, and Jacobson 1953), perhaps involving a similar but more complex version of the system underlying the sense of taste in mammals (see page 283).

◆ *Stimulus Intensity and Temporal Change.* The ability to perceive small differences in intensity of an olfactory stimulus is the basis for detecting concentration gradients, permitting orientation to the stimulus source. Ability to detect rapidly changing patterns of olfactory stimuli is probably limited. The potential usefulness of chemical signals in communication between individuals is thus affected. The amount of information that can be transmitted in a given time, especially over long distances, is restricted. There are several ways that animals can minimize this problem (Wilson and Bossert 1963). Compounds that diffuse rapidly may be used, and transmission may be in a moving medium. The slime molds have a special method. They produce alternately and in rapid succession a signal and a second substance that destroys it, thus generating a pattern of concentric waves. Shaffer (1957) believes that this temporal pattern of waves passing over the amoeboid cells elicits and orients their movement toward the center of aggregation. Even with these specializations the chemical senses probably cannot compete with audition and vision in the rapid communication of social information. On the other hand, the extreme sensitivity of chemoreceptors and their long fade-out time gives chemical signals a particular advantage in some circumstances (Wilson and Bossert 1963).

Olfactory receptors can respond to an enormous range of concentrations. The electroantennogram of the male silkworm moth reveals a response to the female's sex attractant over a concentration range of 10^{12}, with different response curves for the several geometric isomers of the substance (Schneider 1963). These antennal response curves suggest an ability to detect but not to distinguish low concentrations. Intensity discrimination at higher concentrations is potentially more effective and in the vicinity of the female moth would permit direct orientation to her.

◆ *Spatial Properties.* The source of an olfactory stimulus is normally some distance from the animal. It will be difficult to find, when the only clue is the diffusion gradient from the source. This requires sampling of the stimulus concentration at different points. The sampling can be made simultaneously by receptors on different parts of the body as

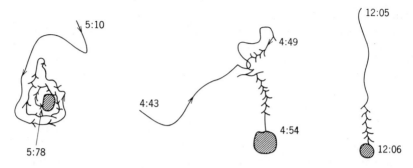

Figure 8-3   *Planaria* approaching a food source. When it reaches the region where chemical stimuli from the source form a steep concentration gradient, lateral movements of the head apparently facilitate successive intensity comparisons and thus localization of the source. Numbers represent time. After Koehler 1932.

in eels (Teichmann 1959), or successively by the same receptors, as in *Paramecium* and flatworms (Koehler 1932, Figure 8-3).

More efficient localization is possible if the medium is moving with respect to the source and the animal can detect the direction of the movement. A male salamander can locate a female from more than a mile downstream by moving upstream as long as he can detect her scent (Twitty 1959, 1961). Several kilometers may separate a silkworm moth from a female and yet be no barrier if the wind is blowing (Jacobson and Beroza 1963). But in still air he must be within one meter to find her (Schwinck 1954, Wilson and Bossert 1963, Figure 8-4). In moving air the male moves upwind until he loses the scent. His subsequent behavior varies from species to species. The male silkworm moths used by Schwinck were a domesticated flightless strain. On losing the scent they backed up and tried again, often in a zigzag path. Other flying species drop to the ground and begin to search on foot, as in the beetle, *Geotrupes* (Kettlewell 1946, Steiner 1953).

A chemist, R. H. Wright (1958), has pointed out that an odor carried in an air stream is distributed in an irregular manner because of turbulence. Under certain conditions the scent will be broadcast in a series of gusts rather than as a steady stream. At greater distances from the source the spacing of the gusts increases. An animal might be able to orient to the source by reference to the interval between gusts. Wright points out that an animal could facilitate its own detection by discharging the chemical in a series of pulses. Except in the slime molds (see page 279), in which something like this occurs, the temporal pattern of emission of such chemical stimuli is unknown.

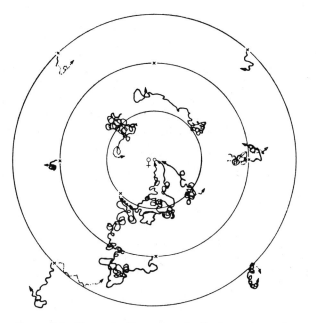

Figure 8-4 The male silkworm moth, *Bombyx mori*, may be unable to find a female even when she is only a meter away if there is no moving air. The concentric circles are one meter apart. Tracks of the males are for one-hour periods. After Schwinck 1954.

TASTE

The methods for assessing the qualitative properties of taste stimuli are the same as those used for olfaction. Either we determine the range of stimuli which evoke a given response, or we attempt to train the animal to distinguish between stimuli. It is important to bear in mind the difference in the significance of data obtained by these two methods. A blowfly or a butterfly will extend its proboscis and attempt to feed if the labellum or foot is stimulated by a sugar solution. Many studies have been made of the kinds of stimuli which facilitate or inhibit this response (Dethier 1953b, 1956, 1963, Hodgson 1955).

◆ *Qualitative Aspects.* Feeding blowflies distinguish acceptable and unacceptable tastes, but within these categories they seem unable to discriminate between substances. Acceptable compounds generally are sugars. All sugars, nutritious or not, are effective if they include certain molecular configurations. A variety of other compounds including acids, salts, and organic substances are rejected. Training experiments with other insects suggest that unacceptable compounds are not necessarily indistinguishable from one another, though the sugars are probably not distinguished. Bauer (1938), for example, trained water beetles to distinguish between sodium chloride and quinine and concluded that there are probably four taste modalities equivalent to sweet, salt, acid, and bitter. Different substances within the same group are likely to be confused. Von Frisch (1934) reached a similar conclusion with honeybees.

◆ *Physiology of Taste in Blowflies.* The physiological basis of the sense of taste in blowflies has been the subject of a remarkable series of electrophysiological experiments (Hodgson and Roeder 1956, Hodgson 1957). Each chemosensory hair on the fly's labium is supplied with three neurons (Dethier 1955). Only the two neurons that pass to the tip of the hair appear to be involved in taste. The third, which is attached to the base of the hair, is responsive to mechanical stimulation. A method of monitoring electrical activity in a single hair was developed.

The two types of spike generated in each hair were assumed to come from the two neurons used for taste. One of the chemosensory neurons responds to sugars and mediates the feeding response; the other responds to acids, salts, and alcohols, and mediates the rejection response. Further studies of several kinds of sugars revealed striking consistency between sugars that evoked feeding and sugars that stimulated activity in the 'sugar' fiber (Hodgson 1957). Here there is a simple mechanism to explain the stimulus filtering that takes place in feeding. As Hodgson points out, there are several complications. By some as yet undetermined mechanism, activity of one fiber seems to inhibit the other, emphasizing the contrast between the two classes of stimuli (see Dethier 1963). Further work has revealed a fourth neuron which is stimulated by water and additional receptors which seem to respond to proteins. In butterflies and the potato beetle there may be still more modalities. (Takeda 1961, Stürckow 1960).

The existence of sugar receptors in flies and butterflies (Minnich 1922, 1929) is consistent with their dependence on carbohydrates as a staple diet. The diet of other invertebrates may include fats and proteins as well as carbohydrates (e.g. wireworms, Thorpe et al. 1947), and we might expect to find taste receptors with different properties. The chemoreceptors of the crayfish, *Cambarus*, which lives on a diet of decaying meat, respond to amino acids (Hodgson 1958). The specific receptors for alkaloids in the potato beetle, *Leptinotarsa*, are related to the presence of alkaloids in the solanaceous plants upon which these insects feed, although in this case they are most concerned with the rejection of unsuitable host plants (Stürckow 1959, see page 233). A knowledge of the animal's natural history is a prerequisite for exploring properties of these receptor systems if the appropriate compounds to present in physiological tests are to be found (Hodgson 1955). Frequently the list of test compounds represents the stock of a chemical storeroom. Often stimuli are chosen on the basis of human experience. More fruitful results are likely to come from a selection of stimuli based on appreciation of the stimuli to which the animal is exposed in nature.

As with olfaction, the sense of taste is more versatile in mammals than in insects. The taste buds on a dog's tongue contain receptors with a range of specificity and considerable overlap. It is the constellation of activity in a range of receptors that determines the outcome of any one stimulus. Behavioral experiments have established the four main taste modalities, sweet, sour, salt, and bitter. Water should be added to the list. Electrodes placed in a taste bud receptor or a single fiber of a mammalian afferent nerve register activity elicited by several compounds such as salt and hydrochloric acid (Pfaffmann 1959b). The total effect depends on the simultaneous activity of other fibers. Table 8-1 shows the provisional diagram constructed by Cohen, Hagiwara, and Zotterman (1955) to portray the basis of four of the modalities. It is already clear that such a diagram oversimplifies the situation. A fifth modality, sweet, should now

Table 8-1 Response of Taste Receptor Fibers in the Cat and Carp

	Fiber type	Water	Salt	Acid	Quinine	Sucrose	Saliva
Cat	1	+	−	+	+		
	2	−	+	+	−		
	3	−	−	+	−		
	4	−	−	−	+		
Carp	1a	−	+	+	−	+	+
	1b	−	+	+	−	+	−
	2	−	+	+	+	+	+
	3a	−	−	+	−	+	+
	3b	−	−	+	−	+	−
	4a	−	+	−	−	−	−
	4b	−	+	+	−	−	−
	5	−	−	+	+	−	−
	6	−	−	+	−	−	+
	7	−	−	+	−	−	−

After Cohen, Hagiwara, and Zotterman 1955, and Konishi and Zotterman 1963.

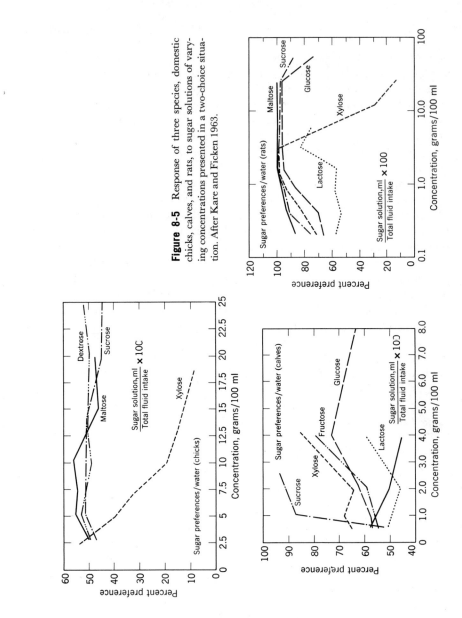

Figure 8-5 Response of three species, domestic chicks, calves, and rats, to sugar solutions of varying concentrations presented in a two-choice situation. After Kare and Ficken 1963.

be added. Sugar fibers are rare in the cat but are common in the guinea pig. This diagram implies a coding system based on presence or absence of activity in certain fibers. But there is good reason to think that the relative degree of activity in parallel fibers may be equally or more important. As Pfaffmann (1959b) expresses it, the sensory code might read $A > B =$ salty, $B > A =$ sweet, the sensation depending on the balance of activity in two fibers.

A system depending on the balance of activity in two fibers is probably capable of greater precision than one depending on the absolute activity level of a single fiber. This point is well illustrated by the overlapping responsiveness of 'warm' and 'cold' fibers in temperature perception (Zotterman 1959).

Just as in insects, species differences in the capacities of mammalian taste receptors relate to the animals' food habits. Cats are quite insensitive to sugar; dogs and rats show moderate responsiveness; guinea pigs, hamsters, and rabbits are still more responsive (Beidler 1961). Since most species seem to have at least a few fibers of all types, it is possible that mammalian species differences in responsiveness to sweet, sour, and bitter are largely a result of differing frequencies of the various types of receptors (Beidler 1963). Differences in the frequency of receptor types may also account for intraspecific variation such as is found between Swedish and Japanese populations of carp, the ecological significance of which is not known. Japanese carp are highly sensitive to bitter substances and relatively insensitive to sugar; the Swedish carp reverse this pattern (Konishi and Zotterman 1963). Additional physiological studies of specific feeders such as herbivores, which depend on particular plants, and fish-eating animals, will perhaps reveal more examples of species differences in the physiology of taste.

The existence of taste modalities does not imply that compounds falling within one modality are indistinguishable or that they elicit the same behavioral responses. Study of the preference of rats and chicks for different sugar shows, at high concentrations, a clear rejection of xylose. But the same sugar at high concentrations becomes increasingly attractive to calves (Kare and Ficken 1963). Other sugars have different preference ratings (Figure 8-5). The relative importance of taste receptors in vertebrates is suggested by the number of taste buds characteristic of each (Table 8-2). The behavioral significance of such variations has yet to be established, however.

◆ *Intensity, Temporal and Spatial Aspects.* In this discussion of the sense of taste most of our attention has been concentrated on the qualitative aspects. Most taste receptors adapt at a moderate rate making possible

Table 8-2 Number of Taste Buds in the Circumvallate Papillae of Some Mammals

Animal	Number of taste buds in circumvallate papillae
Chipmunk	750
Hare	1200
Rhesus monkey	1800
Opossum	2900
Wombat	3500
Dog	8000
Pronghorn antelope	48,000

From Beidler 1963.

accurate estimates of stimulus intensity. The temporal and spatial patterns of taste stimuli are relatively unimportant. Because contact with the body surface is normally required, direct location of the source becomes possible.

The idea that chemical 'shapes' may be perceived by insects has often been discussed but a good case has never been established. The scent trails left by ants consist of fluid from the tip of the abdomen. They are polarized in the sense that the shape of the fluid drop sometimes points in the ant's direction of travel. But there is no indication that lost ants refer to the shape of the marks to tell direction (Carthy 1958, Wilson 1962).

CONCLUSIONS ON STIMULUS FILTERING IN CHEMORECEPTION

We need to know "what the actual physiological differences might be between animals responding differently to the same chemical stimuli. Are they differences limited to the chemoreceptors themselves? Do the chemoreceptors act as highly selective filters, activated only by one or a few chemicals? Are there central nervous mechanisms which differentiate a variety of signals coming from a single chemoreceptor cell responding to a variety of chemicals?" (Hodgson 1955).

The responsibility for much of the specificity of responsiveness to chemical stimuli is apparently relegated to the actual receptors. They achieve their effects either as sense organs specific to certain stimuli or as a mosaic of receptors which respond to specific stimuli with constellations of activity. There is a temptation to think of a series of connections between sensory neurons and motor neurons such that a given stimulus inevitably excites a certain group of receptors, which just as inevitably transmit their excitation to certain motor neurons, eliciting the appropriate behavioral response. Such a model requires minimal involvement of the central nervous system, which would serve primarily as a relay station.

There are many reasons for regarding this explanation of the filtering of chemical stimuli as incomplete. Temporal variation in responsiveness to the same stimulus is difficult to explain by a receptor mechanism alone. For example, we know that a rat deprived of salt distinguishes between water and salt solutions at lower concentrations than a normal rat. The same effect can be achieved by adrenalectomy, which upsets the animal's metabolism in such a way that salts are lost in the urine. The lowered salt threshold that results might be associated with a peripheral change in sensitivity in the rat's taste buds or with some central change. The threshold of taste receptors determined by electrophysiological methods is unchanged after adrenalectomy (Pfaffmann 1959a). Nevertheless, a peripheral mechanism seems to be involved, for further work suggests that salt concentration in the saliva bathing the receptors is the significant variable (Pfaffmann 1963). Salinity is perceived by its contrast with this level of salivary stimulation. If the background level falls, as it well might with a salt deficit, sensitivity to salt will be increased.

Under natural conditions changes of response threshold often have a cyclic quality, rising and falling with periodical changes in the physiological state of the animal. A hungry blowfly or butterfly will lower its proboscis to more dilute sugar solutions than a satiated one (reviewed in Dethier and Bodenstein 1958). Receptor adaptation plays some part (see page 143). There is clear evidence for central interaction in some of Dethier's studies (1953b), however, in which stimuli have been independently applied to chemoreceptors on right and left legs of a blowfly. When sugar is applied to one leg a salt solution of a certain concentration will inhibit the feeding response whether it is applied to the same leg or a contralateral one. Furthermore, the response threshold is lower with bilateral stimulation, also implying central interaction. While receptor adaptation may cause a temporary cessation of feeding the main causes of satiation seem to be central. Satiation results normally from central inhibition arising from the presence of sugar in the foregut (Dethier and Bodenstein 1958, see page 144).

Rhythmical changes in olfactory responsiveness may occur. In women the sense of smell for certain compounds varies with the phase of the estrous cycle. The lactone, exaltolide, has an odor most women smell but cannot be smelled by most men. A man injected with estrogen can smell the odor (Le Magnen 1953). Injection of androgens into women raises their threshold for certain odors (review in Beidler 1961). The mechanism of this sensitization is not known.

The discovery by Le Magnen (1949, quoted by Hodgson 1955) that injection of certain substances into the blood stream of a human patient lowered the olfactory threshold to the same substances is suggestive, however. Is the effect mediated peripherally or centrally? The same phenomenon occurs with taste stimuli, so that a substance injected into the bloodstream may actually be tasted. As with taste, the concentration of substances in fluids circulating around the receptor may provide the explanation (Pfaffmann 1963).

Other types of changes in olfactory responsiveness may take place, implying central effects. The responses to sustained chemical stimuli may become adapted or habituated. Adapation is by definition a function of the receptors and is characterized by a rapid recovery of responsiveness after cessation of thé stimulus. Recovery following habituation is much slower or absent, and there is clear evidence of central nervous involvement. For example, in human subjects the subjective experience of a salt taste may wane while the receptors are still discharging rapidly, and the same thing occurs in olfaction (Beidler, quoted by Pfaffmann 1959a).

Central and peripheral factors in adaptation and habituation can be clearly separated in the taste receptors of insects. Each chemosensory hair on the labium of a blowfly can become completely adapted without limiting the responsiveness of adjacent hairs. A contribution of central processes can be observed as well, for if the chemoreceptors on one leg are adapted there is a decrement in responsiveness in other legs (Dethier 1952).

New patterns of olfactory responsiveness may be acquired. We have already discussed examples of conditioning to chemical stimuli in honeybees. The mechanism of acquisition of new patterns of responsiveness is probably central rather than peripheral. But the evidence is scant. The striking examples of olfactory conditioning in insects discovered by Thorpe and his colleagues (Thorpe 1963) would be very appropriate subjects for physiological study. Has a fruit fly raised on peppermint, which chooses the odor of peppermint in an olfactometer, been permanently sensitized to peppermint at the receptor level? Or are its olfactory receptors unchanged? The irreversible nature of the conditioning suggests that receptor function might indeed be modified. In the honeybee the lability of the conditioning makes this unlikely. Even in our present state of knowledge it is obvious that a complete account of stimulus filtering will have to take account of both central and peripheral factors.

BEHAVIORAL FUNCTIONS OF CHEMORECEPTION

In surveying the functions of the chemical senses in animals we are only skimming the surface of a huge and rapidly expanding subject. The increasing interest of physicists and chemists in the problems of biology has given special impetus to investigations of the relationships between organisms and the chemical characteristics of their environment. Every month new discoveries are reported. We shall first consider interactions with the physical environment and members of other species, then encounters with members of the same species.

◆ *Selection of an Environment.* Chemoreception frequently provides a basis for selection of an environment. Terrestrial insects can detect water at a distance and orient toward or away from it (Fraenkel and Gunn 1940, Carthy 1958, Dethier 1963). Aquatic organisms are highly responsive to chemical characteristics of the water in which they live, such as its carbon dioxide or oxygen content or its acidity, and adjust their movements accordingly (see page 102). Animals of marine and brackish water, for example, the three-spined stickleback (Baggerman 1957), are often highly responsive to salinity.

Responsiveness to the chemical characteristics of river water appears to be an important part of the direction finding of salmon in their spectacular spawning runs. Salmon are born in the headwaters of freshwater streams or rivers or, in more recent times, in hatcheries. After early development in these streams the young fish go downstream to the ocean where, depending on the species, they are to spend the next two to seven years. Tagging studies have established that they then return to the waters where they were hatched to spawn themselves. How do they find their natal stream? Fish are extremely sensitive to the chemical characteristics of their environment (Hasler 1957, Teichmann 1959), and a series of experiments involving blocking the nostrils has established that the particular chemical composition of the home stream provides the homing cue. Responsiveness to the stream is apparently acquired in youth and retained through the years spent in the sea (Hasler 1960). A sample of the water induces strong electrical activity in the olfactory bulbs in contrast with water from other areas. There seems to be a very general sensitization to home stream water as a result of early experience (Hara et al. 1965).

The habitat of many animals is provided by other organisms, especially plants. The chemical senses play a vital role in the location of such habitats, either at a distance by olfaction or at close range by actually tasting the substrate. The different scents of the various species of pine trees guide the movements of the parasitic fly, *Drino bohemica*, in their search for the larvae upon which they lay their eggs (Monteith 1955, 1956, 1958). Human body odor attracts the louse, *Pediculus* (Wigglesworth 1953). Quite specific chemical stimuli attract some ectoparasites to their hosts. Watermites living in the gills of different species of freshwater bivalves respond only to water passed over their particular hosts (Welsh 1931). Carbon dioxide and other factors elicit the approach of female mosquitoes to animals (Laarman 1960). Thus the characteristics of the environment merge with those of food. The same applies to many insects, whether they respond to chemical stimuli from plants, animal hosts, or decaying organic matter (Laing 1937, see page 235).

◆ *Predator-Prey Relationships.* Chemoreception is important in the detection of prey animals by predators. It is sometimes used for long-range perception, as in sharks and the moray eel (Bardach, Winn, and Menzel 1959), although often only after prey has been located by other means, as in the bee-hunting digger wasp (see page 237). In *Hydra* the chemical senses participate both in the sensitization of certain nematocysts and in the sensitization of the feeding response by reduced glutathione which is released from the wounded prey (see page 13).

Potential prey animals also detect predators by chemical means (Passano 1957, Pfeiffer 1963a-c). Many hunted mammals, for example, are acutely sensitive to the smell of predators, and a stalking predator must approach from downwind if it is to have any chance of successful capture. The response of hamsters to the smell of a polecat is considered elsewhere (see page 628). Among aquatic animals various small fishes respond to water in which a predatory pike has been swimming (Göz 1941). A minnow stops swimming and sinks slowly to the bottom, minimizing the stimuli that might elicit attack (see page 236). Salmon swimming upstream may turn back if they smell the skin of mammals in the water. A tentative identification of the substance involved has been made (review in Pfeiffer 1963a, c). Some aquatic invertebrates, such as molluscs, perform escape maneuvers when they smell potential predators, especially starfish (e.g. Weber 1924, see page 245).

The chemical sensitivity of predators may be exploited by prey species in defense mechanisms. Substances noxious to at least some enemies may be produced and delivered either at a distance by diffusion or spraying, or at close range by sting or bite (Eisner 1960a, Roth and Eisner 1962). The effectiveness of such chemical repellents is evident from the frequent occurrence of Batesian mimics, species harmless themselves but sufficiently similar to the noxious species they mimic that predators avoid them (e.g. Brower and Brower 1960). Consider the European earwig, *Forficula auricularia* (Eisner 1960b), which has two pairs of glands opening from the third and fourth abdominal segments; 2-methyl and 2-ethyl-p-benzoquinone are the main components in their secretion. It can be sprayed in different directions by the same twisting movements of the abdomen that direct the orientation of the pincers at the end of the abdomen. It is effective as a defense against ants and frogs, though it seems to have little effect on praying mantids, *Hierodula patellifera*, birds, and mice. The situation is reminiscent of insect-repellent substances in plants which are effective against some enemies but are rarely effective against all (page 233). Indeed, some insects derive noxious substances directly from plants that they feed on, so becoming distasteful to predators (Brower and Brower 1964). These relationships must be in a constantly dynamic state, with prey animals evolving repellents and predators evolving tolerance for them.

◆ *Commensal Relationships.* Some of the most intricate exchanges of chemical stimuli are found in symbiotic relationships in which pairs of species live in close association, each deriving advantage from the association (Davenport 1955). In several cases chemical stimuli seem to be responsible for maintaining the association. For example, the polychaete worm, *Podarke pugettensis*, sometimes lives with starfish, and worms are attracted by water that has passed over the appropriate host species (Figure 8-6). The same is true of the crab, *Pinnixa chaetopternana*, which lives within the occupied tubes of certain polychaete species. Tests of responsiveness to water from other species of worm were negative (Davenport et al. 1960).

A further complication occurs in the relationship between the sea anemone, *Stoichactis*, and the fish, *Amphiprion*, which lives among its tentacles. The fish gains protection from the anemone and probably drops fragments of food for it. However, to remain in such close contact with the anemone, *Amphiprion* must avoid discharging the nematocysts that cover the tentacles. The mucus on its skin has the property of raising the threshold for nematocyst discharge. The lack of this property in the mucus of a fish that has been isolated from anemones for six weeks or more is of special interest. To reestablish a relationship such a fish must go through a period of acclimation, first making only tentative contact with the tentacles, causing occasional nematocyst discharge. Immunity is reacquired gradually. The active principle in the mucus has not been identified, though some of its chemical properties are known (Davenport and Norris 1958).

A special symbiotic relationship exists between flowers and the insects,

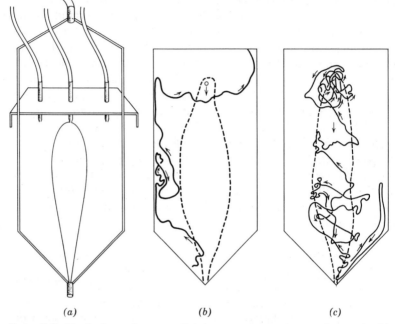

(a)   *(b)*   *(c)*

Figure 8-6   Track of a marine worm, *Podarke pugettensis,* in water passed over a starfish with which it is commensal: (*a*) experimental arrangement, (*b*) track of a worm with control solution, (*c*) track with a host factor at the middle inlet. After Davenport, Camougis, and Hickok 1960.

birds, and bats that pollinate them (Baker 1963). There is ample evidence of mutual evolution. Flower odors elicit approach and exploration by animals collecting nectar and pollen or eating petals. One of the most remarkable cases is the orchid, *Ophrys,* blossoms of which are pollinated by male bees and wasps attempting to copulate with them. The bees collect nothing; the association may more properly be termed parasitic rather than symbiotic (Baerends 1950). Not only do these flowers resemble the female of the hymenopteran which pollinates them, but they also mimic her odor as well (Kullenberg 1956, Stebbins and Ferlan 1956); thus we can speak of olfactory as well as visual mimicry.

PHEROMONES: INTRASPECIFIC CHEMICAL STIMULI

The essence of an act of communication is the reception of information by an organism through a stimulus that it perceives from the external environment. This definition includes not only the kind of stimulus exchange between individual animals that we intuitively accept as communicative but also responses to stimuli from the inanimate environment. All exteroceptive processes are potentially included. It is not easy to rephrase the definition to separate these phenomena. Is withdrawal from the smell of a predator any different from withdrawal from water of high salinity? A perusal of the examples of chemoreceptor mechanisms that we have just considered suggests a valid separation.

The basic components of a communication system are a sender, a receiver, and a medium or channel for signal transmission. The relationship between sender and receiver is one-sided in most of the examples we have considered. One participant attempts to maximize the efficiency of information transfer; the other is at best neutral and may try to minimize it. Only in symbiotic relationships do we find the synergistic interplay between sender and receiver that characterizes most intraspecific communication systems. Both participants are committed to the strategy of maximizing the efficiency of exchange. Generally there is the possibility of communication in both directions. Judged by these criteria, communication includes systems which have mutual value for both sender and receiver. This may involve animals of different species, as in symbiotic relationships, or the interspecific use of auditory alarm signals. Nevertheless, the most elaborate developments occur in intraspecific systems of communication, in chemical systems as well as with the other modalities.

Chemical signals that are exchanged between members of the same species are given the special name of 'pheromones,' a term derived from the Greek *pherein,* to carry, and *horman,* to excite (Karlson and Butenandt 1959, Karlson 1960). They are defined as "substances that are secreted by an animal to the outside and cause a specific reaction in a receiving individual of the same species in which they release a specific reaction, for example, a definite behavior or a developmental process." A surge of interest among biochemists and endocrinologists has led to dramatic advances in recent years in our knowledge of the compounds involved and the behavioral and physiological mechanisms that they participate in.

◆ *Dispersal and Aggregation.* Characteristic patterns of spatial distribution are sometimes achieved by chemical stimuli. Some animals tend to aggregate, especially species which have evolved reliable means of chemical or physical defense. Their bright colors and conspicuous behavior maximize the rate at which predators will learn to avoid them. Dense aggregations are one of several complex 'aposematic' characters (Cott 1957). Lycid beetles often have such aposematic traits. In one species Eisner and Ka-fatos (1962) have shown that chemical stimuli—signals in a communication system—are involved not only in defense but also in achieving aggregation. Only males aggregate, collecting around other males concealed in cloth bags or on unoccupied twigs where aggregations have occurred recently. The roosting aggregations of some butterflies are based at least partly on a chemical attraction (Crane 1955). When worker honeybees find a good source of food they release a scent, that attracts other workers (Renner 1960, Boch and Shearer 1963). Geraniol is one component, but at least four compounds are involved and the most effective seems to be citral (Wilson 1965). The same behavior occurs at the hive entrance and, when swarming is taking place, at new nest locations. In each case its function is to attract other bees.

If a chemical signal is to induce aggregation of members of the same species, and them alone, species specificity is required. This is the case in one phase of the life history of a slime mold. The vegetative phase, in which separate amoebae feed on bacteria, is followed by the fruiting phase in which amoebae congregate and cooperate to form a stalked spore-producing body (Bonner 1959, Shaffer 1962). During aggregation a group of amoeboid cells begins to produce a substance, acrasin, which diffuses outward, attracting other cells. These cells are also stimulated to produce the attractive substance, generating a kind of chemical relay system, so that the attractive center gradually increases in size. The effects are species-specific.

In a chemical signal system that relies upon diffusion for dispersal of the stimulus, the diffusion gradient provides the orienting cues to the respondents. If signal production continues for a long period, a long-lived substance may accumulate, especially in a limited volume of medium, and so eliminate any diffusion gradient. An unstable substance maintains a steeper concentration gradient. Acrasin has this quality, losing its attractive property in a matter of minutes. Some slime molds have evolved a further refinement. The instability of acrasin results from an enzyme that destroys its effectiveness. In some species the two compounds are produced alternately so that waves of acrasin diffuse out from the organizing center, apparently increasing the range over which responding cells can orient to the center.

Thus far we have considered mechanisms of aggregation. The chemical senses also participate in dispersal. Populations of the flour beetle, *Tribolium confusum*, tend to disperse at high densities (Naylor 1959). Secretions of the thoracic and abdominal glands are responsible for this dispersal. They contain quinones, similar in structure to those the earwig uses to repel predators.

Many mammals, especially nocturnal species, have specialized skin glands and behavior patterns for depositing their secretions on objects in their environment (Schaffer 1940, Bourlière 1955, Wynne-Edwards 1962). Localized latrine areas are also frequent, and the deposition of urine on objects or on the surface of the body is widespread. In spite of the huge literature on the natural history of such behavior, there is little information on what effects the chemical signals so generated have on other individuals. Sometimes they seem to assist dispersal. Male shrews have especially large and rank glands on the flanks. In females these glands are smaller, but they are more noticeable during anestrus than in estrus. These animals are solitary and the secretions may facilitate dispersal. The glands are minimally active when females are in estrus (Pearson 1946, Crowcroft 1957). More direct information is needed on the functions and chemical structure of such signals, following up, for example, the intriguing similarity that some of them bear to the sex steroid hormones (e.g. civetone, Figure 8-10, Wilson and Bossert 1963).

◆ *Individual and Group Recognition.* Circumstantial evidence suggests that some of these mammalian chemical signals also convey individual identity. Dogs can distinguish the trails left by different dogs and men, though they have difficulty with the odor of identical twins (Schmid 1935, Kalmus 1955, Figure 8-7). By a conditioning technique Göz (1941) showed that minnows can distinguish between water samples in which different individual members of their school have been living. The ability to make such discriminations by chemical means is undoubtedly exploited in the natural behavior of many animals, though experimental evidence is again lacking. Strangers to a group may be detected by smell, as in honeybees, where the distinctiveness of colony odors seems to result from slight variations in diet from group to group (Kalmus and Ribbands 1952). Lange (1960) obtained similar results with ants, in which the odor of nest material also has an effect. Dietary variations probably play a role in the individuality of odors in several species (Wilson and Bossert 1963). The difference must often lie in subtle variations in the proportions of compounds in a complex mixture. Neuhaus (1956a) has found an acute ability in dogs to distinguish between mixtures of odors in slightly different proportions.

◆ *Alarm Substances.* Another class of pheromones function to signal the presence of danger. The response that they elicit differs with the species, ranging from alerting, withdrawal, and hiding in many cases to, in some ants, approach, searching, and even attack (Maschwitz 1964). Karl von Frisch, familiar for his early studies of the behavior of honeybees, was

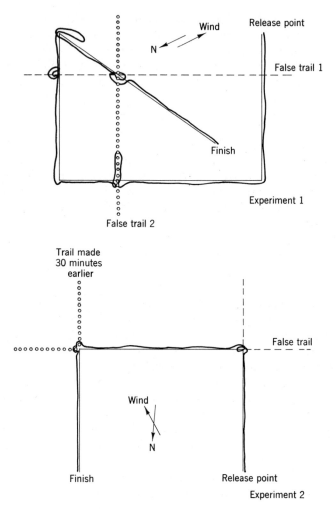

Figure 8-7 A police dog distinguishes the scents of several other dogs. In experiment 1 the trails of two other dogs induce only momentary confusion. In experiment 2 a false trail is distinguished from a fresh track laid by the same dog 30 minutes earlier. After Schmid 1935.

also a pioneer in the study of these alarm substances. He showed that a wounded minnow, *Phoxinus laevis,* releases a substance from special cells in the epidermis, which induces other members of the school to flee for shelter (von Frisch 1941, Pfeiffer 1963a, b). Similar effects have been recorded in many European, Asian, and North American ostariophyean fishes (Pfeiffer 1963c). The typical response varies with the habitat of the fish. Some bottom-living species plough up the substrate and disappear in a cloud of mud; others become motionless. Several surface-living species form a tight school and may leap from the water (Schutz 1956). A tiny piece of skin or a single drop of dilute skin extract elicits dramatic responses from fish in a large aquarium. The same responses are found in amphibian tadpoles (Eibl-Eibesfeldt 1949, Kulzer 1954). Something similar may occur in *Paramecium*, in *Drosophila*, and even in mice (Heintz 1954).

Ants and other hymenopterans produce many pheromones. Those produced by the mandibular or anal glands, depending on the species, often serve as alarm substances (Wilson 1963a, 1965, Wilson and Bossert 1963, Maschwitz 1964). Several of the compounds responsible have been identified by Pavan and others (Figure 8-8). The stimulus properties of the alarm signal and the response to it have been studied in detail in ants of the genus *Pogonomyrmex* by Wilson and Bossert. This substance is effective

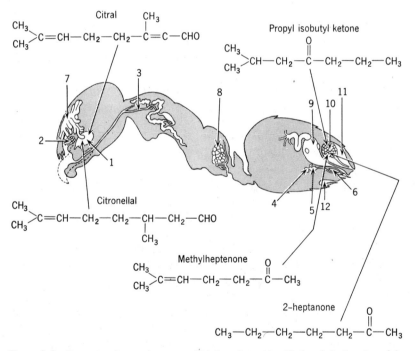

Figure 8-8 Some ant alarm substances which have been identified and the location of the glands which secrete them. Citral identified from *Atta rubropilosa*, citronellal from *Acanthomyops clariger*, propyl isobutyl ketone from *Tapinoma nigerrimum*, methylheptenone in *Tapinoma* and other species, and 2-heptanone from *Iridomyrmex pruinosus*. The exocrine gland system represents *Iridomyrmex humilis*. After Wilson and Bossert 1963, Wilson 1963b.

only over distances of 3 to 5 cm and fades out in about 30 seconds. The resulting diffusion gradient helps other ants to locate the source. If other ants are sufficiently aroused they will relay the signal so that the alarm is broadcast throughout the group. In these studies theoretical predictions about spatial and temporal properties of such a diffusing compound coincided well with experimental results. The response elicited varies with the concentration of the signal. Approach occurred at low intensities and aggression or retreat at high intensities. This parallels the alternative escape responses of many other organisms to danger stimuli from the external environment (see page 162).

◆ *Sex Pheromones.* The pheromones that act over the longest distances are those that elicit approach and copulatory behavior. Windborne scents may attract male moths to females from 2000 meters and considerably more under favorable conditions (Jacobson and Beroza 1963). Distant responses to chemical stimuli are recorded not only in insects but also in crustacea, fish, reptiles and amphibia, and mammals. Taking account of the extraordinary sensitivity of the olfactory receptors on the male moth's antennae, Wilson and Bossert (1963, Bossert and Wilson 1963) have calculated the active space of a female gypsy moth, *Porthetria dispar,* with various wind velocities (Figure 8-9).

The slow fading of the particular compounds used permits communication over great distances, in marked contrast with alarm substances that fade more rapidly. This illustrates the way in which the properties of a chemical communication system can be adjusted to the functions it performs. On the one hand there is instant discharge of an alarm signal that fades quickly, providing a concentration gradient for localization. On the other hand discharge of a sexual signal can be delayed until the environmental conditions are optimal for dispersal of a long-lasting signal, with a wind of a certain velocity. This provides the means both for dispersal of the signal and for orienting the approach of the male. There is a burgeoning literature on the chemical nature and synthesis of sex pheromones (Butenandt et al. 1959, Jacobson and Beroza 1963, Wilson and Bossert 1963) and several of these substances have been identified (Figure 8-10).

Knowledge of the structure of these and other pheromones has led Wilson and Bossert to try to predict those compounds most likely to be used for different purposes. They argue that if many species are using pheromones simultaneously there will be a premium on species specificity in communication systems requiring 'privacy.' The number of possible types of molecules increases sharply with increasing numbers of carbon atoms, and on this basis they argue that small molecules are likely to be

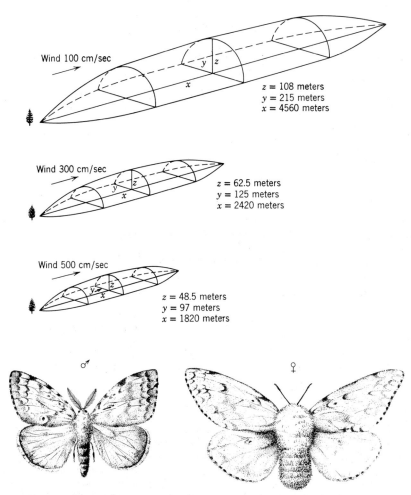

Wind 100 cm/sec

$z = 108$ meters
$y = 215$ meters
$x = 4560$ meters

Wind 300 cm/sec

$z = 62.5$ meters
$y = 125$ meters
$x = 2420$ meters

Wind 500 cm/sec

$z = 48.5$ meters
$y = 97$ meters
$x = 1820$ meters

♂   ♀

Figure 8-9   The distance and area from which female gypsy moths can recruit males with their sex attractant chemical may be calculated by reference to gas diffusion laws and analysis of turbulence. Note the male's large antennae. After Wilson and Bossert 1963.

less commonly used than those with at least five carbon atoms. A similar prediction derives from the knowledge that very small molecules are less efficient in stimulating insect olfactory receptors than large molecules. On the other hand, an upper limit of molecular size will be set by the energy cost of synthesizing and transporting larger molecules, and Wilson and Bossert conclude that "the great majority of pheromones can be expected to contain between 5 and 20 carbon members and have molecular weights between 80 and 300." With sex attractants, in which the

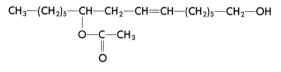

CH₃—(CH₂)₂—CH=CH—CH=CH—(CH₂)₈—CH₂—OH

Bombykol

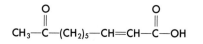

Gyplure

Honeybee queen substance

Civetone   Muskone

Figure 8-10   Sex pheromones in insects and mammals. Bombykol is the sex attractant of the female silkworm moth, *Bombyx mori*. Four geometric isomers of the diene groupings were tested by Butenandt and Hecker (1961), but only 10-*trans*, 12-*cis* was as effective as bombykol. Gyplure is the sex attractant of the female gypsy moth, *Porthetria dispar*. Honeybee queen substance may be secondarily a sex attractant. Civetone, secreted by the para-anal glandular pouch of the civet, *Viverra zibetha*, functions for defense and possibly also as a sex attractant and territory marker. Muskone is secreted by the preputial glands of the musk deer, *Moschus moschiferus*, and probably functions as a sex pheromone or territory marker. After Wilson and Bossert 1963.

demands for species specificity are greatest, molecular size would be expected to exceed that in, say, alarm or recruiting substances. The molecular weight of seven of the latter ranged from 114 to 218; four sex pheromones ranged from 225 to 298; more recent analyses also seem to bear out the prediction (Wilson and Bossert 1963, Wilson 1965).

The identification and synthesis of the sex attractant, bombykol, produced by female silkworm moths was a dramatic event in the study of pheromones (Butenandt et al. 1959, Figure 8-10). Important in itself, this discovery also led to Schneider's remarkable studies of the sensory aspects of the communication system in which bombykol participates (see page 277). Although female antennal chemoreceptors may be stimulated by a variety of odors but not by bombykol, those of the male are specifically responsive to this substance and other closely related compounds (Schneider 1957). This work led to tests between species, presenting the sex pheromone of one moth to males of other species. The results were unexpected. In a group of seven saturniid moth species some males were stimulated to sexual behavior by pheromones from females of other species as well as by those from their own (Table 8-3), and electrical activity in their antennae could also sometimes be recorded (Schneider 1962).

Similar examples of behavioral responses of male moths to sex pheromones of other species have been noted in studies of the European moths,

Table 8-3 Response of Male Saturniid Moths to the Sex Attractant of Females of Various Species.

Male	H.p.	H.ca.	H.ce.	H.e.	A.p.	R.o.	P.c.	B.m.	Bombykol
Hyalophora promethea	++O OOO OOOO	++O OOO OOOO	OO				OOO OOO OOOO	O	OOOO
H. calleta	+++ OOO OOOO	+++ +++ OO	+OO	O			+++ ++++ OOO OO	O	OOO
H. cecropia	OOO OOO ++		+++ +OO OO				OOO O		
H. euryalis	OOO O	OOO	++O OOO O	++ OOO			OOO OO		
Antheraca pernyi							OOO		
Rothschildia orizaba									
Philosamia cynthia	+O OO	O		OO	+OO		+O OO	OOO OO	OO
Bombyx mori	+OO ++	+++ +O++ +++O			+++ ++O O	+++ OOOO	+++ ++O OOOO	+	+

The bombykol used was 10-*trans*-12-*trans*-hexadecadienole, the least effective of the four isomeres of Bombyx sex attractant. + = positive reaction (vibration of antennae and wings); O = no reaction. After Schneider 1962.

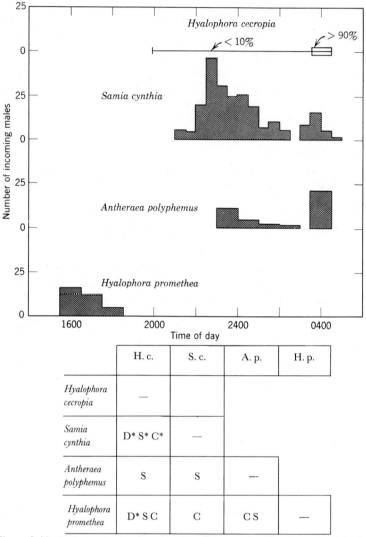

Figure 8-11 Isolating mechanisms in night-flying moths. The time of activity is recorded by number of males coming to a caged female. The block diagram shows suggested isolating mechanisms. D, difference in season of flight; S, species-specific sex attractant; C, difference in time of flight; *, incomplete isolation. After Wilson and Bossert 1963.

Lymantria monacha and *L. dispar* (Schwinck 1955), and other species (Barth 1937, Table 8-4). If these species are sympatric how can they retain their specific identity? In *Lymantria* a seasonal difference in sexual activity seems to be important. Wilson and Bossert (1963) reviewed

Schneider's results, considering the different seasons and times of day at which the same moths were active. The conclusions, based upon several earlier studies, suggested that a combination of timing, chemical signal specificity, and sensory mechanisms responding to signals play a crucial role in reproductive isolation. A circadian rhythm of responsiveness to sex pheromones has been demonstrated in some male moths (Shorey and Gaston 1965). Thus pheromone specificity is by no means the only possible method of restricting responses to members of the same species (Figure 8-11).

Thus far we have considered the triggering of more or less immediate behavioral responses by chemical stimuli. There may also be longer-term physiological consequences of chemical stimuli, sensitizing animals to new types of external stimuli. The control of caste development in termites and hymenopterans is achieved by pheromones which shift the whole process of morphological development. In honeybees the fate of developing females is determined by the 'queen substance' (Figure 8-10), which is produced by the mandibular glands of the queen. As long as this substance is ingested only worker females are produced. But if the queen dies, this substance is no longer produced and the behavior of the sterile female workers is changed. They are released from inhibition and begin construction of queen cells, and new queens are formed (Butler, Callow, Johnston and Johnston 1961). The ovaries of some workers also mature, and they become capable of laying drone-destined eggs. As in termites, the pheromone must achieve its effect by drastically changing the endocrine balance (Lüscher 1956, 1960).

Table 8-4   The Response of Pyralid Male Moths to Female Sex Attractant from Their Own and Other Species.

Male	Female					
	P.i.	E.k.	E.e.	G.m.	Ac.g.	Ap.g.
Plodia interpunctella	+	◯	◯	◯	◯	◯
Ephestia kühniella	+	+	+	◯	◯	◯
E. elutella	+ +	+ +	+	◯	◯	◯
Galleria mellonella	+	◯	◯	+	+ +	◯
Achroia grisella	◯	◯	◯	+ +	+	◯
Aphomia gularis	◯	◯	◯	◯	◯	+

The response of male Pyralid moths to female sex attractant from their own and other species. + = stimulated, ◯ = no reaction, + + = copulation attempted. After Barth 1937.

Behavior may be affected by external chemical stimuli in mammals as well (Parkes and Bruce 1961). Olfactory stimuli may have immediate effects, eliciting approach to other members of the same species, or permitting discrimination between males and females and between estrous and anestrous females (Lipkow 1954, Le Magnen 1953, Beach and Gilmore 1949, Godfrey 1958, Eisenberg 1963). Surely many of the mammalian chemical signals that we have considered as having a dispersal function contribute to the immediate control of sexual behavior as well. Longer-term effects have also been demonstrated, however. For example, the introduction of a male mouse to a group of females induces synchrony in their estrous cycles, even if the male is caged separately. No effect results if females are rendered anosmic by destroying their olfactory bulbs. Mutual exchange of chemical stimuli between females can also affect the pattern of estrus and pseudopregnancy (review in Parkes and Bruce 1961).

Exposure of a female to a strange male, for 12 hours in the early days of pregnancy or to his odor in nest material, causes her to abort and return to an estrous condition. The introduction of a male of a different strain has the strongest pregnancy-blocking effect, a strange male of the same strain has a lesser but still significant effect, but removing the father and then putting him back has no effect. Evidently individual and species differences in these chemical signals are of great significance. The introduction of females also causes no pregnancy blocking. Perhaps most intriguing of all is the absence of pregnancy blocking when a strange male is introduced to a female whose mate is left with her (Parkes and Bruce 1961). Pheromones can evidently impose long-term changes upon reproductive physiology, in turn sensitizing or desensitizing the animal to other new external stimuli.

The production of pheromones participating in reproduction should occur in the appropriate season and be correlated with the period of gonad growth. The activity of many mammalian skin glands varies seasonally and with the estrous cycle. In some mammals, such as the female short-tailed shrew, *Blarina brevicauda*, glandular activity is minimal at the time of sexual receptivity (Pearson 1946). In other mammals, such as some kangaroo rats, *Dipodomys*, glandular activity is maximal at the time of breeding (Quay 1953). In such cases castration sometimes reduces glandular activity while injections of sexual steroids restore it. The lateral gland of the short-tailed shrew is unaffected by gonadectomy.

A parallel may be found in insects. We have already noted that the gonads of most insects are less important in maintaining sexual behavior than the corpora allata. In an elegant series of studies on cockroaches Barth (1961, 1962) found that production of the female sex pheromone that triggers copulatory behavior in the male depends on the presence of the corpora allata and is independent of the gonads. The production of the sex attractant follows a definite temporal pattern, assuming a dominant role in determining the time at which breeding will take place.

◆ *Parent-Young Relationships.* Chemical stimuli produced by the parent may elicit responses in the young, and vice versa. For example, the location of the mother's teats by kittens probably depends partly on olfactory cues (see page 678). The smell of young mammals and their birth membranes plays a part in eliciting responses from the parent, such as eating the placenta or retrieving young displaced from the nest (Blauvelt 1955, 1956, Beach and Jaynes 1956, Rheingold 1963). Klopfer has evidence that individual recognition of her kid by a mother goat has an olfactory basis, stemming from her experience of the birth fluids (Klopfer, Adams, and Klopfer 1964). The chemical stimuli have not been identified and their specificity is not known. There are numerous cases of responses to the smell of individual young. For example, flying foxes, *Pteropus,* can locate their own young in a group even when they are quiet and concealed in cloth bags (Kulzer 1958, 1961, Nelson 1964).

A striking example of specific chemical stimuli emitted by young has been found in the jewel fish, *Hemichromis bimaculatus* (Kühme 1963). If water in which young jewel fishes have been swimming is introduced to an aquarium, the parents will orient to the point of inflow and show fanning and other patterns of parental behavior (Figure 8-12). The attachment will continue for two to three weeks, until the time that the separation would normally take place. The break can be hastened by replacing young fry with older fish and can be postponed by replacing older offspring with younger ones. The brood period of one female was extended to five weeks by manipulation of chemical stimulation from young fish. Evidently the chemical stimuli emitted by the young change with age. In a choice situation parents will select the stimuli from their own young in preference to those of other species and those of other parents of the same species. The young fish themselves also orient to water from young of their own species and avoid chemical stimuli from other species. Further studies show that chemical signals facilitate schooling of the young fish (Kühme 1964).

◆ *Trail Laying.* We have touched several times on the significance of chemical stimuli in orienting the behavior of other members of the species. The long-lasting effectiveness of chemical signals is put to special use by animals in laying trails that other members of the species can follow. Glands on the feet of many mammals suffice to make a trail, as in dogs.

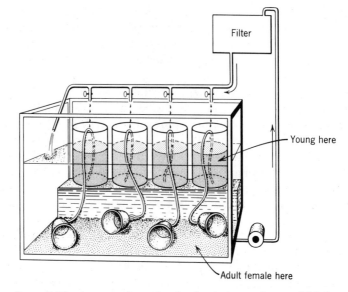

Figure 8-12   Apparatus for testing the chemical attractiveness of fish fry to parental fish. After Kühme 1963.

Male bumblebees lay trails by biting twigs or leaves and leaving a deposit from their mandibular glands, though the function of this behavior is still uncertain (Frank 1941, Haas 1946). In the meliponine bee, *Trigona postica*, trails laid by workers are followed by other foraging bees and serve to help recruit new visitors to a rich food source (Lindauer 1961, Figure 8-13). This behavior is well developed in ants; Wilson (1962) found them to have an intricate and highly efficient system.

The odor trail of the fire ant, *Solenopsis saevissima,* is secreted by the Dufour's gland (Figure 8-8) and released through the extruded sting. The trail is laid in a series of streaks. When a worker finds a rich and large food source it returns to the nest, laying a trail as it goes. This trail leads other ants to the food and they also lay trails as they return if the food supply persists. The trail substance is volatile and falls below threshold concentration for eliciting a response in about two minutes (Figure 8-14), so that the trails to an exhausted food source soon cease to be followed and the foragers look elsewhere. Experimental estimates of the accuracy of trail following lead to the conclusion that the trail laying of ants provides a system of communicating direction and distance which is as efficient as the dance of honeybees (page 544), though with a greater energy expenditure and slower recruitment rate.

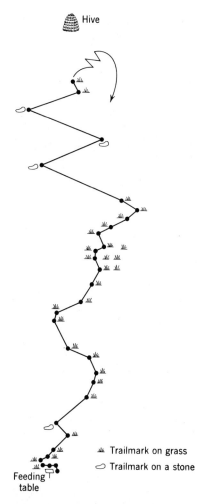

Hive

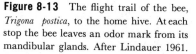

⊿⊾ Trailmark on grass
◯ Trailmark on a stone

Feeding
table

Figure 8-13 The flight trail of the bee, *Trigona postica*, to the home hive. At each stop the bee leaves an odor mark from its mandibular glands. After Lindauer 1961.

CHEMICAL COMMUNICATION SYSTEMS

What are the special properties of a communication system that relies on the chemical sense, as compared with the other sensory modalities? Wilson and Bossert (1963) have shown that the versatility of chemical systems is much greater than had been suspected. Numerous species-

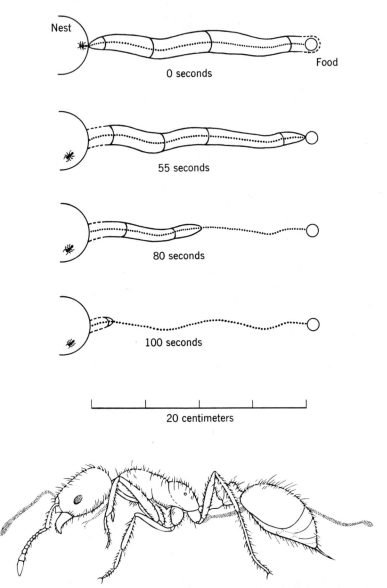

Figure 8-14 The fire ant, *Solenopsis saevissima,* lays a pheromone trail with sting extended. The trail is not continuous but is put down at intervals. The effective shape of the trail changes rapidly as the secretion evaporates. After Wilson 1962, Bossert and Wilson 1963.

specific signals are available, and the number of possible combinations becomes almost infinite if they can be mixed in different proportions.

The characteristics of diffusion rate, emission rate, and response threshold provide further opportunities for a species to vary the information transmitted by a signal (Wilson 1965).

The demands for species specificity of the signals vary with the function, being maximal with sex pheromones and less when interspecific communication is not disadvantageous, as with alarm substances. Trail substances may demand as high a degree of species specificity as sex pheromones. Tests of the interspecific effectiveness of chemical signals in ants and fish have shown that alarm substances do indeed elicit responses from members of other species. The trail substances of ants, on the other hand, generally evoke responses only from members of the same species (Wilson and Pavan 1959, Wilson 1962, Maschwitz 1964). The sex pheromones of moths are sometimes interspecifically effective, but the chance for errors is minimized by restriction of activity of related, sympatric species to different seasons or times of day.

The qualitative properties of chemical stimuli coupled with the great sensitivity of chemoreceptors are thus well exploited in the communication systems of animals. The distinctive temporal properties of chemical stimuli, which unlike auditory and many visual stimuli persist after emission for varying lengths of time, also find application. The potential durability of chemical signals makes possible their transmission over great distances. They may continue to be conveyed in the absence of the animal.

On the other hand, there are circumstances in which a less durable stimulus is advantageous. Here a highly volatile substance is used, as in trail-laying ants. Short-lived signals also permit animals to exploit the sensitivity of chemoreceptors to variations in stimulus intensity, so that, for example, both dogs and ants can detect variations in the age of trails they are following. In this case and in other types of chemical signals such as alarm substances, the response of the animal may change with stimuli of different intensities.

Even chemical signals that fade relatively rapidly have a long life compared with visual and auditory signals, and the use of temporal patterning in designing complex communicatory signals is accordingly limited. The slowly adapting nature of the receptors imposes a similar restriction. We should not overlook the possibility that rapidly adapting chemoreceptors may yet be discovered, however. Furthermore, the method that slime molds use for reducing the life of chemical signals, secreting an enzyme that destroys the effectiveness of the original signal, might prove to be even further refined in other animals.

Slowly adapting chemical receptor systems are likely to be the general rule, for the only inherent spatial property of a chemical signal is its gradient of diffusion. Even when the ability to register stimulus intensity is well developed, orientation to a diffusion gradient is not possible at great distances. Orientation over longer distances can be achieved only by relying on movement of the medium that provides orientation and carries the signal quickly to distant points. An alternative method of conveying spatial information is to lay a trail of chemical markers with a certain orientation. As Wilson (1962) has shown in his ant studies, this method can be developed not only into a remarkably sophisticated method of communicating direction and distance, but also, by incorporating a system of recruitment, into a means of communicating the relative richness of a distant food source. There is food for thought in Wilson's conclusion that the ants convey as much information in their system of chemical trails as honeybees transmit in their hive dances, which have been regarded as a uniquely advanced method of invertebrate communication.

REFERENCES

Adey, W. R. 1959. The sense of smell. In *Handbook of Physiology*, ed. by J. Field, Sec. 1, Vol. 1:535–548. American Physiological Society, Washington, D.C.

Adrian, E. D. 1928. *The Basis of Sensation*. Christophers (Publishers), London.

Autrum, H. 1950. Die Belichtungspotentiale und das Sehen der Insekten (Untersuchungen an Calliphora und Dixippus). *Z. vergl. Physiol.*, **32**:176–227.

Baerends, G. P. 1950. Specializations in organs and movements with a releasing function. *Symp. Soc. Exp. Biol.*, **4**:337–360.

Baggerman, B. 1957. An experimental study on the timing of breeding and migration in the three-spined stickleback (*Gasterosteus aculeatus* L.). *Arch. Néerl. Zool.*, **12**:105–317.

Baker, H. G. 1963. Evolutionary mechanisms in pollination biology. *Science*, **139**:877–883.

Bardach, J. E., H. E. Winn, and D. W. Menzel. 1959. The role of the senses in the feeding of the nocturnal reef predators *Gymnothorax moringa* and *G. vicinus*. *Copeia*, 1959:133–139.

Barth, R. 1937. Herkunft, Wirkung und Eigenschaften des weiblichen Sexualduftstoffes einiger Pyraliden. *Zool. Jahrb., Abt. Allg. Zool. Physiol.*, **58**:297–329.

Barth, R. H., Jr. 1961. Hormonal control of sex attractant production in the Cuban cockroach. *Science*, **133**:1598–1599.

———. 1962. The endocrine control of mating behavior in the cockroach *Byrsotria fumigata* (Guérin). *Gen. Comp. Endocrinol.*, **2**:53–69.

Bauer, L. 1938. Geschmacksphysiologische Untersuchungen an Wasserkäfern. *Z. vergl. Physiol.*, **26**:107–120.

Beach, F. A. and R. W. Gilmore. 1949. Response of male dogs to urine from females in heat. *J. Mammal.*, **30**:391–392.

——— and J. Jaynes. 1956. Studies of maternal retrieving in rats. III. Sensory cues involved in the lactating female's response to her young. *Behaviour*, **10**:104–125.

Beidler, L. M. 1961. The chemical senses. *Ann. Rev. Psychol.*, **12**:363–388.

———. 1963. Dynamics of taste cells. In *Olfaction and Taste*, ed. by Y. Zotterman, Vol. 1:133–148. The Macmillan Company, New York.

Blauvelt, H. 1955. Dynamics of the mother-newborn relationship in goats. In *Group Processes* (transactions of the first conference, 1954), ed. by B. Schaffner: 221–258. Josiah Macy Jr. Foundation, New York.

———. 1956. Neonate-mother relationship in goat and man. In *Group Processes* (transactions of the second conference, 1955), ed. by B. Schaffner: 94–140. Josiah Macy Jr. Foundation, New York.

Boch, R. and D. A. Shearer. 1963. Production of geraniol by honeybees of various ages. *J. Insect Physiol.,* **9:**431–434.

Bonner, J. T. 1959. *The Cellular Slime Molds.* Princeton University Press, Princeton.

Bossert, W. H. and E. O. Wilson. 1963. The analysis of olfactory communication among animals. *J. Theoretical Biol.,* **5:**443–469.

Bourlière, F. 1955. *The Natural History of Mammals.* Alfred A. Knopf, New York.

Brower, L. P. and J. van Z. Brower. 1960. Experimental studies of mimicry: reaction of toads to bumble bees and their asilid-fly mimics. *Proc. 11th Int. Congr. Ent.,* Vol. 3, Symp. 4:258.

——— and ———. 1964. Birds, butterflies and plant poisons: a study in ecological chemistry. *Zoologica,* **49:**137–159.

Butenandt, A. 1955. Über Wirkstoffe des Insektenreiches. II. Zur Kenntnis der Sexual-Lockstoffe. *Naturw. Rdsch.,* **8:**457–464.

———, R. Beckmann, D. Stamm, and E. Hecker. 1959. Über den Sexual-Lockstoff des Seidenspinners Bombyx mori. Reindarstellung und Konstitution. *Z. Naturf.,* **14b:**283–284.

Butler, C. G., R. K. Callow, F. R. S. Johnston, and N. C. Johnston, 1961. The isolation and synthesis of queen substance, 9-oxodec-*trans*-2-enoic acid, a honeybee pheromone. *Proc. Roy. Soc. Lond., B,* **155:**417–432.

Carthy, J. D. 1958. *An Introduction to the Behaviour of Invertebrates.* George Allen and Unwin, London.

Cohen, M. J., S. Hagiwara, and Y. Zotterman. 1955. The response spectrum of taste fibres in the cat: a single fibre analysis. *Acta. Physiol. Scand.,* **33:**316–332.

Cott, H. B. 1957. *Adaptive Coloration in Animals.* Methuen and Company, London.

Crane, J. 1955. Imaginal behavior of a Trinidad butterfly, *Heliconius erato hydara* Hewitson, with special reference to the social use of color. *Zoologica,* **40:**167–196.

Crowcroft, P. 1957. *The Life of the Shrew.* Max Reinhardt, London.

Davenport, D. 1955. Specificity and behavior in symbioses. *Quart. Rev. Biol.,* **30:**29–46.

——— and K. S. Norris. 1958. Observations on the symbiosis of the sea anemone *Stoichactis* and the pomacentrid fish, *Amphiprion percula. Biol. Bull.,* **115:**397–410.

———, G. Camougis, and J. F. Hickok. 1960. Analyses of the behaviour of commensals in host-factor. I. A hesionid polychaet and a pinnotherid crab. *Anim. Behav.,* **8:**209–218.

Dethier, V. G. 1952. The relation between olfactory response and receptor population in the blowfly. *Biol. Bull.,* **102:**111–117.

———. 1953a. Chemoreception. In *Insect Physiology,* ed. by K. D. Roeder: 544–576. John Wiley and Sons, New York.

———. 1953b. Summation and inhibition following contralateral stimulation of the tarsal chemoreceptors of the blowfly. *Biol. Bull.,* **105:**257–268.

———. 1955. The physiology and histology of the contact chemoreceptors of the blowfly. *Quart. Rev. Biol.,* **30:**348–371.

———. 1956. Chemoreceptor mechanisms. In *Molecular Structure and Functional Activity of Nerve Cells.* American Institute of Biological Sciences, Washington, D.C.

———. 1963. *The Physiology of Insect Senses.* Methuen and Company, London.

——— and D. Bodenstein. 1958. Hunger in the blowfly. *Z. Tierpsychol.,* **15:**129–140.

Eibl-Eibesfeldt, I. 1949. Über das Vorkommen von Schreckstoffen bei Erdkrötenquappen. *Experientia,* **5:**236.

Eisenberg, J. 1963. The behavior of heteromyid rodents. *Univ. Calif. Publ. Zool.*, **69**:1–114.

Eisner, T. 1960a. The effectiveness of arthropod defensive secretions. *Proc. 11th Int. Congr. Ent.*, Vol. 3, Symp. 4:264–268.

———. 1960b. Defense mechanisms of arthropods. II. The chemical and mechanical weapons of an earwig. *Psyche* (Cambridge), **67**:62–70.

——— and F. C. Kafatos. 1962. Defense mechanisms of arthropods. X. A pheromone promoting aggregation in an aposematic distasteful insect. *Psyche* (Cambridge), **69**:53–61.

Fraenkel, G. S. and D. L. Gunn. 1940. *The Orientation of Animals.* Oxford University Press, London.

Frank, A. 1941. Eigenartige Flugbahnen bei Hummelmännchen. *Z. vergl. Physiol.*, **28**:467–484.

Frisch, K. von. 1919. Über den Geruchsinn der Biene und seine blutenbiologische Bedeutung. *Zool. Jahrb., Abt. Allg. Zool. Physiol.*, **37**:1–238.

———. 1934. Über den Geschmackssinn der Biene. Ein Beitrag zur vergleichenden Physiologie des Geschmacks. *Z. vergl. Physiol.*, **21**:1–156.

———. 1941. Über einen Schreckstoff der Fischhaut und seine biologische Bedeutung. *Z. vergl. Physiol.*, **29**:46–145.

———. 1950. *Bees: Their Chemical Senses, Vision and Language.* Cornell University Press, Ithaca.

Godfrey, J. 1958. The origin of sexual isolation between bank voles. *Proc. Roy. Phys. Soc. Edinb.*, **27**:47–55.

Göz, H. 1941. Über den Art- und Individualgeruch bei Fischen. *Z. vergl. Physiol.*, **29**:1–45.

Haas, A. 1946. Neue Beobachtungen zum Problem der Flugbahnen bei Hummelmännchen. *Z. Naturf.*, **1**:596–600.

Hainer, R. M., A. G. Emslie, and A. Jacobson. 1953. An information theory of olfaction. *Ann. N.Y. Acad. Sci.*, **58**:158–174.

Hara, T. J., K. Veda, and A. Gorbman. 1965. Electroencephalographic studies of homing salmon. *Science*, **149**:884–885.

Hasler, A. D. 1957. Olfactory and gustatory senses of fishes. In *The Physiology of Fishes*, ed. by M. E. Brown, Vol. 2:187–209. The Academic Press, New York.

———. 1960. Guideposts of migrating fishes. *Science*, **132**:785–792.

Heintz, E. 1954. Actions répulsives exercées sur divers animaux par des substances contenues dans la peau ou le corps d'animaux de même espèce. *Comp. Rend. Séanc. Soc. Biol.*, Paris, **148**:585–588, 717–719.

Hodgson, E. S. 1955. Problems in invertebrate chemoreception. *Quart. Rev. Biol.*, **30**:331–347.

———. 1957. Electrophysiological studies of arthropod chemoreception. II. Responses of labellar chemoreceptors of the blowfly to stimulation by carbohydrates. *J. Insect Physiol.*, **1**:240–247.

———. 1958. Electrophysiological studies of arthropod chemoreception. III. Chemoreceptors of terrestrial and freshwater arthropods. *Biol. Bull.*, **115**:114–125.

——— and K. D. Roeder. 1956. Electrophysiological studies of arthropod chemoreception. I. General properties of the labellar chemoreceptors of Diptera. *J. Cell. Comp. Physiol.*, **48**:51–75.

Jacobson, M. and M. Beroza. 1963. Chemical insect attractants. *Science*, **140**:1366–1373.

Kalmus, H. 1955. The discrimination by the nose of the dog of individual human odours and in particular of the odours of twins. *Brit. J. Anim. Behav.*, **3**:25–31.

——— and C. R. Ribbands. 1952. The origin of the odours by which honeybees distinguish their companions. *Proc. Roy. Soc. Lond., B.*, **140**:50–59.

Kare, M. R. and M. S. Ficken. 1963. Comparative studies on the sense of taste. In *Olfaction and Taste*, ed. by Y. Zotterman, Vol. 1:285–297. The Macmillan Company, New York.

Karlson, P. 1960. Pheromones. *Ergeb. Biol.*, **22**:212–225.

——— and A. Butenandt. 1959. Pheromones (ectohormones) in insects. *Ann. Rev. Ent.*, **4**:39–58.

Kettlewell, H. B. D. 1946. Female assembling scents with reference to an important paper on the subject. *Entomologist,* **79:**8–14.

Klopfer, P., D. K. Adams, and M. S. Klopfer. 1964. Maternal "imprinting" in goats. *Proc. Nat. Acad. Sci.,* **52:**911–914.

Koehler, O. 1932. Beiträge zur Sinnesphysiologie der Süsswasserplanarien. *Z. vergl. Physiol.,* **16:**606–756.

Konishi, J. and Y. Zotterman. 1963. Taste functions in fish. In *Olfaction and Taste,* ed. by Y. Zotterman, Vol 1:215–233. The Macmillan Company, New York.

Kühme, W. 1963. Chemisch ausgelöste Brutpflege-und Schwarmreaktionen bei *Hemichromis bimaculatus* (Pisces). *Z. Tierpsychol.,* **20:**688–704.

———. 1964. Eine chemisch ausgelöste Schwarmreaktion bei jungen Cichliden (Pisces). *Naturwissenschaften,* **51:**120–121.

Kullenberg, B. 1956. Field experiments with chemical sexual attractants on aculeate hymenoptera males. *Zool. Bid. Uppsala,* **31:**253–354.

Kulzer, E. 1954. Untersuchungen über die Schreckreaktion der Erdkrötenkaulquappen (*Bufo bufo* L.). *Z. vergl. Physiol.,* **36:**443–463.

———. 1958. Untersuchungen über die Biologie von Flughunden der Gattung *Rousettus* Gray. *Z. Morph. Ökol. Tiere.,* **47:**374–402.

———. 1961. Über die Biologie der Nil-Flughunde (*Rousettus aegyptiacus*). *Natur. Volk,* **91:** 219–228.

Laarman, J. J. 1960. The plasticity of response patterns in host-seeking mosquitoes. *Proc. 11th Int. Congr. Ent.,* Vol. 3, Symp. 5:60–61.

Laing, J. 1937. Host-finding by insect parasites. I. Observations on the finding of hosts by *Alysia manducator, Mormoniella vitripennis* and *Trichogramma evanescens. J. Anim. Ecol.,* **6:**298–317.

Lange, R. 1960. Über die Futterweitergabe zwischen Augehörigen verscheidener Waldameisen. *Z. Tierpsychol.,* **17:**389–401.

Le Magnen, J. 1953. L'olfaction. Le fonctionnement olfactif et son intervention dans les régulations psycho-physiologiques. *J. Physiol. Path Gén.,* **45:**285–326.

Lindauer, M. 1961. *Communication Among Social Bees.* Harvard University Press, Cambridge.

Lipkow, J. 1954. Über das Seitenorgan des Goldhamsters (*Mesocricetus auratus auratus* Waterh.). *Z. Morph. Ökol. Tiere,* **42:**333–372.

Lüscher, M. 1956. Hemmende und fördernde Faktoren bei der Entstehung der Ersatzgeschlechtstiere bei der Termite *Kalotermes flavicollis* Fabr. *Rev. Suisse Zool.,* **63:**261–267.

———. 1960. Hormonal control of caste differentiation in termites. *Ann. N.Y. Acad. Sci.,* **89:** 549–563.

Maschwitz, U. 1964. Gefahrenalarmstoffe und Gefahrenalarmierung bei sozialen Hymenopteren. *Z. vergl. Physiol.,* **47:**596–655.

Minnich, D. E. 1922. A quantitive study of tarsal sensitivity to solutions of saccharose, in the red admiral butterfly, *Pyrameis atalanta* Linn. *J. Exp. Zool.,* **36:**445–457.

———. 1929. The chemical sensitivity of the legs of the blow-fly, *Calliphora vomitoria* Linn., to various sugars. *Z. vergl. Physiol.,* **11:**1–55.

Moncrieff, R. W. 1946. *The Chemical Senses.* John Wiley and Sons, New York.

Monteith, L. G. 1955. Host preferences of *Drino bohemica* Mesn. (Diptera: Tachinidae), with particular reference to olfactory responses. *Can. Ent.,* **87:**509–530.

———. 1956. Influence of host movement on selection of hosts by *Drino bohemica* Mesn. (Diptera: Tachinidae) as determined in an olfactometer. *Can. Ent.,* **88:**583–586.

———. 1958. Influence of food plant of host on attractiveness of the host to tachinid parasites with notes on preimaginal conditioning. *Can. Ent.,* **90:**478–482.

Mullins, L. J. 1955. Olfaction. *Ann. N.Y. Acad. Sci.,* **62:**247–276.

Naylor, A. F. 1959. An experimental analysis of dispersal in the flour beetle, *Tribolium confusum*. *Ecology*, **40**:453–465.

Nelson, J. E. 1964. Vocal communication in Australian flying foxes (Pteropodidae; Megachiroptera). *Z. Tierpsychol.*, **21**:857–870.

Neuhaus, W. 1956a. Die Riechschwelle von Duftgemischen beim Hund und ihr Verhältnis zu den Schwellen unvermischter Duftstoffe. *Z. vergl. Physiol.*, **38**:238–258.

———. 1956b. Die Unterscheidungsfähigkeit des Hundes für Duftgemische. *Z. vergl. Physiol.*, **39**:25–43.

Parkes, A. S. and H. M. Bruce. 1961. Olfactory stimuli in mammalian reproduction. *Science*, **134**:1049–1054.

Passano, L. M. 1957. Prey-predator recognition in the lower invertebrates. In *Recent Advances in Invertebrate Physiology*, ed. by B. T. Scheer: 37–49. University of Oregon Publications, Oregon.

Pearson, O. P. 1946. Scent glands of the short-tailed shrew. *Anat. Rec.*, **94**:615–629.

Pfaffmann, C. 1959a. The sense of taste. In *Handbook of Physiology*, ed. by J. Field, Vol. I, Sec. I:507–533. American Physiological Society, Washington, D.C.

———. 1959b. The afferent code for sensory quality. *Amer. Psychologist*, **14**:226–232.

———. 1963. Taste stimulation and preference behavior. In *Olfaction and Taste*, ed. by Y. Zotterman, Vol. 1:257–273. The Macmillan Company, New York.

Pfeiffer, W. 1963a. Alarm substances. *Experientia*, **19**:113–168.

———. 1963b. The fright reaction in North American fish. *Can. J. Zool.*, **41**:69–77.

———. 1963c. Vergleichende Untersuchungen über die Schreckreaktion und den Schreckstoff der Ostariophysen. *Z. vergl. Physiol.*, **47**:111–147.

Prosser, C. L. and F. A. Brown, Jr. 1961. *Comparative Animal Physiology* (2nd edition). W. B. Saunders Company, Philadelphia.

Quay, W. B. 1953. Seasonal and sexual differences in the dorsal skin gland of the kangaroo rat (*Dipodomys*). *J. Mammal.*, **34**:1–14.

Ratliff, F. and C. G. Mueller. 1957. Synthesis of "on-off" and "off" responses in a visual-neural system. *Science*, **126**:840–841.

Renner, M. 1960. Das Duftorgan der Honigbiene und die physiologische Bedeutung ihres Lockstoffes. *Z. vergl. Physiol.*, **43**:411–468.

Rheingold, H. L. 1963. *Maternal Behavior in Mammals*. John Wiley and Sons, New York.

Rose, J. E. and V. B. Mountcastle. 1959. Touch and kinesthesis. In *Handbook of Physiology*, ed. by J. Field, Sec. 1, Vol. I:387–429. American Physiological Society, Washington, D.C.

Roth, L. M. and T. Eisner. 1962. Chemical defenses of arthropods. *Ann. Rev. Ent.*, **7**:107–136.

Schaffer, J. 1940. *Die Hautdrüsenorgane der Säugetiere*. Urban and Schwarzenberg, Berlin and Vienna.

Schmid, B. 1935. Über die Ermittelung des menschlichen und tierischen Individualgeruches durch den Hund. *Z. vergl. Physiol.*, **22**:524–538.

Schneider, D. 1957. Elektrophysiologische Untersuchungen von Chemo-und Mechanorezeptoren der Antenne des Seidenspinners *Bombyx mori* L. *Z. vergl. Physiol.*, **40**:4–41.

———. 1962. Electrophysiological investigation on the olfactory specificity of sexual attracting substances in different species of moths. *J. Insect. Physiol.*, **8**:15–30.

———. 1963. Electrophysiological investigation of insect olfaction. In *Olfaction and Taste*, ed. by Y. Zotterman, Vol. 1:85–103. The Macmillan Company, New York.

Schwinck, I. 1954. Experimentelle Untersuchungen über Geruchssinn und Strömungswahrnehmung in der Orientierung bei Nachtschmetterlingen. *Z. vergl. Physiol.*, **37**:19–56.

———. 1955. Freilandversuche zur Frage der Artspezifität des weiblichen Sexualduftstoffes der Nonne (*Lymantria monacha* L.) und des Schwammspinners (*Lymantria dispar* L.). *Z. angew. Ent.*, **37**:349–357.

Schutz, F. 1956. Vergleichende Untersuchungen über die Schreckreaktion bei Fischen und deren Verbreitung. *Z. vergl. Physiol.,* **38**:84–135.

Shaffer, B. M. 1957. Aspects of aggregation in cellular slime moulds. I. Orientation and chemotaxis. *Am. Naturalist,* **91**:19–35.

———. 1962. The acrasina. In *Advances in Morphogenesis,* ed. by M. Abercrombie and J. Brachet. Vol. 2:109–182. The Academic Press, New York.

Shorey, H. H. and L. K. Gaston. 1965. Sex pheromones of noctuid moths. V. Circadian rhythm of pheromone-responsiveness in males of *Autographa california, Heliothis virescens, Spodoptera exigua* and *Trichoplusia ni* (Lepidoptera: Noctuidae). *Ann. Entomol. Soc. Amer.,* **58**:597–600.

Slifer, E. H. 1955. The detection of odors and water vapor by grasshoppers (Orthoptera, Acrididae) and some new evidence concerning the sense organs which may be involved. *J. Exp. Zool.,* **130**:301–317.

Stebbins, G. L. and L. Ferlan. 1956. Population variability, hybridization, and introgression in some species of *Ophrys. Evolution,* **10**:32–56.

Steiner, G. 1953. Zur Duftorientierung fliegender Insekten. *Naturwissenschaften,* **40**:514–515.

Stürckow, B. 1959. Über den Geschmackssinn und den Tastsinn von *Leptinotarsa decemlineata* Say (Chrysomelidae). *Z. vergl. Physiol.,* **42**:255–302.

———. 1960. Elektrophysiologische Untersuchungen am Chemorezeptor von *Calliphora erythrocephala* Meigen. *Z. vergl. Physiol.,* **43**:141–148.

Takeda, K. 1961. The nature of impulses of single tarsal chemoreceptors in the butterfly, *Vanessa indica. J. Cell. Comp. Physiol.,* **58**:233–245.

Teichmann, H. 1959. Über die Leistung des Geruchssinnes beim Aal [*Anguilla anguilla* (L.)]. *Z. vergl. Physiol.,* **42**:206–254.

Thorpe, W. H. 1963. *Learning and Instinct in Animals.* Harvard University Press, Cambridge.

———, A. C. Crombie, R. Hill, and J. H. Darrah. 1947. The behaviour of wireworms in response to chemical stimulation. *J. Exp. Biol.,* **23**:234–266.

Twitty, V. C. 1959. Migration and speciation in newts. *Science,* **130**:1735–1743.

———. 1961. Experiments on homing behavior and speciation in *Taricha.* In *Vertebrate Speciation,* ed. by W. F. Blair:415–459. University of Texas Press, Austin.

Walls, G. L. 1942. *The Vertebrate Eye.* Cranbrook Institute of Science, Bloomfield Hills, Michigan.

Weber, H. 1924. Ein Umdreh- und Fluchtreflex bei *Nassa mutabilis. Zool. Anz.,* **60**:261–269.

Welsh, J. H. 1931. Specific influence of the host on the light responses of parasitic water mites. *Biol. Bull.,* **61**:497–499.

Wigglesworth, V. B. 1953. *The Principles of Insect Physiology* (5th edition). Methuen and Company, London.

Wilson, E. O. 1962. Chemical communication among workers of the fire ant, *Solenopsis saevissima* (Fr. Smith). 1–3. *Anim. Behav.,* **10**:134–164.

———. 1963a. The social biology of ants. *Ann. Rev. Ent.,* **8**:345–368.

———. 1963b. Pheromones. *Sci. Amer.,* **208**(5):100–114.

———. 1965. Chemical communication in the social insects. *Science,* **149**:1064–1071.

——— and W. H. Bossert. 1963. Chemical communication among animals. *Recent Prog. Hormone Res.,* **19**:673–716.

——— and M. Pavan. 1959. Glandular sources and specificity of some chemical releasers of social behavior in dolichoderine ants. *Psyche* (Cambridge), **66**:70–76.

Wright, R. H. 1958. The olfactory guidance of flying insects. *Can. Ent.,* **90**:81–89.

Wynne-Edwards, V. C. 1962. *Animal Dispersion in Relation to Social Behaviour.* Oliver and Boyd, Edinburgh and London.

Zotterman, Y. 1959. Thermal sensations. In *Handbook of Physiology,* ed. by J. Field, Sec. 1, Vol. 1:431–458. American Physiological Society, Washington, D.C.

nine

MECHANISMS OF RESPONSIVENESS
TO LIGHT

Properties of light that are perceived • Sensitivity of photoreceptors •
Perception of color and polarization • Spatial properties of light stimuli
• Form vision and its physiological basis • Perception of distance: the
visual cliff.

PHYSICAL CHARACTERISTICS OF LIGHT AND VISION

Only a small proportion of the total spectrum of radiant energy is
perceived by living organisms as light (Figure 9-1). It is no coincidence
that the same part of the spectrum penetrates water most readily, a reminder of the aquatic origin of life (Brett 1957). The overwhelming importance of light in animal perception is due to its reflection from objects
in the environment and to the transmission of these reflected rays in
straight lines, thus preserving the relative spatial properties of the reflecting object.

Qualitative properties of light are also important to vision. Variations
in the surface characteristics of objects affect the amount of reflected light
and its wavelength, and this is perceived by some animals as relative
brightness and color. Some animals are able to perceive an additional
feature of light, namely its plane of polarization. These are reasons enough
for the development of photoreceptors as means of exploring the environment, especially when we add the crucial significance to life of the solar
cycle of light and darkness (Brett 1957).

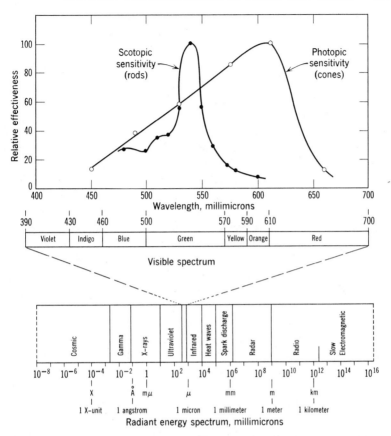

Figure 9-1 Animals perceive only a small part of the total spectrum of radiant energy as light. The two sensitivity curves here are for the sunfish, *Lepomis*, in dim light near the minimum threshold for scotopic sensitivity (10 millilamberts) and in much brighter light (photopic sensitivity). Maximal sensitivity is assigned a value of 100 in each case. From Brett 1957.

Light receptors in animals are almost ubiquitous. We can only touch upon the huge literature dealing with their structure, physiology, and biological significance (e.g. Walls 1942, Duke-Elder 1958, Ratliff 1962). Here our main concern is with the stimulus filtering involved in vision. We can consider this under four headings: the sensitivity of photoreceptors, and the perception of the qualitative, temporal, and spatial properties of light. Sensitivity will be dealt with first because it bears upon other properties of photoreceptors. We will be primarily concerned with the vertebrate eye and the compound eyes of crustacea and insects. There will be only passing mention of the cephalopod eye and the simple eyes or ocelli of arthropods and other invertebrates.

◆ *Sensitivity of Light Receptors.* The threshold of responsiveness of photoreceptors cannot be discussed without also considering variations in eye structure. Structure is, in turn, intimately related to the animal's way of life.

We might expect to find striking differences, for instance, between the eyes of strictly diurnal animals and those of animals that are partly or entirely nocturnal. At night sensitivity is at a premium, and there are many adaptations for its improvement. Large eyes can collect more light than small ones. This tendency reaches an extreme in deep-sea fishes and in some nocturnal birds, in which the eyes come to occupy a major portion of the head. Other nocturnal adaptations include "a widely dilated pupil to allow the maximum amount of light to enter, and a large spherical lens set far back from the cornea to place the optical centre near the retina so that light transmitted through the dioptic system is concentrated into a small image of the maximum possible brightness" (Duke-Elder 1958, Figure 9-2). Sometimes a special structure, the tapetum lucidum, reflects back light which has passed through the retina. Most important are the specializations in the organization of the actual photosensitive cells and their connections in the retina.

There are two main types of retinal cells in vertebrates, cones which are typical of diurnal animals and rods which characterize those that are nocturnal. The rods are so arranged that many of them converge on the same bipolar cells, which in turn converge upon a smaller number of ganglion cells. Thus information received over an appreciable area of the retina is pooled, resulting in greater sensitivity than in a cone-rich retina where there is less convergence and summation.

A different mechanism makes the compound eye of nocturnal crustacea and insects (Waterman 1961) more sensitive than that of diurnal forms (Wigglesworth 1953, Dethier 1953). In the diurnal type of 'apposition' compound eye each ommatidium functions as an independent optical unit with its own focusing and receptor systems, isolated from its neighbors by a sheath of pigment cells. The image received by the eye as a whole consists of a mosaic of points of light of varying brightness. In the nocturnal 'superposition' type of eye the pigment sheaths are incomplete and the lens systems of adjacent ommatidia cooperate to produce a single image, thus making maximum use of the light impinging on the eye (Figure 9-3).

◆ *Changes in Sensitivity.* The great sensitivity of the eyes of nocturnal animals is achieved at a sacrifice of spatial information. The high degree of

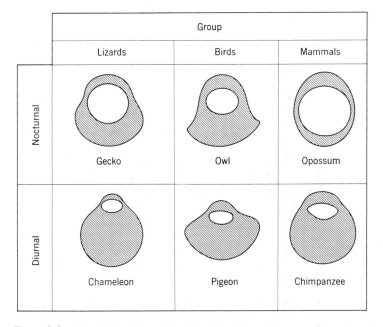

Figure 9-2   The relative sizes of the lenses in the eyes of some nocturnal and diurnal animals. After Walls 1942.

convergence in the subretinal layers of a rod-rich vertebrate eye results in uncertainty about precisely which point of the retina is stimulated at any one moment. The maximum certainty about position occurs with cone-rich eyes, with a minimum of convergence but with a lower sensitivity. There is probably a similar contrast between the apposition and superposition compound eyes of arthropods, the latter providing a less accurate determination of stimulus position but greater sensitivity, although there is still no proof of this point (Waterman 1961).

Confronted with this element of incompatibility between position perception and sensitivity, many animals have evolved means of varying the properties of their photoreceptors according to the degree of illumination. Processes of light and dark adaptation serve to decrease or increase the sensitivity of the actual receptor cells. This adaptation is achieved either by changes in the properties of one receptor type, as in insects (Dethier 1953) or, in vertebrates, by switching from cone vision to rod vision. The vertebrate solution requires a mixture of the two receptor types in the retina, which occurs commonly, making activity possible under a wide range of lighting conditions.

Changes in the relative distribution of shielding pigment in the eye also occur. In the superposition compound eyes of arthropods the pig-

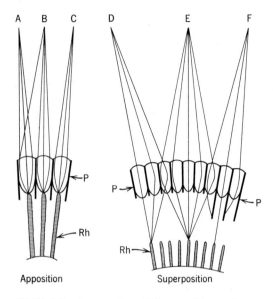

Figure 9-3 A comparison of the apposition and superposition types of compound eyes. A to F, light sources, P, pigment, Rh, rhabdom. At the right-hand side of the superposition eye the pigment is shown in the light-adapted condition. After Wigglesworth 1953.

ment may migrate toward the receptor cells in bright light, making possible the apposition type of image formation (Figure 9-3). The pigment probably also serves as a constricting pupil, reducing the amount of light entering each ommatidium (Milne and Milne 1959, Bernhard and Ottoson 1960, Waterman 1961). There are close parallels in vertebrate eyes. Migrations of shielding pigment occur during dark adaptation in fish and frogs, exposing the rods in the retina (Duke-Elder 1958). In some vertebrates, especially fish, the photosensitive cells change shape (Brett 1957). In others the light-reflecting properties of the tapetum lucidum may vary. Finally, the dimensions of the pupil in vertebrate eyes may change, controlling the amount of light entering the eye and affecting the depth of the visual field that is in focus.

◆ *Intensity Perception.* Thus there are several ways that visual sensitivity can be changed, with reciprocal loss or gain of acuity. But estimates of sensitivity alone tell little about the visual world of an animal. We also need to know what differences cf intensity can be perceived. On this subject there is much less information available, and existing reports are conflicting (see Duke-Elder 1958). This conflict is caused in part by lack of control over absolute light intensity, which directly affects intensity discrimination. Another complication is the difficulty in controlling variation in stimulus image size in experiments with animals. Nevertheless, the generalization that intensity discrimination is most efficient in bright light and with large stimulus areas is probably accurate.

QUALITATIVE PROPERTIES OF LIGHT STIMULI

◆ *Wavelength Discrimination: Color Vision.* Two characteristics of light can be regarded as qualitative properties: wavelength and the plane in which the light waves are vibrating, the plane of polarization.

Animals perceive a limited range of wavelengths as visible light. For man, most other vertebrates, and a few insects the range is from 390 mμ in the violet to 760 mμ in the red (see Figure 9-1). In most insects visible light extends from about 300 mμ in the ultraviolet to 650 mμ in the orange-red. The honeybee is typical in this respect.

Within these ranges there is wide variation in the region of maximum sensitivity. In some crustacea and insects there is a single peak, usually in the blue-green or green. In others there is a second peak in the ultraviolet (Dethier 1953, Waterman 1961). The honeybee is far more sensitive to ultraviolet, around 350 mμ, than to any other wavelength (Daumer 1956).

The conditions of experimentation on color vision must be carefully defined (Goldsmith 1961). For example, in several invertebrates (Waterman 1961, Milne and Milne 1959) there is a shift of sensitivity away from the red end of the spectrum as the eye becomes adapted to darkness. This Purkinje shift is especially characteristic of vertebrates (see Figure 9-1), in which the peaks of the curves for photopic (light-adapted) and scotopic (dark-adapted) sensitivity differ by as much as 70 mμ. In man the peaks are at 554 mμ in the yellow-green, and at 510 mμ in the blue-green, a difference associated with the changeover from cone to rod vision.

Wavelength sensitivity is affected by the presence of color in the cornea or lens or in oil droplets in the retina. Color occurs especially in species which are active in very bright light—certain lizards and birds. Yellow and orange droplets may shift the maximum sensitivity well into the orange. The sensitivity of these animals to red and relative insensitivity to blue must help in reducing chromatic aberration (Walls 1942, Wald 1959).

In addition to wide variation in the visible spectrum and responsiveness within that spectrum, the ability to separate colors varies. Color vision is the capacity to discriminate between different wavelengths irrespective of variations in stimulus intensity and overall receptor responsiveness. This capacity is widespread among both invertebrates (e.g. Dethier 1953, Waterman 1961) and vertebrates (e.g. Walls 1942, Duke-Elder 1958). Furthermore, there is good evidence that at least one insect, the honeybee, sees the visible spectrum as a series of relatively discrete categories or colors (von Frisch 1914, 1964, Daumer 1956). Daumer shone colored lights through feeding dishes made of quartz which, unlike glass, is transparent to ultraviolet. The colors seen by bees correspond in principle with the spectral colors experienced by man. Although the wavelength limits differ, the categories can be arranged in a color circle (Figure 9-4). A mixture of the longest (588 mμ) and shortest (360 mμ) wavelengths the honeybee sees creates a new color, 'bee purple,' which is distinguished from all other colors. Mixtures of wavelengths that have opposite positions on the color circle, such as ultraviolet and blue-green or purple and blue, are not distinguished from white light. The discovery was made in the following manner. Bees were first trained to a food reward at a broad spectrum of light from a xenon lamp. Then colors were added to determine whether any combination would be confused with the full spectrum. A mixture of 15 percent 360 mμ and 85 percent 490 mμ was confused with 'bee white.' Combinations of other colors that by themselves were readily distinguished were also treated as bee white. Evidently the phenomenon of complementary colors is a characteristic of honeybee vision.

Some insects cannot distinguish between light of different wavelengths. The same is true of many vertebrates, especially those that are nocturnal. Apparently in animals with rod-rich retinas color vision has been sacrificed for sensitivity. But many fish (e.g. Herter 1953), amphibia (e.g. Birukow 1949), reptiles, birds (e.g. Hess 1956), and some mammals

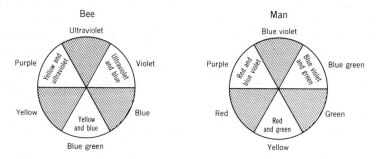

Figure 9-4　Color circles for the honeybee and man. The primary colors are hatched. Intermediate colors are made by the mixing of adjacent primary colors; complementary colors are in opposite sectors. After Daumer 1956.

such as squirrels and primates that have cones in the retina can distinguish colors, some only very roughly, others with precision.

◆ *Polarized Light Reception.* The plane of vibration of light rays can be affected by the properties of a surface from which they are reflected. Some organisms detect the plane of polarization. For example, there is a consistent relationship between the pattern of plane polarization of light from the sky and the position of the sun, and some invertebrates can tell direction with this information even when the sun is obscured.

Use of the polarization plane of light from blue sky in honeybee orientation was discovered by von Frisch in 1949. Since that time the capability has been found in many other arthropods, both terrestrial and aquatic (Stockhammer 1959, Waterman 1961). Perception of the plane of polarization is widely used as a means of orientation in space.

Attempts to demonstrate the same ability in vertebrates and other invertebrates have failed, except for experiments with *Octopus* (Moody and Parriss 1961, Rowell and Wells 1961, Moody 1962) which provide one of the few demonstrations of polarized light perception based on training. The orientation of *Octopus* to polarized light is apparently based upon complex structural elements of the retina known as rhabdoms. Electron microscopy has shown that these structures bear a remarkable similarity to the retinulas of arthropods. They contain the visual pigment and are the basis of the polarized light sensitivity of cephalopods (Zonana 1961).

Man is the only vertebrate known to be able to see polarized light. Some people can see "Haidinger's brushes," dark, hourglass shapes around the macula lutea, at right angles to the plane of polarization (Stockhammer 1959). We seldom use this ability and generally are not conscious of it.

TEMPORAL PROPERTIES OF LIGHT STIMULI

Sensitivity to temporal change in a pattern of light is related to the adaptation rates of the receptors. Photoreceptors generally adapt quickly, thus maximizing responsiveness to temporal changes of stimulation. It is useful to distinguish between (1) the effects of repeated stimulation of single groups of light receptors, and (2) successive changes in the patterns of stimulation of populations of receptors, as occur in the perception of movement of a stimulus object across the visual field.

When a flickering light is presented to an animal it is possible to determine the rate of flicker that the eye is just unable to distinguish. This is called the 'flicker-fusion frequency.' If it is exceeded, the light no longer seems to flicker. One way of measuring this frequency is an electro-retinogram, the pattern of electrical activity in the retina when it is exposed to the flickering light. In man the flicker-fusion frequency is about 40 flashes per second. The number of retinal cells stimulated also affects the flicker-fusion frequency, implying some kind of interaction between adjacent retinal elements. This interaction will be mentioned in our discussion of movement perception (Bartley 1951).

Brightness affects the responsiveness to temporal change. Granit (1955) has shown that the flicker-fusion frequency increases in brighter light. This occurs in cats, guinea pigs, and pigeons, the details varying from species to species. In pigeons the flicker-fusion frequency increases in a smooth curve, whereas there are breaks in the curves for the cat and guinea pig. Variations in the shape of the curve seem to be related to the density of rods in the retina. Rods are abundant in the guinea pig, less so in the cat, and relatively rare in the pigeon. In the cat and guinea pig the lower parts of the curves presumably represent the results with scotopic vision, and the upper parts represent photopic vision. It also appears that an eye rich in cones can distinguish much more rapid flicker rates than a rod-rich eye. In the pigeon, rates as high as 150 flashes per second are resolved (Granit 1955, 1959).

The poorer temporal resolution of a rod eye is thus another sacrifice made for the sake of high sensitivity. The position of the stimulated spot is also less readily determined with a rod eye. Thus as Walls (1942) points out it is misleading to say, as some have done, that rod eyes are more sensitive to movement than cone eyes; "rather it is that they are too crude to afford any phases of vision except movingness and brightness."

There is a parallel in the 'slow' and 'fast' compound eyes of insects (Autrum 1950, Autrum and Stöker 1952). Slow eyes are characteristic of relatively slow-moving and often nocturnal insects such as cockroaches and grasshoppers. For them flicker-fusion frequency may be as low as five or ten flashes per second. The fast eyes of rapidly flying diurnal insects such as bees and flies may resolve flicker frequencies as high as 265 per second. Similar but less striking variation occurs in crustacea (Waterman 1961). As in vertebrates, the fusion frequencies rise with increasing light intensity. Fast eyes also seem to have better acuity than slow ones, another parallel with cone and rod retinas.

Thus far we have discussed on-off stimulation at one point. In actual movement perception, the image shifts across the receptor surface, resulting in on-off stimulation of successive retinal units. The perception of movement implies a process of integration of the temporal stimulation of separate units, and it is a challenge to understand how this is done.

Much known about the compound eyes of insects results from 'optomotor' experiments (see Kalmus 1949, Carthy 1958, Hassenstein 1961).

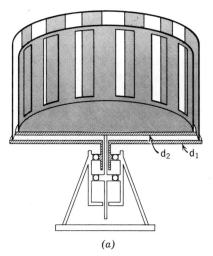

(a)

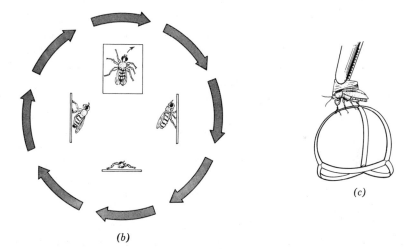

(b)

(c)

Figure 9-5   The optomotor response. A turning drum with vertical stripes creates
the illusion of movement as long as stripes can be distinguished. More precise control
of stimulus patterns is achieved with a second, inner drum that has slots in the wall,
as shown in (a). In (b) the measure of response is the head orientation or posture of a
fruit fly. In (c) the measure is the direction that the beetle takes when it reaches
a fork in the Y-maze globe that it passes beneath it. After Kalmus 1949, Hassenstein
1961.

Insects placed in the center of a revolving drum with vertical stripes on
the inner surface change their posture when the stripes are moved (Figure
9-5). The postural adjustment can be used as an index for movement

perception, especially with the refinement devised by Hassenstein (1961). This consists of a "Y-globe maze," a device which the beetle *Chlorophanus viridus* will cling to and pass between its feet. The response depends on the normal habit of this beetle, which is to walk upside down on vegetation. Thus the beetle normally supports its own weight during locomotion, and the Y-globe maze must approximate the weight of the beetle to elicit locomotion. In the experiments the beetle is suspended in the center of an optomotor apparatus. Whenever it comes to an intersection, it must make a choice. The direction taken is influenced by the movement of the visual field, and the beetle generally turns in the same direction as the movement of the field as long as it can be perceived.

By combining this sensitive measure of response with an elaborate arrangement of screens to restrict the insect's view, Hassenstein (1961) and Reichardt (1961) have been able to establish some of the principles governing movement detection in insects. A series of successive distinct stimuli impinging on different parts of the eye create an illusion of movement, just as in man. This illusion is a boon for the experimenter because such stimuli are much easier to control than a continuously moving image. When successive light stimuli are presented to the beetle, an optomotor response is evoked if the ommatidia so stimulated are no more than two ommatidia apart. Only two ommatidia need be stimulated. If more are stimulated, the effects summate, evoking stronger responses.

If the time interval between successive stimuli is varied, the maximum effect is found when stimuli are about a quarter of a second apart. The response is weaker with shorter or longer intervals. Even so, some effect can still be detected with intervals of up to 10 seconds, implying detection of rates of movement slower than that of the minute hand of a clock. Evidently some physiological aftereffect persists for as long as 10 seconds after the first ommatidium is stimulated. The order of presentation determines the apparent direction of movement. Reversal of order reverses the orientation of the response.

Hassenstein and Reichardt went on to demonstrate unexpected relationships between response and stimulus intensity, stimulus lightening and darkening, and the temporal ordering of stimuli, implying a process of multiplication of the effects of stimuli upon adjacent ommatidia. Such methods can be used as a means of exploring the mechanisms that underlie the processes of perception (reviews in Wooldridge 1963, Bullock and Horridge 1965).

◆ *Other Aspects of Movement Perception.* There are several distinct problems in understanding movement perception. We can separate simple detection of a moving image from the tasks of determining the rate of movement, the position of the stimulus object, and its direction of movement. It is possible for an animal to detect movement and probably rate of movement without forming more than a crude impression of its spatial properties. Indeed, there is some incompatibility between the requirements for the perception of these different characteristics.

Consider the determination of the position of a moving object by a compound eye. The visual angle of adjacent ommatidia is important; the smaller it is, the more precisely the position of a moving object can be detected. Another limiting factor is the acceptance angle of each ommatidium. If each ommatidium functioned as an independent unit, the larger the acceptance angle the less precise would be the determination. However, integration of information from overlapping fields can actually sharpen responsiveness to the position of a moving object (Burtt and Catton 1954), and the amount of overlap is in fact considerable in many compound eyes (Waterman 1961). Presumably, the loss in spatial perception results in a gain in movement perception; the more overlap there is, the more ommatidia stimulated by movement between two points, and the smaller the minimal detectable displacement of the image (Exner 1891).

Much of the movement seen by insects is created by their own locomotion in walking or flying; movement in the horizontal plane becomes critical. In flies and many insects that are capable fliers the ommatidial angle is about twice as large in the horizontal plane as in the vertical (Autrum 1949). There are also variations of ommatidial angle on different parts of the eye, with the largest angles where the rates of movement are greatest. In these cases the sacrifice of visual acuity results in a gain in movement perception. We are reminded of the similar compromise in vertebrate eyes between the high acuity of cones and the high sensitivity and responsiveness to movement of rods.

Vertebrate eyes are not without special structures for detecting movement. They are seen most clearly in the eyes of birds, whose lives are dominated more by the visual sense than are the lives of any other vertebrate group. One special structure is the fovea, in which cones are packed closely together, giving maximal acuity. In most birds the cones are densely distributed on the walls of a pit. Pumphrey (1961) has hypothesized that this arrangement maximizes sensitivity to movement. An image passing across the fovea will have a high rate of apparent movement up and down the walls of the foveal pit and may thus be more readily noticed. By the same token, the ability to follow a moving object should be more efficient because any deviation from the line of sight would result in a maximal displacement of the image on the retina.

The pecten is another unique object in the avian eye. This conical structure projects from the blind spot where the optic nerve enters the eye. It carries a rich supply of blood vessels, and an important function is undoubtedly the provision of nutrients for the retina. In this way entry of light into the retina itself is not impeded by blood vessels. A further function of the pecten may be facilitation of movement perception. The elaborate folding of the pecten in many species casts a broken shadow on the retina which may increase the conspicuousness of an image moving across it (Menner 1938). Although the evidence is still equivocal, the fact that, in general, the birds with the largest and most elaborate pectens, such as the diurnal birds of prey, are the most sensitive to movement may not be accidental.

The neural mechanisms underlying movement perception in vertebrates are now beginning to be understood. We have already seen that flicker-fusion frequencies vary widely in different species and in the same species under different lighting conditions. But when an image moves across the retina cooperation of adjacent receptors must take place, as Hassenstein has shown in insects. Such interaction has been demonstrated in the eyes of frogs and cats (Adrian and Matthews 1928, Hartline 1938, Barlow 1953a, b, Kuffler 1953, Maturana et al. 1960) and will be discussed in detail in the next section.

The neural mechanisms in the retina are clearly more than mere simple devices that transmit information about the temporal and spatial patterns of illumination on the receptor mosaic (Ratliff, Miller, and Hartline 1958). By sacrificing accuracy concerning relatively unimportant information, features which are significant are more accurately perceived. For many organisms environmental movement is of great significance, whether it originates outside the animal or is created by the animal's own movement. Mechanisms for the perception of such movement have taken a high evolutionary priority, often at the expense of information about the spatial properties of light stimuli.

SPATIAL PROPERTIES OF LIGHT STIMULI

The fact that light travels in straight lines is the main reason for the tremendous elaboration of light receptors throughout the animal kingdom. In invertebrates and vertebrates alike, receptor systems which exploit the directionality of light as a means of perceiving the environment have evolved (Milne and Milne 1959). We can discuss the perception of the spatial properties of light stimuli under headings that emphasize the increasing precision of responses to this directional property: (1) limitations of the field of view of whole eyes, (2) perception of the direction of stimuli within the visual field, (3) discrimination of spatially different arrays of light stimuli, and (4) perception of distance.

◆ *The Visual Field.* Light can only be received by an eye that is oriented to the source. The acceptance angle of the eye depends on the curvature of its surface, whether it be the array of lenses of a compound eye or the single lens of a cephalopod or vertebrate eye. The shape of the retina and the size of the pupil must also be taken into account (Duke-Elder 1958).

In vertebrates the field of each eye averages rather constantly about 170 degrees (Duke-Elder 1958). The main variation occurs in the placing

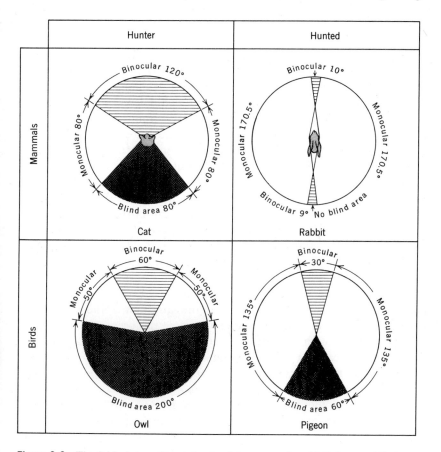

Figure 9-6   The field of view of hunted animals is panoramic, with little or no blind area in the horizontal plane. Hunters have large areas of binocular vision and sizeable blind areas. After Duke-Elder 1958.

of the two eyes with respect to one another. A large binocular field facilitates depth perception but reduces the overall visual field. We find that, in general, animals which are hunted and thus cannot afford to have a large blind area, have a large visual field with relatively little overlap between the two eyes. Hunters, on the other hand, have a smaller visual field, and a large proportion of it is binocular (Figure 9-6).

The compound eye of arthropods may be almost spherical with a total acceptance angle of about 300 degrees. Thus there can be a large binocular field without reducing the total field of view. This occurs with the huge eyes of such predatory insects as dragonflies. Good vision seems to be less crucial for hunted invertebrates than for hunted vertebrates. Their eyes are usually small and they possess fewer ommatidia than predatory arthropods.

◆ *Perception of the Direction of Light Stimuli: Acuity.* The capacity to distinguish the direction of a light stimulus and, by implication, to discriminate between stimuli coming from different directions, must ultimately depend on the acceptance angle of the individual receptor units. This is true whether the receptors are ommatidia or groups of rods and cones. The relationship has been beautifully demonstrated by von Buddenbrock and Schulz (see von Buddenbrock 1952) by examining the 'light-compass' reaction of many arthropods. If a single light is visible to them, they set a temporary course subtending a certain angle to the light. If the light is moved, the course shifts appropriately. By this means the investigators demonstrated the minimal angular displacement of the light eliciting a course change. This angle is directly related to the acceptance angle of the individual ommatidia in the species concerned. The larger the angle, the further the light must be moved to induce a change in the animal's course (Figure 9-7).

Variations in ommatidial angle in different parts of a compound eye also affect acuity and may even occur in the same ommatidium in different planes. The fact that the horizontal angle of acceptance is greater than the vertical in parts of the eye of the honeybee (see page 327) means that acuity is greater in the vertical plane than it is in the horizontal (see Wigglesworth 1953). Acuity is probably greater in the apposition eye than in the superposition compound eye (see page 319).

In vertebrates the most sensitive, rod-rich eyes also sacrifice much acuity because many rods converge upon the same optic nerve fiber. In cone-rich eyes there is less convergence, and in the fovea the ratio of cones to nerve fibers tends to approach unity. In some birds this condition may even prevail over the whole retina. This fact, together with the great density of cones per unit area, may permit many diurnal birds to see as

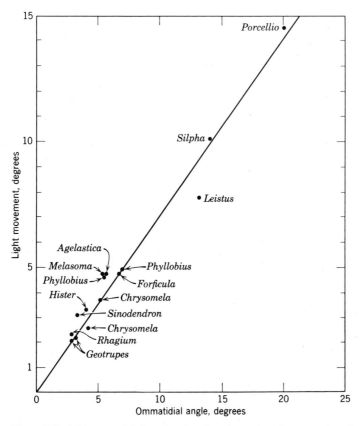

Figure 9-7   The ommatidial angle of various invertebrate genera plotted against the angular change in direction of a light source required to induce a change of course. After von Buddenbrock 1952.

clearly over the whole visual field as we do in the direct line of sight. The acuity of some small passerine birds is estimated at 1.5 minutes of arc, as compared with 0.5 minute in man. Again there is close agreement with the angle subtended by cones in the retina. These considerations lead to the conclusion that some of the larger predatory birds, such as eagles, probably have a greater visual acuity than man (Donner 1951, reviewed in Pumphrey 1961).

The concentration of receptor cells in certain parts of vertebrate retinas, like the areas on arthropod compound eyes with small ommatidial angles, results in an especially high acuity on certain visual axes. Such areas, often enclosing a pit-like fovea, are widespread in vertebrates. In some

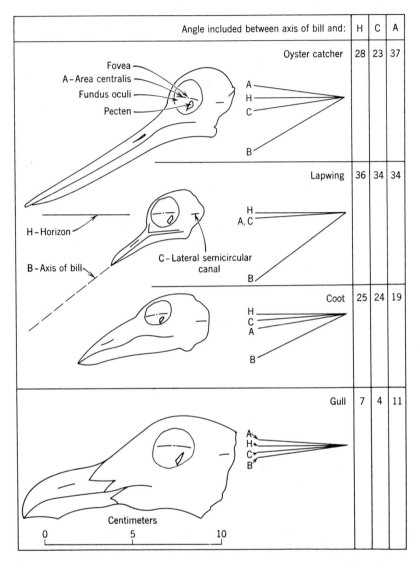

Figure 9-8 These birds each tend to hold the head with the ribbon-like area centralis and the lateral semicircular canals in a horizontal position. A, area centralis, H, horizontal, C, the lateral semicircular canal, and B, bill. The birds are an oyster catcher, *Haematopus ostralegus,* a lapwing, *Vanellus vanellus,* a coot, *Fulica atra,* and a herring gull, *Larus argentatus.* After Duijm 1958.

animals, such as ungulates, the concentration is of rods rather than cones, presumably resulting in a local area of high sensitivity. In diurnal vertebrates dense areas of cones are the rule. The arrangements vary widely.

A fovea may be central or temporal, i.e. on the posterior wall of the eye, or there may be both a central and a temporal fovea in each eye. By this means some birds are able to use a different fovea in monocular and binocular fixation of an object. In some species there is a long ribbonlike area extending horizontally across the retina (Wood 1917). This area is noticeably more common in birds that live in open habitats, like seabirds and waders, and is relatively rare in woodland birds, suggesting a correlation with the importance of the horizon in the birds' frame of reference. This interpretation is reinforced by Duijm's (1958) demonstration that the apparent deviation of the ribbonlike area from the horizontal in some species is corrected by the position in which the bird normally holds its head (Figure 9-8).

The presence of a clearly marked fovea may have an important effect on the way in which visual exploration of the environment takes place. Either the head or the eye must be turned for careful examination of an object in the peripheral field. Fixed eyes are the rule, although movements within the orbit do occur in many fishes, some reptiles (e.g. the chameleon), and in mammals, especially the foveate primates. Where the retina is homogeneous, whether it is rod-rich or cone-rich, such eye movements are rare. In birds, in which foveas are common, movement may be achieved by the very mobile neck.

In man the slight, constant movements of the eye are crucial for sustained vision. This can be experimentally established by keeping the projected image on the same point of the retina. A small mirror is attached to a contact lens and reflects light to one spot on the retina. After a few moments the image seems to disappear. To be restored, it must either be flickered or moved to another point on the retina (Riggs et al. 1953, reviewed in Mueller 1961). In addition to these very small 'saccadic' eye movements there are larger movements which scan the boundaries of figures during exploration of the visual field, perhaps playing an important role in the discrimination of shapes—the process of form vision (Hebb 1949).

PERCEPTION OF SPATIAL ARRAYS
OF LIGHT STIMULI: FORM VISION

It is one thing to demonstrate that an animal has sufficient visual acuity to distinguish two edges of a figure, perhaps a square, and quite another to determine the manner in which that whole shape is seen. To what extent do animals see and distinguish shapes as we do, by referring to the properties of squares, triangles, circles and ovals, rectangles and rhomboids, and stars and stripes? The answers to this question seem to vary widely from animal to animal and according to the shapes we consider.

◆ *Octopus Form Vision.* The small, simple eyes of invertebrates are clearly capable of distinguishing between simple shapes. Many experiments have demonstrated the responsiveness of various invertebrates to black shapes in an arena, clearly implying a capacity for simple form vision (review in Carthy 1958). The actual parameters of the effective stimuli are not known for these species. In the more highly developed simple eye of *Octopus,* our understanding of the basis of form vision is developing rapidly as a result of the intensive studies of Boycott (1954), Sutherland (1960), Young (1961), and others.

By training captive octopuses to associate one shape with reward and another with an electric shock, the capacity for form vision can readily be demonstrated. There is no doubt that an octopus is fully capable of reacting to distinct shapes rather than simply to differences in area or outline (Young 1961). Some discriminations are made more easily than others (Figure 9-9). Octopuses, like rats, more readily confuse circles and squares than vertical and horizontal rectangles (Lashley, see Munn 1950, Beach et al. 1960). The difficulty experienced with oblique rec-

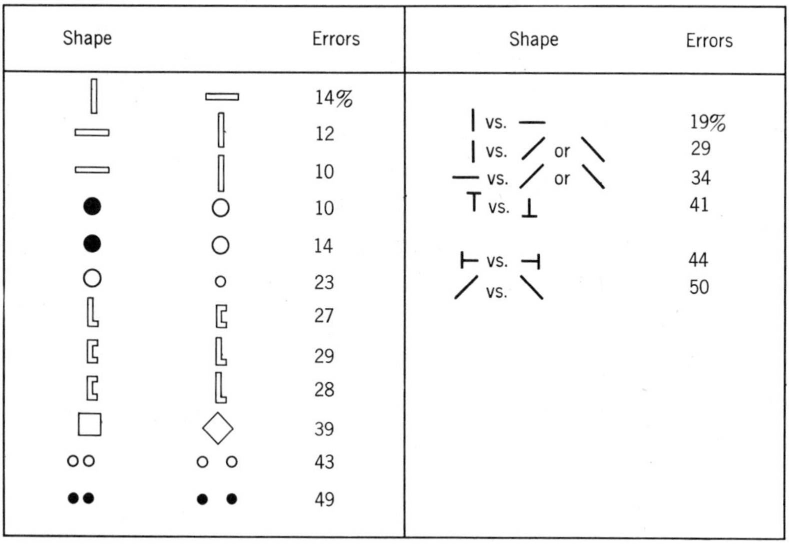

Shape		Errors	Shape	Errors
ǁ	▭	14%	ǀ vs. —	19%
▭	ǁ	12	ǀ vs. ╱ or ╲	29
—	ǁ	10	— vs. ╱ or ╲	34
●	○	10	⊤ vs. ⊥	41
●	○	14		
○	○	23	⊢ vs. ⊣	44
Ɩ	Ɛ	27	╱ vs. ╲	50
Ɛ	Ɩ	29		
Ɛ	Ɩ	28		
□	◇	39		
○ ○	○ ○	43		
●●	● ●	49		

Figure 9-9 An octopus distinguishes some shapes more effectively than others in a shock or reward training situation. After Young 1961.

tangles is especially revealing. If two rectanges at right angles to one another are arranged so that one is vertical and the other is horizontal, they are readily distinguished: but if both are oblique, though still at right angles, they are not distinguished.

This peculiarity led Sutherland (1960) to investigate the dimensions that are relevant to shape discrimination by the octopus. The dimensions he discusses include absolute vertical extent of a shape, vertical extent relative to area, ratio of vertical to horizontal extent, contour relative to area, and number of re-entrants. As a result of careful examination of these possibilities he predicted accurately which figures might be expected to be confused. Sutherland believes that the octopus relies largely upon the horizontal and vertical extent of figures in making its discriminations —hence the confusion between oblique rectangles at right angles, whose horizontal and vertical extents are the same (Figure 9-10, b3 and b4).

Tests with more elaborate figures suggest that the horizontal aspect is analyzed more fully than the vertical, correlating with the frequent occurrence of oval and dendritic fields in the retina with the long axis horizontal. In addition, the vertical axis is differentiated by gravity, illumination, and other clues not available for the right-left axis (Young 1961). Thus up-down differences are recognized more easily than right-left as is the case with various vertebrates (e.g. Figure 9-10, c5 and c6 are more readily distinguished than c7 and c8). The hypothesis predicts that some up-down differences such as those in d1 should be difficult for the octopus to distinguish, and tests confirm this.

If the ability to discriminate shapes depends on the horizontal position of the retina, cooperation of the gravity orientation mechanism is implied. In *Octopus* this ability is a function of the paired statocysts (Dijkgraaf 1961, see page 532). Tests of the visual discriminatory ability of *Octopus* were made following bilateral statocyst removal (Wells 1963). The eyes were no longer held horizontal (Figure 9-11), and learning tests revealed that the first two figures of Figure 9-9 could no longer be distinguished.

Thus Sutherland's hypothesis seems to stand up well in the face of experimental evidence. Although such characters as figure area may be referred to in some cases, the horizontal and vertical extents are the properties of a figure most significant for the octopus eye (Sutherland 1960). These properties in turn will have a profound effect on the way that an octopus perceives its environment.

Octopus has a spontaneous preference in a feeding situation for shapes whose properties cannot be accounted for in the way described. A stimulus-filtering mechanism tends to restrict responsiveness to a certain subclass of the total array of perceptible shapes while an octopus is feeding. The effects can readily be overridden by training but are clearly evident in the behavior of experimentally naive animals. The significant

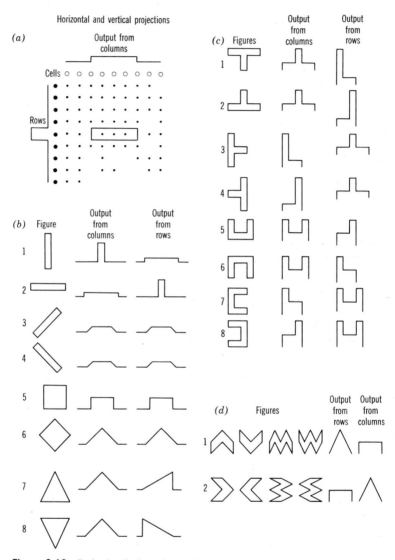

Figure 9-10   Sutherland's hypothesis of shape discrimination in *Octopus*. Part (*a*) shows how horizontal and vertical projections of a figure on the retina, here a rectangle, are supposed to be derived. Parts (*b*) through (*d*) show the projections of various types of figure. In (*d*) are pairs of figures that should be confused according to the hypothesis. The predictions are confirmed. From Young 1961 after Sutherland.

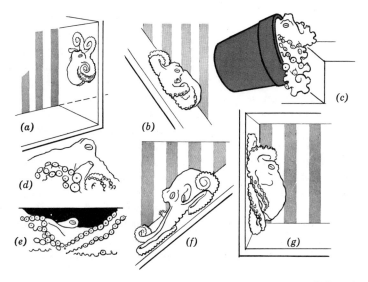

Figure 9-11   An *Octopus* maintains orientation to gravity by means of bilateral statocysts. The slit pupil remains roughly horizontal whatever the orientation of the animal (*a* through *e*). But when the statocysts are removed the eyes are no longer held horizontal (*f, g*). At the same time the ability to distinguish certain pairs of figures is lost. After Wells 1963.

properties, which include movement of a figure along its long axis in the direction of its pointed end, are probably characteristics of some of the animals which are its natural prey (Sutherland and Muntz 1959). If this spontaneous preference were fixed and immutable, the results of all the training experiments would have been different. Moreover, they would have ceased to be a reliable guide to the potential properties of the octopus eye for form vision. Studies of form vision in honeybees may have been confused over a similar issue.

◆ *Honeybee Form Vision.* Most of what we know about the capacities of compound eyes for form vision comes from training studies and spontaneous preference tests of honeybees. When honeybees are seeking sources of nectar and pollen they readily alight upon colored, flowerlike shapes. If the choice of some shapes is rewarded with food, the bees can be trained to approach and alight on them, implying a capacity for form vision. In the absence of experimental training they show spontaneous preferences.

Foraging honeybees prefer to alight on shapes with a broken outline. The radial pattern of most flowers is preferred, but other shapes elicit some responses. A lattice may be as attractive as a star. Exhaustive experiments by Hertz, Wolf, and others (reviewed in Carthy 1958) suggest that attractiveness is a function of the degree of flicker the figure generates in the bee's eye as it flies over. We have already seen that the high flicker-fusion frequency of the eyes of fast-flying insects such as the honeybee permits the perception of a wide range of flicker frequencies (see page 324). The role of flicker was further implied by an experiment in which the effect of movement was examined. Moving shapes are more attractive than stationary ones (Wolf and Zerrahn-Wolf 1937).

All the attempts to train honeybees to distinguish between shapes by associating some with food have been complicated by this spontaneous responsiveness to flicker. In one experiment Hertz (1935) found that the bees could be trained to distinguish solid figures from broken ones, but not solid from solid, or broken from broken (Figure 9-12). On the basis of this and similar experiments, it has been concluded that differences in flicker patterns are the sole basis for form discrimination in the honeybee.

In contrast with this interpretation, Hertz found some evidence of discrimination between simple forms. Sakagami (1956) reached a similar conclusion by presenting simple figures against a checkerboard background. The results of some of von Frisch's experiments on hive recognition and the use of orientation to landmarks by honeybees also implies a capacity for more conventional form vision. In some other Hymenoptera, such as the wasps *Philanthus* and *Ammophila*, the use of landmarks implies a better ability to discriminate simple forms than would be expected from the flicker-vision theory alone (Tinbergen and Kruyt 1938, von Beusekom 1948). The same applies to studies of the effects of the flower patterns called honey guides, which lead honeybees and bumblebees to the centers of flowers (Manning 1956, Daumer 1958). It is difficult to avoid the sus-

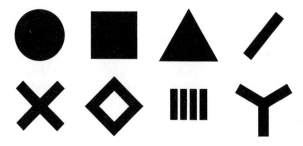

Figure 9-12   Honeybees have great difficulty distinguishing shapes within one row, but they have no difficulty distinguishing two shapes one from each row. After Hertz 1935.

picion that the results of training experiments in which food rewards are used have been confused by stimulus filtering appropriate to the context of searching for flowers but not necessarily dominating vision in other situations to the same extent.

◆ *Form Vision in Mammals.* The form vision of several species of mammals has been intensively studied. In general, the principles of human vision are applicable. Perhaps the most intensive experiments have been done with rats, mainly by Lashley (see Munn 1950, Beach et al. 1960). The history of these experiments is an illuminating comment on the key role of methods in training experiments.

The first attempts to demonstrate form vision in rats led to the conclusion that rats are deficient in detail vision. The demonstrations were conducted in an apparatus with the visual symbols placed near the exits.

In complete contrast, later studies revealed an excellent ability for form vision. These were conducted with a platform from which the animal was required to jump directly at the patterns. The different results were presumably caused by the greater motivation on the Lashley jumping stand. The closer proximity in time of the pattern, and either punishment (falling into a net below) or reward (access to food) may also have been important. Allowing for the rather poor visual acuity of the rat's rod retina, and the fact that rats may not depend too much on vision in nature, Lashley concluded that

one must be impressed by the similarity of the rat's discriminative behavior to the perceptual impressions of the human observer. If a series of patterns is ranked in order of the conspicuousness of the figures for the human eye, that order will have a high predictive value for the rate at which the rat can learn the figures. Stimuli to which the rat transfers in equivalence tests are those obviously similar for man. Figure-ground relations seem to be determined in much the same way for both. Both distinguish complex figures by discovering limited part-figures as cues (Lashley 1938, quoted in Munn 1950, p. 152).

Bearing these arguments in mind, Fantz (1961, 1965) showed that human babies spend more time fixating complex figures than simple ones. They show special interest in concentric circles and checkerboard patterns (Figure 9-13). There is a thought-provoking parallel not only with the rat but also with honeybees. Our knowledge of the incessant movements of the human eye suggests that flicker patterns may be as significant to the human eye as to the compound eyes of insects!

Just as physiological studies of arthropod vision have proceeded hand in hand with behavioral analysis, so also in recent years have dramatic advances in understanding the physiological basis of form vision in vertebrates accompanied behavioral studies. We already know that a large

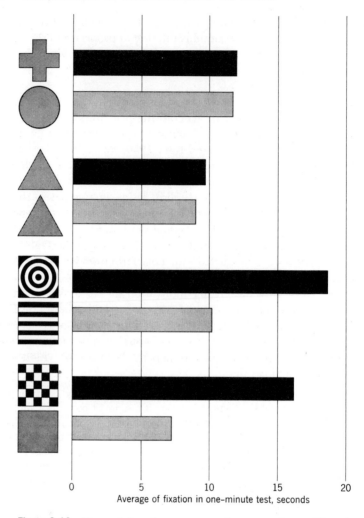

Average of fixation in one–minute test, seconds

Figure 9-13   Human infants fixate more complex patterns longer. The pairs of patterns were presented together. Patterns were red or red on white. After Fantz 1961.

part of the process of integration of incoming information takes place in the eye itself.

◆ *Frog Form Vision.* By shining small spots of light on the retinas of frogs and monitoring the electrical activity of the underlying ganglion cells, the response of different retinal units has been determined. The responsiveness of different units varies. Some respond to both onset and cessation of illumination (on-off units), others only to one or the other (off and on units, Hartline 1938). On units have a maintained discharge that builds up rather slowly. The discharge of the off units often persists several seconds after the light is extinguished (Barlow 1953a).

There is evidence that these types serve different functions. The off units are concentrated in the posterior part of the retina. They probably aid the frog in orienting accurately to a fly before striking at it and are especially easy to stimulate with a moving image. It is well known that frogs will accept only moving objects as food (Maier and Schneirla 1935, Maturana et al. 1960).

By keeping an electrode in one ganglionic cell and moving a spot of light about the retina, it is possible to plot the size of the retinal field of that cell. Off units have a receptive field about one millimeter in diameter. This seems very large for the purpose of accurate location of an object until we remember the great degree of overlap between adjacent fields. Thus the pattern of activity in neighboring and overlapping retinal fields of off units will reveal the position of the image with some accuracy. With on-off cells the size of the receptive fields "would be nicely filled by the image of a fly at two inches" (Barlow 1953b). On-off cells are highly sensitive to movement.

Of most general interest, perhaps, is the demonstration that the activity of a stimulated on-off unit is reduced by simultaneous stimulation of adjacent units. This phenomenon, called lateral inhibition, was first discovered in the eye of the crustacean, *Limulus* (Hartline et al. 1956, Figure 9-14). It has the effect of inducing a maximum level of nervous activity around the contrasting margins of an image on the retina—an important fact in understanding the neural basis of form vision.

In addition to the three types of retinal units described in the frog by Hartline (1938), Maturana, Lettvin, McCulloch, and Pitts (1960) discovered two more, which led them to redefine the properties of the other units as well. The on units they describe as 'sustained edge detectors.' This description distinguishes them from the newly defined 'convex edge detectors.' The latter have similar properties, but respond most strongly to an advancing edge if it is convex rather than straight. The on-off units correspond with their 'changing contrast detectors,' a name that implies both responsiveness to movement and the property of lateral inhibition, which emphasizes margin contrast. Off units become 'dimming detectors.' The fifth category of retinal units, 'dark detectors,' are continuously active. Their discharge rate is related to the light intensity, with a maximum in darkness and a minimum in strong light. These units are slower to adapt than the other types and are thus best suited to register light

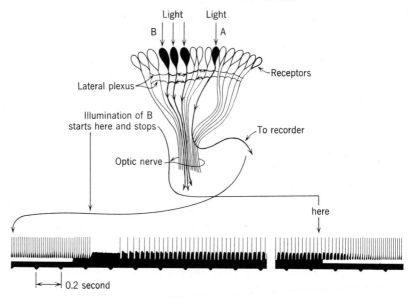

Figure 9-14   Activity of a steadily illuminated ommatidium in the eye of the horseshoe crab, *Limulus* (A) is inhibited when nearby ommatidia (B) are illuminated. After Hartline, Wagner, and Ratliff 1956.

intensity. They do not respond to sharp changes of intensity or to movement.

Here in the frog's eye is a remarkably diverse set of receptor systems, overlapping on the retinal surface, each with a rather different function. They are concerned with transforming simple retinal images into categories of information biologically relevant to the animal.

◆ *Cat Form Vision.* There is good evidence for similar processes in cats. As in the frog, the ganglion cells in the retina of cats have overlapping retinal fields. The level of activity in a given field is reduced by illumination of the areas around it (Kuffler 1953). Unlike the frog, in which the center area of an on-off unit responds both to onset and cessation of light stimulus, the receptive fields in the eye of a light-adapted cat are often arranged with an on center and an off periphery. The center and periphery are, however, antagonistic to each other when stimulated together (Figure 9-15). This reaction again differs from that in the frog, which in the surrounding area inhibits the center area while itself giving no overt response to light. In the cat inhibition works both ways. Nevertheless, the mechanism achieves the same effect of increasing contrast of a figure against its background. Both mechanisms may be described as exhibiting lateral inhibition (Barlow, Fitzhugh, and Kuffler 1957).

These same investigators described the effects that follow dark adaptation in the cat's eye. A loss of visual acuity is to be expected (page 318). It had always been assumed that this loss was a result of an increase in the size of receptive fields during dark adaptation. Barlow and his associates have demonstrated a different kind of change that also contributes to the loss of sensitivity. In dim light the off area in the periphery of the field stops responding and lateral inhibition ceases to occur (Figure 9-15). Thus the loss of visual acuity results from lowered responsiveness to contrast. In their preparations the increase in receptive field was too slight to be significant, but a greater increase may occur in other types of retinal units. There are probably several changes of retinal organization taking place in dark adaptation, and the effects upon the filtering of visual stimuli are likely to be many and varied.

The mechanisms we have discussed so far establish some basic principles of information transmission from the receptors but are of little help in establishing how this information permits form vision. By monitoring the activity of single neurons in the striate cortex, the visual center in the cat's brain, Hubel and Wiesel (1959, 1962) have been able to take the analysis further. These brain cells, like the ganglion cells, subtend retinal fields in the cat's eye. They also have on and off areas that are mutually inhibitory. The shape and arrangement of these areas differ from the concentric patterns of the retina, however (Figure 9-16).

By using a rectangular spot of light instead of a circular one, striking

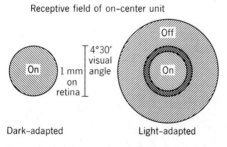

Receptive field of on-center unit

On — 1 mm on retina — 4°30′ visual angle

Off — On

Dark-adapted   Light-adapted

Figure 9-15 Proposed organization of the receptive field of an on-center unit, light and dark adapted in the retina of a cat. "On" or "off" responses to a long flash occur when the stimulus falls in the region so labeled. The positions of these areas have been inferred from area threshold curves and have not been determined directly. After Barlow, Fitzhugh, and Kuffler 1957.

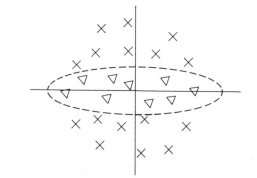

Receptive field
on retina

1 second

Locus of
stimulation

1° light spot

a

b

c

d

e

f

5° light spot

(a)

Figure 9-16 (a) Responses of a cell in the striate cortex of a cat to a 1° spot of light on the retina. The receptive fields are on the contralateral side from the eye stimulated; there was no response from stimulation of the ipsilateral eye. The receptive field or the retina is mapped on the right; x areas are excitatory, Δ areas are inhibitory. (b, c) A receptive field of another type with an excitation center and an inhibitory periphery. In (b) a rectangular spot of light, 1° x 8°, with its center in the middle of the receptive field is rotated to seven other positions. In (c) one end of a 1° x 5° light slit remains in the center of the receptive field during the rotation. After Hubel and Wiesel 1959.

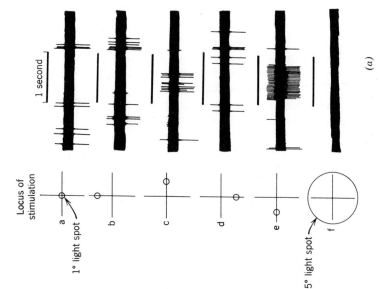

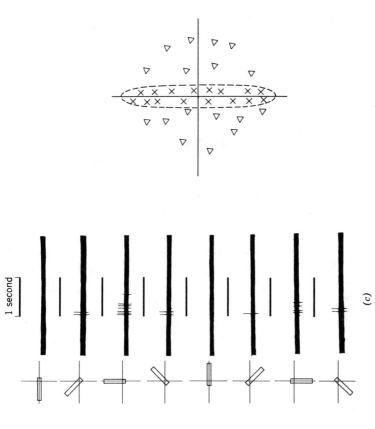

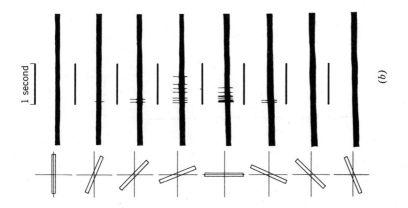

(c)

(b)

1 second

1 second

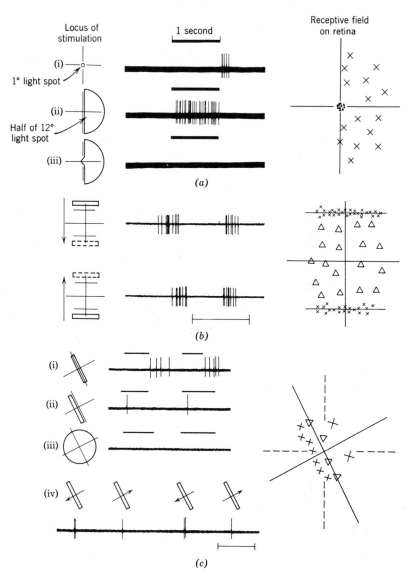

Figure 9-17 In (*a*) a 1° spot of light covers the inhibitory region (i), whereas in (ii) half of a 12° circle of light reaches the eye. When the circle is extended to include the inhibitory area activity ceases. In (*b*) the slow movement of a 1° x 8° slit up and down across the receptive field results in bursts of cortical action potentials each time the light crosses an excitatory region. Part (*c*) shows the response of the ipsilateral eye to (i) an obliquely oriented 1° x 10° slit of light covering the central region, and (ii) the flanking region to the left. In (iii) a 12° spot covers the entire receptive field, and in (iv) an oblique 1° x 10° slit is moved transversely in two directions, eliciting a strong response in one direction and a weak response in the other. After Hubel and Wiesel 1959.

variations were demonstrated in the responses of different units to movement of the image in different directions. A unit with a long on area surrounded by an off zone responded strongly to a vertical rectangle of light, but not at all to the same rectangle when it was presented horizontally (Figure 9-16). Other areas responded differently to a rectangle when it was moved from up to down and vice versa, or when it was shifted along the oblique axis (Figure 9-17). These differences in responsiveness to movement in different directions can be related to varying strengths of the inhibitory relationships in different directions, with the strongest response occurring when the image moved from the off area to the stronger of the two on areas.

Barlow, Hill, and Levick (1964) have found ganglion cells in the retina of the rabbit that respond selectively to the direction and speed of movement of an image as well as to localized dimming and brightening. This response indicates still further sophistication in the peripheral analysis of incoming stimuli. It is becoming evident that the mechanism of lateral inhibition, elaborated upon by whatever processes intervene between the retina and the striate cortex, can achieve much more than a simple emphasis of figure-ground contrast. With appropriate arrangement of fields upon the retina, it can also provide a basis for achieving responsiveness to images with a specific shape, size, orientation, and direction of movement. Perhaps something of this kind is responsible for the peculiarities of form vision in *Octopus,* which we described earlier.

These, then, are some of the stimulus-filtering processes that intervene in the visual pathway between the retina and the brain. They result in a profound reorganization of the incoming information. The physiological investigations of these mechanisms are just beginning. The role of eye movements in form vision has been the subject of much discussion (e.g. Hebb 1949). Foveate animals that use eye or head movements in exploring the visual field must rely in part on eye movements in form discrimination. Experiments with a fixed image on the human retina (page 333) show that considerable form vision in the region of the fovea is possible without eye movements. Moreover, the curious ways in which coherent parts of such a fixed image disappear and reappear must point to more complex physiological processes than those we have outlined earlier (Pritchard 1961). It is a challenge to the physiologist to explain how such mechanisms work.

THE PERCEPTION OF DISTANCE

A complete account of the spatial properties of light stimuli must include a consideration of the dimension of depth. Many animals can certainly perceive distance, but we are largely ignorant of the cues that they use. There are a number of possibilities, some involving only one eye, others both. In animals, as in man, the most accurate estimates of close distances are made through binocular vision.

◆ *Cues to Distance.* The predatory larvae of dragonflies seize living prey by the rapid extension of their jawed labial mask. The distance to the prey is judged by binocular vision, and the mask is extended only when the object reaches the distance that intersects the position of maximum extension of the mask (Baldus 1926). Here we may assume that the degree of convergence of the visual axes provides the distance clue. The disparity between the images that the same object subtends to each eye, the basis of stereoscopy, may also provide information about depth, but we do not know whether animals exploit this principle.

A variety of monocular clues is also available, including (1) relative size: the distance of a familiar object may be judged by its size; (2) linear perspective: parallel lines apparently converge as they move further away; (3) aerial perspective: texture, color, and clarity change with distance; (4) nearness to the horizon: distant objects tend to approach the horizon; (5) interposition: if one object overlaps another, it must be closer; (6) accommodation: at close range the circles of blurring which surround the image of an object out of focus may give clues to distance; (7) light and shade: in certain circumstances shadows may give an impression of depth; (8) movement parallax: as an eye is moved in the visual field, near objects show more relative movement than distant ones. These are the main methods upon which a monocular judgment of distance may be based (Walls 1942, Gibson 1950, Graham 1951).

Little is known about which of these clues animals use. Domestic chicks evidently respond to the shadows cast by grains of corn, for they are less ready to eat grains whose shadows have been eliminated (Benner 1938, Hess 1961). Most of the evidence we have is of a somewhat anecdotal nature. A major reason for this is the difficulty of conducting animal experiments. One outstanding exception is the work of Gibson and Walk (1960, Walk 1965) on the so-called 'visual cliff.'

◆ *'Visual Cliffs.'* Most animals are subject to injury from falling. Many avoid cliffs, and this can be demonstrated under experimental conditions. A room is provided with a false glass floor. On one side of the room there is a second floor immediately below the glass. On the other side is a similar floor, but a foot below the glass. Animals are released on a bridge down the middle of the room and are required to walk on the glass, either on the 'shallow' side or the 'deep' side.

Domestic chicks invariably choose the shallow side, and the same is true of kittens, kids, and lambs. A kid placed on the glass over the deep side refuses to put its feet down, and backs up in a posture of defense with front legs rigid and hind legs limp. In this state of immobility the kid could be pushed forward across the glass until its head and field of vision crossed the edge of the surrounding solid surface. Then it would relax and spring forward upon the surface (Gibson and Walk 1960). Clearly the distance of the floor beneath the glass is perceived and responded to. Rats behave similarly as long as they cannot reach the glass with their vibrissae before choosing.

The value of this situation lies in the control the experimenter has over the visual clues by which the distance of the floor is judged, especially

Figure 9-18   A kitten at the edge of a 'visual cliff.' The cliff is no real hazard; a glass pane covers the apparent chasm. After a photograph in Tinbergen 1965.

since chicks and rats make little use of binocular cues. If checkerboard patterns are placed on the floor, two monocular cues available to judge distance are (1) relative size and density of the pattern and (2) movement parallax as the animal moves along the bridge. By making the pattern on the deep side larger than that on the shallow side, relative size and density can be eliminated. Rats and chicks still chose the shallow side, implying the use of movement parallax. If movement parallax is eliminated by placing the pattern immediately beneath the glass on both sides, but with smaller squares on the deep side, the chicks step off each side of the bridge indiscriminately. Rats show some preference for the shallow side, suggesting that they use both relative size and movement parallax as clues to depth (Figure 9-18). There is some evidence that the response to relative size is acquired, while responses to movement parallax appear on the rat's first encounter with such visual stimuli. The responsiveness of chicks and gulls on a visual cliff also seems to be affected by prior experience (Emlen 1963, Tallarico and Farrell 1964).

Gibson and Walk's experiments emphasize the dramatic results that can sometimes be achieved with simple apparatus. Perhaps others will follow suit in exploring the neglected subject of distance perception in animals.

CONCLUSIONS ON STIMULUS FILTERING IN VISION

Much reorganization of visual information takes place in the process of transmission to the brain. Mechanisms in the eyes of frogs and cats account in part for responsiveness to certain specific shapes, orientations, and movements. What more must be postulated to explain the entire process of stimulus filtering in vision? In particular, how much can be explained in terms of the normal mode of functioning of the visual pathway, and to what extent does the process imply special filtering mechanisms which are called into play only during the course of certain reactions? We can pose these questions with respect to cases of specific responsiveness, and also in relation to temporal changes of responsiveness.

Behavioral studies have established many examples of responsiveness to specific visual stimuli (page 237). Some are the result of the normal functioning of the visual system. The insect compound eye is especially responsive to flickering stimuli, and the responsiveness of feeding honeybees to the radial patterns of flowers may be simply responsiveness to the broken outlines perceived as a high rate of flickering in the honeybee's eye as it flies over.

The same relationship has also been demonstrated in other insects in a courtship situation. The role of movement in evoking the courtship responses of male butterflies is well established. The critical experiments of Magnus (1958) established an increase of responsiveness of fritillary butterflies with more rapid flicker rates, up to about 140 stimulus changes per second (page 241). Beyond this rate, which is much faster than the normal butterfly wingbeat, responsiveness declines. Electrophysiological studies revealed a flicker-fusion frequency at 150 stimulus changes per second. Thus it appears that the male fritillary butterfly simply responds more strongly to higher rates of flicker as long as he can perceive them. We are once more reminded of honeybees and flower patterns.

Male houseflies also respond to flickering stimuli during courtship. By experimenting with models with a broken outline and other models moved at a rapid rate, Vogel (1957) found an increase of responsiveness up to 270 stimulus changes per second, and beyond this a decline. The flicker-fusion frequency is estimated from electrophysiological studies at 265 per second (Autrum 1950).

Although we cannot be sure that this reliance on flicker vision is equally extreme in all situations (page 338), it is evidently widespread. Perhaps it should be regarded as one of the normal concomitants of vision with the compound eye. Because the limits of the flicker-fusion frequency are set by retinal mechanisms, we can regard this as a peripheral stimulus filter.

In vertebrates peripheral mechanisms aid the frog in responding to flies as food and help the cat to descry form. Some behavioral experiments have probably also involved mechanisms of this kind. For example, most of the stimulus parameters that Tinbergen and Perdeck (1950) found effective in evoking the pecking by gull chicks at a red bill spot (page 388) are also rendered conspicuous by peripheral mechanisms in various birds (Weidmann and Weidmann 1958, Weidmann 1961, Marler 1961, Hailman 1962). Thus the young chick may peck primarily at what to it is a small conspicuous object. It is thus not surprising that 'supernormal' stimuli which are more effective than the stimuli that naturally evoke the response can be devised (see page 390).

There are other cases of responsiveness to specific visual stimuli that cannot be explained in this way. For example, the responsiveness of different butterflies to species-specific wing color (page 258) has never been correlated with variations in the spectral sensitivity curves of their eyes. The responsiveness to particular shapes of butterflies (page 257), dragonflies (page 258), and spiders (page 254) is difficult to explain by peripheral filtering. The possibility of lateral inhibition has not yet been fully explored, however. In vertebrates as well, some of the examples of specific responsiveness to owls in mobbing and other responses of birds cannot be explained by peripheral filtering.

When periodic changes in visual responsiveness occur, as when a male *Heliconius* butterfly visits red objects for courting and yellow objects for feeding (page 256), a temporal change in the stimulus-filtering process is implied (Crane 1955). Pierid butterflies respond to yellowish-white objects while courting, to any color, especially yellow and blue, while feeding, and to green and blue-green while looking for a place to lay eggs (Ilse 1941). Whether peripheral changes in wavelength sensitivity take place with these shifts of preference, or whether central changes are responsible, we do not know.

A similar shift in responsiveness with time is implied in many animals, vertebrate and invertebrate, that respond to different spatial configurations or shapes when feeding, drinking, fighting, escaping, or mating. We are far from understanding the underlying physiological mechanism involved. No doubt the complete picture will include efferent control over visual functions, as in audition (Granit 1955, Livingstone 1959). In this case central mechanisms will have to be involved as well. We should also bear in mind that the distinction between peripheral and central mechanisms is less readily applied to vision than, for example, to chemoreception. From an embryological point of view the eye itself is part of the vertebrate central nervous system.

REFERENCES

Adrian, E. D. and R. Matthews. 1928. The action of light on the eye. Part III. The interaction of retinal neurones. *J. Physiol.*, **65**:273–298.

Autrum, H. 1949. Neue Versuche zum optischen Ausflösungsvermögen fliegender Insekten. *Experientia*, **5**:271–277.

——. 1950. Die Belichtungspotentiale und das Sehen der Insekten (Untersuchungen an Calliphora und Dixippus). *Z. vergl. Physiol.*, **32**:176–227.

—— and M. Stöker. 1952. Über optische Verschmelzungsfrequenzen und stroboskopisches Sehen bei Insekten. *Biol. Zbl.*, **71**:129–152.

Baldus, K. 1926. Experimentelle Untersuchungen über die Entfernungslokalisation der Libellen (*Aeschna cyanea*). *Z. vergl. Physiol.*, **3**:475–505.

Barlow, H. B. 1953a. Action potentials from the frog's retina. *J. Physiol.*, **119**:58–68.

——. 1953b. Summation and inhibition in the frog's retina. *J. Physiol.*, **119**:69–88.

——, R. Fitzhugh, and S. W. Kuffler. 1957. Change of organization in the receptive fields of the cat's retina during dark adaptation. *J. Physiol.*, **137**:338–354.

——, R. M. Hill, and W. R. Levick. 1964. Retinal ganglion cells responding selectively to direction and speed of image motion in the rabbit. *J. Physiol.*, **173**:377–407.

Bartley, S. H. 1951. The psychophysiology of vision. In *Handbook of Experimental Psychology,* ed. by S. S. Stevens: 921–984. John Wiley and Sons, New York.

Beach, F. A., D. O. Hebb, C. T. Morgan, H. W. Nissen (Eds.). 1960. *The Neuropsychology of Lashley*. McGraw-Hill Book Company, New York.

Benner, J. 1938. Untersuchungen über die Raumwahrnehmung der Hühner. *Z. wiss. Zool.*, 151:382–444.

Bernhard, G. G. and D. Ottoson. 1960. Studies on the relation between the pigment migration and the sensitivity changes during dark adaptation in diurnal and nocturnal Lepidoptera. *J. Gen. Physiol.*, 44:205–215.

Beusekom, G. von. 1948. Some experiments on the optical orientation in *Philanthus triangulum* Fabr. *Behaviour*, 1:195–225.

Birukow, G. 1949. Die Entwicklung des Tages - und des Dämmerungssehens im Auge des Grasfrosches (*Rana temporaria* L.). *Z. vergl. Physiol.*, 31:322–347.

Boycott, B. B. 1954. Learning in *Octopus vulgaris* and other cephalopods. *Pubbl. Staz. Zool. Napoli*, 25:67–93.

Brett, J. R. 1957. The eye. In *The Physiology of Fishes*, ed. by M. E. Brown, Vol. 2:121–154. The Academic Press, New York.

Buddenbrock, W. von. 1952. *Vergleichende Physiologie*, Vol. 1. Sinnesphysiologie. Verlag Birkhäuser und Cie. A.G., Basel.

Bullock, T. H. and G. A. Horridge. 1965. *Structure and Function in the Nervous Systems of Invertebrates*, Vol. 1. W. H. Freeman and Company, Publishers, San Francisco.

Burtt, E. T. and W. T. Catton. 1954. Visual perception of movement in the locust. *J. Physiol.*, 125:566–580.

Carthy, J. D. 1958. *An Introduction to the Behaviour of Invertebrates*. George Allen and Unwin, London.

Crane, J. 1955. Imaginal behavior of a Trinidad butterfly, *Heliconius erato hydara* Hewitson, with special reference to the social use of color. *Zoologica*, 40:167–196.

Daumer, K. 1956. Reizmetrische Untersuchung des Farbensehens der Bienen. *Z. vergl. Physiol.*, 38:413–478.

————. 1958. Blumenfarben, wie sie die Bienen sehen. *Z. vergl. Physiol.*, 41:49–110.

Dethier, V. G. 1953. Vision. In *Insect Physiology*, ed. by K. D. Roeder: 488–522. John Wiley and Sons, New York.

Dijkgraaf, S. 1961. The statocyst of *Octopus vulgaris* as a rotation receptor. *Pubbl. Staz. Zool. Napoli*, 32:64–87.

Duijm, M. 1958. On the position of a ribbon-like central area in the eyes of some birds. *Arch. Néer. Zool.*, 13(Suppl. 1):128–145.

Duke-Elder, S. 1958. *System of Ophthalmology*. Vol. I. The Eye in Evolution. Henry Kimpton, London.

Emlen, J. T. 1963. Determinants of cliff edge and escape responses in herring gull chicks in nature. *Behaviour*, 22:1–15.

Exner, S. 1891. *Die Physiologie der Facettikten Augen von Kresben und Insekten*. Deuticke, Leipzig and Vienna.

Fantz, R. L. 1961. The origin of form perception. *Sci. Amer.*, 204(5):66–72.

————. 1965. The ontogeny of perception. In *Behavior of Nonhuman Primates*, ed. by A. M. Schrier, H. F. Harlow, and F. Stollnitz: 365–403. The Academic Press, New York.

Frisch, K. von. 1914. Der Farbensinn und Formensinn der Biene. *Zool. Jahrb., Abt. Allg. Zool. Physiol.*, 35:1–182.

————. 1949. Die Polarisation des Himmelslichtes als orientierender Faktor bei den Tänzen der Bienen. *Experientia*, 5:142–148.

————. 1964. *Aus dem Leben der Bienen*. Springer Verlag, Berlin.

Gibson, E. J. and R. D. Walk. 1960. The 'visual cliff.' *Sci. Amer.*, 202(4):64–71.

Gibson, J. J. 1950. *The Perception of the Visual World*. Houghton Mifflin Company, Boston.

Goldsmith, T. H. 1961. The color vision of insects. In *Light and Life*, ed. by W. D. McElroy and B. Glass: 771–794. Johns Hopkins Press, Baltimore.

Graham, C. H. 1951. Visual perception. In *Handbook of Experimental Psychology*, ed. by S. S. Stevens: 868–920. John Wiley and Sons, New York.

Granit, R. 1955. *Receptors and Sensory Perception*. Yale University Press, New Haven.

———. 1959. Neural activity in the retina. In *Handbook of Physiology*, ed. by J. Field, Sec. 1, Vol. I:693–712. American Physiological Society, Washington, D.C.

Hailman, J. P. 1962. Development of species recognition in gulls. Quoted in *Behavioral Aspects of Ecology* by P. H. Klopfer. Prentice-Hall, Englewood Cliffs.

Hartline, H. K. 1938. The response of single optic nerve fibers of the vertebrate eye to illumination of the retina. *Amer. J. Physiol.*, **121**:400–415.

———, H. G. Wagner, and F. Ratliff. 1956. Inhibition in the eye of *Limulus. J. Gen. Physiol.*, **39**:651–673.

Hassenstein, B. 1961. Wie sehen Insekten Bewegungen. *Naturwissenschaften*, **48**:207–214.

Hebb, D. O. 1949. *The Organization of Behavior*. John Wiley and Sons, New York.

Herter, K. 1953. *Die Fischdressuren und ihre sinnesphysiologischen Grundlagen*. Akad.-Verlag, Berlin.

Hertz, M. 1935. Die Untersuchungen über den Formensinn der Honigbiene. *Naturwissenschaften*, **23**:618–624.

Hess, E. H. 1956. Natural preferences of chicks and ducklings for objects of different colors. *Psychol. Rep.*, **2**:477–483.

———. 1961. Shadows and depth perception. *Sci. Amer.*, **204**(3):139–148.

Hubel, D. H. and T. N. Wiesel. 1959. Receptive fields of single neurones in the cat's striate cortex. *J. Physiol.*, **148**:574–591.

——— and ———. 1962. Receptive fields, binocular interaction and functional architecture in the cat's visual cortex. *J. Physiol.*, **160**:106–154.

Ilse, D. 1941. The colour vision of insects. *Proc. Roy. Phil. Soc. Glasgow*, **65**:68–82.

Kalmus, H. 1949. Optomotor responses in Drosophila and Musca. *Physiol. Comp. Oecol.*, **1**:127–147.

Kuffler, S. W. 1953. Discharge patterns and functional organization of mammalian retina. *J. Neurophysiol.*, **16**:37–68.

Livingston, R. B. 1959. Central control of receptors and sensory transmission systems. In *Handbook of Physiology*, ed. by J. Field, Sec. 1, Vol. 1:741–760. American Physiological Society, Washington, D.C.

Magnus, D. 1958. Experimentelle Untersuchungen zur Bionomie und Ethologie des Kaisermantels *Argynnis paphia* L. (Lep. Nymph.) *Z. Tierpsychol.*, **15**:397–426.

Maier, N. R. F. and T. C. Schneirla. 1964. *Principles of Animal Psychology*. Dover Publications, New York.

Manning, A. 1956. The effect of honey-guides. *Behaviour*, **9**:114–139.

Marler, P. 1961. The filtering of external stimuli during instinctive behaviour. In *Current Problems in Animal Behaviour*, ed. by W. H. Thorpe and O. L. Zangwill: 150–166, Cambridge University Press, Cambridge.

Maturana, H. R., J. Y. Lettvin, W. S. McCulloch, and W. H. Pitts. 1960. Anatomy and physiology of vision in the frog (*Rana pipiens*). *J. Gen. Physiol.*, **43**(6, Part 2):129–175.

Menner, E. 1938. Die Bedeutung des Pecten im Auge des Vogels für die Wahrnehmung von Bewegungen. *Zool. Jb., Abt. Allg. Zool. Physiol.*, **58**:481–538.

Milne, L. J. and M. Milne. 1959. Photosensitivity in invertebrates. In *Handbook of Physiology*, ed. by J. Fields, Sect. 1, Vol. 1:621–645. American Physiological Society, Washington, D.C.

Moody, M. F. 1962. Evidence for the intraocular discrimination of vertically and horizontally polarized light by *Octopus. J. Exp. Biol.*, **39**:21–30.

——— and J. R. Parriss. 1961. The discrimination of polarized light by *Octopus*: A behavioural and morphological study. *Z. vergl. Physiol.*, **44**:268–291.

Mueller, C. G. 1961. Visual sensitivity. *Ann. Rev. Psychol.,* **12**:311–334.

Munn, N. L. 1950. *Handbook of Psychological Research on the Rat.* Houghton Mifflin Company, Boston.

Pritchard, R. M. 1961. Stabilized images on the retina. *Sci. Amer.,* **204**(6):72–78.

Pumphrey, R. J. 1961. Sensory organs: hearing. In *Biology and Comparative Physiology of Birds,* ed. by A. J. Marshall, Vol 2:69–86. The Academic Press, New York.

Ratliff, F. 1962. Some interrelationships among physics, physiology, and psychology in the study of vision. In *Psychology: A Study of a Science,* ed. by S. Koch. McGraw-Hill Book Company, New York.

———, W. H. Miller, and H. K. Hartline. 1958. Neural interaction in the eye and the integration of receptor activity. *Ann. N.Y. Acad. Sci.,* **74**:210–222.

Reichardt, W. 1961. Autocorrelation, a principle for the evaluation of sensory information by the central nervous system. In *Sensory Communication,* ed. by W. A. Rosenblith: 303–317. Massachusetts Institute of Technology Press, Cambridge.

Rowell, C. H. F. and M. J. Wells. 1961. Retinal orientation and discrimination of polarized light by octopuses. *J. Exp. Biol.,* **38**:827–831.

Sakagami, S. F. 1956. Zur Wahrnehmungspsychologie der optischen Dressur bei der Honigbiene. Beitrag I: Dressierbarkeit gegen konturarme *Figur* gestellt auf konturreichem *Grund. J. Fac. Sci. Hokkaido Univ.* (Ser. 6, Zool.), **12**:333–361.

Stockhammer, K. 1959. Die Orientierung nach der Schwingungsrichtung linear polarisierten Lichtes und ihre sinnesphysiologischen Grundlagen. *Ergeb. Biol.,* **21**:23–56.

Sutherland, N. S. 1960. Theories of shape discrimination in *Octopus. Nature,* **186**:840–844.

——— and W. R. A. Muntz. 1959. Simultaneous discrimination training and preferred directions of motion in visual discrimination of shape in *Octopus vulgaris* Lamarck. *Pubbl. Staz. Zool. Napoli,* **31**:109–126.

Tallarico, R. B. and W. M. Farrell. 1964. Studies of visual depth perception: an effect of early experience on chicks on a visual cliff. *J. comp. physiol. Psychol.,* **57**:94–96.

Tinbergen, N. 1965. *Animal Behavior.* Time-Life Books, New York.

——— and W. Kruyt. 1938. Über die Orientierung des Bienenwolfes (*Philanthus triangulum* Fabr.). III. Die Bevorzugung bestimmter Wegmarken. *Z. vergl. Physiol.,* **25**:292–334.

——— and A. C. Perdeck. 1950. On the stimulus situation releasing the begging response in the newly hatched herring gull chick (*Larus argentatus argentatus* Pont). *Behaviour* **3**:1–39.

Vogel, G. 1957. Verhaltensphysiologische Untersuchungen über die den Weibchenbesprung des Stubenfliegen-Männchens (*Musca domestica*) auslösenden optischen Faktoren. *Z. Tierpsychol.,* **14**:309–323.

Wald, G. 1959. The photoreceptor process in vision. In *Handbook of Physiology,* ed. by J. Field, Sect. 1, Vol. I:671–692. American Physiological Society, Washington, D.C.

Walk, R. D. 1965. The study of visual depth and distance perception in animals. *Adv. Study Behav.,* **1**:99–154.

Walls, G. L. 1942. *The Vertebrate Eye.* Cranbrook Institute of Science, Bloomfield Hills, Michigan.

Waterman, T. H. 1961. Light sensitivity and vision. In *The Physiology of the Crustacea,* ed. by T. H. Waterman, Vol. 2:1–64. The Academic Press, New York.

Weidmann, R. and U. Weidmann. 1958. An analysis of the stimulus situation releasing foodbegging in the black-headed gull. *Brit. J. Anim. Behav.,* **6**:114.

Weidmann, U. 1961. The stimuli eliciting begging in gulls and terns (Abstract). *Anim. Behav.,* **9**:115–116.

Wells, M. J. 1963. The orientation of Octopus. *Ergeb. Biol.,* **26**:40–54.

Wigglesworth, V. B. 1953. *The Principles of Insect Physiology* (5th edition). Methuen and Company, London, and E. P. Dutton and Company, New York.

Wolf, E. and G. Zerrahn-Wolf. 1937. Flicker and the reactions of bees to flowers. *J. Gen. Physiol.,* **20:**511–518.

Wood, C. A. 1917. *The Fundus Oculi of Birds.* Lakeside Press, Chicago.

Wooldridge, D. E. 1963. *The Machinery of the Brain.* McGraw-Hill Book Company, New York.

Young, J. Z. 1961. Learning and discrimination in the octopus. *Biol. Rev.,* **36:**32–96.

Zonana, H. V. 1961. Fine structure of the squid retina. *Bull. Johns Hopkins Hospital,* **109:**185–205.

ten

BEHAVIORAL FUNCTIONS OF VISION

Location of environments and food • Predator-prey relations • The
evolution of cryptic and aposematic coloration • Visual mimicry •
The symbiotic relationship of pollinating insects and flowering plants •
Evolution of social releasers, functioning in aggregation and dispersal,
individual, sexual, and species recognition • Properties of visual communication systems.

Vision is the most important sensory modality in the environmental control of
the behavior of vertebrate animals and many invertebrates. The unique
spatial properties of light stimuli provide the commonest basis for obstacle
avoidance in rapid locomotion, and oriented responses are given to many
different types of remote visual stimuli (page 543). Much of the research
on eliciting and sensitizing effects of the environment on behavior has
been concerned with visual stimuli. Until recently most discussions of the
origin and evolution of animal communication signals have been based
on visual systems (e.g. Lorenz 1935, 1941, Tinbergen 1940, 1952, 1954).

LOCATION OF ENVIRONMENTS

◆ *Direction Finding.* In the late nineteenth and early twentieth centuries
many researchers were concerned with the role of light in the control of
orientation of movements. Using the work of botanists on the 'tropisms'
of plant gametes and unicellular algae as a point of departure, Jacques

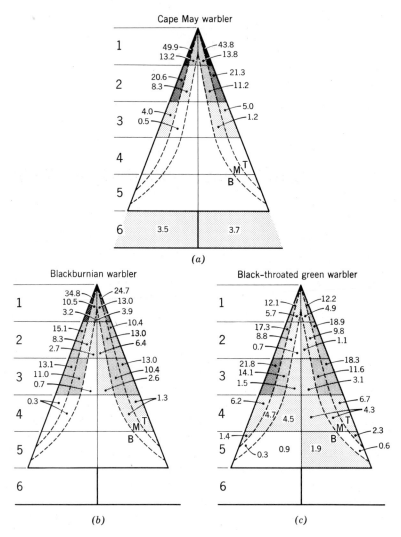

Figure 10-1   The foraging zone of five species of wood warblers, Parulidae, in conifers. The preferred habitats are shaded to show intensity of use, the darker shading representing the heaviest use. Relative amount of time on the left, relative number of observations on the right. (*a*) Cape May warbler, *Dendroica tigrina*, (*b*) blackburnian warbler, *D. fusca,* (*c*) black-throated green warbler, *D. virens,* (*d*) bay-breasted warbler, *D. castanea,* and (*e*) myrtle warbler, *D. coronata*. Each branch was divided into the base (B), the middle zone of old needles (M), and the terminal zone of new needles and buds (T). After MacArthur 1958.

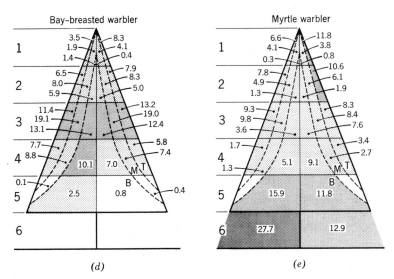

(d)   (e)

Loeb introduced zoologists at the turn of the century to the subject of simple orientation mechanisms. He inspired others to explore further, and many important investigators during that period, A. Alverdes, S. J. Holmes, A. Kuhn, and S. O. Mast, and others still active today such as W. von Buddenbrock and O. Koehler, made the orientation mechanisms of invertebrates a major target of their research. The work of a whole generation was admirably summarized by Fraenkel and Gunn (1940), much of it concerned with responses to light.

Positive and negative phototaxes are widespread among invertebrates as a means of selecting environments. The sign of response may be adjusted to variations in the external stimulus situation and to changes in physiological state. The unicellular flagellate, *Euglena,* which requires light for photosynthesis, moves toward a dim light but away from a very bright one. Newly hatched blowfly larvae are photopositive, a response that favors dispersal from the place of hatching. Later they become photonegative and hide from predators. The tendency of some fruit flies to move away from light as the temperature rises or humidity falls reduces the chance of desiccation under natural conditions (Pittendrigh 1958).

The orientation of the body may be based on the direction of incident light, as with the so-called 'dorsal light reaction' in which the animal maintains posture by keeping the dorsal side toward light, which will usually be sunlight from above (page 526). Here, too, the sign of the response may vary. Hawkmoth caterpillars, for example, present their dorsal surface to light when they are young. They gradually change to

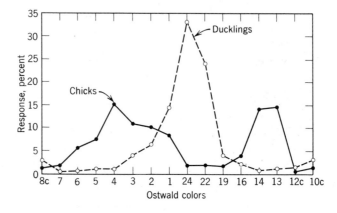

Figure 10-2 The color preferences of inexperienced ducklings and chicks, measured by relative number of pecks delivered to each color. The red end of the spectrum is to the left of the graph, the violet end to the right. From Hess 1960.

a ventral light reaction as they mature so that they hang upside down under natural conditions (de Ruiter 1956). The older larvae are so colored as to be camouflaged by countershading, and they begin to hang upside down with the dark belly upward at about the time that the counter-shading becomes fully developed.

◆ *Selection of Habitat.* Birds and other vertebrates make use of visual stimuli for the selection of more specific environments (Lack 1933, 1944, 1947, Svärdson 1949). MacArthur (1958) has shown that five species of warblers living in the same spruce forest select different parts of the tree for their activities and use different tactics in foraging for food (Figure 10-1). We know little of the mechanisms underlying these variations in habitat selection. In reviewing this subject Klopfer and Hailman (1965, also Klopfer 1962) point out that mechanical consequences of a certain body size, position and length of the legs and feet, and size of the bill may all affect an animal's choice of habitat (see Hinde 1959, Kear 1962). Although such physical determinants must often be involved (e.g. Davis 1957, Hildén 1965), they are not always obvious.

Preliminary tests on one species, the chipping sparrow, suggest that visual characteristics of the environment also play a part (Klopfer and Hailman 1965). Wild and hand-raised sparrows placed in a chamber with pine boughs on one side and oak boughs on the other chose the pine, the natural habitat preference of the population from which the experimental subjects were drawn. This occurred in spite of the equalization of perching opportunities by the provision of artificial perches. It is difficult to avoid the conclusion that the preference for pine is largely based on vision. The role of vision in habitat selection is a new realm of investigation which awaits exploration.

◆ *Food Selection.* The habitat that an animal occupies may in turn determine the food objects encountered, shaping in large measure the feeding pattern of the species. The structure of the feeding equipment may play a part (see page 131). Direct visual stimuli from the food are not to be ignored, but little work has been done on nonpredatory species. Stimuli that evoke pecking at grain have been analyzed in chicks. Small, rounded, three-dimensional objects elicit most responses (Fantz 1957). The shadows resulting from directional lighting are important cues (Hess 1961) and so is color.

Chicks peck most at blue and orange objects. By contrast, ducklings show a strong preference for green objects (Hess 1956, 1960, Figure 10-2). It is tempting to speculate on the significance of the difference. Although the blue preference of chicks is difficult to relate to any natural food, ripe seeds, their staple diet, are often orange in color. Ducklings, on the other hand, feed on aquatic weeds and, more especially, on the insects that live on them. A preference for pecking at green objects may well aid in the location of proper food (Collias 1962). Kear (1964) has shown that the preference for green recurs in many ducks and geese (Table 10-1). Young magpie geese peck at green and yellow objects, similar in color to the seeds of swamp grasses that are found in their gizzards (Davies 1961).

There are a myriad of unanswered questions concerning the sensory basis of food selection. To what extent does vision play a role in the different selection of herbaceous plants which African ungulates make while feeding on the same sward (Talbot 1962)? Comparative investigation of habitat and food selection is in its infancy. It could become one of the most fruitful links between ecological and behavioral studies.

Table 10-1 Pecks at Colored Spots by Various Waterfowl Groups and Some Other Precocial Birds

	Red	Orange	Yellow	Green	Blue-green	Blue
Geese	14.0	11.2	12.7	30.5	16.6	15.0
Diving ducks	12.1	13.3	19.2	26.7	15.8	12.9
Dabbling ducks	10.4	8.0	18.9	27.3	18.0	17.5
Gulls	27.0	25.0	15.7	8.2	13.3	11.0
Coot, Gallinule	30.0	23.7	13.5	12.8	12.4	7.6
Pheasant	6.3	7.0	20.7	29.3	20.0	16.7

The values are percentage preferences, averaged from pair choices. After Kear 1964.

LIGHT AND PREDATOR-PREY RELATIONSHIPS

Predator and prey are in constant battle, the one striving for successful capture, the other struggling constantly to avoid that capture. Many animals are both hunter and hunted. In the predator-prey relationship the visual sense plays an extremely important role, for the directional properties of light provide ideal cues for orienting a quick, accurate attack. Predatory animals, both vertebrate and invertebrate, have the best-developed eyes in the animal kingdom. Prey animals have a host of characteristics that aid in concealing them from the predator's view.

◆ *Vision and the Hunter.* The prey-catching actions of many predators are elicited by the rather unspecific stimuli presented by moving objects within a certain size range (page 236). Selectivity of prey items is for many predators merely a function of the habitat in which they hunt or the consequence of more specific responsiveness at a later phase during prey capture. There are exceptions. Young cuttlefish, *Sepia*, for example, capture small crustaceans by approaching them and stabbing at them with their tentacles (Wells 1962). These movements are elicited by prey animals which are behind glass; visual stimuli must be responsible. Only live, moving crustaceans (*Mysis*) elicited an appreciable number of prey-catching movements from newly hatched *Sepia*. A moving *Mysis* model elicited some responses but other models were ineffective. Experienced animals were less selective than naive ones.

Predators must avoid triggering premature flight by their intended prey. Hence many predators are stealthy in their approach to within striking distance and are cryptically colored, though seldom with as much elaboration or subtlety as prey animals. An alternative is to assume the guise of some nonpredatory animal, or even of the prey itself (Brower, Brower, and Westcott 1960). Such 'aggressive mimicry' is not uncommon, though mimicry is more commonly used as a means of defense than for attack (Cott 1957).

◆ *Vision and Parasitic Birds.* Several groups of birds including cuckoos, cowbirds, and finches lay eggs in the nests of other birds and leave the young to be reared by them. If the host can perceive the alien egg, it may abandon the nest, build over the foreign egg, or eject it from the nest. Experiments show that the host does not actually identify its own eggs but recognizes the presence of one that is different (Rensch 1925). Thus if four parasitic eggs are placed in a nest with one of the host's eggs, the host ejects its own egg. The discriminatory ability is greatest in species that are the normal hosts of parasites (Rensch 1925), attesting to the mu-

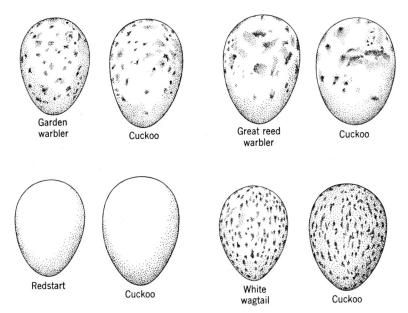

Figure 10-3   The eggs of individual European cuckoos, *Cuculus canorus,* often match closely the eggs of the host selected, both in color and size. The difference in egg size of host and parasite may represent the discriminatory ability of the host balanced against any advantage the cuckoo may gain from a larger egg. After Welty 1962.

tual evolutionary history of parasite and host. The ability of hosts to distinguish egg markings has led to the evolution of egg mimicry in parasitic cuckoos, with different races or 'gentes' of the parasite having different eggs and specializing in different hosts. Often the mimicry is so precise that it is difficult for the human observer to distinguish eggs of parasite and host (Chance 1922, Jourdain 1925, Baker 1942, Southern 1954, Figure 10-3). Usually there is a slight size difference. Hamilton and Orians (1965) suggest that this difference may correspond with the minimal discriminable size difference perceptible to the host, while allowing the parasite the slight advantage gained by the larger egg.

In the parasitic weaverbirds there is also evidence of mimicry in the appearance of the young (Nicolai 1964). In the corners of the mouths of both parasites and hosts, which are weaver finches of a different family, there are brilliant light-reflecting pads which direct the feeding responses of the parents in the dark interiors of the nests (Figure 10-4). Some of the parasitic weavers even seem to learn the song of their host.

Parasites may be subject to attack by hosts. A remarkable behavior pattern which seems to function in reducing such a hazard has been de-

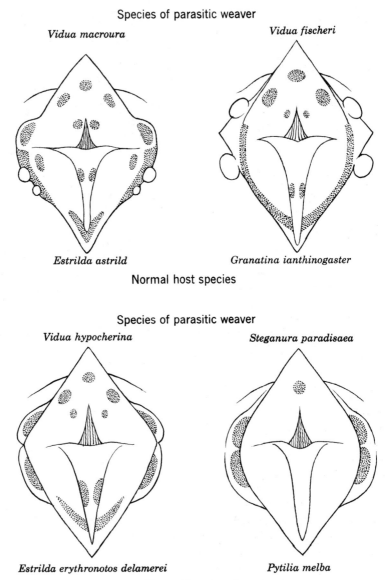

Species of parasitic weaver

Vidua macroura   *Vidua fischeri*

Estrilda astrild   *Granatina ianthinogaster*

Normal host species

Species of parasitic weaver

Vidua hypocherina   *Steganura paradisaea*

Estrilda erythronotos delamerei   *Pytilia melba*

Normal host species

Figure 10-4   Patterns of spots, colors, and reflecting surfaces on the palate of nest-ling finches are assumed to guide the parent in placing food in the semidarkness of a closed nest. Species of parasitic weavers, *Vidua* and *Steganura,* have similar nestling mouth markings to their normal hosts—here species of *Estrilda, Granatina,* and *Pytilia.* After Friedmann 1960 from Neunzig.

scribed in an American brood parasite, the brown-headed cowbird, *Molothrus ater* (Selander and La Rue 1961). The visual stimuli presented by the cowbird in a special head-down posture induce other species to preen its feathers. The preening probably reduces the chance of aggression between host and parasite, and may even permit the establishment of a temporary bond between them during the period before laying when the cowbird has the nest under surveillance. The cowbirds' behavior is all the more remarkable considering the absence of mutual preening with members of their own species.

◆ *The Hunted.* The first recourse of a prey animal is to conceal itself from its predators. Cott (1957) has reviewed the many methods of concealment. They include a general resemblance to the colors of the environment, with both static and dynamic elements; specific resemblance to common objects in the environment such as bark or leaves; the elimination of three-dimensional lighting effects by countershading; disruptive coloration that breaks up the outlines of the body as a whole or of a particular structure such as the eye; and concealment of the shadow, by crouching low or by structures that conceal the shadow from above. Once discovered, the animal may sham death, minimizing the most widespread stimulus for prey catching, movement.

Protective coloration and patterns must be considered in relation to (1) the sensory capacities of the predators which have shaped these characteristics of the prey, (2) the behavior of predator and prey and the ranges at which attack and flight occur, and (3) the environment in which the encounter takes place. Cursory examination of a zebra behind the fence of a zoo does not suggest protective coloration. Consideration of Figure 10-5, however, suggests that a protective interpretation of the zebra pattern should be seriously considered.

The hunted animal may give false visual orienting clues to the predator. An alarmed squid assumes cryptic coloration and, as it takes flight, ejects a conspicuous cloud of ink which remains to distract the predator while the squid flees to safety. Another version of false position clues occurs in 'flash colors.' Brightly colored structures are conspicuously exposed while the animal is in rapid and often erratic motion. They are suddenly concealed as motion stops. The animal seems to disappear as it alights, and the human eye searches for the colored object. The wriggling tail autotomized by an attacked lizard is another example of distracting a predator. Many color patterns seem to be designed to divert a predator's first attack to the least vulnerable parts of the body (Cott 1957).

As another avenue of escape the prey animal can suddenly change its appearance to something startling or intimidating (Figure 10-6*b, d*) and so ward off the predator, or at least make it hesitate, gaining time for escape. Sudden increase in apparent body size occurs in animals as varied as insects, fishes, lizards, toads, and owls when startled by a predator, an action sometimes dramatized by bright colors.

The effectiveness of the visual stimuli generated by such defensive

Figure 10-5   The principle of disruptive margins. Place the book in an upright position and back across the room until the zebra or "pseudozebra" disappears. The figures with disruptive edges also disappear first, illustrating the principle of the zebra pattern. After Cott 1957.

(a)   (c)

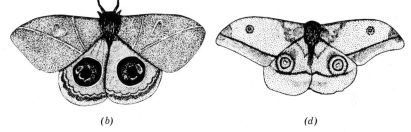

(b)   (d)

Figure 10-6   Intimidation displays of moths. (*a*) The resting posture of an *Automeris medusae* male, (*b*) a female of the same species following disturbance. Part (*c*) shows a *Nudauriela dione* male preparing for flight. In (*d*) the same moth in display after disturbance. After Blest 1957b.

movements has been demonstrated experimentally by Blest (1957a, b). Some moths and butterflies, usually cryptic in their general coloration, have conspicuous eyespot patterns on their hindwings. They expose these in a series of special movements when they are suddenly disturbed, perhaps by a bird alighting nearby (Figure 10-6). Similar visual stimuli presented on an illuminated screen had a maximal effect in scaring birds away from food (Figure 10-7). Shading to produce a pair of three-dimensional "eyes" created the strongest stimulus of all. Small birds are also highly responsive to the paired eyes of owls (page 249), and Blest suggests that these moths and butterflies may be mimicking them: "it is clear that the most effective type of model of all is one which is solid in appearance, circular, and composed of concentric elements. Such a pattern is inevitably more or less eyelike. It may be deduced from these experiments that the eyespot patterns borne on the wings of good mimics such as *Caligo* or *Precis* may well approach the most effective patterns possible for the order of size to which they belong" (Blest 1957a). Such patterns also attract the eyes of human infants (page 339), and may have high stimulating value for many vertebrate eyes.

Some potential prey animals have evolved chemical means of defense

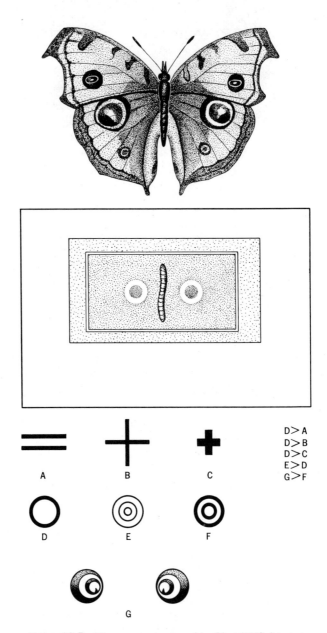

$$D>A$$
$$D>B$$
$$D>C$$
$$E>D$$
$$G>F$$

A   B   C

D   E   F

G

Figure 10-7   The arrangement used by Blest (1957a) to test the response of birds to eyespot patterns such as those on the wings of the butterfly *Precis almana* given here. A model is projected onto a screen behind a mealworm placed on a slide where the bird has been trained to take food. The relative effectiveness of the models in alarming the birds is shown below. After Blest 1957b.

(page 290). Chemical protection from predators is associated with the production of visual stimuli of a distinctive type, including what is known as 'aposematic' or warning coloration (Cott 1957). Predators that attack aposematic animals encounter these noxious chemicals and quickly learn to avoid them. The visual stimuli presented help the predator to make quick and accurate identification of the stimulus pattern in the future. Many different animal groups have evolved a similar basic pattern, which includes (1) black and white, yellow, orange, and red coloration permanently displayed, (2) an arrangement of the colors in bold, simple patterns, (3) movement in open view of potential predators, with no attempt at concealment, (4) slow, conspicuous movements in locomotion, (5) the adoption of postures when alarmed that maximize presentation of the color patterns, and (6) clumping, which insures minimal losses to naïve predators. The use of conspicuous black and white contrasts has an obvious physiological explanation, but the conspicuousness of red, orange, and yellow to many vertebrate eyes has yet to be explained in physiological terms. These are not necessarily the colors to which a predator's eyes are most sensitive, especially in dim light.

Animals with chemical defenses are often mimicked by other animals, themselves harmless, which have evolved resemblance to a noxious species. There is ample evidence that such mimics gain advantage from the resemblance, provided that their numbers stay below those of the model (Brower 1960, Ford 1964).

Animals sometimes draw a predator's attention to themselves, thus diverting it from mate, nest, or offspring. Disablement and distraction movements are best known in birds disturbed near their nests and young. They flop around conspicuously, often simulating a broken wing (Armstrong 1947) and displaying conspicuous plumage features as they lure the predator away from their offspring. Sometimes they mimic an attractive prey object. Some shorebirds, for example, perform a 'small mammal' distraction display. Twitching movements give the impression of moving legs, and the feathers are raised, making them furlike (Duffey, Creasey, and Williamson 1950). Visual elements dominate the stimulus situation that is thus presented to the predator.

◆ *Vision in Commensalism and Symbiosis.* The association between pollinating insects and plants is largely responsible for the enormous variety of specifically distinct flower patterns of angiosperms (Grant 1963). Chemical characteristics (page 292) and mechanical structure of the flower can determine which insects will pollinate a given plant. Nevertheless, the visual stimuli they present are often important.

Individual honeybees and other pollinating insects often tend to specialize on certain types of flowers. Many flowering plants that are not seasonally isolated are potentially interfertile with their sympatric relatives. Reproductive isolation can be achieved by providing conspicuous sensory cues that attract pollinating agents from a distance. The same cues also provide the pollinators with a means of distinguishing the flowers from those of related species, encouraging flower constancy. Many flowering plants rely on the species-specific appearance of their blooms for reproductive isolation. This has led to great diversification of flower structure and has in turn provided the taxonomists with convenient characters for identifying and classifying plant species. Taxonomists rely much more on floral characters when dealing with plants that have flower-constant pollinators than in classifying plants that have indiscriminate pollinators (Grant 1949, 1963, Figure 10-8), a situation parallelled in the taxonomy of birds (page 386).

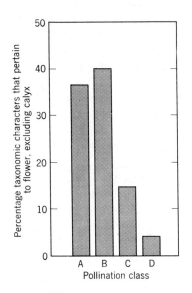

Figure 10-8   The relative importance of floral characters in the taxonomy of flowering plants is related to the manner of pollination. The plant groups plotted here are pollinated (A) by birds, (B) by bees and long-tongued flies, (C) by promiscuous and unspecialized insects, and (D) by wind and water. After Grant 1949.

The function of attracting pollinators and guiding them to the stamens, pistils, and nectaries has favored the evolution of many structures that generate visual stimuli. Colors are widely exploited. In plants pollinated by insects the flowers are most often blue, yellow, and ultraviolet, colors to which the eyes of the pollinators are most sensitive (page 321). Red is rare because most insects are blind to it. Red, however, is a predominant color in flowers pollinated by birds, and is sometimes found in flowers pollinated by bats (Baker 1963), as well as in fruits dispersed by birds. We have already noted evidence that red is a conspicuous color to vertebrate eyes (page 351).

The radial pattern of many flowers is particularly stimulating to the compound eyes of insects (page 238). Manning (1956) has shown that once bees alight on the edges of petals, special markings or honey guides lead them to the nectaries. A differential distribution of color can achieve a similar effect. Daumer (1958) studied the colors of flowers, paying special attention to the distribution of ultraviolet (Figures 10-9, 10-10), by far the brightest color to the honeybee's eye.

The plant-insect relationship is taken to remarkable extremes in a group of orchids in which each species mimics the appearance and odor of a different species of bee. The male pollinates the flower while attempting to copulate with it (Baerends 1950, Meeuse 1961).

Interspecific associations of vertebrates such as are found in flocks composed of several species of birds may also depend on visual stimuli. These mixed flocks are especially notable in the tropics (Moynihan 1960,

Figure 10-9   These figures are drawn from photographs taken with a quartz lens to pass visible and ultraviolet light. The first of each pair is with a yellow filter, the second with an ultraviolet filter. In *Helianthus rigidus,* above, and *Oenothera biennis,* below, striking ultraviolet patterns emerge, unseen by man. They occupy the most sensitive part of the pollinating bee's visual spectrum. From Daumer 1958.

1962) and seem to have resulted in the evolution of similar plumage types in their member species. The assumption of specifically indistinct plumage patterns in the nonbreeding season by some species of birds may minimize the stimuli for aggression (page 167) and provide common visual signals for group integration, thereby favoring the formation of interspecific groupings (Moynihan 1960, 1962, Hamilton and Barth 1962).

The similarity of the plumage patterns of female weaver finches may be correlated with the phenomenon of interspecific flocking (Emlen 1957). In open-country species of Australian grassfinches that form interspecific nomadic flocks in the dry seasons, bill color seems to play a special role in the maintenance of the flock. Immelmann (1962) studied seven species that formed mixed flocks, two with red bills, two with yellow bills, and three with green. He discovered that interspecific flocks always form from species with similar bill color.

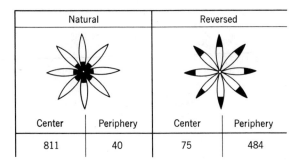

Natural		Reversed	
Center	Periphery	Center	Periphery
811	40	75	484

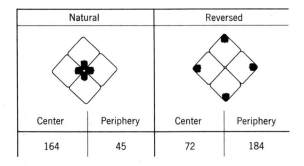

Natural		Reversed	
Center	Periphery	Center	Periphery
164	45	72	184

Figure 10-10　Models of flowers attract honeybees. In these experiments petals of *Helianthus rigidus,* in the first row, and *Oenothera biennis,* in the second row, are arranged under cellophane with the "honey guides" either at the center or at the periphery. The number of visits to the center and edge of the patterns so formed are given below each configuration. After Daumer 1958.

INTRASPECIFIC VISUAL SIGNALS: SOCIAL RELEASERS

The major developments of intraspecific systems of visual communication are found in diurnal insects, fishes, lizards, birds, and primates. Communication in these animals has been a major area of investigation occupying many pioneer workers in animal behavior, including Whitman, Craig, Huxley, Lorenz, and Tinbergen. Because visual signals lend themselves to direct study by human observers, processes of visual communication figure prominently in the theoretical developments of the last 50 years. Lorenz (1935) derived many of his theories from study of the structures and behavior patterns of fish and birds—so-called displays that function to transmit visual signals to other animals. A landmark is Tinbergen's paper, published in 1948, on social releasers and the experimental method required for their study. Most of its examples are taken from visual signals. The term social releaser refers to an intraspecific communication signal. Some phenomena are more readily studied in visual signals than in auditory or chemical signals, especially the mode of origin of signaling structures and their transformation in the course of evolution, a process known as 'ritualization.'

→ *Characteristics of Visual Signals.* Some predictions can be made about the characteristics that visual signals are likely to have. Colors are exploited by animals that have color vision. Red, orange, and yellow are colors especially conspicuous to vertebrate eyes under natural conditions. Contrast and temporal change both make for greater conspicuousness. The distance over which a signal is used and the background against which it is perceived must also be considered. At close range the possibility of environmental interference is minimal and the requirement for conspicuousness is reduced. Subtle, changing patterns of form, color, and movement can be exploited. At long range the emphasis shifts to simple, stereotyped, conspicuous patterns.

For example, in ground-dwelling primates that live in cohesive groups, such as rhesus monkeys and baboons, most visual signaling is done at close range. We find a complex of subtle and changing systems of signals with many different parts of the body contributing to the signal, particularly the face (e.g. Hinde and Rowell 1962, Andrew 1964, Hall and DeVore 1965). By comparison, the visual signals of many birds, which communicate over greater distances, are simpler and much more stereotyped (e.g. the goldeneye duck, Dane and Van der Kloot 1964; see page 387).

Visual signals are potentially durable, a mixed blessing. Conspicuous patterns on the external body surface that aid in intraspecific communication can be a hindrance when the animal must hide from a predator.

Many methods have been evolved for switching visual signals on and off by movements of head, body, limbs or tail, gills, extensions of the body surface, hair or feathers, and by changes in the dispersion of chromatophores that permit both concealment in times of danger and a pattern of temporal change during signaling. Animals that are relatively immune to predators or those such as polygamous lek birds that gain a disproportionate reproductive advantage from their social signals, can exploit permanent visual signals to the full (see page 382).

Durable visual signals, like chemicals, can be placed in the environment to continue to function in the absence of the signaling animal. The marking of trees by deer in the rut and the trails left by migrating ungulates are examples. The bowerbirds of Australia and southeastern Asia prepare an ornamented arena which is the focus of the courtship displays of the male (Marshall 1954). Such marking of the environment is much less common than with chemical signals. Visual signals lack the dynamic fade-out of chemical signals, and their very permanence limits the information content of such sign posts.

◆ *Visual Signals in Aggregation and Dispersal.* The distribution of members of a species in space has a crucial bearing on their exploitation of environmental resources. There is a multiplicity of mechanisms by which different patterns of distribution are achieved, and in many of them visual signals are prominent. Vision is crucial in forming and maintaining schools of fish. Blinding may eliminate schooling (Keenleyside 1955). A dorsal fin with a conspicuous black patch is an important visual signal in the schooling of *Pristella riddlei.* To an isolated individual a school of these fish with amputated fins was less attractive than a school of intact fish (Figure 10-11). Visual signals must be important in the formation of aggregations in many birds and mammals.

Figure 10-11   The fish *Pristella riddlei,* showing black fins which are a visual aid in schooling. After Keenleyside 1955.

There is more information on visual signals that encourage dispersal. Animals may avoid one another on sight, or they may direct signals at one another, eliciting withdrawal. There are simple signals generated by the animal and compound visual situations that involve perception of a complex of environmental factors as well (page 384). Simple stimuli include the red breast of the male chaffinch (page 167) and the comb of hens (Collias 1943, Marks, Siegel, and Kramer 1960). A hen with a

Figure 10-12 The head-up posture is a widespread signal in fighting behavior in many passerine families. Top row, from left, *Parus major* (Paridae), *Catharus minimus* (Turdidae), and *Agelaius phoeniceus* (Icteridae). Second row, *Fringilla coelebs* (Fringillidae), *Molothrus ater* (Icteridae), and *Erithacus rubecula* (Turdidae). Bottom, *Cassidix mexicanus* (Icteridae). From Marler 1961.

large comb is likely to win in a fight with a hen that has a smaller comb. Removal of the comb and wattles reduces her chances of winning, and such 'dubbed' birds end up with low status in the dominance hierarchy.

Special postures and movements are often used to display these signal structures. A preliminary review of the underlying principles is possible. Aggressive displays often involve an increase in *apparent* size. Larger animals dominate smaller ones in many species, and intimidating or re-pelling signals often maximize this particular property. A case in point is the head-up posture used in territorial defense by several species of birds (Tinbergen 1959, Marler 1961, Figure 10-12).

Presentation of the main fighting weapons, with or without maximiza-tion of size, occurs in many displays. Darwin (1872) gave many exam-ples of the incorporation of preparations for attack into threat displays in documenting his principle of serviceable associated habits. The main weapons of many birds are the bill and wings, and these are often maxi-mally presented to the opponent in a 'head-forward' posture (Andrew 1961). Gulls use the head-up and head-forward threat postures in some-what different situations (Tinbergen 1959, Figure 10-13). Birds that use the feet in fighting often assume an upright threat posture from which they can readily strike at the opponent.

Mammals also tend to present the weapons in threat. Darwin gives the dog as an example. Here the main emphasis is on the teeth. Ungu-lates emphasize not the teeth but the horns and feet, their main weapons. These are often marked and colored (Hingston 1933), enhancing their conspicuousness. There is often a correlation between display movements and markings as in cichlid fishes (Baerends and Baerends-van Roon 1950).

Visual displays communicating aggression are often highly variable, in contrast with sexual displays which are often more stereotyped. Aggres-sive displays of mammals (Eisenberg 1963) and birds (Brown 1964, Fig-ure 10-14) often appear in a graded series, varying along a continuous spectrum from attack to flight. This graded quality may make possible the communication of slight changes in motivation, facilitating the reso-lution of territorial and other conflicts.

The communicatory role of most displays is largely a matter of infer-ence and circumstantial evidence. However, by observing many aggres-sive encounters between titmice, Stokes (1962a, b) was able to correlate various postures with the behavior of the opponent (Figure 10-15). If an aggressive birds faces its rival with wings raised, its opponent is more likely to flee than when it does not raise its wings. If it fluffs its feathers the opponent is more likely to attack. Four sympatric species behaved in similar fashion, responding to one another's displays. This relative

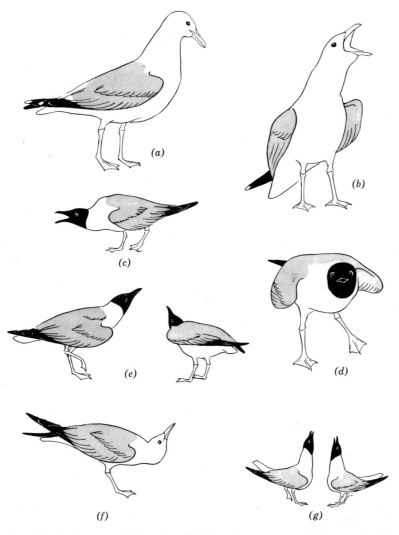

Figure 10-13   Intraspecific threat in gulls. Their main weapons in fighting are the bill and wings. (*a*) Aggressive upright posture and (*b*) oblique postures of herring gull, *Larus argentatus;* (*c* to *e*) forward postures of black-headed gull, *L. ridibundus;* (*f*) Hartlaub's gull, *L. novae-hollandiae;* and (*g*) little gull, *L. minutus.* The differences between these postures are associated with differences in the probability of aggression or escape and are responded to appropriately by other birds. The aggressive upright indicates a readiness to attack, the oblique a less vigorous threat. The forward postures, shown for several species, indicate that the bird displaying will probably not attack but will fight if attacked. After Tinbergen 1959.

A Comparison of Activities in a Dominant Steller's Jay in Relation to Its Crest Angle and the Resistance of Its Opponent

Activity	Resistance of opponent	Postulated agonistic arousal	Modal crest angle
Foraging	None	Slight	0°
Supplanting:			
No increase in crest angle	Slight if any	Slight	30°
Increase in crest angle	Moderate	Moderate	40°
Aggressive sidling	High	High	80°
Combat	Extreme	Extreme	90°

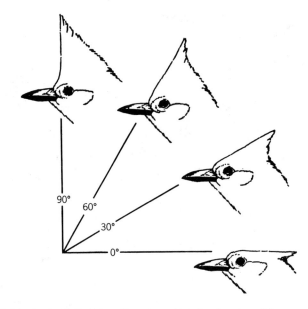

Figure 10-14 In the Steller's jay, *Cyanocitta stelleri*, the elevation of the crest relates to the degree of agonistic arousal. After Brown 1964.

lack of specificity may be related to interspecific competition for food. In such circumstances a species may gain advantage from postures that resemble those of sympatric competitors. In titmice, as in many animals, "threat postures are rather conservative in their rate of evolutionary divergence" (Stokes 1962b).

◆ *Individual Recognition.* There is abundant evidence of individual recognition based on visual cues in animals. Dominance hierarchies, for example, are based on a capacity for individual recognition. Characteristics

					Reaction of Opponent				
		Great tit				Blue tit			
Action		Attack	Escape	Stay	Significance level	Attack	Escape	Stay	Significance level
Erect crest	Yes	7	40	55	not	21	3	76	<.01
	No	3	46	51		18	37	45	
Body feathers	Yes	17	21	62	<.01	20	5	75	<.01
erect	No	3	47	50		21	25	54	
Facing rival	Yes	6	64	30	<.01	19	34	47	<.01
	No	4	33	63		15	33	52	
Wings raised	Yes	5	75	50	not	21	27	52	<.01
	No	5	41	54		13	48	39	
Body	Yes	5	55	40	not	20	35	45	not
Horizontal	No	4	40	56		20	29	51	

Figure 10-15 The signal value of postures of the great tit, *Parus major,* and blue tit, *Parus caeruleus,* can be evaluated by their effect on the reaction of the opponent. Two of the several postures are illustrated. Left, facing rival with body horizontal; right, crest and body feathers erect. The results are expressed as percentages. Some actions change reactions of the opponent significantly. After Hinde 1952 and Stokes 1962b.

of the face are particularly important (Nice 1943). Guhl and Ortman (1953) found that disguising the head and neck of hens was the most effective way to make them strangers to their companions. The degree of intrapopulation variability of the head characters of birds is often higher than that of other parts of the body, a possible correlation with the need for individual variability in certain externally visible characters (Marler 1961). The extreme variation in the coloration of many newly hatched precocial birds may be another adjustment permitting individual recognition of young by their parents. There is good evidence that such recognition develops within a few days in gulls and terns, whose young leave the nest early (Davies and Carrick 1962).

The fact that man himself relies heavily upon facial characters in individual recognition could bias his judgments about where most individuality is to be found in animals. Nevertheless, the great variability in the arrangement of the nostrils of gorillas that Schaller (1963) relied on

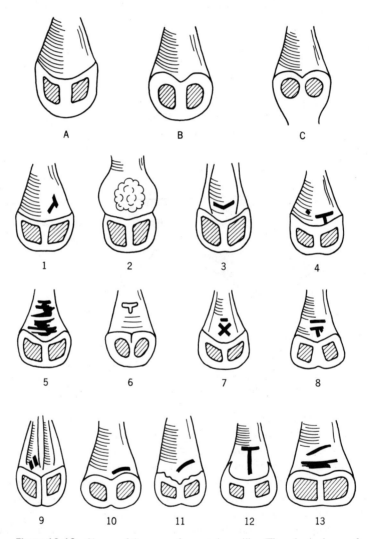

Figure 10-16   Shapes of the noses of mountain gorillas. Three basic shapes of the nasal wing are shown in A through C. The individuals of one group are shown in 1 through 13. Heavy black marks indicate prominent wrinkles. Not drawn to scale. After Schaller 1963.

for identification of individual animals in the field may not be accidental (Figure 10-16). Although many selective factors encourage homogeneity in the visual signals of a species, there are some that favor heterogeneity. The provision of characters for quick accurate individual recognition is one of these.

◆ *Visual Alarm Signals.* The commonest visual signals eliciting alertness, alarm, and flight are provided by the very actions of flight. The tail-flicking movements of many birds preparing to fly probably function in this way (Andrew 1956). The fin flicking of fishes communicates danger (Keenleyside 1955). In some ungulates the act of taking flight is often presaged by a leap into the air and the spreading of a patch of white hair on the rump, providing a conspicuous and effective alarm signal (Hingston 1933). Display of the white markings of rabbits and hares seems to serve a similar function (Wynne-Edwards 1962).

Another type of alarm signal may be generated by rapid changes of color in the integument. This occurs in many animal groups, both invertebrate (e.g. the cuttlefish, Wells 1962) and vertebrate (e.g. man). It is especially well developed in fish, many of which will blanch to a cryptic coloration that matches the background when they are alarmed. This color change may serve as an alarm signal, though concealment from predators is undoubtedly another major function of chromatophore contraction in fish.

In comparison with auditory communication systems the evolution of specialized visual alarm systems seems to have occurred rarely. We have noted the great reliance that predators place on their visual sense while hunting. It is difficult for a potential prey animal to emit a visual alarm signal to its companions without also making itself more conspicuous to a predator. The demands of crypticity can thus drive many animals to rely upon other senses to signal alarm.

◆ *Sexual Signals.* Many visual signals are directed partly or entirely toward members of the opposite sex, coordinating reproductive activities. These signals ensure that each mate does the appropriate thing at the right time. Like any external stimulus they may facilitate some behavior patterns as well as inhibiting others. Many sexual signals serve to reduce distance, a necessary prelude to mating. Aggression must be inhibited before distance can be reduced. Reproduction often involves a chain of stimulus-response interactions between the partners, in which each link elicits certain actions and also prepares the mate for the next signal in the sequence (page 251).

Static sexual signals are often presented by adults, either constantly or during the period of reproduction. The species-specific wing color of female butterflies, for instance, is critical in eliciting the courtship responses of males (page 258). Plumage characters of male and female zebra finches determine whether a male will attack or court a newcomer (page 243).

The degree of sexual dimorphism in external morphology is affected by a variety of ecological factors, some of which have nothing to do with the generation of sexual communication signals. A connection with reproduction is sometimes clearly implied, however. In a few bird species such as phalaropes and button quail, the sexual roles are reversed. Females compete for the favors of males, and the female is larger and more handsomely adorned. In many animal groups there is a correlation between polygyny and extreme sexual dimorphism, ranging from certain grouse and grackles in which males may weigh twice as much as females to the extreme example of the Alaska fur seal in which the male may be six times as heavy as the female (Bartholomew 1953, Amadon 1959). Intense aggressive interaction between males in competition for females together with delayed maturity, seems to be the evolutionary basis of their large size and excessive ornamentation (Selander 1965).

Even in sexually dimorphic species posture may be important in eliciting sexual responses from the partner (page 87). A thorough analysis has been made of the sexual responses of cockerels to taxidermic models set in various postures (Fisher and Hale 1957, Carbaugh, Schein, and Hale 1962). Plumage differences between rooster and hen proved to have little effect. The maximum number of sexual responses was elicited by a crouching model. Tail, head, and body were presented alone and together in different orientations. The head alone elicited a surprising number of responses, though practically no complete copulations. A prone head added to a body raised the level of sexual behavior, but the main role of the head in this context seems to be the orientation of the mounting behavior of the rooster. The head alone also contributes to the orientation of roosters (Figure 10-17).

The temporary assumption of sexual color patterns is especially important in fishes such as *Badis badis* (Barlow 1963) and various cichlids (Baerends and Baerends-van Roon 1950, Neil 1964). The colors may be associated with particular postures, as in the guppies studied by Baerends, Brouwer, and Waterbolk (1955). In some mouth-brooding cichlids of the genus *Haplochromis* the function of color patterns is particularly intricate (Wickler 1962). Males have spots on the anal fin that resemble eggs. During spawning the female snaps up the eggs and also snaps at the male's spots, which are close to his genital pore. In this way the eggs in her mouth are certain to be fertilized.

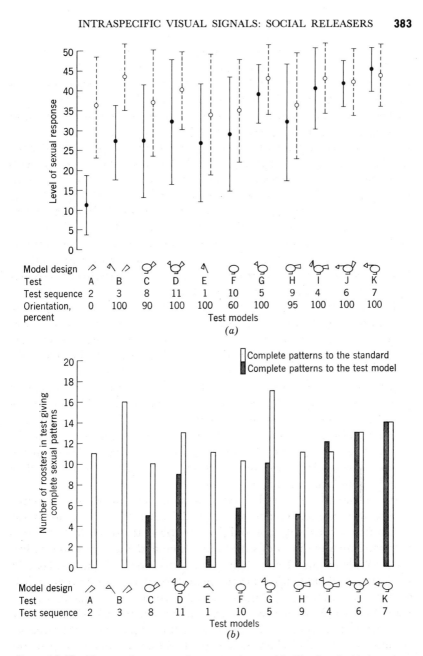

Figure 10-17 The sexual responses of roosters to hen models. The data in (*a*) show the mean ±1 standard deviation for the experimental model (solid lines) and the control model (dotted lines) that day. The percentages below indicate the relative number of tests with correct anterior-posterior orientation. In (*b*) the number of complete sexual patterns evoked by each test model is compared with a standard control, a realistic taxidermic model. After Carbaugh, Schein, and Hale 1962.

The dynamic properties of visual signals are often critically important in eliciting responses from the opposite sex. This applies to the claw-waving movements of fiddler crabs (Crane 1957). An elegant example comes from fireflies (Buck 1937). At mating time the male firefly, *Photinus pyralis*, flashes at regular intervals while in flight. The female climbs a blade of grass and remains there, flashing in reply to any nearby flashing male. How she recognizes his flashes is not known, but it may be because of the regular interval of his flashing, about 5.8 seconds. Her response is to flash back to the male about 2 seconds later. This time interval is critical, ranging from 1.6 to 2.4 seconds, according to the temperature. A male does not respond to other males' signals, but will approach a light of any size, color, and duration that flashes 2 seconds after he does. Flashes are exchanged between male and female as the male approaches, until he reaches and mates with her. In one experiment males were made to flash 2 seconds after another male by pinching. These males were approached just as though they were females.

How do sympatric species of fireflies avoid confusion? In some parts of the southeastern United States as many as a dozen species may be active at the same time (McDermott 1917), and a practiced observer can distinguish them by their manner of flashing (Figure 10-18). But the problems of interspecific isolation have so far received no attention.

Lizards employ a series of rapid push-ups in their displays, the temporal pattern varying from species to species (Carpenter 1962, 1963). By the use of an ingenious machine attached to the head of a plastic lizard, Hunsaker (1962) imitated the push-up patterns of different species. Females of two species chose to associate with a model displaying at the tempo of their own species in preference to a model moving at random or like another species (Figure 10-19).

In contrast with the graded nature of many aggressive displays, courtship patterns are often highly stereotyped, irrespective of variation in the motivation of the displaying bird (Morris 1957). In one of the few studies involving measurement of variability Dane and Van der Kloot (1964, Dane, Walcott, and Drury 1959) found that some of the displays the goldeneye duck uses in pair formation and copulation are extraordinarily stereotyped in form and duration (Figure 10-20). Such stereotypy presumably stems from the need for clear, unambiguous signals that function in reproductive isolation. In the face of this requirement the need for communicating subtle changes in motivation that dominates the structure of many threat displays probably has had little influence.

A distinctive property of many visual signals is their compound nature, involving a pattern of stimuli coming from several parts of the body. Actually, the stimulus may be more complex still, encompassing other objects in the environment, such as a territory, a display ground, or particular objects, such as a nest. Emlen (1957) believes that when a female weaverbird establishes a sexual bond she responds to the nesting habitat and the nesting frame built by the male, as well as to the male's displays. The display structures of bowerbirds, often ornamented by objects of a particular color, are special cases. Within them the males display to females, sometimes while holding objects in their bills (Marshall 1954, Gilliard 1963). The colors of male plumage and adornments of the bower are closely related. In one group there is an inverse relationship between them—the brighter the bower the duller the plumage.

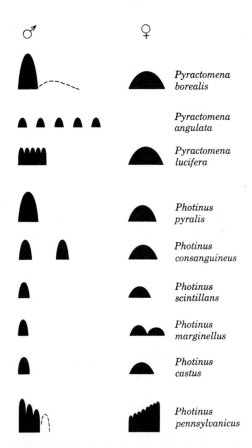

Figure 10-18 The flashing pattern of nine species of fireflies. The height of the traces is roughly proportional to light intensity. After McDermott 1917.

In many species of birds the male plumage is considerably more striking than the plumage of the female. The vividness of males is often probably the result of selection pressure for distinctiveness and has led to repercussions in the classification of these birds (Marler 1957). Avian taxonomists rely heavily on external features in evaluating relationships and may be

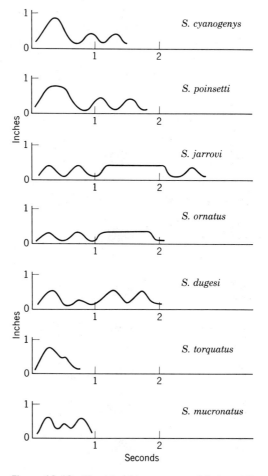

Figure 10-19 Head-bobbing patterns of *Sceloporus* lizards, determined by cinematography. The depth of the bob is represented on the ordinate. When female *S. torquatus* and *S. mucronatus* were given a choice of two models bobbing with both patterns, each female consistently associated with the species-specific pattern. After Hunsaker 1962.

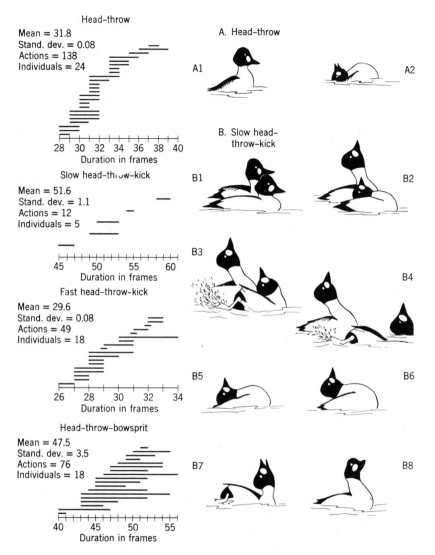

Head-throw
Mean = 31.8
Stand. dev. = 0.08
Actions = 138
Individuals = 24

28 30 32 34 36 38 40
Duration in frames

Slow head-throw-kick
Mean = 51.6
Stand. dev. = 1.1
Actions = 12
Individuals = 5

45   50   55   60
Duration in frames

Fast head-throw-kick
Mean = 29.6
Stand. dev. = 0.08
Actions = 49
Individuals = 18

26   28   30   32   34
Duration in frames

Head-throw-bowsprit
Mean = 47.5
Stand. dev. = 3.5
Actions = 76
Individuals = 18

40   45   50   55
Duration in frames

A1   A. Head-throw   A2

B. Slow head-
throw-kick
B1   B2
B3
B4
B5   B6
B7   B8

Figure 10-20   The courtship displays of male American goldeneyes, *Bucephala clangula,* are extremely stereotyped. Sequences of the head-throw (A1, 2), slow head-throw-kick (B1-8, rear bird) and fast head-throw-kick (bird in foreground, B1-4) are drawn from photographs (Dane, Walcott, and Drury 1959). At the left are measurements of the temporal pattern of these displays and one other, the head-throw-bowsprit. Time on the abscissa is measured in movie frames. The range of durations of each individual male measured is indicated by each horizontal bar. Dane and Van der Kloot 1964.

led by extremely divergent external characters to think that species are less closely related than they are. Mayr (1942) has shown that this is in fact the case. The average number of species per genus in birds of paradise (2.4), hummingbirds (2.6), and grouse (1.6) may be compared with the average number in birds that rely less on visual sexual signals, such as owls (4.5), wrens (4.0), and goatsuckers and nighthawks (3.5). The first three families provide many examples of natural hybrids, both interspecific and intergeneric; thus their members are more closely related than taxonomists have thought (Mayr 1942, Sibley 1957).

Hybridization in nature must normally be disadvantageous when the offspring are infertile, as is frequently the case, when they are ill-adapted to the ecological niches of the parental species, or when they have difficulty finding a mate (Sibley 1961). The occurrence of hybridization must greatly enhance the selection pressure for sexual signals to become specifically distinct. Conversely, insular races and species which live where the fauna is less diverse are under less pressure for specific distinctiveness; in these circumstances males often revert to female-like plumage patterns (Lack 1947, Sibley 1957).

The extremes of plumage ornamentation and sexual dimorphism such as are found in hummingbirds, birds of paradise, certain shorebirds, and some grouse are often associated with a particular kind of social system. Instead of there being a durable pair bond, the contact between male and female is brief. The males display, females visit them, and copulation occurs. The females then leave to lay eggs and raise young on their own. The brevity of the pair bond allows little opportunity for the correction of errors. This has presumably placed special emphasis on the plumage characteristics that are attractive to the female, resulting in extremely distinctive plumage patterns and displays.

◆ *Parent-Young Relationships.* Vision is important in eliciting the approach of young fish to their parents (page 624) and in evoking the following responses of newly hatched precocial birds (page 635). There are cases of specific and even individual recognition of young by parents (Davies and Carrick 1962, Myrberg 1964).

Perhaps the most thoroughly analyzed exchange of visual signals between parents and young is the pecking of young gulls at the bill of the parent. The chicks are fed regurgitated food, which is presented to them in the tip of the parent's bill. Several observers noted that initially the young herring gull chick does not peck at food, but focuses attention on the red spot at the tip of the lower mandible of the parent's yellow bill. Eventually it strikes the food and eats it. Tinbergen and Perdeck (1950) investigated the effectiveness of shapes, colors, and patterns in evoking this response

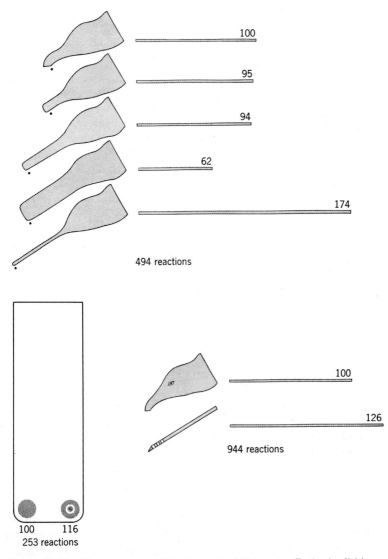

Figure 10-21 The supernormal bill. A long thin bill is more effective in eliciting a pecking response from herring gull chicks than an outline closely resembling the head of an adult gull. The position of the chick's bill at the beginning of the test is indicated by the spot. When a pointed "bill" with stripes is compared with a three-dimensional model of a herring gull's head, the striped model is most effective. A comparison of two spots, one solid as in a herring gull's bill spot, the other formed of concentric circles, results in more pecking at the circles. Compare these models with Figure 9-13. After Tinbergen and Perdeck 1950.

by presenting flat cardboard models one at a time for 30 seconds each. Scores were taken of the number of pecks given in each presentation. It had been previously established that movement was critical in evoking a response, and in these experiments the models were always moved. Before each test the parent's feeding call was imitated.

The form and color of the head could be varied in many unnatural ways without affecting the pecking response. Remarkably, the presence or absence of a head made little difference! The experimenters therefore focused attention on the bill. The color of the spot on the bill, and the degree of its contrast with the whole bill, had a strong effect on the pecking response. High contrast and a red color evoked the most pecks. Evidently red has special significance; a bill colored entirely red evoked more responses than any other solid color, though a red spot on a yellow bill was still more effective.

The position of the spot and the shape of the bill also were important. A long, thin model was most effective (Figure 10-21). A red spot near the tip of the bill evoked the most responses. An irregularity in the bill's outline, such as might be provided by a piece of food, increased the number of pecks. Orientation of the bill relative to the chick was important. Most pecks were directed at a model pointed downward with its tip low in the chick's visual field. In addition, a model evoked more responses when held close to the chick. The key characteristics of the visual stimuli evoking the maximal pecking response may be summarized as follows: (1) movement, (2) a definite shape, (3) 'lowness,' (4) 'nearness,' (5) pointing down, (6) a patch at the tip characterized by red color and high contrast, and (7) something protruding outside the outline of the bill.

Another interesting achievement was the creation of a model that was more effective than a naturalistic head and bill in evoking the chick's response. Such a 'supernormal' stimulus was provided by a long, thin, red rod with three white rings near the tip (Figure 10-21).

Studies of other species of gulls and terns have led to the same conclusions. Red produces the most pecking responses. There are some interspecific differences of special interest, such as the high responsiveness of young, wide-awake terns, *Sterna fuscata*, to black models. This is one of the few black-billed species (Cullen 1962). Nevertheless, the general predisposition to peck at red objects is striking. The conspicuousness that red seems to have for many animals (page 351) is apparent here. Perhaps oil droplets on the retina maximize responsiveness to long wavelengths (Weidmann 1961, Quine and Cullen 1964). Other comparative studies have shown the important roles of contrast, shape, and orientation in many species. Movement of the bill can be replaced by an on-off flicker (Collias and Collias 1957). These same characters contribute to the conspicuousness of visual stimuli in other vertebrates (e.g. Fantz 1961, page 339). Approaching the problem from another point of view, Hailman (1962) notes that 30 of the 44 gulls in the genus *Larus* have some bright red on the adult's bill during the breeding season. Of the remainder, four have a contrasting bill tip (yellow on black or vice versa). Some of the remaining species feed their young in a different way than other gulls. Young kittiwakes, *Rissa tridactyla*, poke their bills down the parent's throat (Cullen 1957)—the interior of the mouth is bright red.

In species in which the young peck at the parent's bill to get food there has evidently been convergence of adult bill characteristics. The trend has been toward an approximate match of the shape and color of the bill spot with the predisposition of chicks to respond to particular stimuli—a predisposition that they probably share with other vertebrates as well.

CONCLUSIONS ON THE USE OF VISION IN COMMUNICATION

There is abundant exploitation of the special properties of light that animals can perceive. Perhaps the most distinctive attribute of the visual sense is responsiveness to the directionality of light rays and the associated ability to distinguish spatial patterns. Cases in which form and color combine to generate different types of visual signals are numerous. Characteristics of such spatial patterns may be changed independently, permitting the development of compound signals in which several independent variables contribute to the response. Nowhere is this compounding better seen than in the visual signals of primates in which eyes, brows, mouth, ears, body, limbs, and tail may all combine in different ways to generate a great variety of graded signals (Andrew 1964, Marler 1959, 1965).

Alternatively, the several elements in a visual signal may be compounded in a very stereotyped fashion, the many constituents establishing a high degree of redundancy and ensuring a maximal rate and accuracy of signal recognition. The lead established in quantitive studies of the degree of stereotypy in the displays of goldeneye will be a fruitful one to follow (Dane, Walcott, and Drury 1959, Dane and Van der Kloot 1964).

The rapid adaptation rates of visual receptors also permit exploitation of temporal patterns in the design of visual signals. The possibilities range from the simple pattern of firefly flashing, through the complex trains of movement in the displays of lizards and the long sequences of display actions in birds such as the goldeneye.

A survey of systems of visual signaling raises many questions about the physiology of the eye. The evident conspicuousness of yellow, orange, and red colors to many vertebrates has not been adequately explained. The physiological basis of the particular attractiveness of certain kinds of spatial patterns, especially broken and concentric designs, has yet to be explored. It is intriguing that human children and bees show much the same kind of preferences in this respect (Fantz 1961, 1965). At the opposite pole there are characters facilitating concealment that are exploited in various ways to achieve cryptic coloration.

Only physiological study can provide the explanation for the myriad filtering mechanisms that are a part of the visual sense. The tremendous progress in the last few years promises an exciting future (Jung 1961). The prospects are especially bright if the suggestion made by Barlow (1961) in a symposium on sensory mechanisms is followed: "It is foolish to investigate sensory mechanisms blindly—one must always look at the ways in which animals make use of their senses. It would be surprising if the use to which they are put was not reflected in the design of the sense organs and their nervous pathways—as surprising as it would be to find a bird's wing to be like a horse's hoof."

REFERENCES

Amadon, D. 1959. The significance of sexual differences in size among birds. *Proc. Amer. Phil. Soc.,* **103:**531–536.
Andrew, R. J. 1956. Intention movements of flight in certain passerines, and their use in systematics. *Behaviour,* **10:**179–204.
———. 1961. The displays given by passerines in courtship and reproductive fighting: a review. *Ibis,* **103a:**315–348.
———. 1964. The displays of the primates. In *Evolutionary and Genetic Biology of Primates,* ed. by J. Buettner-Janusch, Vol. 2:227–309. The Academic Press, New York.
Armstrong, E. A. 1947. *Bird Display and Behaviour.* Lindsey Press, London.
Baerends, G. P. 1950. Specializations in organs and movements with a releasing function. *Symp. Soc. Exp. Biol.,* **4:**337–360.
——— and J. M. Baerends-van Roon. 1950. An introduction to the study of the ethology of cichlid fishes. *Behaviour Suppl.,* **1:**1–243.
———, R. Brouwer, and H. Tj. Waterbolk. 1955. Ethological studies on *Lebistes reticulatus* (Peters). I. An analysis of the male courtship pattern. *Behaviour,* **8:**249–334.
Baker, E. C. S. 1942. *Cuckoo Problems.* H. F. and G. Witherby, London.
Baker, H. G. 1963. Evolutionary mechanisms in pollination biology. *Science,* **139:**877–883.
Barlow, G. W. 1963. Ethology of the Asian teleost *Badis badis.* II. Motivation and signal value of the colour patterns. *Anim. Behav.,* **11:**97–105.
Barlow, H. B. 1961. Possible principles underlying the transformations of sensory messages. In *Sensory Communication,* ed. by W. A. Rosenblith: 217–234. Massachusetts Institute of Technology Press, Cambridge.

Bartholomew, G. A. Jr. 1953. Behavioral factors affecting social structure in the Alaska fur seal. *Transactions 18th North American Wildlife Conference:* 481–501.

Blest, A. D. 1957a. The function of eyespot patterns in the Lepidoptera. *Behaviour,* 11:209–256.

———. 1957b. The evolution of protective displays in the Saturnioidea and Sphingidae (Lepidoptera). *Behaviour,* 11:257–309.

Brower, J. van Z. 1960. Experimental studies of mimicry. IV. The reactions of starlings to different proportions of models and mimics. *Amer. Nat.,* 94:271–282.

Brower, L. P., J. van Z. Brower, and P. W. Westcott. 1960. Experimental studies of mimicry. 5. The reactions of toads (*Bufo terrestris*) to bumblebees (*Bombus americanorum*) and their robberfly mimics (*Mallophora bomboides*), with a discussion of aggressive mimicry. *Amer. Nat.,* 94:343–355.

Brown, J. L. 1964. The integration of agonistic behavior in the Steller's jay *Cyanocitta stelleri* (Gmelin). *Univ. Calif. Publ. Zool.,* 60(4):223–328.

Buck, J. B. 1937. Studies on the firefly. II. The signal system and color vision in *Photinus pyralis. Physiol. Zool.,* 10:412–419.

Carbaugh, B. T., M. W. Schein, and E. B. Hale. 1962. Effects of morphological variations of chicken models on sexual responses of cocks. *Anim. Behav.,* 10:235–238.

Carpenter, C. C. 1962. A comparison of the patterns of display of *Urosaurus, Uta,* and *Streptosaurus. Herpetologica,* 18:145–152.

———. 1963. Patterns of behavior in three forms of the fringe-toed lizards (*Uma*-Iguanidae). *Copeia,* 1963(2):406–412.

Chance, E. P. 1922. *The Cuckoo's Secret.* Sidgwick and Jackson, London.

Collias, E. C. and N. E. Collias. 1957. The response of chicks of the Franklin's gull to parental bill-color. *Auk,* 74:371–375.

Collias, N. E. 1943. Statistical analysis of factors which make for success in initial encounters between hens. *Amer. Nat.,* 77:519–538.

———. 1962. The behaviour of ducks. In *The Behaviour of Domestic Animals,* ed. by E. S. E. Hafez: 565–585. The Williams and Wilkins Company, Baltimore.

Cott, H. B. 1957. *Adaptive Coloration in Animals.* Methuen and Company, London.

Crane, J. 1957. Basic patterns of display in fiddler crabs (Ocypodidae, genus *Uca*). *Zoologica,* 42:69–82.

Cullen, E. 1957. Adaptations in the kittiwake to cliff-nesting. *Ibis,* 99:275–302.

Cullen, J. M. 1962. The pecking response of young wideawake terns *Sterna fuscata. Ibis,* 103b:162–173.

Dane, B., C. Walcott, and W. H. Drury. 1959. The form and duration of the display actions of the goldeneye (*Bucephala clangula*). *Behaviour,* 14:265–281.

——— and W. G. Van der Kloot. 1964. An analysis of the display of the goldeneye duck (*Bucephala clangula* (L.)). *Behaviour,* 22:282–328.

Darwin, C. 1872. *The Expression of the Emotions in Man and the Animals.* John Murray (Publishers), London.

Daumer, K. 1958. Blumenfarben, wie sie die Bienen sehen. *Z. vergl. Physiol.,* 41:49–110.

Davies, S. J. J. F. 1961. The orientation of pecking in very young magpie geese *Anseranas semipalmata. Ibis,* 103a:277–283.

——— and R. Carrick. 1962. On the ability of crested terns, *Sterna bergii,* to recognize their own chicks. *Aust. J. Zool.,* 10:171–177.

Davis, J. 1957. Comparative foraging behavior of the spotted and brown towhees. *Auk,* 74:129–166.

Duffey, E., N. Creasey, and K. Williamson. 1950. The 'rodent-run' distraction-behaviour of certain waders. Part 1. Field observations on the purple sandpiper. *Ibis,* 92:27–33.

Eisenberg, J. 1963. The behavior of heteromyid rodents. *Univ. Calif. Publ. Zool.,* **69**:1–114.

Emlen, J. T. 1957. Display and mate selection in the whydahs and bishop birds. *The Ostrich,* **28**(4):202–213.

Fantz, R. L. 1957. Form preferences in newly hatched chicks. *J. comp. physiol. Psychol.,* **50**:422–430.

——. 1961. The origin of form perception. *Sci. Amer.,* **204**(5):66–72.

——. 1965. Ontogeny of perception. In *Behavior of Nonhuman Primates,* ed. by A. M. Schrier, H. F. Harlow, and F. Stollnitz: 365–403. The Academic Press, New York.

Fisher, A. E. and E. B. Hale. 1957. Stimulus determinants of sexual and aggressive behavior in male domestic fowl. *Behaviour,* **10**:309–323.

Ford, E. B. 1964. *Ecological Genetics.* Methuen and Company, London.

Fraenkel, G. S. and D. L. Gunn. 1940. *The Orientation of Animals.* Oxford University Press, London.

Friedmann, H. 1960. The parasitic weaverbirds. *U.S. Nat. Mus. Bull.,* **223**:1–196.

Gilliard, E. T. 1963. The evolution of bowerbirds. *Sci. Amer.,* **209**(2):38–46.

Grant, V. 1949. Pollination systems as isolation mechanisms in angiosperms. *Evolution,* **3**:82–97.

——. 1963. *The Origin of Adaptations.* Columbia University Press, New York.

Guhl, A. M. and L. L. Ortman. 1953. Visual patterns in the recognition of individuals among chickens. *Condor,* **55**:287–298.

Hailman, J. P. 1962. Development of species recognition in gulls. Quoted in *Behavioral Aspects of Ecology* by P. H. Klopfer. Prentice-Hall, Englewood Cliffs.

Hall, K. R. L. and I. DeVore. 1965. Baboon social behavior. In *Primate Behavior,* ed. by I. DeVore: 53–110. Holt, Rinehart and Winston, New York.

Hamilton, T. H. and R. H. Barth, Jr. 1962. The biological significance of season change in male plumage appearance in some new world migratory bird species. *Amer. Nat.,* **96**:129–144.

Hamilton, W. J., III. and G. Orians. 1965. Evolution of brood parasitism in altricial birds. *Condor,* **67**:361–382.

Hess, E. H. 1956. Natural preferences of chicks and ducklings for objects of different colors. *Psychol. Rep.,* **2**:477–483.

——. 1960. Sensory processes. In *An Introduction to Comparative Psychology,* ed. by R. H. Waters, D. A. Rethlingshafer, and W. E. Caldwell: 74–101. McGraw-Hill Book Company, New York.

——. 1961. Shadows and depth perception. *Sci. Amer.,* **204**(3):139–148.

Hildén, O. 1965. Habitat selection in birds. *Ann. Zool. Fenn.,* **2**:53–75.

Hinde, R. A. 1952. Behaviour of the great tit (*Parus major*) and some other related species. *Behaviour Suppl.,* **2**:1–201.

——. 1959. Behaviour and speciation in birds and lower vertebrates. *Biol. Rev.,* **34**:85–128.

—— and T. E. Rowell. 1962. Communication by postures and facial expressions in the rhesus monkey (*Macaca mulatta*). *Proc. Zool. Soc. Lond.,* **138**:1–21.

Hingston, R. W. G. 1933. *The Meaning of Animal Colour and Adornment.* Edward Arnold and Company, London.

Hunsaker, D., II. 1962. Ethological isolating mechanisms in the *Sceloporus torquatus* group of lizards. *Evolution,* **16**:62–74.

Immelmann, K. 1962. Biologische Bedeutung optischer und akustischer Merkmale bei Prachtfinken (Aves: Spermestidae). *Verh. Dtsch. Zool. Ges., Zool. Anz.* Suppl. **25**:369–374.

Jourdain, F. C. R. 1925. A study on parasitism in the cuckoos. *Proc. Zool. Soc. Lond.,* **1925**:639–667.

Jung, R. 1961. Neuronal integration in the visual cortex and its significance for visual information. In *Sensory Communication*, ed. by W. A. Rosenblith: 627–674. Massachusetts Institute of Technology Press, Cambridge.

Kear, J. 1962. Food selection in finches with special reference to interspecific differences. *Proc. Zool. Soc. Lond.*, **138**:163–204.

——. 1964. Colour preference in young Anatidae. *Ibis*, **106**:361–369.

Keenleyside, M. H. A. 1955. Some aspects of the schooling behaviour of fish. *Behaviour*, **8**:183–248.

Klopfer, P. 1962. *Behavioral Aspects of Ecology*. Prentice-Hall, Englewood Cliffs.

—— and J. P. Hailman. 1965. Habitat selection in birds. *Adv. Study Behav.*, **1**:279–303.

Lack, D. 1933. Habitat selection in birds, with special reference to the effects of afforestation on the Breckland avifauna. *J. Anim. Ecol.*, **2**:239–262.

——. 1944. Ecological aspects of species-formation in passerine birds. *Ibis*, **86**:260–286.

——. 1947. *Darwin's Finches*. Cambridge University Press, Cambridge.

Lorenz, K. Z. 1935. Der Kumpan in der Umwelt des Vogels. *J. Orn.* **83**:137–213, 289–413.

——. 1941. Vergleichende Bewegungsstudien an Anatinen. *J. Orn.*, **89** (Suppl. 3): 194–293.

MacArthur, R. H. 1958. Population ecology of some warblers of northeastern coniferous forests. *Ecology*, **39**:599–619.

McDermott, F. A. 1917. Observations on the light-emission of American Lampyridae. *Can. Ent.*, **49**:53–61.

Manning, A. 1956. The effect of honey-guides. *Behaviour*, **9**:114–139.

Marks, H. L., P. B. Siegel, and C. Y. Kramer. 1960. Effect of comb and wattle removal on the social organization of mixed flocks of chickens. *Anim. Behav.*, **8**:192–196.

Marler, P. 1957. Specific distinctiveness in the communication signals of birds. *Behaviour*, **11**:13–39.

——. 1959. Developments in the study of animal communication. In *Darwin's Biological Work*, ed. by P. R. Bell: 150–206. Cambridge University Press, Cambridge.

——. 1961. The evolution of visual communication. In *Vertebrate Speciation*, ed. by W. F. Blair: 96–121. University of Texas Press, Austin.

——. 1965. Communication in monkeys and apes. In *Primate Behavior*, ed. by I. DeVore: 544–584. Holt, Rinehart and Winston, New York.

Marshall, A. J. 1954. *Bower-birds*. Oxford University Press, London.

Mayr, E. 1942. *Systematics and the Origin of Species*. Columbia University Press, New York.

Meeuse, B. J. D. 1961. *The Story of Pollination*. The Ronald Press Company, New York.

Morris, D. 1957. "Typical intensity" and its relation to the problem of ritualisation. *Behaviour*, **11**:1-12.

Moynihan, M. 1960. Some adaptations which help to promote gregariousness. *Proc. 12th Int. Orn. Congr.* (1958), Vol. 2:523–541.

——. 1962. The organization and probable evolution of some mixed species flocks of neotropical birds. *Smithsonian Misc. Coll.*, **143**(7):1–140.

Myrberg, A. A., Jr. 1964. An analysis of the preferential care of eggs and young by adult cichlid fishes. *Z. Tierpsychol.*, **21**:53–98.

Neil, E. H. 1964. An analysis of color changes and social behavior of *Tilapia mossambica*. *Univ. Calif. Publ. Zool.*, **75**:1–58.

Nice, M. M. 1943. Studies in the life history of the song sparrow. II. The behavior of the song sparrow and other passerines. *Trans. Linn. Soc. N.Y.*, **6**:1–328.

Nicolai, J. 1964. Der Brutparasitismus der Viduinae als ethologisches Problem. *Z. Tierpsychol.*, **21**:129–204.

Pittendrigh, C. S. 1958. Adaptation, natural selection and behavior. In *Behavior and Evolution*, ed. by A. Roe and G. G. Simpson: 390–416. Yale University Press, New Haven.

Quine, D. A. and J. M. Cullen. 1964. The pecking response of young arctic terns *Sterna macrura* and the adaptiveness of the "releasing mechanism." *Ibis,* **106:**145–173.

Rensch, B. 1925. Verhalten von Singvögeln bei Aenderung des Gelenges. *Orn. Monatsbericht,* **33:**169–173.

Ruiter, L. de. 1956. Countershading in caterpillars. An analysis of its adaptive significance. *Arch. Néerl. Zool.,* **11:**285–341.

Schaller, G. B. 1963. *The Mountain Gorilla.* University of Chicago Press, Chicago.

Selander, R. K. 1965. On mating systems and natural selection. *Amer. Nat.,* **99:**129–141.

—— and C. J. La Rue, Jr. 1961. Interspecific preening invitation display of parasitic cowbirds. *Auk,* **78:**473–504.

Sibley, C. G. 1957. The evolutionary and taxonomic significance of sexual dimorphism and hybridization in birds. *Condor,* **59:**166–191.

——. 1961. Hybridization and isolating mechanisms. In *Vertebrate Speciation,* ed. by W. F. Blair: 69–88. Texas University Press, Austin.

Southern, H. N. 1954. Mimicry in cuckoo's eggs. In *Evolution as a Process,* ed. by J. Huxley, A. C. Hardy, and E. B. Ford: 219–232. George Allen and Unwin, London.

Stokes, A. W. 1962a. Agonistic behaviour among blue tits at a winter feeding station. *Behaviour,* **19:**118–138.

——. 1962b. Comparative ethology of great, blue, marsh, and coal tits at a winter feeding station. *Behaviour,* **19:**208–218.

Svärdson, G. 1949. Competition and habitat selection in birds. *Oikos,* **1:**157–174.

Talbot, L. M. 1962. Food preferences of some East African wild ungulates. *E. Afr. Agric. For. J.,* **27:**131–138.

Tinbergen, N. 1940. Die Übersprungbewegung. *Z. Tierpsychol.,* **4:**1–40.

——. 1948. Social releasers and the experimental method required for their study. *Wilson Bull.,* **60:**6–51.

——. 1952. "Derived" activities; their causation, biological significance, origin, and emancipation during evolution. *Quart. Rev. Biol.,* **27:**1–32.

——. 1954. The origin and evolution of courtship and threat display. In *Evolution as a Process,* ed. by J. S. Huxley, A. C. Hardy, and E. B. Ford: 232–250. George Allen and Unwin, London.

——. 1959. Comparative studies of the behaviour of gulls (Laridae): a progress report. *Behaviour,* **15:**1–70.

—— and A. C. Perdeck. 1950. On the stimulus situation releasing the begging response in the newly hatched herring gull chick (*Larus argentatus argentatus* Pont). *Behaviour,* **3:**1–39.

Weidmann, U. 1961. The stimuli eliciting begging in gulls and terns. (Abstr.) *Anim. Behav.,* **9:**115–116.

Wells, M. J. 1962. *Brain and Behaviour in Cephalopods.* Heinemann, London.

Welty, J. C. 1962. *The Life of Birds.* W. B. Saunders, Philadelphia and London.

Wickler, W. 1962. Ei-Attrappen und Maulbrüten bei afrikanischen Cichliden. *Z. Tierpsychol.,* **19:**129–164.

Wynne-Edwards, V. C. 1962. *Animal Dispersion in Relation to Social Behaviour.* Oliver and Boyd, Edinburgh and London.

eleven

RESPONSIVENESS TO
MECHANICAL DISTURBANCE: AUDITION

Perception of the physical properties of a sound wave • Pressure and displacement receptors • Responsiveness of insect sound receptors to frequency and intensity • Location of sounds • Vertebrate hearing • Stimulus filtering in audition.

PHYSICAL PROPERTIES OF SOUND WAVES AND RECEPTORS

A moving object generates disturbance in the surrounding medium and in the substrate. If the disturbance is great enough it becomes perceptible some distance from the point of origin. The vibrations permit recognition of the moving object's presence, and also the perception of its direction, distance, and temporal pattern of movement. The ability of animals to perceive such mechanical disturbances or sounds is exploited while they explore their environment, avoid danger, locate food, and communicate with members of their own species.

The structures that animals have evolved to enable them to hear sounds are many and varied. The mode of action of these devices determines the functions that hearing can serve. One receptor type may be better than another for locating a sound source but be less well suited for determining the frequency of vibration. Variations occur because different kinds of receptors respond to different properties of sound waves. As the vibrating molecules of the surrounding medium transmit the sound from the source they generate a wave of pressure change. Some sound receptors respond to the actual displacement of molecules, others register changes in pressure (Autrum 1936, 1941, Pumphrey 1940).

◆ *Pressure and Displacement Receptors.* How do these two types of receptors work? To be sensitive to molecular displacement a membrane or hair must be light and freely suspended so that it responds to slight movements of the medium. If a membrane mediates the response, the sound wave must have free access to both sides of it. In a pressure-sensitive system, however, the membrane must be heavier and the sound wave must be shielded from its inner surface. The chamber within is kept at some stable reference pressure, usually equal to that of the atmosphere. It may be that smaller hearing organs more closely approximate displacement systems, hence the specialization of arthropods in this type of receptor. A diagrammatic representation of the two types of membrane systems is given in Figure 11-1. Also shown are their counterparts in the pressure receptive mammalian ear, and the sensory hair and tympanal receptor organs of insects, which respond to particle displacement.

◆ *The Properties of Sound Waves.* A radiating sound wave can convey information about several of the properties of the moving object that generates the disturbance. The extent or amplitude of the movement is represented by the intensity of the sound perceived, i.e. loudness. Loudness perception is necessarily relative because the amplitude of the sound reaching a listener declines with the square of the distance over which it has traveled and is further affected by interactions with the intervening environment. Within limits the time the disturbance occurs can be determined, for sound travels at a constant speed, irrespective of its intensity. In air at room temperature the velocity of sound is about 1130 feet per second (340 meters per second). It travels faster in hot air than in cold. In water the velocity of sound is more than four times greater than in air.

Another temporal property of sound is the manner of vibration of the original movement, which is reflected in the pattern of disturbance of the molecules of the surrounding medium. The rate of vibration, measured in cycles per second, is represented by the frequency of the sound, which is perceived subjectively as pitch. If we picture the sound as a waveform, the distance between successive peaks decreases as the frequency increases (Table 11-1). Since the velocity is constant irrespective of frequency, the reduction in wavelength results in an increased cycle frequency.

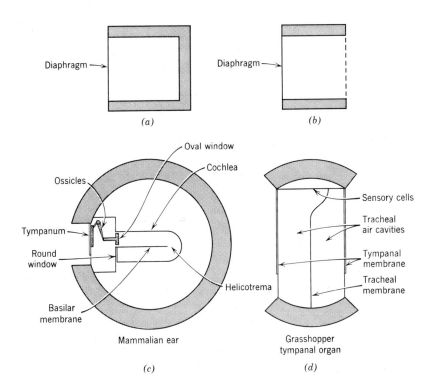

Diaphragm →

Diaphragm →

(a)

(b)

Oval window

Cochlea

Ossicles

Tympanum →

Round window

Basilar membrane

Helicotrema

Mammalian ear

(c)

Sensory cells

Tracheal air cavities

Tympanal membrane

Tracheal membrane

Grasshopper tympanal organ

(d)

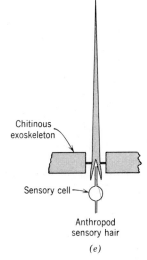

Chitinous exoskeleton

Sensory cell →

Anthropod sensory hair

(e)

Figure 11-1 Schematic diagrams of (a) pressure and (b) displacement receptors and their counterparts in (c) mammalian and (d, e) insect hearing organs. (c) The tympanum receives sound pressure waves only from its outer side. The ossicles of the middle ear conduct movements from the tympanum to the oval window and the inner ear. (d) The tympanal organ of grasshoppers responds to particle displacement on both sides of opposing tympanal membranes which are coupled to the tracheal membrane through the tracheal air cavities. Movement of the tracheal membrane activates the sensory cells of the crista acustica. The thin portion of the tympanal membranes permits free movement. Another type of displacement receptor, the mobile hairs of arthropods (e), articulate with the exoskeleton and activate a sensory cell at the base. After Haskell 1961 from Pumphrey, and after Autrum 1963.

Table 11-1   Pitch of Some Musical Notes and Their Physical Characteristics

Octaves above or below (−) middle C	Frequency, cycles/sec	Wavelength, feet
−2 (C$_2$)	65.5	17.26
−1 (C$_3$)	131	8.63
0 (C$_4$)	262	4.31
1 (C$_5$)	524	2.15
2 (C$_6$)	1048	1.08
3 (C$_7$)	2096	.54
4 (C$_8$)	4192	.27
5 (C$_9$)	8384	.14

From Bergeijk, Pierce, and David 1960.

Natural sounds seldom contain a single frequency. Multiples of the basic frequency or harmonics are often present, and a broad spectrum of sound frequencies or noise may also be included. Variation in the vibration frequency of sound-producing organs is widely exploited by animals as a means of generating communicatory sounds.

Sounds also have spatial properties that depend on the distance and direction of the source. The vibratory movement of the medium radiates from the sound source unless it is channeled. Thus directional information can be derived if the receptors can register the appropriate property of the sound. Perception of sound direction is obviously crucial for animals which use audition to analyze their environment. We shall see that pressure and displacement receptor systems handle this problem in different ways.

To determine the distance to a sound source it is necessary to register its direction at two points in the sound field, either successively or at the same time. This determination has rarely been achieved by animals as far as we know, although some owls have a remarkable ability to localize prey in three dimensions by sound (page 420). If the intensity of a sound at the source is fairly constant, its loudness at a given point in the field can give information about the distance of the source. Many natural sounds do have a characteristic amplitude, particularly communicatory sounds that animals themselves generate.

We can summarize the properties of sounds of significance to organisms under the same headings that we have used for the other sensory modalities.

1. *Qualitative properties.* Just as the wavelength of light is perceived by some organisms as a particular color, so the wavelength of sounds is perceived as the qualitative property pitch, even though it depends on the

temporal frequency characteristics. As color mixtures are perceived as hues, so different sound frequencies may combine to give a distinctive spectral structure, which we detect as the tonal quality of a sound.

2. *Intensity.* A wide range of sound intensities can be distinguished. In general, sound receptors adapt relatively quickly and are thus suited for perceiving rapid changes in intensity. Nevertheless, they do not adapt as rapidly as most visual receptors.

3. *Temporal properties.* Frequency variations are perceived by many organisms. Both intensity and frequency variation are commonly used as a means of coding information in acoustical communication. Sound vibrations are much slower than those of light, and low-frequency sounds are perceived not as tones but as a series of separate events. Thus there is a point at which temporal and qualitative properties of sounds overlap.

4. *Spatial properties.* A sound can convey information about the direction and distance of its source if transmission is not disturbed by irregularities of the intervening medium.

INSECT SOUND RECEPTORS

➤ *Receptor Organs.* To perceive a sound some receptor structure must be set in motion relative to another part of the body, and the differential movement of the body parts must be detected by mechanoreceptors. In insects perhaps the simplest form of sound receptor is a movable hair on the body surface, articulated at its base, with sensory cells to detect any movement relative to its socket (Figure 11-1e). The hair may be moved directly by the sound wave, or the sound may excite some other part of the body, such as a limb, which in turn sets hairs in motion on the articular membrane (Autrum 1963).

Alternatively, the special mechanoreceptors called chordotonal sensillae are appropriately placed to detect differential movements of certain parts of the body (Haskell 1961, Dethier 1963). Sometimes they are placed within a leg to detect vibration that is transmitted through the substrate. Then they are combined with accessory sensory structures in a subgenual organ, named for its position which is often just below the knee. In many insects chordotonal sensillae also occur at the base of the antennae in the Johnston's organ. This remarkable structure, which also functions in proprioception, is excited when sound moves the flagellum of the antenna (Risler 1955), permitting both detection of sound and determination of its direction (Tischner 1953, Keppler 1958). Johnston's organs are especially well developed in male mosquitoes, which locate females by their wing sounds, and in the whirligig beetle, *Gyrinus,* which

Table 11-2   Insect Hearing Organs and Some of Their Characteristics

Receptor	Groups	Stimulus	Range, kc/sec
Tympanal organ	Orthoptera	Airborne	0.1 −100
	Homoptera	”	0.1 − 50
	Lepidoptera	”	1 −250
	Heteroptera	Waterborne, perhaps also airborne	2 − 40
Johnston's organ	All insects	Airborne, many other stimulus types	0.05− 0.5
Subgenual organ	Orthoptera Plecoptera Lepidoptera Hymenoptera Hemiptera	Substrate vibration	0.1 − 10
Scattered chor- dotonal sensillae	All insect orders	Proprioceptors, may respond to air- or waterborne vibration	probably 0.5 − 1
Hair sensillae	All insect orders	Tactile, high intensity airborne sounds	0.05− 10

After Haskell 1961.

uses Johnston's organ to locate the source of disturbances of the water surface (see page 502).

The most elaborate sound receptors associated with the chordotonal sensillae of insects are tympanal organs, which occur in several groups and are especially characteristic of orthopterans (Table 11-2). Their essential features are a membranous drum with a tracheal air sack behind it and sensory cells so arranged that they are stimulated by movements of the drum or of the tracheal walls. The air sack connects with the tracheal system or with a paired tympanal chamber, giving sound access to both sides of the tympanum (Figure 11-2).

Tympanal organs, like Johnston's organ, subgenual organs, and hair sensillae function as displacement receptors and do not seem to be responsive to changes in pressure. Depending on the habitat of the animal and the placement of the receptors, they respond to vibrations in air, in water, or in the substrate.

◆ *Responsiveness to Frequency.* How do insect hearing organs respond to the qualitative and other properties of sound waves? First we can consider the range of frequencies to which they are tuned. Generally, hearing organs are sensitive to a wide range of frequencies. Thus tympanal organs of some grasshoppers respond to frequencies from 800 or 1000 cycles/sec well into the supersonic range, around 100 kc/sec. In some crickets the range is lower, between about 300 cycles/sec and 8 kc/sec (Autrum 1963). Responses to frequencies as high as 240 kc/sec have been detected in the tympanal nerve of a moth (Roeder and Treat 1957). Within this range there may be some tuning in the sense that the threshold is minimal for certain frequencies (Figure 11-4). In grasshoppers the zone of maximal sensitivity lies near 5 to 20 kc/sec, depending on the species. In crickets it is lower and in moths it is much higher, enabling them to perceive the cries of bats.

The frequency range of other types of insect hearing organs is narrower and lower than that of tympanal organs (Figure 11-3). Subgenual organs and other vibration receptors usually fail to respond above 2 to 8 kc/sec (Autrum 1963). With hair sensillae the cutoff is still lower, around 2 to 3 kc/sec. Again there is a zone of maximum responsiveness, much lower than that of tympanal organs.

Sharp tuning has been found in the Johnston's organ of mosquitoes which responds between about 150 and 550 cycles/sec. In the male *Aedes*

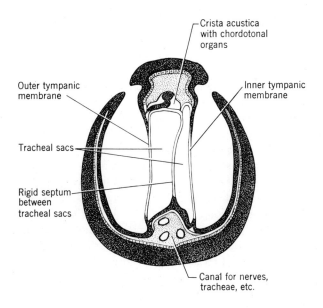

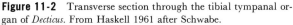

Figure 11-2   Transverse section through the tibial tympanal organ of *Decticus*. From Haskell 1961 after Schwabe.

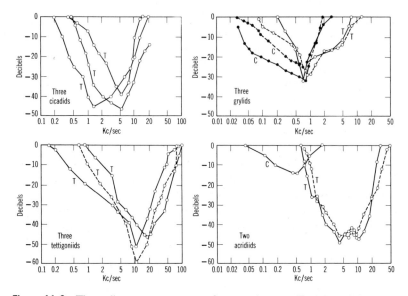

Figure 11-3 The auditory response ranges of tympanal organs, T, and cercal hair sensillae, C. After Katsuki and Suga 1960.

aegypti the maximal responsiveness corresponds with the wing tone of the female, and it can be shown that the antennae are used in locating her. The male wing tone, which is higher in frequency, is above the maximal limit of the Johnston's organ and is not heard (Roth 1948, Tischner and Schief 1954, Figure 11-4).

Are insects able to distinguish between two frequencies that are within their audible range? Answers to this question have for the most part been obtained electrophysically with some corroboration from behavioral experiments. For tympanal organs the answer is essentially negative. The pattern of activity in the temporal nerve shows no synchrony with the frequency of the sound stimulus. In experiments on the responses to artificial songs, orthopterans show no sign of distinguishing between different frequencies (review in Haskell 1961, Schwartzkopff 1962a, Autrum 1963 etc.). Subgenual organs do not seem to permit any frequency discrimination (Autrum 1963). Only with hair and antennal receptors is there a physiological mechanism for detailed frequency discrimination. If sensory hairs on the anal cerci of cockroaches or grasshoppers are stimulated by low-frequency sound, impulses that have the same frequency as the sound or some multiple of it can be detected in the cercal nerve (Pumphrey 1940). The same is true of the Johnston's organs of male mosquitoes

(Tischner 1953). Whether this potentiality for discrimination of low frequencies is in fact exploited in behavior is uncertain.

Thus many insects possess the equipment to distinguish sound frequencies between about 100 and 800 cycles/sec by means of sensory hairs and antennal receptors. Hair sensillae and tympanal organs of the same insect sometimes respond to very different frequencies (Table 11-2), providing a means of distinguishing between high and low frequencies (Katsuki and Suga 1960). In the higher part of the auditory range detected by tympanal organs, from about a kilocycle into the supersonic, frequency discrimination seems to be rudimentary or absent. Most of the communicatory sounds of insects are in this upper range. It is obvious that some property other than frequency must also be important.

◆ *Responsiveness to Intensity.* The sensitivity of the various auditory organs of insects is exceedingly great and approaches the limits of what is physically possible in some cases (Autrum 1963). The range of sound intensities that can be heard is correspondingly wide. A number of physiological mechanisms exist to make the organs acutely sensitive to variations in loudness.

Perhaps the most thorough study of an auditory system, on the tym-

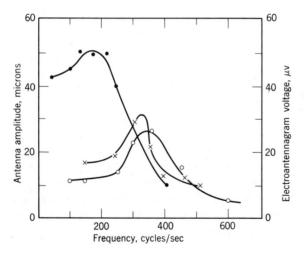

Figure 11-4   The antennal receptor responses of the mosquito, *Aedes aegypti:* x-x, electroantennagram voltage against sound frequency; o-o, amplitude of male antennal movement in microns plotted against frequency of a constant intensity sound; •-•, same but for females. After Haskell 1961.

panal organ of moths, assumes special interest in light of the knowledge that there are only two acoustical neurons in each tympanal organ (Roeder 1963). This relatively simple system has some remarkable properties. As with other tympanal organs the frequency of the sound used as a stimulus can vary widely without any visible effect on the pattern of activity in the two sensory cells. A change in sound intensity has several obvious effects, however. The response to a pure tone is a rapid sequence of action potentials which rapidly decrease in frequency. If the same tone is presented at greater intensities the action potentials are more frequent and last longer. As the sound intensity is increased further it is evident that there is more than one type of action potential. Apparently the two sensory cells have different thresholds. Careful examination of the temporal relationship between presentation of a sound stimulus and the first action potential reveals yet other means of intensity discrimination; the louder the sound the shorter the response latency, and the more intense the sound the longer the train of activity that follows a brief sound pulse.

Roeder has thus demonstrated several methods for intensity discrimination in the tympanal organ of the moth. The same principles probably apply to hair sensillae and to the more complex tympanal organs of orthopterans. The addition of more neural elements with differing thresholds would refine still further the ability to detect changes in the amplitude of sounds.

◆ *Responsiveness to Temporal Change.* Since sound frequency cannot be detected over most of the audible range, changes in frequency cannot be heard other than as variations in loudness. In the low-frequency range perceived by hair sensillae frequency variation might be detected, but the possible limits have not been explored. Although the possibility of perceiving temporal changes in frequency seems limited, tympanal organs are ideally suited to register patterns of amplitude change. They adapt relatively rapidly and, as Roeder has shown, they have several ways of responding accurately to variations in amplitude. The ability to perceive the temporal pattern of amplitude change or modulation has been exploited by insects as a means of coding information into the sounds they use for communication (page 433). This is in striking contrast to vertebrates, as we shall see.

◆ *Responsiveness to Spatial Properties.* The hearing organs of insects are displacement receptors. Since the pattern of molecular displacement of the medium has an inherent directional property, the position of the source in space can be determined directly. Thus a hair or an antenna vibrates along the path of the sound. Given suitable sensory equipment at the base to detect the direction in which the structure is vibrating, the direction of the source may be detected directly. A hair may be so articulated that it can vibrate in only one plane, and it can then respond to sound from only two directions. The same applies to the membrane of a tympanal organ, which responds most strongly to sounds striking it at right angles. Thus if a tympanal organ is isolated and stimulated by sounds coming from different angles, its directionality is immediately apparent (Pumphrey 1940, Figure 11-5a). In an intact animal the polar diagram of sensitivity of the tympanal organs will be rather different because of obstruction and diversion of the sound by the insect's body. But the directionality persists (Figure 11-5b, e.g. Autrum, Schwartzkopff, and Swoboda 1961) so that scanning movements permit localization of the sound source. It has been shown, by destroying the receptors on one side, that only one receptor is needed for localization by these methods.

Binaural clues can be important too. The shadowing of the sound by the insect's body creates a difference of intensity on the two sides of the body when the sound is coming from one side. A comparison of activity of the tympanal nerves on each side of the body gives another immediate clue to the direction of the sound source, without the need for scanning movements.

The actual mechanism of sound localization in insects has been most intensively studied in moths, which give evasive reactions to the sounds of hunting bats (Roeder 1963). Their tympanal organs are very sensitive to the high frequencies that bats use in echolocation. Experiments with artificial bat sound pulses reveal that the moth's escape responses are sometimes oriented away from the sound source, particularly if the moth is some distance from the point of origin. At close range nondirectional responses are more typical (Figure 7-5).

The orientation is based on differences in the intensity of stimulation of the two tympanal organs. The sound shadow created by the moth's body is especially marked at the high sound frequencies used by bats. Sound reflection and the consequent sound shadowing are greatest when the wavelength of the sound is less than the size of the obstructing object. Bats use ultrasonic pulses for echolocation for the same reason.

We have already noted four methods available to the moths for the perception of sound intensity: (1) the interval between action potentials, (2) the number of acoustical cells responding (one or both), (3) the action potential generation time, and (4) the number of action potentials evoked. Although the first two methods will permit the perception of sound intensity if only one ear is used, the last two may be ambiguous unless comparisons between two ears are made (Roeder 1964). Thus the moth can-

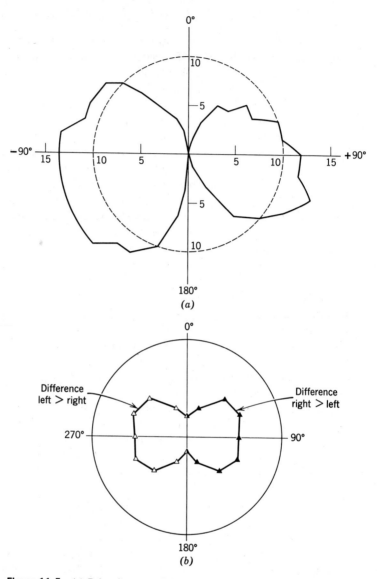

Figure 11-5 (*a*) Polar diagram of the sensitivity of an isolated tympanic organ of *Locusta migratoria*. Sensitivity is plotted radially and minimal sensitivity is arbitrarily taken as zero. The 0- to 180-degree line is the sagittal plane of the animal. (*b*) Sensitivity of a tympanal organ is an intact *Locusta*. The potential in the tympanal nerve is used as an index of responsiveness, expressed in relative values as differences between the potential on the right and left sides. After Pumphrey 1940 and Autrum, Schwartzkopff, and Swoboda 1961.

not apprehend the generation time of the first action potential as such since it lacks an independent means of knowing the moment of sound arrival. But a difference in spike generation time in response to the same sound arriving at right and left ears will reveal where the sound is loudest, which in turn tells the direction of the sound source. At one ear the number of action potentials generated is also an ambiguous index of sound intensity. For example, the same number might be generated by a brief, loud sound and a long, softer sound. Yet binaural differences in the number of action potentials evoked by the same sound would be a reliable measure of differences in sound intensity and therefore of the direction of the source. Perhaps if the sound stimuli had a standard duration, as tends to be the case with the pulses of a cruising bat, the number of spikes generated would be a less ambiguous register of sound intensity.

Of the two methods of sound localization by binaural intensity differences, Roeder (1964) has shown that differences in spike generation time at the two ears serve to orient the evasive action of moths. The orientation disappears at close range, apparently because the response of the tympanal organs becomes saturated by the loud sound, so that binaural intensity differences cease to be perceptible. The diving response that is elicited by loud sounds seems to be mediated by the brief interval between action potentials that occurs in such circumstances.

Other types of binaural comparison that are used by vertebrates for sound localization cannot be exploited by insects. Differences in time of arrival at the two ears are too slight to be detectable. Binaural phase differences cannot be detected without a means of frequency analysis, and the same applies to differences in tonal quality. The instantaneous binaural comparison of the intensity of bat pulses is used by moths for quick evasive action. There is no time for scanning, and the localization that is achieved is probably only approximate. The sustained and repetitive patterns of sound in insect songs allow ample time for a listening insect to scan with its auditory receptors and thus achieve a much more accurate localization of the source.

VERTEBRATE SOUND RECEPTORS

◆ *Receptor Structures.* The basic hearing organ of vertebrates is the ear, but there are other receptor systems that can participate in the detection of mechanical disturbances in the surrounding medium. The lateral line organs of fish and aquatic amphibians are reminiscent of the hair sensillae of insects (Figure 11-6). Like them they respond directly to flow of water on the body surface or in the lateral line canals and are thus displace-

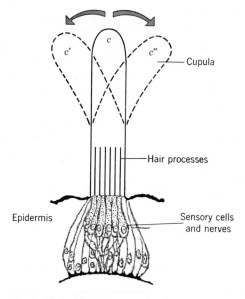

Figure 11-6 The sensory cells of the neuromasts along the lateral line of a bony fish. The cupula projects into the water and, when deflected by movement of the medium, stimulates hair processes of the sensory cells. After Lowenstein 1957 from Dijkgraaf.

ment receptors. As such they can give information about the direction of the source (Lowenstein 1957, Dijkgraaf 1962, Tavolga and Wodinsky 1963). They are mainly responsive to transients rather than steady frequencies, such as are generated by erratically moving objects or by the movements of the fish's own body. Low-frequency sounds below 800 cycles/sec or even lower stimulate lateral line receptors, however, and synchrony of discharge with the stimulus frequency has been recorded. Nevertheless, the ability to perceive sound vibrations lies primarily with the inner ear, the removal of which greatly reduces a fish's ability to respond to sounds.

Mechanoreceptors of other types may also respond to sounds. There is evidence that the Herbst corpuscles in the legs of birds permit them to respond to low-frequency sounds conducted through the substrate (Schwartzkopff 1949). A possible auditory function of the elongated bristles on the face of many birds (rictal bristles) and mammals (vibrissae) has yet to be explored.

All vertebrates have an inner ear with the same essential structure, consisting of a pars superior which has semicircular canals for the perception of gravity and movements of the head in space, and a pars inferior for the perception of sound. There may or may not be middle and outer ears to conduct and transform sounds from the body surface to the inner ear.

The tissues of fishes generally have about the same density as water, so that sounds impinging upon the surface of the head can pass directly to the inner ear. No outer ear is required, though there may be channeling of sound through tissues of low density. Nor is there any of the apparatus of a middle ear such as an eardrum and ossicles to conduct sound to the inner ear. But some groups of fishes have a different structure which serves an analogous function. This is the gas-filled swimbladder which connects with the inner ear either directly by means of anterior diverticula (e.g. mormyrids and labyrinthine fishes) or by 'Weberian ossicles' (ostariophysine fishes, von Frisch 1936, Poggendorf 1952, Jones and Marshall 1953, Tavolga and Wodinsky 1963). With such a link there is a considerable improvement in hearing ability.

The external auditory meatus of whales is greatly reduced. Some, perhaps most, of the sound that they hear must be conducted directly to the middle ear through the intervening skin and blubber (Dudok van Heel 1962).

In terrestrial animals an outer ear assumes important functions. It comprises the external pinna and the external auditory meatus. The mammalian pinna, for example, increases the area over which sound energy is abstracted, makes the ear directional, and prevents the generation of wind noise in the meatus (Pumphrey 1961). Studies of the acoustical properties of a movable pinna are badly needed. Birds lack a pinna, presumably because of the drag that it would cause during flight. The covering of feathers over the meatus must hinder hearing to some extent, but it is required to reduce the wind noise that would otherwise reach intolerable levels in the open meatus during flight. Nevertheless, bats have retained and enlarged their pinnae in spite of the aerodynamic disadvantages (Pumphrey 1961).

The meatus conducts sound from the surface to the tympanum. It serves as a resonator, amplifying certain frequencies and roughly tuning the ear to be particularly sensitive within a certain range. The resonant frequency of the external meatus of man corresponds closely to the frequency to which he is most sensitive (Bergeijk, Pierce, and David 1960).

The middle ear transmits sound mechanically from the eardrum to the relatively dense and incompressible fluid behind the oval window of the inner ear. In birds the transmission is achieved by a single rod, the columella, and in mammals by a chain of three ossicles. The force of the movement at the oval window in a bird is increased since it is smaller than the tympanum. In mammals the lever action of the ossicles also changes the tympanal vibrations to movements of smaller amplitude but greater force at the oval window (Békésy 1962). The ossicles can serve a protective function. Very loud sounds elicit contraction of muscles attached to the ossicles in the middle ear, reducing the transmission to the inner ear and so alleviating the possibility of damage.

Sensory hairs within the inner ear are the ultimate transducers of mechanical vibrations into nerve impulses. These hairs resemble the lateral line organs of fish and may have been derived from them (Pumphrey 1950).

There are two ways in which the hairs can be excited by sound. In fish the hairs are covered with jelly in which one or more dense calcareous particles or 'otoliths' are incorporated. A sound passing through the ear causes differential movement of the otolith and the underlying hair 'macula' stimulating the sensory cells. The otolith organ in the sacculus is particularly involved, though in some fish the parts of the ear normally concerned with gravity perception may also respond to sound (Lowenstein 1957, Moulton 1963).

In terrestrial vertebrates the conduction of sound to the inner ear along a specific pathway, through the cochlea, leads to the excitement of the sensory hairs. Sound is conducted from the oval window down one side of the cochlea tube, the scala vestibuli. After a delay it goes through a hole at the tip, the helicotrema, and comes back down the other side of the tube, the scala tympani. It is then dispersed from the round window into the cavity of the middle ear. The 'basilar membrane' and its sensory hairs, the organ of Corti, are incorporated in the dividing wall (Figure 11-7).

A sound passing up the scala vestibuli causes vibration in the basilar membrane. The movements exert a shear force on the hair cells and a sound is perceived. The point in the cochlear tube with the maximal amplitude of displacement of the membrane varies with the frequency of the sound stimulus (Figure 11-8). Locating the point of maximal stimulation permits us to determine the sound frequency, with further information at least for lower frequencies, derived from the temporal pattern of neural activity at certain points in the cochlea. By analogy with skin sensations, Békésy (1960) has shown how perception of the point of maximal displacement can be sharpened by a process of lateral inhibition similar to that occurring in vision (Figure 11-9). The ears of terrestrial vertebrates respond to pressure changes in the surrounding medium rather than to molecular displacement. The same is probably true of aquatic mammals and of fish that use the air bladder in hearing. The mechanism of hearing in fish that lack a sound transformer such as the

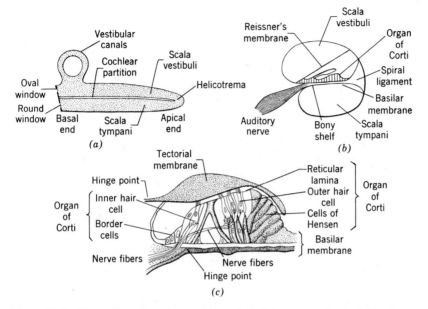

Figure 11-7 The cochlea of vertebrates, (*a*) unrolled, (*b*) in cross section, and (*c*) enlargement of (*b*). After Bergeijk, Pierce, and David 1960.

air bladder is still in doubt. Lateral line organs, on the other hand, are known to be displacement receptors.

Given hearing equipment of the type we have described, what are the capabilities of vertebrates in perceiving the various types of information that sounds can convey?

◆ *Responsiveness to Frequency.* The range of frequencies heard by vertebrates is as variable as in invertebrates. Many conform to patterns similar to that of man. Figure 11-10 shows a fish, a bird, and a mammal each with a frequency range from a minimum of about 100 cycles/sec to a maximum of 10 to 20 kc/sec. The many deviations from this pattern are of interest. Fishes that rely upon direct stimulation by way of calcareous otoliths can hear sounds within a limited frequency range—between perhaps 100 and 2000 cycles/sec depending on the species. In species that have some connection between the swimbladder and the inner ear, the upper frequency limit is raised twofold or more. There is a corresponding improvement in the ability to distinguish between sounds of different frequencies. They are sensitive to a 3 percent difference, as compared with 9 percent in species that do not use the swimbladder (Dijkgraaf 1960, Tavolga and Wodinsky 1963).

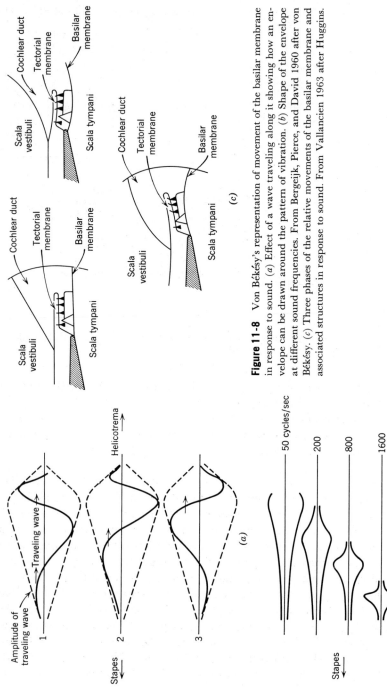

Figure 11-8 Von Békésy's representation of movement of the basilar membrane in response to sound. (*a*) Effect of a wave traveling along it showing how an envelope can be drawn around the pattern of vibration. (*b*) Shape of the envelope at different sound frequencies. From Bergeijk, Pierce, and David 1960 after von Békésy. (*c*) Three phases of the relative movements of the basilar membrane and associated structures in response to sound. From Vallancien 1963 after Huggins.

Frogs and reptiles hear various ranges of frequencies, with an upper limit that is generally lower than in birds. Birds have about the same frequency range as man. The frequency to which the ear is most sensitive varies. In general, this correlates with the size of the bird, a crow being most sensitive around 1 to 2 kc/sec, a smaller bird such as the bullfinch around 3 kc/sec. Such a relationship would be expected since the resonant frequency of the auditory meatus will increase with decreasing size. Exceptions to the rule are some owls which, even when they are large, are most sensitive to sounds as high as 6 kc/sec, apparently implying a relationship with their habit of hunting by ear at night (Schwartzkopff 1955). Birds are better than most mammals and approach men in their ability to distinguish between sounds differing slightly in frequency (Table 11-3). The fact that their cochlea is much shorter than that of mammals must imply a significant central factor in the process of frequency discrimination (Schwartzkopff 1955).

The ears of mammals respond to a range of frequencies from a lower limit of about 50 cycles/sec to an upper one that varies from as low as 20 kc/sec in man, to 100 kc/sec in some rodents (Schleidt 1952), and higher

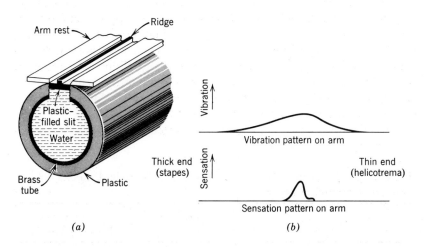

(a)   *(b)*

Figure 11-9   (*a*) Apparatus used by von Békésy to illustrate analogies between skin sensation and hearing. The plastic in the slit tapers in thickness and therefore in elasticity from one end of the tube to the other. With an arm on the rest the subject feels vibrations set up in the water by a piston with maximal stimulation at a certain point. The point moves up and down the tube with changes in the vibration frequency. (*b*) The localization of the sensation is sharper than the actual vibration pattern of the plastic membrane. This suggests a parallel with 'lateral inhibition' in vision and shows the possibility of accurate localization of the point of maximal vibration on the basilar membrane. From Bergeijk, Pierce, and David 1960 after von Békésy.

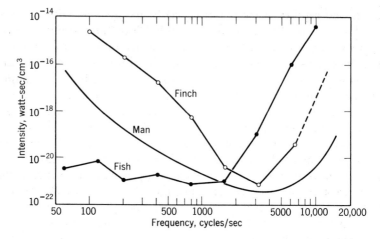

Figure 11-10 Sound frequency thresholds for man, a finch, *Pyrrhula*, and a fish, *Amiurus*. After Schwartzkopff 1960, from Poggendorf 1952.

for some bats. In general, the upper limit increases as the animal's size decreases (Schwartzkopff 1960). Exceptions to this approximate rule are the whales and porpoises. They have a very high upper frequency limit, which relates to their use of high-frequency sounds for echolocation in a manner similar to that of bats (see page 500). Within this frequency range the capacity to discriminate between different frequencies is acute and must in part be a result of the long cochlea. Man, for instance, can detect a 0.3 percent frequency difference (Table 11-3).

Sound frequency has a significance for vertebrates that is absent in in-

Table 11-3 Frequency Discrimination in Man, Three Bird Species, and the Fishes *Phoximus* and *Sargus*

Species	Optimal range, cycles/sec	Discrimination threshold, percent
Homo sapiens	1000–3000	0.3
Melopsittacus undulatus	1000–3000	0.3–0.7
Loxia curvirostra	1000–3000	0.3–0.7
Columba livia	1000–2000	6
Phoxinus laevis	400–1000	3
Sargus annularis	150–450	<9–15

From Schwartzkopff 1955, after Ranke, Knecht, Wassiljew, and Dijkgraaf.

sects. Their ability to distinguish variations in frequency provides a new dimension of hearing that is extensively exploited in their systems of vocal communication, which consequently differ strikingly from those of insects.

◆ *Responsiveness to Intensity.* The sensitivity of vertebrate ears is remarkable. The amplitudes to which parts of the human ear respond begin to approach the dimensions of Brownian movement (Békésy and Rosenblith 1951). Within the range of sound intensities that can be heard there are several physiological mechanisms that permit discrimination of intensity differences. These include variation in the number of nerve impulses generated by a sound and in the number of nerve fibers involved (Davis 1961). The large numbers of sensory elements permit an intermingling of slow and rapidly adapting receptors, receptors with differing thresholds, and central neurons responding to on and off stimulation (Katsuki 1961). These find a special application in detecting binaural differences in response to a sound.

◆ *Responsiveness to Temporal Change.* Responsiveness to both amplitude and frequency of sounds in vertebrates makes the detection of temporal change of these properties possible. A conflict can arise between the requirements for frequency determination and the perception of rapid temporal patterns (Licklider 1951). When making an analysis of the structure of brief sounds, it is impossible to make simultaneous estimates, with equal accuracy, of both the frequency and the time of starting and finishing of the sound. In a sense, an accurate picture of frequency is necessarily accompanied by an approximate picture of the temporal pattern. To put it in another way, a brief sound has to be 'smeared' out for a longer period (Joos 1948) in order for an accurate estimate of frequency to be made. Conversely, if an accurate picture of the beginning and termination of such a brief sound is to be made, we have to be content with an approximate picture of frequency structure.

The sound spectrograph, now widely used in the analysis of natural sounds, takes account of this paradox. It has two filter settings, wide band and narrow band, to perform each of these functions. With the narrow band-pass filter there is a long time constant, which smears the sound out and gives an accurate picture of frequency. The wide band-pass filter has a short time constant and gives an accurate picture of the time pattern at the expense of some distortion of the picture of frequency.

The same principles probably affect the responses of auditory receptors. Thus very brief sounds below about 10 milliseconds in duration are heard by us as clicks which have no definite pitch. As the duration is increased the pitch gradually becomes evident, and beyond about 50 milliseconds we hear the sound as a pure tone (Stevens and Davis 1938). It has even been suggested that the time constant of the human ear can be varied between 20 and 250 milliseconds, according to the task which is being performed (Gabor 1947).

A high degree of damping in the inner ear would favor the perception of the temporal properties of sounds. The scala vestibuli of birds is not a clear passage as in mammals, but is filled with folds and processes from the tegmentum vasculosum (Schwartzkopff and Winter 1960, Schwartz-kopff 1963, Figure 11-11). These obstructions must have the effect of bringing the system to rest more quickly in birds than in mammals, so sharpening responsiveness to sounds that follow one another rapidly. Schwartzkopff (1957) finds some electrophysiological support for this contention. The more rapid temporal patterns of sounds used in avian communication as compared with those of mammals must be a reflection of such a difference in ability for temporal discrimination (Pumphrey 1961, Schwartzkopff 1957). Thorpe (1963) has evidence for an acute temporal sense and for very quick auditory reaction times in the behavior of pairs of duetting birds, one following the other with great speed and accuracy.

✦ *Perception of Spatial Properties of Sounds.* The ability of fish to determine the direction of a sound source has rarely been explored. They do not seem to locate sound sources readily. Species that use a median swimbladder in hearing must surely experience difficulty. But localization of a source should be possible with the displacement perception of lateral line organs and also with an otolith if it is directly stimulated through the tissues of the head.

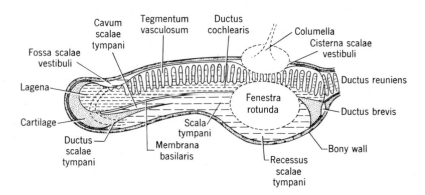

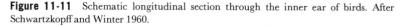

Figure 11-11 Schematic longitudinal section through the inner ear of birds. After Schwartzkopff and Winter 1960.

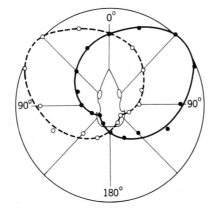

Figure 11-12   Polar diagram of the sensitivity of the bullfinch's ear to a 3.2 kc/sec sound; ●-●, right ear, o-o, left ear. The diagram is based on measurements of the cochlear potential. After Pumphrey 1961 from Schwartzkopff.

The pressure-responsive nature of the ears of other vertebrates compels them to use binaural comparisons for the most part in localizing the source of a sound. The presence of the head as a sound obstruction provides some monaural cues, however. A person with one ear can scan for the direction of maximal stimulation. With complex sounds containing a range of frequencies another monaural cue is available. We have noted that the degree of sound shadowing depends on the relationship between wavelength and the size of the obstructing object. Thus the spectral structure of a sound may differ on the two sides of the head. If the sound is familiar, variations in the tonal quality heard at one ear can give an instantaneous clue to the direction of the sound source.

In the intact animal binaural cues are undoubtedly most important. If the ears are far enough apart there are differences in arrival time and in phase at the right and left sides, as well as intensity differences resulting from the sound shadow of the head. In man all three methods are used. With smaller animals the temporal differences are greatly reduced and, as in insects, binaural intensity differences become the dominant cue. Thus small birds seem to rely mainly on intensity differences (Schwartzkopff 1950, 1952, 1962c, Figure 11-12). Larger birds and mammals probably use a combination of methods. In addition, the tonal quality of complex sounds may provide binaural as well as monaural cues.

The facility with which a particular sound can be localized depends on its characteristics. Sound shadowing and changes in tonal quality vary with the relationship between head size and wavelength. Differences in arrival time are best determined if the sound contains abrupt discontinuities or transients, whereas phase differences require a relatively sustained sound. The analysis of phase differences is also affected by the sound frequency, for they become ambiguous when the wavelength is less than twice the distance between the ears. Thus low frequencies are best for locating sound by phase differences, and high frequencies are best for intensity differences. The easiest sounds to locate are those that provide cues for all methods, requiring a wide frequency spectrum and sharp discontinuities. Such cues are provided by the clicks and the pips commonly used in psycho-acoustical experiments. Here are implications for the evolution of communication signals that are readily located (see page 464).

Owls have an uncanny ability to locate prey by sound (Payne 1962). The wide head maximizes binaural time differences. The extraordinary bilateral asymmetry of the outer ear in some species may have a function (Pumphrey 1948, Freye 1953). Preliminary attempts to explore this possibility electrophysiologically failed to establish a systematic asymmetrical response, apparently because the bilateral differences in structure are under dynamic control (Schwartzkopff 1962b, 1963). The asymmetry may enable owls to determine the distance of a sound source as well as its direction.

STIMULUS FILTERING IN AUDITION

◆ *Role of Peripheral Filtering.* The structure of hearing organs has a profound effect in determining which of the several properties of a sound wave are perceived. Displacement receptors register the direction of the source directly, pressure receptors only indirectly. Vertebrate receptors provide the organism with an accurate determination of the frequency structure of a sound. In general, those of arthropods do not. But they give an accurate determination of the temporal pattern of change of loudness.

Some organisms are responsive to certain specific sound patterns (see page 435). Orthopterans, for example, respond to the particular properties of songs of their own species and not to those of other species (Walker 1957). The same is true of some species of birds (e.g. Thorpe 1958, Falls 1963, see page 457). To what extent can the structure and response characteristics of receptors and their peripheral neural structures account for this more specific kind of stimulus filtering?

Haskell (1956) monitored the electrical activity in the tympanal nerve of grasshoppers evoked by recordings of natural and artificial sounds. The pattern of amplitude modulation in a natural song was clearly represented in the nerve's response. Yet the same was true of other sounds with different patterns of change in loudness. There was no evidence that the pattern of the species' own song was especially effective in stimulating the tympanal organs. However, in the bullfrog there seems to be a correspondence between the frequency spectrum a sound must have to evoke male calling and the frequencies to which different parts of the ear respond best (Capranica 1965).

The process by which the chaffinch acquires its song (page 684) is characterized by a predisposition to learn a certain specific class of sounds within which the normal species-specific song is included. Again a process of stimulus filtering is implied. Physiological studies are beginning to reveal how such specificity of responsiveness might be achieved.

All the main receptor systems are supplied by efferent fibers carrying impulses from the brain to various points in the sensory pathway, including the receptors themselves. These efferent fibers apparently modulate the function of the receptor systems (Granit 1955, Livingston 1959). Sometimes the only effect is a general facilitation or inhibition of the whole pathway, but more specific control is possible. The effects are clearly demonstrated in studies of audition.

◆ *Habituation.* Several types of modification of the responsiveness to sounds are accompanied by measurable changes in activity of the auditory pathway. Habituation is the process by which repetition of a given stimulus sometimes results in a loss of responsiveness (see page 642). Electrodes inserted into the brain of a cat, in the cochlear nucleus, the first synaptic relay from the ear, reveal a clear burst of activity when a tone is played into the cat's ear. If the click is repeated at intervals of 2 seconds —too widely spaced for adaptation of the receptors to occur—the response to successive stimuli wanes and eventually disappears. If the tone is replaced by another at a different frequency, 1 kc/sec instead of 3 kc/sec, responsiveness reappears, demonstrating that the previous loss was specific to the particular frequency (Jouvet and Hernández-Peón 1957, Hernández-Peón and Brust-Carmona 1961). Here is a direct physiological parallel with the behavioral process of habituation taking place at a point in the auditory pathway which is very close to the ear itself. The mechanism controlling this decline of responsiveness has not been definitely identified, but there are some good hints. Thus stimulation of efferent fibers arriving in the cochlear nucleus from the next stage in the auditory pathway, the superior olive, has a similar effect of reducing the amplitude of responses to a click in the cochlear nucleus (Galambos 1956). Having eliminated the muscles of the middle ear as a possible cause of this effect, the process of inhibition is assumed to take place somewhere within the cochlea itself. Here the results are general ones lowering responsiveness over the whole pathway, but we can see how more subtle effects might be achieved, raising the sensitivity to certain types of auditory stimuli and lowering it to others. The highly patterned activity in the efferent pathways must surely serve a more complex function than general inhibition.

➤ *Reticular Formation and Attention.* Another anatomical structure implicated in the efferent control of receptor function, and in the whole problem of the physiological basis of 'attention,' is the reticular system of the vertebrate brain (Hernández-Peón 1961). This area of the brain receives branches from all the main receptor systems and also gives rise to efferent fibers that connect with the receptors. In mammals it is involved in the control of sleeping and waking, and apparently in more specific kinds of stimulus filtering. Thus Jouvet and Hernández-Peón's cats failed to show any habituation of the cochlear nucleus after destruction of the reticular system in the mesencephalon. In experiments with other sensory modes stimulation of the reticular system affected the responsiveness of peripheral receptors (Livingston 1959). The efferent fibers from the superior olive in the auditory pathway may also have a functional connection with the reticular system.

Changes in responsiveness of the auditory pathway of cats during shifts of attention are seen in unanaesthetized cats which are distracted by various kinds of stimuli (Hernández-Peón, Scherrer, and Jouvet 1956). The auditory responses to click stimuli are clearly seen in the cochlear nucleus when the cat is relaxed. If a live mouse or the odor of fish is presented, engaging the cat's attention, the amplitude of the auditory responses evoked by the click is reduced until the distracting stimuli are removed. Again we assume that the reticular system is involved.

Of these electrophysiological studies none are more exciting than those that seek to establish the changes taking place in types of sensory learning which are more complex than habituation (Galambos 1958, Hernández-Peón and Brust-Carmona 1961). For example, a cat that had been habituated to a sound stimulus showed a revived response in the cochlear nucleus when the same sound was paired with a painful shock as an unconditioned stimulus. After several such paired presentations, with the sound preceding the shock, the sound continued to evoke a clear response in the cochlear nucleus when it was presented alone. When it was repeated the rate of habituation was slower than previously (Marsh, McCarthy, Sheatz, and Galambos 1961). Moreover, by monitoring activity at other points in the auditory pathway, on into the cerebral cortex, these investigators showed that after conditioning the amplitude of signals in the auditory pathway rose above the initial level. Thus conditioning seems to involve active facilitation of certain types of responsiveness, not just an absence of inhibition. The same may even be true of the process of habituation. Although waning of responsiveness can occur in the cochlear nucleus and in higher centers as well, there may be no waning at some of the intermediate locations. The interaction of inhibiting and facilitating effects that seems to be implied has also been inferred from behavioral studies of habituation (Hinde 1960).

The processing of information from sound signals impinging on the ear can clearly take place at many points in the auditory pathway. We have observed several examples of changes of responsiveness that are at least partly the result of changes in the pattern of efferent control over the auditory pathway, sometimes at the level of the receptors themselves. Mechanisms for ensuring responsiveness to specific temporal patterns of sound (see page 438) may also exist at the receptor level. In any event, we shall see dramatic advances in our understanding of the physiology of stimulus filtering in audition in the next few years.

REFERENCES

Autrum, H. 1936. Über Lautäusserungen und Schallwahrnehmung bei Arthropoden. I. Untersuchungen an Ameisen. Eine allgemeine Theorie der Schallwahrnehmung bei Arthropoden. *Z. vergl. Physiol.*, **23**:332–373.

——. 1941. Über Gehör und Erschütterungssinn bei Locustiden. *Z. vergl. Physiol.*, **28**:580–637.

——. 1963. Anatomy and physiology of sound receptors in invertebrates. In *Acoustic Behaviour of Animals*, ed. by R. G. Busnel: 412–433. Elsevier Publishing Company, Amsterdam.

——, J. Schwartzkopff, and H. Swoboda. 1961. Der Einfluss der Schallrichtung auf die Tympanal-Potentiale von *Locusta migratoria* L. *Biol. Zbl.*, **80**:385–402.

Békésy, G. von. 1960. *Experiments in Hearing*. (Trans. and ed. by E. G. Wever.) McGraw-Hill Book Company, New York.

——. 1962. The gap between the hearing of external and internal sounds. *Symp. Soc. Exp. Biol.*, **16**:267–288.

—— and W. A. Rosenblith. 1951. The mechanical properties of the ear. In *Handbook of Experimental Psychology*, ed. by S. S. Stevens: 1075–1115. John Wiley and Sons, New York.

Bergeijk, W. A. van, J. R. Pierce, and E. E. David, Jr. 1960. *Waves and the Ear*. Doubleday and Company, New York.

Capranica, R. 1965. *The Evoked Vocal Response of the Bullfrog*. Massachusetts Institute of Technology Press, Cambridge.

Davis, H. 1961. Peripheral coding of auditory information. In *Sensory Communication*, ed. by W. A. Rosenblith: 119–141. Massachusetts Institute of Technology Press, Cambridge.

Dethier, V. G. 1963. *The Physiology of Insect Senses*. Methuen and Company, London.

Dijkgraaf, S. 1960. Hearing in bony fishes. *Proc. Roy. Soc. Lond., B*, **152**:51–54.

——. 1962. The functioning and significance of the lateral-line organs. *Biol. Rev.*, **38**:51–105.

Dudok van Heel, W. H. 1962. Sound and Cetacea. *Netherlands J. Sea Res.*, **1**:407–507.

Falls, J. E. 1963. Properties of bird song eliciting responses from territorial males. *Proc. 13th Int. Orn. Congr.*, Vol. 1:259–271.

Freye, H. A. 1953. Die Asymmetrie des Ohres der Waldohreule (*Asio otus* L.). *Beitr. Vogelk.*, 3:231–234.

Frisch, K. von 1936. Über den Gehörsinn der Fische. *Biol. Rev.*, 11:210–246.

Gabor, D. 1947. Acoustical quanta and the theory of hearing. *Nature*, 159:591–594.

Galambos, R. 1956. Suppression of auditory nerve activity by stimulation of efferent fibers to cochlea. *J. Neurophysiol.*, 19:424–437.

————. 1958. Electrical correlates of conditional learning. In *The Central Nervous System and Behavior*, ed. by M. A. B. Brazier. Josiah Macy Jr. Foundation, New York.

Granit, R. 1955. *Receptors and Sensory Perception*. Yale University Press, New Haven.

Haskell, P. T. 1956. Hearing in certain Orthoptera. I, II. *J. Exp. Biol.*, 33:756–766, 767–776.

————. 1961. *Insect Sounds*. H. F. and G. Witherby, London.

Hernández-Peón, R. 1961. Reticular mechanisms of sensory control. In *Sensory Communication*, ed. by W. Rosenblith: 497–520. Massachusetts Institute of Technology Press, Cambridge.

———— and H. Brust-Carmona. 1961. Functional role of subcortical structures in habituation and conditioning. In *Brain Mechanisms and Learning*, ed. by J. F. Delafresnaye: 393–412. Council for International Organizations of Medical Sciences Symposium, Oxford.

————, H. Scherrer, and M. Jouvet. 1956. Modification of electrical activity in cochlear nucleus during 'attention' in unanesthetized cats. *Science*, 123:331–332.

Hinde, R. A. 1960. Factors governing the changes in the strength of a partially inborn response, as shown by the mobbing behaviour of the chaffinch (*Fringilla coelebs*). III. The interaction of short-term and long-term incremental and decremental effects. *Proc. Roy. Soc. Lond., B*, 153:398–420.

Jones, F. R. H. and N. B. Marshall. 1953. The structure and functions of the teleostean swimbladder. *Biol. Rev.*, 28:16–83.

Joos, M. 1948. Acoustic phonetics. *Language Suppl.*, 24(2):3–136.

Jouvet, M. and R. Hernández-Peón. 1957. Mécanismes neurophysiologiques concernant l'habituation, l'attention et le conditionnement. *Electroenceph. Clin. Neurophysiol. Suppl.*, 6:39–49.

Katsuki, Y. 1961. Neural mechanism of auditory sensation in cats. In *Sensory Communication*, ed. by W. A. Rosenblith: 561–583. Massachusetts Institute of Technology Press, Cambridge.

———— and N. Suga. 1960. Neural mechanism of hearing in insects. *J. Exp. Biol.*, 37:279–290.

Keppler, E. 1958. Über des Richtungshören von Stechmücken. *Z. Naturf.*, 13b:280–284.

Licklider, J. C. R. 1951. Basic correlates of the auditory stimulus. In *Handbook of Experimental Psychology*, ed. by S. S. Stevens: 985–1039. John Wiley and Sons, New York.

Livingston, R. B. 1959. Central control of receptors and sensory transmission systems. In *Handbook of Physiology*, ed. by J. Field, Sec. 1, Vol. 1:741–760. American Physiological Society, Washington, D.C.

Lowenstein, O. 1957. The acoustico-lateralis system. In *The Physiology of Fishes*, ed. by M. E. Brown, Vol. 2:155–186. The Academic Press, New York.

Marsh, J. T., D. A. McCarthy, G. Sheatz, and R. Galambos. 1961. Amplitude changes in evoked auditory potentials during habituation and conditioning. *Electroenceph. Clin. Neurophysiol.*, 13:224–234.

Moulton, J. M. 1963. Acoustic behaviour of fishes. In *Acoustic Behaviour of Animals*, ed. by R. G. Busnel: 655–693. Elsevier Publishing Company, Amsterdam.

Payne, R. S. 1962. How the barn owl locates prey by hearing. *The Living Bird*, 1:151–159.

Poggendorf, D. 1952. Die absoluten Hörschwellen des Zwergwelses (*Ameirus nebulosus*) und Beiträge zur Physik des Weberschen Apparates der Ostariophysen. *Z. vergl. Physiol.*, 34:222–257.

Pumphrey, R. J. 1940. Hearing in insects. *Biol. Rev.,* **15**:107–132.

———. 1948. The sense organs of birds. *Ibis,* **90**:171–199.

———. 1950. Hearing. *Symp. Soc. Exp. Biol.,* **4**:3–18.

———. 1961. Sensory organs: hearing. In *Biology and Comparative Physiology of Birds,* ed. by A. J. Marshall, Vol. 2:55–68. The Academic Press, New York.

Risler, H. 1955. Das Gehörorgan der Männchen von *Culex pipiens* L., *Aëdes aegypti* L. und *Anopheles stephensi* Liston (Culicidae), eine vergleichend morphologische Untersuchung. *Zool. Jahrb., Abt. Anat. Ontog.,* **74**:478–490.

Roeder, K. D. 1963. *Nerve Cells and Insect Behavior.* Harvard University Press, Cambridge.

———. 1964. Aspects of the noctuid tympanic nerve response having significance in the avoidance of bats. *J. Insect Physiol.,* **10**:529–546.

——— and A. E. Treat. 1957. Ultrasonic reception by the tympanic organ of noctuid moths. *J. Exp. Zool.,* **134**:127–157.

Roth, L. M. 1948. A study of mosquito behavior. An experimental laboratory study of the sexual behavior of *Aedes aegypti* (Linnaeus). *Amer. Midl. Nat.,* **40**:265–352.

Schleidt, W. M. 1952. Reaktionen auf Töne hoher Frequenz bei Nagern. *Naturwissenschaften,* **39**:69–70.

Schwartzkopff, J. 1949. Über Sitz und Leistung von Gehör und Vibrationssinn bei Vögeln. *Z. vergl. Physiol.,* **31**:527–608.

———. 1950. Beitrag zum Problem des Richtungshörens bei Vögeln. *Z. vergl. Physiol.,* **32**:319–327.

———. 1952. Untersuchungen über die Arbeitsweise des Mittelohres und das Richtungshören der Singvögel unter Verwendung von Cochlea-Potentialen. *Z. vergl. Physiol.,* **34**:46–68.

———. 1955. On the hearing of birds. *Auk,* **72**:340–347.

———. 1957. Untersuchung der akustischen Kerne in der Medulla von Wellensittichen mittels Mikroelektroden. *Zool. Anz. Suppl.,* **21**:374–379.

———. 1960. Vergleichende Physiologie des Gehörs. *Fortschr. Zool.,* **12**:206–264.

———. 1962a. Vergleichende Physiologie des Gehörs und der Lautäusserungen. *Fortschr. Zool.,* **15**:214–336.

———. 1962b. Zur Frage des Richtungshörens von Eulen (Striges). *Z. vergl. Physiol.,* **45**:570–580.

———. 1962c. Die akustische Lokalisation bei Tieren. *Ergeb. Biol.,* **25**:136–176.

———. 1963. Morphological and physiological properties of the auditory system in birds. *Proc. 13th Int. Orn. Congr.,* Vol. 2:1059–1068.

——— and P. Winter. 1960. Zur Anatomie der Vogel-Cochlea unter natürlichen Bedingungen. *Biol. Zbl.,* **79**:607–625.

Stevens, S. S. and H. Davis. 1938. *Hearing.* John Wiley and Sons, New York.

Tavolga, W. N. and J. Wodinsky. 1963. Auditory capacities in fishes. *Bull. Amer. Mus. Nat. Hist.,* **126**:177–240.

Thorpe, W. H. 1958. The learning of song patterns by birds, with especial reference to the song of the chaffinch, *Fringilla coelebs. Ibis,* **100**:535–570.

———. 1963. Antiphonal singing in birds as evidence for avian auditory reaction time. *Nature,* **197**:774–776.

Tischner, H. 1953. Über den Gehörsinn von Stechmücken. *Acustica,* **3**:335–343.

——— and A. Schief. 1954. Fluggeräusch und Schallwarnehmung bei *Aedes aegypti* L. (Culicidae). *Verh. Dtsch. Zool. Ges.,* **51**:453–460.

Vallancien, B. 1963. Comparative anatomy and physiology of the auditory organ in vertebrates. In *Acoustic Behaviour of Animals,* ed. by R. G. Busnel: 522–556. Elsevier Publishing Company, Amsterdam.

Walker, T. J. 1957. Specificity in the response of female tree crickets (Orthoptera, Gryllidae, Oecanthinae) to calling songs of the males. *Ann. Ent. Soc. Amer.,* **50**:626–636.

twelve

ACOUSTICAL COMMUNICATION

Sound production in animals • The sound repertoire • Acoustical signals and reproduction • Songs of insects • Significance of variation in birdsong • Individual versus specific distinctiveness • Experiments on song recognition in birds • Structure of sound signals in relation to function • Use of graded sound systems in monkeys and apes • Audition, vision, and chemoreception as media for communication.

BEHAVIORAL FUNCTIONS OF HEARING

➤ *Hearing and Other Sensory Modalities.* Deaf animals show surprisingly few abnormalities in their behavior. Captive bullfinches with the cochlea surgically removed are nevertheless able to form pairs, go through normal breeding behavior, and even transmit alarm to one another (Hüchtker and Schwartzkopff 1958). The functions of vision and audition overlap extensively, and one sense can compensate to some extent for loss of the other. Of the two, hearing is more readily dispensed with than vision in diurnal animals. Nevertheless, there are circumstances in which hearing has unique advantages, especially in social behavior but also in the relationship of animals to their physical environments.

The orientation of fishes in space is strongly dependent on their ability to detect water flow and distant mechanical disturbances by the lateral line organs, especially in dark or turbid waters. Air movements are sensed by the hair sensilla and antennal receptors of insects. The approach of predators is often sensed by the ears, hence the advantage of silent flight for owls. The soft fringes on the edges of their flight feathers greatly reduce the noise generated in flight. The reduction is especially marked in the high frequencies above about 15 kc/sec, a range to which many small mammals are particularly sensitive (Thorpe and Griffin 1962). Owls that eat fish are in less danger of being detected by their prey. They lack the fringes on their feathers and their flight is noisier. A special case of the use of hearing in the detection of danger occurs in the moths that give evasive responses to the echolocation pulses of bats (page 245). On the other hand, animals which have some means of protection, such as a bad taste or poison glands, may have conspicuous 'aposematic' sounds as well as colors (see page 369). Batesian mimicry of sounds has also been noted, for example in insects (Haskell 1961) and in birds (Sibley 1955).

Although vision is undoubtedly the dominant sense by which the hunting behavior of predators is controlled, hearing can play an important part. Echolocation systems cannot operate without it (see page 481). Owls rely heavily on hearing when hunting mice at night (Payne 1962), and some predatory insects depend on hearing. Parasitic wasps that lay eggs in the larvae of other species locate their prey through an inch of bark by the noise that they make, apparently with great accuracy (Haskell 1961). But by far the most widespread function of sounds for animals is social communication.

The sense of hearing has unique advantages for communication in the dark or in habitats where vision is impeded. Sound signals can be transmitted at any time and are less drastically affected by environmental conditions than chemical signals. They have the further advantage that rapid signal modulations can be generated by one animal and perceived by another, permitting a quick exchange of information.

➤ *Sound Production in Animals.* Many of the sounds produced by animals incidentally in the course of other activities, such as locomotion and feeding, do communicate in that they provide other animals with information about what is being done. The sounds made by the wings of flying insects are known to elicit responses in others (Haskell 1961, Sotavalta 1963). Many structures are specially designed for the production of sound. Arthropods have a myriad of frictional devices involving almost every pair of movable parts of the body (Dumortier 1963a, b). The conspicuous songs of crickets and grasshoppers are produced in this way, usually by rubbing the elytra together or by rubbing the legs against the elytra (Faber 1953).

The structure of the frictional parts and their associated resonators, which may vary between the sexes or between species, has a direct effect on the sounds produced (Figure 12-1). Sounds are also produced by muscular vibration of membranes, as in the tymbal of cicadas, and by

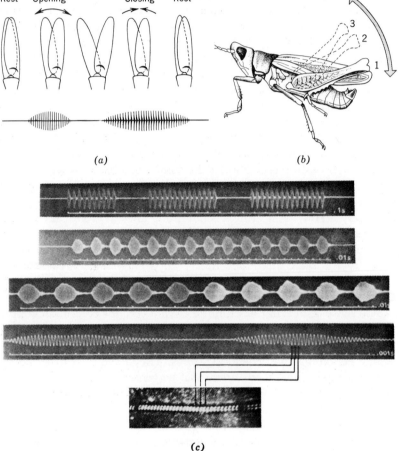

Figure 12-1   (*a*) Diagram of elytron movements of a tettigoniid grasshopper during sound production, with an oscillogram of the sounds produced. (*b*) Stridulatory movements of an acridid grasshopper, which produces sound by rubbing a file on the femur against an enlarged vein on the elytron. (*c*) Oscillograms of a gryllid song on a progressively finer time scale. The last record shows how each tooth on the pars stridens creates one sound wave. After Dumortier 1963b.

banging parts of the body on the ground. A few arthropods make sounds by passing air or water across an orifice; but this method is much more typical of vertebrates (Haskell 1961, Dumortier 1963a, b).

Some fish generate sounds by frictional mechanisms, often using the air bladder as a resonator. Others use the walls of the air bladder as a drum, squirting gas out or passing it from one section to another (Tavolga 1960, 1964, Schneider 1961, Moulton 1963).

In terrestrial vertebrates sound production is usually associated with the respiratory system. Air movements are used to vibrate membranes and the sounds are amplified by resonating chambers. By varying the tension on the membranes, the rate of air flow, and the size of resonators, a wide array of different sounds can be produced. Nonvocal sounds are sometimes produced by striking an object in the environment (woodpeckers, chimpanzees), by slapping parts of the body together (wings in birds, chest beating in gorillas), or in the course of locomotion.

THE SOUND REPERTOIRE

The sounds that a species uses in the course of a life cycle can be recorded and arranged in categories according to their general physical structure. An analysis of this kind gives an estimate of the size of the acoustical repertoire (Table 12-1). Although the information available is rather limited, a general picture of the situation in different taxonomic groupings is beginning to emerge. The maximal repertoire of birds and mammals is larger than that of lower vertebrates and invertebrates. It is surprising that the fish studied so far have a limited repertoire, for sounds travel quickly in water and should provide a good means of communication. The difficulties in locating sound sources in water may be responsible. Anurans and orthopterans have much the same repertoire size. The resemblance carries through to the functions that the sounds serve and even, in some respects, to the physical structure of the sounds employed.

A sound repertoire is a well-defined facet of the behavioral repertoire of many animals. Its study is facilitated by the completeness with which the motor pattern can be described, given the aid of techniques of recording and physical analysis. By such methods it is possible to define the temporal pattern and frequency characteristics of sounds.

The frequency of sounds used is correlated with the auditory capacities of animals. Insects often produce sounds of very high frequencies. Tettigoniid grasshoppers may sing as high as 100 kc/sec, and their tympanal organs are correspondingly sensitive to high frequencies. On the other hand, crickets hear best at much lower frequencies, and their songs are correspondingly lower pitched (Dumortier 1963c, Figure 12-2). A similar relationship is found in birds. The frequency to which the ear is most sensitive, and the dominant frequency of vocalizations, generally bear an inverse relationship to body size, though there are numerous exceptions (Schwartzkopff 1955).

Like any other behavior, vocalization occurs when an animal is in a particular physiological state. The appropriate physiological condition

Table 12-1   Estimated Number of Sound Types in the Adult Repertoire of Various Animal Groups

Animal group	Species	Repertoire	Author
Insects	Various crickets and other orthopterans	1–6 average 4–5	Faber 1953 Alexander 1962 Dumortier 1963c
Fish	Goby, *Bathygobius,* Sea robins, *Prionotus* spp. and toadfish, *Opsanus* spp.	1–2	Tavolga 1960 Moulton 1963 Gray and Winn 1961
Amphibians	Various frogs and toads	Up to 4	Bogert 1960 Blair 1963
Birds	Warblers, finches, doves, partridges, etc.	5–14	Thorpe 1961 Armstrong 1963
Mammals	Various non-human primates	5–17	Marler 1965

The citations refer mainly to review articles.

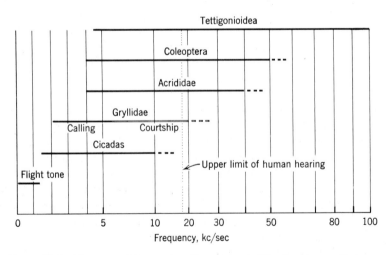

Figure 12-2   The range of frequencies of insect sounds. The dotted upper limits exceed the capacities of the microphone used, and higher frequencies may be present. After Dumortier 1963a.

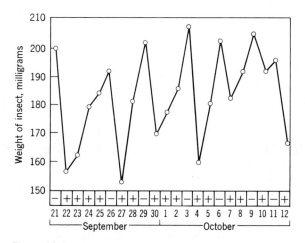

Figure 12-3   The female of the grasshopper, *Chorthippus brunneus*, is responsive, +, to song just after egg laying as indicated by a drop in weight. After Haskell 1961.

may be a transient one, generated by some external stimulus such as a predator or a competitor, and often may occur at any phase of adult life. In other cases long-term physiological cycles restrict vocal patterns to certain phases of the life cycle. Many sounds are confined to animals in reproductive condition and therefore in many cases to certain seasons. Some canids and cervids have male and female sounds that are limited to the breeding season (Tembrock 1963), and the same is true of many birds. Davis (1958) found that the state of gonadal activity in the male rufous-sided towhee, *Pipilo erythrophthalmus*, correlated not only with the frequency of singing but also with subtler aspects of singing behavior such as perch height chosen and the time of the first and last songs in relation to sunrise and sunset. Of the fourteen basic adult sounds of the chaffinch, one of those of the female and six of those of the male are restricted to the breeding season (Marler 1956, Poulsen 1958). Frogs, toads, and fishes produce some of their sound signals solely or most frequently in the reproductive season (Bogert 1960, Gray and Winn 1961, Winn 1964). Most of the vocalizing of insects is associated with reproduction, the correlation being not with gonad growth but with activity of the corpora allata (see page 102, Dumortier 1963c).

In addition to the correlation with long-term reproductive cycles, vocal behavior is associated with short-term patterns as well. A male grasshopper may pass four or five days in silence after mating with a female before resuming song and regaining readiness to mate (Busnel, Dumortier, and Busnel 1956). Similarly, with a species in which the female vocalizes

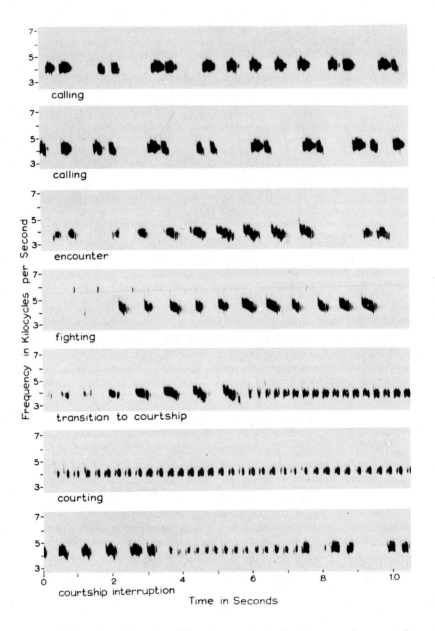

Figure 12-4   Sounds of a cricket, *Teleogryllus commodus*, analyzed on a sound spectograph. The entire vocal repertoire of this species is represented. After Alexander 1962.

in response to male sounds, egg laying is preceded by a period of unresponsiveness which quickly disappears after oviposition (Haskell 1961, Figure 12-3).

◆ *Sounds and Reproduction.* Many animal sounds are subject to cyclic variation with different phases of the breeding cycle and are intimately associated with the complex of reproductive activities. Within this complex several different functions may be served. For example, Alexander (1960, 1962) has shown that male crickets have different sounds for (1) establishing initial contact between the sexes (the calling song), (2) mediating sexual exchanges at close range (the courtship song), (3) use when a courting female moves away (the courtship interruption sound), (4) repelling or dominating other males (the aggressive sound), (5) maintaining contact between the pair after mating (the postcopulatory song), and (6) announcement of presence with functions not yet fully understood (the recognition sound). In almost all crickets sound production is the prerogative of the male. This is not true of acridid grasshoppers in which female calling also occurs.

The functional requirements for cricket calling songs are rather different from those for sounds used in close-range courtship (e.g. 2, 3, 5). At close range the specific identity of the partners has already been established, either by the calling song, chemicals, or other stimuli. Species specificity is less important for such sounds than for the calling song, which is responsible for sexual isolation. There is correspondingly less divergence between sympatric species in these close-range communicatory sounds than in calling songs, and they are softer and simpler in structure (Alexander 1962, Figure 12-4).

What sound properties are exploited to achieve divergence of songs of sympatric species? We have seen that the tympanal organs are not responsive to variations in sound frequency but are acutely sensitive to variations in amplitude. This sensitivity provides a means of generating a great many different signals by varying the pattern of amplitude modulation; it is the basis for specific distinctiveness both in orthoptera and in cicadas (Figure 12-5). More complex sound patterns may be expected in species with large repertoires and in species that occur in sympatry with many relatives. A survey of calling song patterns confirms this prediction (Alexander 1962). Cricket species that are active at the same time and place have different calling songs. Conversely, species that are spatially isolated from one another or breed at different seasons, and that live with few sympatric relatives often have similar sound patterns, both in the song and in the other calls.

The sounds of male insects may elicit responses from other males.

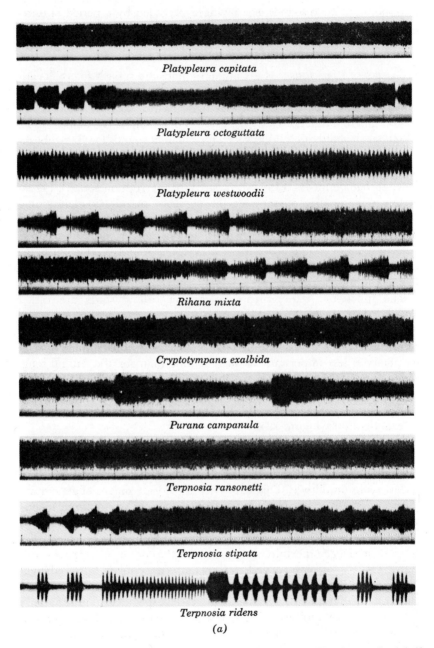

Platypleura capitata

Platypleura octoguttata

Platypleura westwoodii

Rihana mixta

Cryptotympana exalbida

Purana campanula

Terpnosia ransonetti

Terpnosia stipata

Terpnosia ridens
(a)

Figure 12-5   (a) Oscillograms of nine species of cicáda in Ceylon. The time marker is half a second. After Leston and Pringle 1963. (b) Diagrams of some of the patterns of trilling songs of crickets arranged in order of increasing complexity. After Alexander 1962.

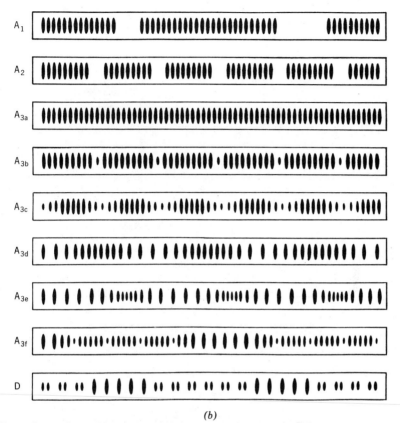

(b)

Sometimes the calling song and the aggressive sounds seem to elicit withdrawal. Thus in sedentary species they function as a means of territorial defense. Males may also sing in reply, either in alternation or in synchrony, and they may aggregate in the process, producing one very loud signal. The function of this synchronized signaling is obscure (Dumortier 1963c).

The marked specific distinctiveness in the calling songs of males presumably enables females to restrict their sexual responses to members of their own species. A few experiments have verified this assumption (Dumortier 1963c).

◆ *Experiments with Artificial Insect Songs.* Walker (1957) studied a group of tree crickets in the eastern United States. The role of song in the reproductive behavior of this group is relatively simple. Only the males sing, by vibrating parts of the wings against each other. There are several different types of song, one of which, the calling song, is given by solitary males and attracts sexually responsive females of the same species.

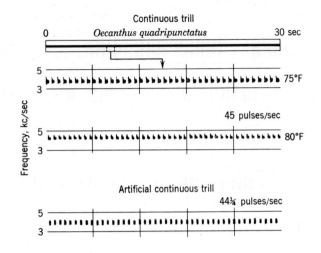

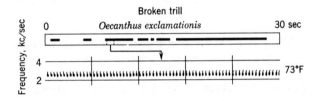

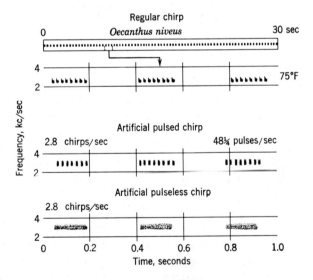

Figure 12-6 The pulse patterns comprising the song of three species of tree crickets and some artificial songs. After Walker 1957.

The calling songs of nine species of tree cricket differ in several ways. There are three main types: continuous trills, broken trills, and regular chirps (Figure 12-6). The pulse rate of these trills and chirps may vary and usually differs markedly in species occurring in the same habitat. The experimental method was to play recorded songs to a female in a special cage and to record responses toward and away from the speaker. Artificial songs were then created, resembling the natural songs in some respects and not in others (Figure 12-6), and played to females in the cage. Females responded only to recorded songs of males of their own species.

Within the group of nine species, three, *Oecanthus quadripunctatus, O. argentinus,* and *O. nigricornis* all have continuous trills which differ in the rate of pulses per second. The next step was to determine whether this difference was responsible for the lack of interspecific responses from the female. The question is complicated by variation of the rate of pulsing with temperature (Figure 12-6). Walker found that the pulse frequency to which a female best responds varies with temperature in an exactly parallel way (Figure 12-7). The essential role of pulse frequency was also confirmed by the use of artificial songs. These were only effective when the pulse rate corresponded with that of the conspecific male at the same temperature. Varying the sound frequency had no effect within the audible range. As a final check he was able to adjust the temperature at which a male of one species was singing to achieve a pulse rate corresponding to another species. At 89°F a male *O. quadripunctatus* sings at a rate of 55.25 pulses per second. A female *O. nigricornis* at 70°F responded positively to a recording of this song which duplicated the pulse rate of a male of her own species at 70°F.

Species that sing broken trills, such as *O. exclamationis,* deliver irregular patterns that might be significant in evoking female responses. However, by comparing the responses to a normal song and to an artificial one that lacked breaks but was otherwise identical, Walker could show that the pulse rate was again the critical factor.

With the regular chirp songs, of which *O. niveus* is the example, the broken rhythm proves to be significant. This could be shown by comparing the responses of females to a continuous trill with the correct pulse rate, regular chirps of the correct duration but unpulsed (Figure 12-6), and a normal song. The last two evoked a response but the first did not. Evidently the breaking up of the trill into chirps is a necessary stimulus for the female's response. The second model evoked a slightly weaker response than the normal song, indicating some role for the pulse rate.

Walker's study illustrates a point which recurs repeatedly in analyses of stimuli exchanged between animals for communication—the extent to which patterns in time are important. Often the pattern is created by

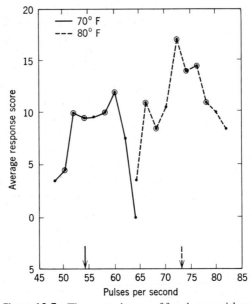

Figure 12-7 The responsiveness of female tree crickets, *Oecanthus nigricornis,* to male songs varies with temperature, with maxima corresponding to the pulse rates of the male song normal for that temperature (arrows on abscissa). After Walker 1957.

temporal variations in the behavior of the animal producing the stimulus. But we have seen one example, in fireflies, where the temporal pattern of stimulus and response assumes significance (see page 384).

The work of Perdeck (1958), together with that of Weih (1951), Loher (1957), Busnel (1963), and others, has revealed a close parallel in the exchange of auditory signals in grasshoppers. Comparing the behavior of two closely related grasshoppers, *Chorthippus biguttulus* and *C. brunneus,* which live together and rarely hybridize, Perdeck demonstrated that the different songs of the two species play a crucial role in keeping them apart. Unlike the tree crickets the two sexes of these grasshoppers answer each other's songs. The males are much more likely to reply to and approach a female than another male. One of the key factors for approach in *C. biguttulus* is the duration of the pause before a female replies to a conspecific male. It must not be more than 2.5 seconds. A male, on the other hand, will reply after an irregular interval. An artificial signal may be quite effective in evoking a male response if it satisfies this requirement of following his song after a certain interval, a close parallel with *Pyralis pyralis.*

In *C. brunneus,* by contrast, the rhythm of reply and answer is only the first phase of the interchange. Both males and females of this species will reply to each other in regular alternation. Then after a variable interval a male will break into a more rapid series of chirps. If his partner is a male it will follow suit. If it is a female it will persist with the original rhythm, and the male will join her. The nature of the response enables the male to select an appropriate mate. Again the frequency of the sound is unimportant as long as it is audible.

In some species sounds within the range of sensitivity of hair sensillae and antennal receptors (page 403) are used in communication and, as might be predicted, the significant properties are rather different from those of orthopteran songs. The wing tone of the female mosquito, *Aedes aegypti,* attracts the male and elicits his mating behavior (Roth 1948, Wishart and Riordan 1959). It has a frequency of about 500 cycles/sec. A loudspeaker or tuning fork emitting such a note elicits approach from considerable distances and can also induce some of the initial actions of mating. The male antenna seems to be so constructed that it resonates mechanically to this frequency, maximizing the responsiveness in this frequency range. The specificity of the receptors probably enables males to detect and locate a female against a high level of background noise.

◆ *Fish and Amphibian Songs.* Playback experiments with fish and amphibians have demonstrated that responses can be elicited with recorded sounds. The grunts of male gobies, *Bathygobius soporator,* encourage female courtship in collaboration with visual stimuli. They also elicit the approach of males (Tavolga 1956, 1958). Similarly in the satinfin shiner, *Notropis analostanus,* territorial males produce single knocks when chasing and during courtship, rapid series of knocks during display fighting, and purring during courtship activities of approach, circling and male passing over nest site. Playback of the knocks tends to elicit aggressive behavior from other males while purring sounds favor courtship activities (Stout 1963). There is evidence that sounds of other species fail to elicit responses in some cases (Delco 1960) but are effective in others (Tavolga 1958).

In frogs and toads playback of the calls of sexually active males attracts ovulating females and elicits calling from other males (Martof and Thompson 1958, Bogert 1960). In one case responsiveness to conspecific calls in preference to those of another sympatric species has been demonstrated (Littlejohn and Michaud 1959). The premium upon specific distinctiveness in calling behavior must be considerable. Bogert (1960) notes that as many as fourteen species of frogs can be heard calling at a single spawning site in parts of Florida, each with a distinctive sound pattern. Study of some species pairs has shown that their calls are more divergent in areas of sympatry than in allopatry, again satisfying the need for specific distinctness (Blair 1958, 1963). In the bullfrog, Capranica (1965) has identified the physical properties of a sound necessary to evoke

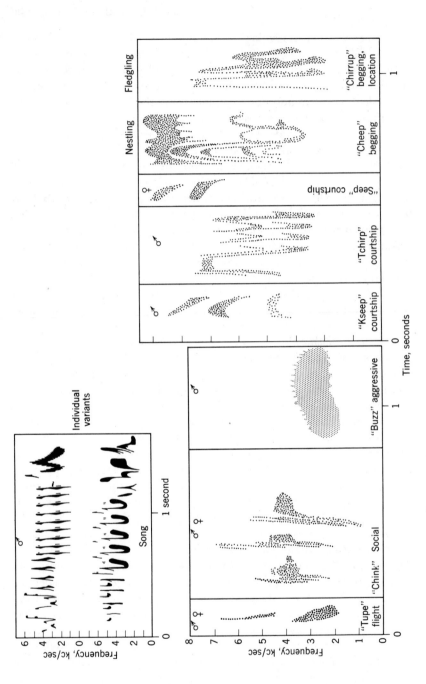

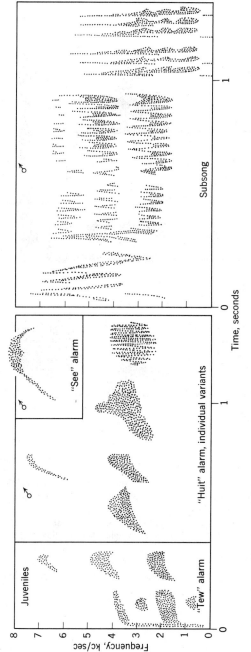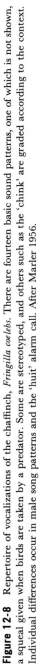

Figure 12-8 Repertoire of vocalizations of the chaffinch, *Fringilla coelebs*. There are fourteen basic sound patterns, one of which is not shown, a squeal given when birds are taken by a predator. Some are stereotyped, and others such as the 'chink' are graded according to the context. Individual differences occur in male song patterns and the 'huit' alarm call. After Marler 1956.

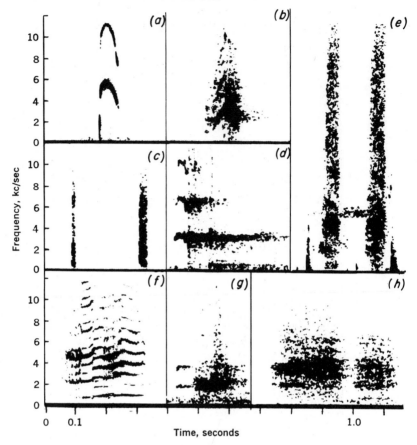

Figure 12-9 Repertoire of vocalizations of the village weaverbird. There are fifteen basic sound patterns, one not shown. Juvenile hunger-distress chirps (*a* and *b*), juvenile contact note while perched (*c*), male and female low-intensity alarms (*d*), male and female high-intensity alarm (*e*), male and female high-intensity distress (*f*), male and female low-intensity threat (*g*), and male high-intensity threat (*h*) are shown on the left-hand page. The male song (*a* and *b*), nest material carrying call (*c*), male announcement of arrival (*d*), two examples of male nest display call (*e*), male scold-chatter call (*f*), male and female copulation call (*g*), and female nest call (*h*) are shown on the right. After Collias 1963.

male calling. Nonetheless, sympatric species do not always have highly divergent calls. Call structure is surely only one of a complex of factors that maintain reproductive isolation (Littlejohn 1959).

BIRDSONG

The vocal repertoire of birds is as rich and varied as any to be found in the animal kingdom. The signals are often highly structured and dis-

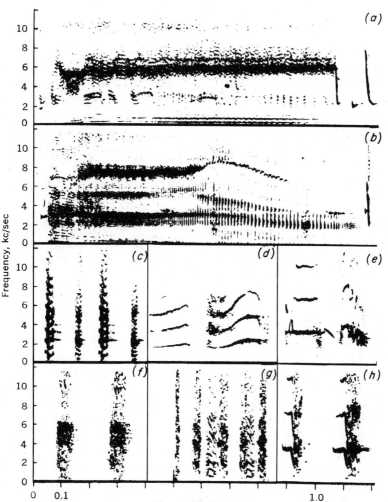

crete, without overlap. Examples of the vocal repertoires of two finches
are shown in Figures 12-8 and 12-9. In the chaffinch and the village
weaver as in the majority of songbirds, one vocal pattern, the song, is
more complex. It is usually though not always the prerogative of males.
It tends to be associated with territorial defense, establishment and maintenance of pair bonds, control of the reproductive cycles of male and
female, or some combination of these (Howard 1920). In some species
the song is less well defined, and it sometimes appears that one of the
simpler sounds, or calls, is taking over the same functions. But for the
majority of passerine birds the song is easily identified. The qualities that

seem musical to human ears have been the subject of a considerable amount of research as well as aesthetic appreciation (Thorpe 1961, Armstrong 1963).

Birdsongs, like insect and frog vocalizations that function wholly or in part as reproductive isolating mechanisms, are likely to be found consistently and distinctively divergent when sympatric species are compared. The existence of such specific distinctiveness has often been noted. Gilbert White (1789) used the song patterns as a means of first distinguishing between three morphologically very similar species of European warbler (Figure 12-10).

The disadvantages that must accrue from confusion with songs of other species, leading to time-wasting errors and dysgenic hybridization, favor specific distinctiveness (Mayr 1942, Huxley 1942, Sibley 1957, 1961). Because many closely related bird species live together in most parts of the world, elaborate arrangements of frequencies and temporal patterns are required to permit unequivocal distinction of each one. Some of the complexities of birdsongs can be thus explained.

Although such an interpretation helps us to understand most of the properties of insect and anuran songs, there is much in birdsong that is less easily explained. Birdsong patterns are extraordinarily variable, not only between but also within species. Careful study of such variation is useful from several points of view. It is a prerequisite for any taxonomic work; and sound production lends itself more readily than most categories of behavior to the study of stereotypy and variability. It can be a fruitful source of hypotheses about the functions of behavior.

We can consider the variation of birdsong at several different levels. How extensive are individual repertoires? How much variation is there within the same population? We can compare the singing patterns of different populations both locally and throughout the geographical range of the species. Finally we can compare species and species groups and so return to the question of species specificity.

◆ *Individual Variation in Birdsong.* Species of birds differ widely in the extent of the individual song repertoire. Some adult birds, for example certain flycatchers, have only one song type (Kellogg and Stein 1953, Stein 1958), and the same is generally true of tree creepers, *Certhia* (Thielcke 1961), and some sparrows (Marler and Isaac 1960a, Marler and Tamura 1962, Borror 1959b, 1961). More commonly, an individual has a small repertoire of two or three song types and distributes its singing time among them. The wood pewee has three basic patterns (Craig 1943) and the chaffinch and the Oregon junco have about the same number (Marler

1952, Marler, Kreith, and Tamura 1962, Konishi 1964). The rufous-sided and brown towhees may have rather more, from four to eight (Borror 1959a, Marler and Isaac 1960b). Meadowlarks and the great titmouse, *Parus major,* are in the same range (Lanyon 1957, Gompertz 1961).

In other birds song variation in the individual occurs at a still more complex level. Borror (1956, 1960) has described a hermit thrush with 13 different song patterns, and a Carolina wren with 22. Individual song sparrows also have from 6 to around 20 songs (Nice 1943, Borror 1961,

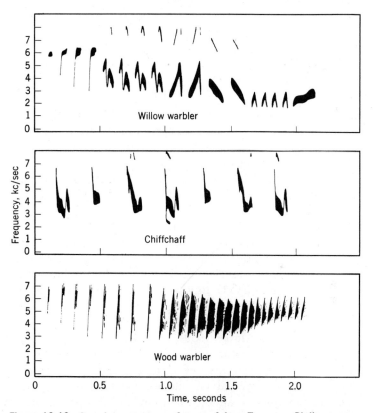

Figure 12-10   Sound spectrograms of songs of three European *Phylloscopus* warblers, used by Gilbert White as the first evidence that they are distinct species. The willow warbler (*Phylloscopus trochilus*) and the chiffchaff (*P. collybita*) are very similar morphologically but have different songs. The first is a short regular song, repeated at intervals, whereas the second rambles on continuously, improvising on two basic notes. The lower record is a wood warbler song (*P. sibilatrix*). After Marler 1960.

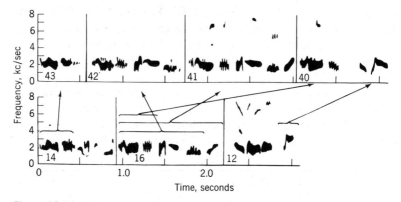

Figure 12-11 The last 4 songs in a sequence of 43 given by a mistle thrush compared with earlier songs in the sequence to show how new themes are produced by the recombination of old phrases.

Mulligan 1963 in press). In these species there is a clear, finite limit to the number of song types so that except for slight variation all songs rendered by an adult individual can be assigned to one of the types. In some other birds this is not the case.

Songs of the mistle thrush are constructed from the combination of about three to five 'syllables' (Figure 12-11). Individual birds have a basic repertoire of about twenty syllable types that can be linked in a variety of ways resulting in many different song types (Marler 1959, Isaac and Marler 1963). The American robin's repertoire is somewhat similar (Konishi 1965). An extreme development in the direction of complexity is found in some of the other thrushes, such as the European blackbird and song thrush. Individuals have a huge repertoire of syllable types which can be recombined in many different ways and which change in structure with time (Messmer and Messmer 1956, Thielcke-Poltz and Thielcke 1960, Hall-Craggs 1962, Marler 1959). In such species the total number of song types sung during the adult life of an individual is enormous.

What is the significance of this wide array of possibilities ranging from species in which each individual has only one song type to others in which the individual repertoire is almost inestimable? We must assume that within the class of so-called bird songs there are sound signals with different functions. And we must also bear in mind the possibility that some aspects of song variation are a manifestation of some kind of primordial exercise in aesthetics (Craig 1943, Hartshorne 1958, Thorpe 1958, 1961, Hall-Craggs 1962). There is indeed evidence that the temporal organization of singing patterns in certain birds shares some of the characteristics of human music (Craig 1943). It is not easy in our present state of ignorance, however, to decide if these same characteristics may not have relevance to the communication system of which they are a part, whether one also regards them as aesthetic or not.

◆ *Within a Population: Individuality.* A comparison of the songs of adjacent individuals in the same population almost always reveals obvious differences. Individuality is as common in birds with small repertoires as in those with large ones. It occurs, for example, in chipping sparrows that have only one song per individual (Borror 1959b, Marler and Isaac 1960a) and in mistle thrushes and blackbirds, with large individual repertoires (Isaac and Marler 1963, Thielcke-Poltz and Thielcke 1960). In view of the increasing attention being given to the use of song in classification of the taxonomically difficult tyrannid flycatchers, it is worth recalling Wallace Craig's (1943) remark that "each individual pewee sings his own kind of song every morning; his individual traits persist throughout the season. . . . The individual traits concern every characteristic of the singing." Songs of individual ovenbirds differ in pitch, speed, and details of phrasing (Weeden and Falls 1959). Oregon juncos show great individuality in the structure of the syllables from which the song is made up (Konishi 1964, Figure 12-12). On the basis of extensive studies on a variety of species, Borror (1961) concluded that two individuals rarely share identical songs.

By extending the description to include groups of individuals, a picture of the diversity of singing patterns at the population level can be obtained. Often we find that in spite of individual variation the members of a population share many properties of the pattern. This is true of the flycatchers that have been studied. Another good example is the white-crowned sparrow which exhibits a high degree of conformity in certain aspects of the singing pattern (Marler and Tamura 1962). In this bird the pattern is consistent from one year to the next and is thus a reasonably stable characteristic of the population. In other species in which there is more variation between individuals, one can still characterize the population by certain singing patterns as in the chaffinch and mistle thrush (Marler 1952, Thorpe 1958, 1961, Isaac and Marler 1963).

Finally there are some species in which the diversity of singing patterns within a population is so great that only a few basic properties of the singing pattern are shared by its members. In the brown towhee, for example, in which the main part of the song is a trill of repeated syllables, an extraordinary range of syllable types has been described within one population (Marler and Isaac 1960b). In this case the birds share the same elemen-

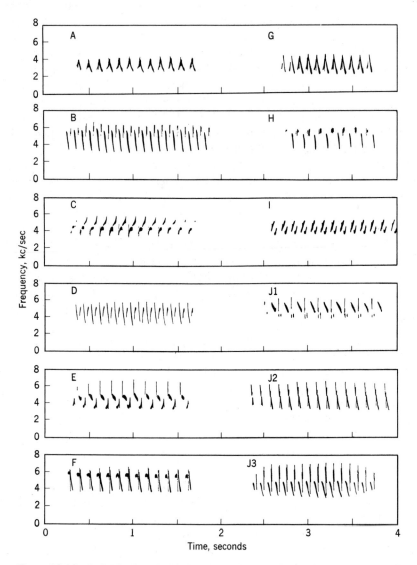

Figure 12-12 Individuality of syllable structure in some Oregon junco songs. J1 to J3 are three song types of one individual. After Marler, Kreith, and Tamura 1962.

tary pattern, with about the same overall duration. Within this basic framework there is a high degree of intrapopulation variability. Mulligan (1963 in press) has described similar variability for the song sparrow. Sometimes it is still more difficult to see what is shared. Such is the case with the Mexican junco, *Junco phaeonotus*, where the great diversity of syllable types is also accompanied by a degree of variation in the temporal patterning within the song so great that it is not easy to define what the songs have in common. Their duration is similar, they generally include two trills, and there is some tendency for the duration of syllables to decrease through the song. Even so, the diversity is more impressive than the conformity (Marler and Isaac 1961).

We find then that in some species the members of a population conform to the same pattern of song. In others there is more diversity, and in some the variation is so great that there are relatively few song characters shared by all members of the population. Differences are sometimes found even among members of the same family. It is a challenge to explain how these contrasts have evolved. Again it is difficult to avoid the conclusion that birdsong is subject to various selective forces, some favoring intrapopulation diversity, others favoring conformity.

◆ *Population Differences.* The singing patterns in separate but adjacent populations of the same species are sometimes very similar. But most studies of this subject have been provoked by the initial impression that interpopulation differences did indeed exist. This impression has been amply verified in many cases. The chaffinch is an example much studied in Europe. Discrete populations, such as are found in the separate valleys in mountainous areas of Scotland, are characterized by the predominance of a particular song type. In the tree creeper, *Certhia brachydactyla*, there are clearly marked local song 'dialects' (Thielcke 1961, Figure 12-13). A somewhat similar phenomenon occurs in the blackcap (Sauer 1955) and in the great titmouse (Gompertz 1961). There is some evidence for local dialects in songs of the mistle thrush (Isaac and Marler 1963). Song dialects in the white-crowned sparrow are thrown into particularly strong relief as a result of the relative homogeneity of song patterns within a population (Marler and Tamura 1962). As a result the differences between separate populations are clear-cut; individual birds can be accurately assigned to their appropriate population on the basis of their pattern of singing (Figure 12-14).

What is the functional significance of such local dialects in birdsong? We think immediately of the possibility that they might somehow aid birds in distinguishing between members of one population and another. There is evidence that membership in a given song dialect can arise in

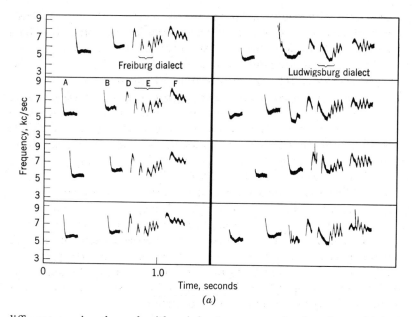

Time, seconds

(a)

different species through either inheritance or adoption (page 684). In either case the dialects may function to help dispersed birds rejoin the population of which they are members. We sorely need experimental evidence on this point. But the possibility must be borne in mind that these dialects may arise indirectly in the course of satisfaction of some other functional requirement, lacking a direct function of their own. One is nevertheless hesitant to regard such a striking and widespread characteristic as an epiphenomenon until other explanations are found wanting.

♦ *Geographic Variation and Character Displacement.* Several studies of song dialects have shown that the patterns are distributed as a kind of mosaic. Each local population is characterized by a song type which distinguishes it from neighboring populations, but which may also recur elsewhere (e.g. the chaffinch, Marler 1952, tree creepers, Thielcke 1961, 1965). If descriptions are carried to wider geographical ranges, we often find variation of another type, in the form of a consistent geographical shift in the dominant song patterns which affects all local populations. General and consistent variations in the song patterns in different parts of the geographical range of the species have been noted in many kinds of birds (e.g. Promptoff 1930, Benson 1948, Thielcke 1961, Thorpe 1961). Borror (1956) has described significant differences in phrase rate and number of phrases in the songs of Florida and Ohio populations of the Carolina

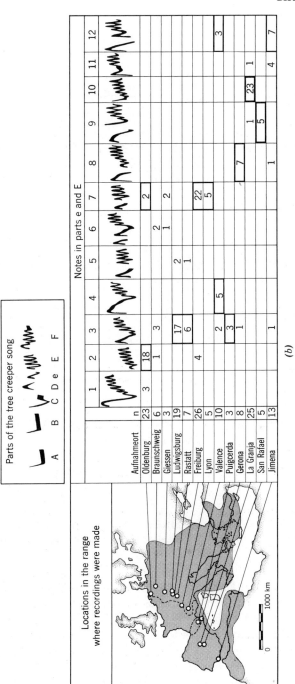

Figure 12-13 (*a*) Sound spectrograms of songs of four male short-toed tree creepers in and around Freiburg, Germany, and four more from Ludwigsburg, 140 kilometers away. (*b*) The occurrence of certain note types in various parts of Europe, showing the mosaic distribution. After Thielcke 1961, 1965.

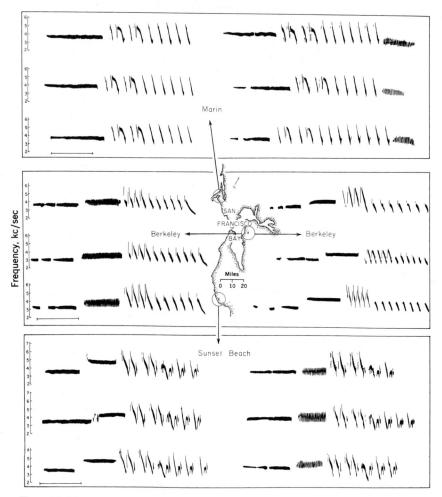

Figure 12-14 Sound spectrograms of songs of male white-crowned sparrows in and around the San Francisco Bay Area. There are clearly marked dialects, characterized particularly by syllable structure in the second part of the song. The time marker is half a second. After Marler and Tamura 1964.

wren. Russian and west European chaffinches seem to differ consistently; the eastern birds have a significantly simpler pattern at the end of the song, made up of fewer notes (Promptoff 1930, Marler 1952). Chipping sparrows have significantly shorter song syllables, more syllables per song, and a more rapid rate in the eastern and midwestern states of the United States than in parts of Mexico (Borror 1959a, Marler and Isaac 1960a).

Is this geographical variation merely incidental to other variations in

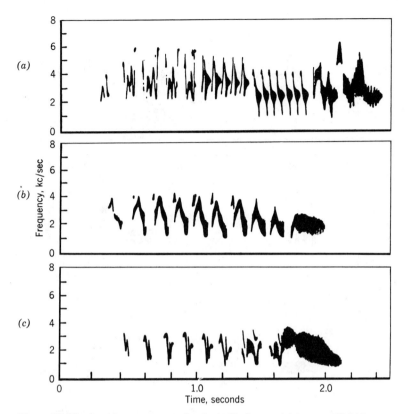

Figure 12-15   Sound spectrograms of male chaffinch song. (*a*) A normal British song. (*b*) Simpler song of a British bird raised in isolation. After Thorpe 1961. (*c*) Song of a blue chaffinch on Tenerife. After Marler 1959.

the characteristics of local populations? Another possibility is that there is an accompanying difference in the associated 'sound environment' within which the song is used, changing the requirements for species specificity. The principle of 'character displacement' (Brown and Wilson 1956) focuses attention on the distributional relationships of pairs of closely related species. When the geographical ranges of two species of animals overlap, competition or the requirement for species specificity may result in selection that accentuates differences between them in the zone of sympatry. Some examples are ecological and morphological in nature, others behavioral. One of the clearest comes from Blair's (1955, 1958, 1963) studies of frog calls. The difference between the calls of two species of *Microhyla* is appreciably greater in the area of overlap than in the allopatric parts of their ranges.

When we compare singing behavior in two continental populations,

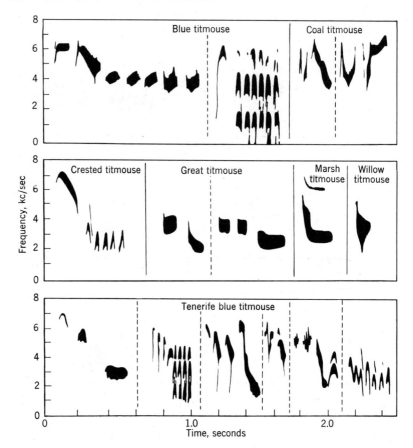

Figure 12-16   Examples of vocalizations of the six species of titmouse in Britain, and the single titmouse species occurring on Tenerife in the Canary Islands. After Marler 1959.

in which each species may be associated with large numbers of closely and distantly related species, it is not easy to interpret species differences. Comparisons between continental and insular populations are more easily interpreted. Islands usually have an impoverished fauna providing an excellent opportunity to detect differences that may arise when a species lives with few or many sympatric relatives.

The Azores, Madeira, and the Canary Islands, with their predominantly west European faunas, provide a number of such comparisons with the fauna of the mainland. The chaffinches of the genus *Fringilla*, for example, are represented by *Fringilla teydea*, endemic in the Canary Islands, and various subspecies of *Fringilla coelebs* in the Azores, Madeira, and Canary Islands. On the mainland *Fringilla coelebs* lives with a rich variety of more or less closely related cardueline and emberizine finches.

On the islands these finches are represented by only a handful of species. On most of the Azores Islands, for example, the only other common finches are *Serinus canaria* and *Carduelis carduelis.* The other songbirds on these islands live in the absence of many of their mainland relatives.

Comparison of mainland and island songs has revealed a number of differences (Lack and Southern 1949, Marler and Boatman 1951, Marler 1960, etc.). Chaffinch songs are consistently simpler on these islands than on the mainland; they lack the elaborate and distinctive end phrase which is so characteristic of chaffinch songs in Europe. This is true in the Azores and Madeira, and even in the Canary Islands, the only place where there are two chaffinches, the common chaffinch, *Fringilla coelebs,* and the blue chaffinch, *Fringilla teydea.* The two occupy separate habitats and are sedentary (Lack and Southern 1949), and both have the same simple song that recurs in the other island forms (Figure 12-15).

The song of the mainland chaffinch is largely learned; birds raised in isolation have a simple song (see page 684). The island birds have reverted to this simpler pattern, as though the circumstances favoring learned elaboration of the mainland song no longer exist in the simpler fauna of the islands.

The blue titmouse, *Parus caeruleus,* shows a trend of a different type. In Great Britain this species lives with five other *Parus* species. In the Canary Islands it is the only *Parus* species, and its songs and calls represent a bewildering variety of sounds. Many of them overlap in structure with sounds used by other members of the genus in Britain (Figure 12-16). Although there is variation in the British titmice (e.g. Gompertz 1961), the vocabularies are nevertheless more restricted than the island form (Marler 1960). Once more interspecific divergence is greatest and most consistent in the areas of sympatry.

The relationship between the willow warbler, *Phylloscopus trochilus,* and the chiffchaff, *P. collybita,* two species that are very similar in morphology but different in behavior, is of special interest. These species are sympatric over much of Europe, and their songs are consistently and distinctively different. In the Canary Islands *P. collybita* is present without *P. trochilus* and sings patterns which overlap both of the songs used by the mainland forms (Marler 1960).

Thus the principle of character displacement can be applied to the geographical variation of birdsong. Although we naturally focus on examples of marked variation, it is worth recalling that there is equally good evidence for a *lack* of geographical variation in the songs of some birds. The corn bunting, *Emberiza calandra,* in the Canary Islands seems to have a song similar to that of the mainland form, and the same is true of the blackbird, *Turdus merula,* and the blackcap, *Sylvia atricapilla* (Marler 1960). Selander and Giller (1961) were unable to detect character displacement in the songs of the grackles, *Cassidix major* and *C. mexicanus,* in an extensive zone of overlap. There is no measurable geographical variation in widely separated populations of meadowlarks (Lanyon and Fish 1958, Lanyon 1962). Borror (1959a, b) finds a similar situation in the towhee, *Pipilo erythrophthalmus,* and the chipping sparrow, *Spizella passerina.* Songs of the flycatcher, *Myiarchus tyrannulus,* vary relatively little over an extensive range in Central America (Lanyon 1960a, Davis 1961). The song patterns of these birds, as of meadowlarks, seem to be more conservative than the external morphology. Lanyon (1960b) was unable to find significant differences in song in widely separated populations of the house wren, *Troglodytes aedon.* It seems unlikely that the requirements for species specificity are identical throughout the whole range in all these cases. If the requirements are not the same we must assume either that selection for species specificity in the song is less severe in some species than in others, or that the song patterns for some reason resist change. We need to know more about the functions and physiological basis of song in these species before anything more than speculation is possible.

◆ *Individuality versus Specific Distinctiveness.* The existence of individual characteristics and species specificity in the same song results in something of a conflict. Accurate species identification demands stable and predictable characters consistent throughout a population. Individuality, on the other hand, calls for diversity within a population. Complex songs allow for resolution of this conflict by permitting diversity within a stereotyped general pattern. In many cases the internal structure of the syllables of the song is the basis for individuality, but the overall temporal pattern remains basically unchanged as, for example, in some thrushes (Stein 1956). But other combinations of stereotyped and variable characters occur.

Birds can discriminate between the songs of different individuals. Field observations support this contention (Armstrong 1963) and experiments confirm it. Hinde (1958) played back recorded songs to captive chaffinches and counted the number of songs given in reply. They responded most strongly to songs resembling their own, implying an ability to distinguish them from other song patterns. When the ovenbird, *Seiurus aurocapillus,* was tested in nature the responses to recorded songs were different (Weeden and Falls 1959). The recorded songs of neighboring males were found to elicit fewer responses than those from males in nonadjacent territories. Recordings of a male's own song were less effective than those of strangers but more effective than those of neighbors, as measured both by latency of the first response and the number of reply songs. There is clearly an ability to distinguish individual songs. The tests conducted here concern behavioral exchanges between males. It is likely that individual recognition is equally important in the relationship between male and female. Although circumstantial evidence indicates this importance (e.g. Marler 1956), experimental evidence is wanting. Individuality in calls is significant in parent-young relationships as well (Thorpe 1961, Armstrong 1963) as in the cliff-nesting guillemot, *Uria aalge,* in which both adults and chicks seem to recognize each other's individual calls (Tschanz 1949).

◆ *Species Song Recognition.* For many years the evidence for specific recognition of songs was indirect and circumstantial. Only recently has experimental support been obtained. Dilger (1956) made extensive tests, presenting both models and sounds of five species of North American thrushes in various combinations. Models alone were attacked more or less indiscriminately. But the addition of a song or, in some cases, of a distinctive call restricted the responses to members of the same species irrespective of the model used. There was occasional confusion. But the one species pair that sometimes responded to each other's sounds, *Catharus fuscescens* and *C. minimus,* is rarely sympatric.

Thielcke (1962) played recorded songs to two morphologically similar sympatric European tree creepers, *Certhia familiaris* and *C. brachydactyla,* finding strong responses only to the conspecific song. Lanyon (1963) conducted similar experiments with male American *Myiarchus* flycatchers in nature, but with a useful refinement. Pairs of dummies and loudspeakers were set up and two songs were played simultaneously so that the male chose between them in making an attack. The clear-cut results provided by this method confirm once more that the males of sympatric flycatchers are quite specific in their responsiveness to song patterns. It also appears that vocal behavior is much more important than external morphology in specific recognition by territorial males. The taxonomy of New World flycatchers is especially difficult; analysis of vocalizations promises to be a valuable aid in understanding species limits and relationships in this group (Lanyon 1960a, 1961, Johnson 1963).

Playback of unmodified song patterns confirms their importance as specific stimuli but does not indicate which of the many properties of a complex song pattern are responsible for the responses. Falls (1963) has explored this question in detail in two North American species, the ovenbird, *Seiurus aurocapillus,* and the white-throated sparrow, *Zonotrichia albicollis.* Normal and modified songs were played to territorial males and their various responses were quantified and compared.

The ovenbird's song consists of several repeated syllables increasing in loudness (Figure 12-17). Reversal of the changes in loudness did not re-

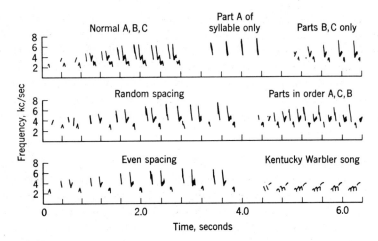

Figure 12-17 Reactions of ovenbirds in the field to playback of normal and experimentally modified songs. Sound spectrograms of some of the test songs are shown. The table is arranged in decreasing order of combined score of responses to the song. An asterisk indicates a significant difference from the reaction to songs of another species. A dagger indicates no significant difference from the reaction to a normal ovenbird song. After Falls 1963.

Type of test song	Increase in song	Time of first sound	Number approaching	Number of birds	Score (* plus †)
1. Normal ABC	8.5*†	3.1*†	30*†	35	6
2. Decreasing loudness	14.0*†	2.7*†	5*†	6	6
3. BC only	13.7 †	1.0*†	5*†	6	5
4. Random spacing	4.3*†	3.5*†	8*	15	5
5. ACB	7.6*†	5.0	11*†	14	4
6. Backward	3.7	2.5*†	3*†	6	4
7. Even spacing	5.5*†	6.5	8*	15	3
8. Kentucky warbler	2.9 †	4.9 †	3	7	2
9. Half speed	2.9 †	8.1 †	0	7	2
10. Double speed	0.9	6.5	1	8	0
11. A only	0.3	11.0	2	6	0
12. Other species	–0.01	8.2	1	21	0

duce the effectiveness of the song significantly. But the introduction of long or randomized intervals between the syllables reduced the response considerably: timing was important. Responses to a Kentucky warbler song, also consisting of a repetitive series, were further evidence of the importance of timing (Figure 12-17). The recorded songs of other species with different temporal patterns elicited no responses. The internal structure of the syllables was experimentally modified. Normally syllables have three parts. Elimination of the first of these had no effect, and a song made up of just the first note was ineffective. Apparently the second and third parts of the syllable are most important. Rearrangement of the order of the three parts reduced the effectiveness of the song. Falls concluded that to elicit the type of reaction studied here, an ovenbird's song must consist of a rather precisely timed series of phrases, each phrase consisting of at least two sounds having a definite form and occurring in a definite order (Falls 1963). It is notable that certain properties of the song are redundant. Weeden and Falls's (1959) previous study showed that individual recognition of song occurs and some characters redundant for specific recognition probably function in individual recognition.

The song of the ovenbird is too complex to be readily synthesized by a signal generator. Falls worked with another species, the white-throated sparrow, *Zonotrichia albicollis*. Its song consists of a series of clear whistled notes, simple enough to be readily synthesized. Some of the notes of the normal song are broken into triplets, and there are also changes in loudness (Figure 12-18). The effectiveness of artificial songs of varying frequency structure and temporal characteristics was compared with that of the normal song. The same playback methods were used. The broken nature of some notes and the occurrence of slurs, which show a high degree of individual variation in the natural song, can be eliminated without reducing the effectiveness of the song. Within broad limits the frequency of the tones can be varied. The limits coincide roughly with the variations encountered in nature. Elimination of variations in loudness leaves the song unimpaired. The presence of frequency differences between some of the notes and the absence of strong harmonics or other overtones are critical.

The temporal pattern of the white-throated sparrow song is important. In nature the duration of the notes is much more variable than the interval between notes. Correspondingly, the duration of notes in artificial songs could be varied widely above a certain minimum without impairing effectiveness in eliciting responses from territorial males. But the introduction of note intervals much beyond the normal maximum made the song ineffective. The duration of the whole song seems to be relatively unimportant (Figure 12-18).

Falls concludes that to be effective in this situation the song must consist of unvarying pure tones within a certain range of pitch. Less important is the presence of notes of different pitch arranged in a certain pattern. The notes should be of a certain minimum length, and the intervals between notes should not exceed a certain maximum (Falls 1963). Once

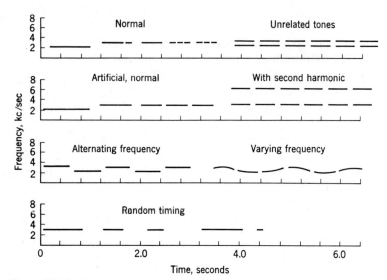

Figure 12-18 Responses of white-throated sparrows in the field to playback of normal and modified song patterns. Sound spectrograms of some of them are shown. The table is arranged in decreasing order of the score for each sound pattern. An asterisk indicates a significant difference from the reaction to songs of another species. A dagger indicates no significant difference from the reaction to a normal white-throated sparrow song. After Falls 1963.

Type of test song	Increase in song	Time of first sound	Number vocal-izing	Number within 20 ft	Number moving	Number of birds	Score (total * and †
1. Normal	11.7*†	2.9*†	159*†	135*†	156*†	159	10
2. Normal pitch change	11.7*	2.9*†	19*	20*†	20*†	21	8
3. Normal note length	9.0*	4.4*†	18*	12*	16*	21	6
4. Three or six notes	6.7*	6.2*	27*	12*	18*	32	5
5. One octave high	4.6*	7.4*	26*	10*	18*	33	5
6. One long note	3.1*	6.5*	23*	8*	18*	29	5
7. Widely spaced	4.3*	8.6	15*	13*	14*	21	4
8. Alternating pitch	1.6	6.8*	27*	12*	18*	34	4
9. Harmonic tones	5.0*	9.2	15	10*	9*	24	3
10. Random timing	1.6	8.4	21*	5	11*	31	2
11. Unrelated tones	2.6	9.1	14	4	6*	23	1
12. Fifteen short notes	2.1	10.4	21	6	13*	33	1
13. Varying pitch	1.3	11.1	21	6	13*	33	1
14. One octave low	0.8	9.3	15	2	7*	32	1
15. Two octaves high	1.5	16.2	9	2	2	32	0
16. Other species	0.02	13.0	31	3	4	69	0

more characteristics that are not necessary to elicit approach, attack, and song from territorial males may be important in other situations such as individual recognition between rival males or in exchanges between males and females.

One of the most interesting aspects of Falls's study is the interplay between experimentation and description of variation in natural behavior. Identification of characteristics that seem important in specific recognition led to experimental manipulation of these characteristics. It would be difficult to find a better example of the value of descriptive work as a preliminary to experimentation.

◆ *Variations in Specific Distinctiveness.* Our emphasis on the importance of a specifically distinctive song in birds must now be balanced by considering some birdsongs that lack specific distinctiveness. The songs of some sympatric species are unusually alike (e.g. Marler 1960). Moreover, a consideration of some of the functions of song suggests that specific distinctiveness is unlikely to be a universal characteristic.

We have noted the occurrence of interspecific territoriality in a number of birds (see page 171). In such circumstances a specifically divergent song might be less effective in repelling intruders than a sound pattern with some characteristics in common with the other species involved. The similarities in voice in North American titmice may be directly related to the interspecific territoriality that they display in areas of sympatry (Dixon 1961). Wherever two species compete actively for some commodity, it is possible that selection for a high degree of species specificity will be held in check in those signals that are used in competitive encounters.

A species may have several kinds of song, some more distinctive than others. Many North American warblers have at least two basic patterns. The 'accented song' is used particularly in establishing territories and pair bonds early in the breeding season. The unaccented song is used later in the season (Ficken and Ficken 1962). The accented songs differ strikingly in sympatric warblers but the unaccented songs are much more similar to one another. Selection for specific distinctiveness is probably less severe after pair bonds and territories have been established.

When songs are employed for stimulation of the female after pair formation, individuality may be important; it is between individual mates that synchrony must be achieved. Furthermore, the song is often used in the context of a constellation of signals generated together. Distinctive visual characters may relieve the song of requirements for strong specific distinctiveness (Smith 1965).

Variations in the need for specific distinctiveness are easier to discern in some of the sound signals which are less bound up with the function of reproductive isolation than song is. Alexander (1962) points out how much less divergent the aggressive and close-range courtship calls of crickets are as compared with the calling song. The same is true of many birds. The direct facilitation of interspecific communication can be a factor here. Consider alarm calls for example. If two sympatric species are endangered by the same predator, they may gain from a similarity in the alarm signals used to announce its presence, thus encouraging interspecific communication. There is ample evidence that such interspecific exchange does occur in bird and mammalian communities, and that it is associated with the use of similar types of signals, even in species which are distantly related (see page 467).

More subtle types of interspecific cooperation can occur. Many finches form into flocks of several species during the nonreproductive season. They perform coordinated movements requiring the interspecific exchange of signals. The flight calls of finches that are used in this situation are much less divergent than their songs (Marler 1957, Figure 12-19). The sounds of the gulls, *Larus argentatus* and *L. fuscus,* used to sound alarm and to attract other gulls to feed, are very similar in structure and elicit interspecific responses. Apparently local abundance of food in the non-breeding season minimizes competition and favors interspecific cooperation (Frings, Frings, Cox, and Peissner 1955).

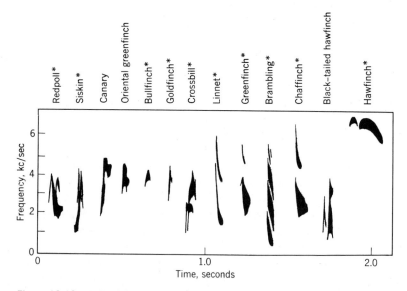

Figure 12-19 Calls of finches given before and during flight tend to conform to the same pattern. Species marked with asterisks are sympatric with most of the others over extensive parts of their ranges. After Marler 1959.

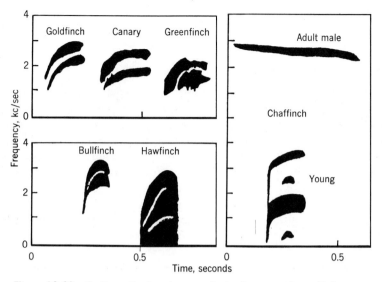

Figure 12-20   Similar calls given by some finches in strong alarm. Only young chaffinches use the low-frequency call. In the adult male chaffinch it is replaced by the upper call. After Marler 1959.

For different reasons very faint sounds may be less subject to selection for specific distinctiveness than loud sounds. The fact that they can be used for communication only at close range increases the likelihood of use between individuals brought together by other means (see page 261). The close range maximizes the chances of specific identification by the external appearance of the calling animal. Several finches use soft alarm calls of similar form (Figure 12-20). The calls probably owe their lack of divergence more to low volume than to the facilitation of interspecific communication (Marler 1957).

Arguments such as this bear on the use of sound and other signals in phylogenetic studies. Strong similarities or dissimilarities in the signals of sympatric species may be difficult to interpret without a knowledge of the function of the signals. By contrast, the comparison of behavior in species which are largely or entirely allopatric is less hazardous and can be a valuable and immediate guide to phylogenetic relationships (e.g. Alexander 1962, Ficken and Ficken 1962, Marshall 1964).

The occurrence of both intraspecific and interspecific communication by alarm calls has been confirmed experimentally, particularly in attempts to control the movements of birds on buildings and airfields by means of recorded sounds. Starlings and crows flee from recordings of distress calls given by a bird when taken in the hand, and aggregate in response to assembly calls (Frings and Jumber 1954, Frings and Frings 1957,

Busnel 1963), and the same effects can sometimes be produced inter-specifically. Tests conducted in France show that recorded distress calls of the European jay also elicit responses from carrion crows (Bremond 1963).

◆ *Structure of Sound Signals in Relation to Function.* Many relationships between structure and function of animal sound signals are obvious. The volume of a sound must be appropriate to the distance over which it is to elicit responses. It is efficient and economical for close-range signals to be softer than long-range ones. Busnel (1963) has tabulated the distances over which various animal sounds can be heard. We have already argued that the function of some sounds require a high degree of specific distinctiveness, and that in others specific distinctiveness has little value and may even be a disadvantage. A further requirement for many sound signals is that the source of the sound can be located, particularly if vision cannot be used.

The methods of sound location used by vertebrates vary in efficiency with different types of sound. It might be expected that sounds whose function involves location will have a form that will maximize the speed and accuracy of localization. We have noted that a series of clicks or pips

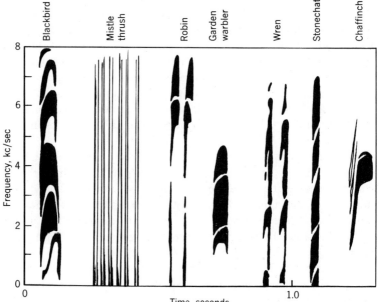

Figure 12-21 Sound spectrograms of calls of several species of British birds used while mobbing an owl. They share the characteristic of being easy to locate. After Marler 1959.

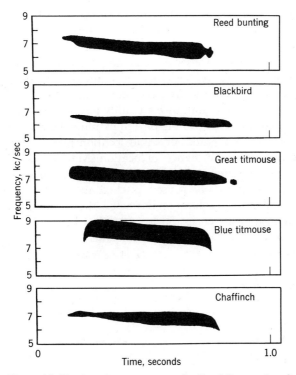

Figure 12-22 Sound spectrograms of calls of five species of British birds used when a hawk flies over. They share the characteristic of being difficult to locate. After Marler 1959.

provides the maximal number of clues (see page 420). The wide range of frequencies provides clues for both intensity and phase differences at the two ears, while the repeated sudden starts and stops, rich in transients, provide a basis for binaural time differences. It is possible for sounds to vary structurally a great deal while satisfying some or all of these requirements. The great majority of animal sounds satisfy them in some degree. A survey of some of the figures of birdsongs and birdcalls (e.g. Figures 12-8, 9, 10) shows how readily most of them can be located. The same characteristics can be found in many sounds of anurans and mammals (e.g. Blair 1958, Bogert 1960, Eisenberg 1963, Andrew 1963, 1964).

Nonetheless, the requirement for locatability is not universal. To illustrate this we can compare two patterns of response to predators that recur in many small birds. If a stationary hawk or owl is encountered the common response is to 'mob' it (see page 248) with approach to within a certain distance, conspicuous display, and loud calls. A sound used in this situation will function most efficiently if it can be readily located. A survey of sounds used by woodland birds in Britain shows that they conform closely to the requirements (Marler 1957, Figure 12-21).

When a hawk flying overhead is sighted the response differs. Instead of conspicuous behavior we see extreme crypticity. Birds in the open flee to the nearest cover. There they crouch low and are still, sometimes giving an alarm call that elicits the same response in members of their own and other species. In this circumstance a readily located call is not necessary. Indeed, it might place the calling bird in extreme danger.

Knowledge of the methods of sound location permits the design of a sound that minimizes the chances of location (Marler 1955). This is done by eliminating time cues, so that the sound fades in and out with no abrupt discontinuities. A pure tone is used, pitched above the frequency maximum for phase difference location but below the optimum for generating binaural intensity differences. Such a sound, a high thin whistle, has a ventriloquial quality and is difficult to locate.

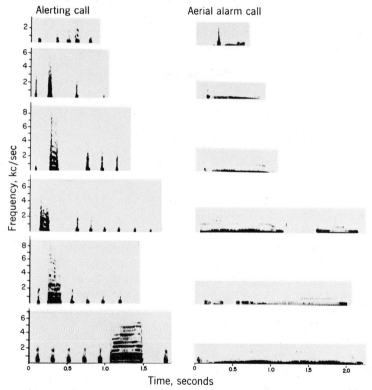

Figure 12-23 Grading of signals in vocal behavior of cockerels. Both the alerting call and the aerial alarm vary in duration according to the intensity of external stimulation. After Konishi 1963.

This type of sound for signaling the presence of a flying hawk has evolved independently in several families of passerine birds (Figure 12-22). It recurs in several North American species, including the robin, *Turdus migratorius*, the wood thrush, *Hylocichla mustelina*, and three titmice, *Parus bicolor, P. inornatus,* and *P. atricapillus* (Brackbill 1959), and in at least four icterid genera (Selander and Giller 1961).

These sounds probably provide as little aid to a predator in locating the calling bird as they do to us. Small birds seem to be more responsive to binaural intensity differences than we are and less responsive to time differences (Schwartzkopff 1950). The same might be true of hawks, although their heads are larger and their ears are further apart than those of small birds. But the elimination of time cues also interferes with one of the methods of binaural intensity discrimination. This method involves the latency of the first response, which is known to provide binaural orientation cues in moths and probably in vertebrates as well (see page 407). The lack of a sharp onset will interfere with the determination of binaural differences in latency.

Some birds have convergently evolved a sound that exploits these methods for minimizing locatability, thus incidentally preparing the way for free interspecific communication. Other species have evolved sounds of variable characteristics, allowing the addition of properties that increase species specificity yet avoiding the maximization of cues for localization. Many avian and mammalian alarm calls have this intermediate structure (Marler 1955, 1957).

SOUNDS OF MONKEYS AND APES

◆ *Grading versus Stereotypy.* The extent of variability in utterances of the same basic sound in different situations is another aspect of the relationship between signal structure and function. As with some visual displays (see page 384) the relative stereotypy of many sound signals is striking, often to the extent that much of the vocal repertoire can be separated into discrete, nonoverlapping categories. Such is the case with the sounds of many birds (Figures 12-8 and 12-9). Some sounds, however, show an extensive degree of grading, the precise form varying with the circumstances in which the signal is emitted (e.g. Konishi 1963, Smith 1965, Figure 12-23). The use of graded sound systems seems to be more extensive in mammals, particularly in higher primates (Marler 1965).

Andrew (1963) makes special mention of the great variability of renderings of some of the sounds emitted by marmosets. Langurs have at least two graded systems, the 'grunt-bark' continuum and the 'squeal-

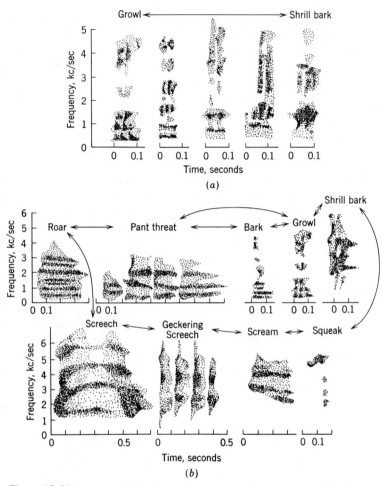

Figure 12-24 (*a*) A graded series of rhesus monkey sounds from the growl to the shrill bark (after Rowell and Hinde 1962). (*b*) A more extensive graded series of rhesus sounds encompassing nine calls. Note the complex relationship between the pant-threat, the bark, and the growl (after Rowell 1962, Rowell and Hinde 1962).

scream' continuum. Other sound signals vary in some degree, although the categories are distinct (Jay 1965). The gibbon's system is probably similar (Carpenter 1940). Baboons have a number of intergrading systems. Of the various adult sounds (Hall and DeVore 1965) the two kinds of grunting grade into each other and perhaps into roaring. The three types of barking also grade into each other, and so do screeching and yakking. Investigators of baboons repeatedly emphasize the difficulty of categorizing sounds.

Nowhere is this intergradation of signals more evident than in the vocal behavior of the rhesus monkey, which has been closely studied (Rowell and Hinde 1962, Altmann 1962, Rowell 1962, Andrew 1963). "One of its most striking features is the possibility of an almost infinite range of intermediates between the main sounds" (Figure 12-24, Rowell and Hinde 1962). Rowell (1962) has analyzed such a graded system used by rhesus monkeys in agonistic situations. A set of nine sounds is listed as follows:

Roar: loud, fairly long noise made by a very confident animal, when threatening another of inferior rank or when protected by the cage from actual contact with the other. *Pant-threat:* a similar noise to the roar, but broken up into short 'syllables,' made by a less confident animal wanting the support of the rest of the group in its attack. *Bark:* rather like a single bark of a dog, given by a threatening animal insufficiently aggressive to move toward the other. *Growl:* differentiated from a bark in being quieter and rather shriller and broken up with very short sound units, like a rolled 'r'; given by a mildly alarmed animal. *Shrill-bark:* the alarm call of the species, probably given to predators in the wild. *Screech:* typically has an abrupt pitch change up and then down. Made when threatening a higher ranking animal, and when excited and slightly alarmed generally. *Geckering screech:* a similar noise to the previous one, but broken into syllables. Made by an animal being threatened by another. *Scream:* shorter than the screech and without the pronounced rise and fall. Made by a losing monkey in a fight while being bitten. *Squeaks:* short, very high pitched noises made by a defeated and exhausted monkey at the end of a fight (Rowell 1962, pp. 93–94).

These nine sounds actually constitute one system linked by a continuous series of intermediates. Moreover, there is one example of multi-dimensional variation, the pant-threat grading independently into three other calls (Rowell 1962, Figure 12-24). This extraordinarily rich system of connected variations encompasses a large part of the adult vocal repertoire.

Some of the higher monkeys and apes seem to have a vocal system in which stereotyped or discrete signals are rare. Signals that can vary in structure in several dimensions account for a major proportion of the repertoire. Characteristics other than signal form can also vary, as in the sounds of many animals. Loudness can vary in accordance with the context in which a sound is used, as in the grunts of langurs described by Jay. More significant perhaps are variations in the temporal pattern of delivery. For example, the "shrill bark" of the baboon is characteristically given just once. The "two-phase bark" is often repeated every two to five seconds for a minute or more. The "doglike bark," on the other hand, is usually given in bursts of from two to four calls. In addition to these distinct ways of delivering different calls, the actual rate may vary according to the circumstances, as in the "two-phase bark." "Grunting" may range from a slow rate of one every two seconds to an extremely rapid sequence, in which other animals may join as a chorus (Hall and DeVore 1965).

These variations in the temporal pattern of delivery of different signals, and of the same signal under different conditions, may be fundamentally related to the kinds of information they can convey, and therefore to the function they can perform.

◆ *Species Distinctiveness in Primate Sounds.* Compared with the calls of birds, many sounds used by primates and other mammals are coarse, lacking the purity of tone and precise patterns of frequency modulation that occur in many passerine birdsongs. Of course birds do make harsh noises and some primates can produce birdlike sounds (Andrew 1963, 1964). Certain sounds of *Colobus* and *Cercopithecus* monkeys are as long and complex in structure as bird sounds (Hill and Booth 1957, Ullrich 1961). Even in the repertoire of rhesus monkeys, langurs, gibbons, and chimpanzees there are relatively pure, drawn-out sounds (rhesus, "clear" calls, Rowell and Hinde 1962; langurs, the "whoop," Jay 1965; gibbons, type 1 "hoots," Carpenter 1940; chimpanzees, "howls" and "moaning hoots," Reynolds and Reynolds 1965). The primate larynx is evidently capable of producing sounds that are musical in tone.

Nevertheless, in the higher forms there seems to be a predominance of sounds that have a relatively wide frequency spectrum, with most of the energy in relatively low frequencies (below 4 or 5 kc/sec) and without much patterning of frequency; the changes in pitch that do occur are slow and are often blurred by noise.

The purer sounds that are produced are often also loud and are used to communicate over distance to maintain group spacing. Coincidentally, the drumming and chest beating of chimpanzees and gorillas, among the more highly structured sounds produced by apes, are distance signals. This coincidence might be related in part simply to the efficiency of transmission over distances. If this is the only correlation, why are many of the closer-range signals of prosimians and monkeys structured, as they seem to be (Andrew 1963, Petter 1965), instead of being bursts of poorly structured noise? It seems likely that the problem of species identification is a factor and that the degree of structuring of sound signals is partly determined by the requirements of specific distinctiveness.

When animals communicate in nature there is always a danger that alien sounds will intrude into the system and cause confusion. There are two situations in which the danger is minimal, (1) when a species is living out of earshot of organisms similar in size and structure, and (2) when sounds are used at sufficiently close range that visual or other cues can confirm the identity of the signaling animal. Both conditions are satisfied in many of the higher primates. In rhesus monkeys, baboons, gorillas, and chimpanzees the social unit is a relatively compact group, permitting almost constant reference to visual cues during communication within the group. Furthermore, these animals live with few close relatives of similar size.

This is in contrast with the condition of, for example, some of the *Cercopithecus* species. In forests of southwestern parts of Ghana they may be within hearing range of as many as six other species of monkeys, either other *Cercopithecus* or species of *Colobus* and *Cercocebus* (Booth 1956). These species occupy different levels in the forest much of the time, and, if this division were consistent, confusion would only be likely to arise between loud signals used for distance communication. Haddow (1952) and Booth (1956) have shown that, in fact, these monkeys frequently mingle in mixed groups when eating certain foods. *Cercopithecus petaurista,* for example, has been seen in mixed feeding parties with *Cercopithecus aethiops, C. campbelli,* and *C. mona.* In such circumstances the possibility of interspecific confusion is greatly increased, and sound signals seem to be correspondingly more highly structured. This structuring may be used, at least in part, to maintain species specificity in part of the vocal repertoire. As a result, an experienced observer can distinguish between these many cohabiting, forest-dwelling monkeys by listening to their sound signals (e.g. Haddow 1952).

Thus the relatively ill-defined structure of most sound signals of the rhesus monkey, baboons, chimpanzees, and gorillas may be correlated with the close-knit, terrestrial, or semiterrestrial social grouping and with the relative isolation from cohabiting species of similar size and structure. These conditions may free them from the need for a high degree of species specificity that demands both structured sounds and a relatively low degree of variability. These species can exploit an alternative type of sound-signaling system that is noisier and simpler in the basic structure of the sounds used, yet more complex in the development of these subtle continuous and multidimensional variations. The variations may serve to communicate more elaborate information than discrete, stereotyped signals can carry (Marler 1965).

AUDITION, VISION, AND OLFACTION
AS COMMUNICATION MEDIA

Given what is known about the types of signals that serve for distance communication and the properties of the receptor systems that respond to them, what generalizations can we make about the advantages and drawbacks of the different sensory modalities?

The sensitivity of olfactory receptors is such as to lend a special advantage to the use of chemical signals when communication over great distances is required. The only requirement is that emission be timed to coincide with movements in the surrounding medium which then aid dispersion, and permit distant location of the source. Auditory receptors can also be very sensitive. Moreover, sound and chemical signals share a characteristic generally lacking in visual signals—that energy can be directed into their production to raise the intensity of the signal above the noise level in the environment. Visual conspicuousness can be maximized by contrast and movement but except for such special cases as organisms that generate light, the intensity of visual signals is limited by ambient lighting. A disadvantage of most visual signals besides their limited value at night is that their transmission is readily impeded by environmental obstructions, whereas chemical and sound signals can bypass obstacles readily. Thus for several reasons vision is likely to be a less satisfactory method of long-distance communication than olfaction or audition. There may be exceptions for some species, such as seabirds. Their environment is unobstructed and well lit, and it provides a homogeneous background for the display of visual signals (e.g. Armstrong 1944).

On the other hand, visual signals have the supreme advantage of easy source location; localization is less accurate with sound signals, and it is slow and uncertain with olfactory signals except under very special conditions. Moreover, the directionality of light makes possible the use of spatial patterns to a degree that is inconceivable with chemical and sound signals. Compound signals with many separate and simultaneously variable elements can be exploited fully, to generate an immensely complex and extensive repertoire of signals. The richness is increased by the variables of color and brightness and the possibility of exploiting rapid temporal patterning. Furthermore, it is possible for some elements of a visual signal to be relatively durable, such as objects in the environment or aspects of external morphology, while others are transient, such as a brief movement or display of a concealed structure. Vision is in many ways the ideal means for close-range communication, when conditions permit. Diurnal animals living in a fairly open environment can best exploit vision. A relatively close-knit society favors the use of visual signals, as does a social organization complex enough to make use of the subtleties of signal complexity that are possible when vision is used. Nowhere are these conditions better satisfied than in some of the higher primates. It is no accident that some of the greatest complexities of communication in such animals as baboons and macaques are found in systems that employ visual signals (Altmann 1962, Hall and DeVore 1965).

When the usefulness of vision is limited by the environment or by the inadequacy of visual receptors, we find an apparently greater reliance on olfaction, for close-range as well as distance communication. The particular advantages of olfaction are the potential durability of the signals and variation in durability according to the substance used. Wilson and Bossert (1963) have shown how these special temporal characteristics of chemical signals can be woven into a communication system of great complexity and sophistication. If the members of a population occupy a reasonably stable position in space, the durability of chemical signals can be exploited, as we find in many nocturnal mammals. The immense variety of compounds that can be generated provides a ready basis not only for specific identification, exploiting the possible specificity of receptor function, but also for colony or individual identification. There is ample signal diversity for generating different signals for different functions.

The relative durability of chemical signals can be a disadvantage in some circumstances, when rapid exchanges between animals call for modification of signal characteristics at short notice. It is here that sound signals reign supreme. Temporal coding reaches its greatest complexity in sounds such as the songs of insects and birds used for distance communication. The transient nature of sound signals also permits rapid exchanges of variable signals. This can be especially valuable in highly mobile species that need brief, accurate exchanges of information.

There is another advantage of sound as a means of communication that is a little more subtle. Some of the occasions for communication between animals are important enough to warrant the cessation of other activities while signals are being generated. But it can be advantageous for ongoing behavior to continue during signal emission in some situations. This is impossible if the process of signal production involves a major part of the animal's motor equipment, as in many types of visual signaling, or in sound production by grasshoppers and crickets. Furthermore, on the perceptual side the eyes must be used to watch the partner during visual communication, which interferes with their use in exploring the environment. On both counts, sound signals have an advantage. The use of respiratory air movements to generate sounds allows signal production to proceed simultaneously with other behavior as, for example, in the flight calls of flocking birds or the soft grunts heard in foraging groups of many social mammals. Sounds can be generated and heard without disrupting other activities.

Thus each modality has its own special advantages and disadvantages. Species that have the necessary sensory equipment are likely to make use of all three distance senses for communication in different situations. Other sensory systems are sometimes involved. The electrical sense of fishes may be an important means of communication (see page 503). The contact chemical sense, taste, can be important in close-range encounters. Perhaps most neglected in studies of communication is the sense of touch, which is known to be important in arthropods (e.g. Liesenfeld 1961, Walcott and Van der Kloot 1959). It may prove to be the most important single modality in social integration of some primate groups. A touch on some part of the companion's body is involved in such activities as social grooming and many types of greeting (e.g. Hall 1962). But the tactile sense is also one of the most difficult to investigate. It is not easy for an observer to interpose himself or his instruments in a tactile communication system in such a way as to register the signals—at least not in the form that they are actually received by the animals themselves.

REFERENCES

Alexander, R. D. 1960. Sound communication in Orthoptera and Cicadidae. In *Animal Sounds and Communication*, ed. by W. E. Lanyon and W. N. Tavolga: 38–92. American Institute of Biological Sciences, Washington, D.C.

———. 1962. Evolutionary change in cricket acoustical communication. *Evolution*, 16:443–467.

Altmann, S. 1962. A field study of the sociobiology of rhesus monkeys, *Macaca mulatta*. *Ann. N.Y. Acad. Sci.*, 102:338–435.

Andrew, R. J. 1963. The origin and evolution of the calls and facial expressions of the primates. *Behaviour*, 20:1–109.

———. 1964. The displays of the primates. In *Evolutionary and Genetic Biology of Primates*, ed. by J. Buettner-Janusch, Vol. 2:227–309. The Academic Press, New York.

Armstrong, E. A. 1944. White plumage of sea-birds. *Nature*, 153:527–528.

———. 1963. *A Study of Bird Song*. Oxford University Press, London.

Benson, C. W. 1948. Geographical voice-variation in African birds. *Ibis*, 90:48–71.

Blair, W. F. 1955. Mating call and stage of speciation in the *Microhyla olivacea—M. carolinensis* complex. *Evolution*, 9:469–480.

———. 1958. Mating call in the speciation of anuran amphibians. *Amer. Nat.*, 92:27–51.

———. 1963. Acoustic behaviour of Amphibia. In *Acoustic Behaviour of Animals*, ed. by R. G. Busnel: 694–708. Elsevier Publishing Company, Amsterdam.

Bogert, C. M. 1960. The influence of sound on the behavior of amphibians and reptiles. In *Animal Sounds and Communication*, ed. by W. E. Lanyon and W. N. Tavolga: 137–320. American Institute of Biological Sciences, Washington, D.C.

Booth, A. H. 1956. The distribution of primates in the Gold Coast. *J. West Afr. Sci. Ass.*, 2:122.

Borror, D. J. 1956. Variation in Carolina wren songs. *Auk*, 73: 211–229.

———. 1959a. Variation in the songs of the rufous-sided towhee. *Wilson Bull.*, 71:54–72.

———. 1959b. Songs of the chipping sparrow. *Ohio J. Sci.*, 59:347–356.

———. 1960. The analysis of animal sounds. In *Animal Sounds and Communication*, ed. by W. E. Lanyon and W. N. Tavolga: 26–37. American Instiute of Biological Sciences, Washington, D.C.

———. 1961. Intraspecific variation in passerine bird songs. *Wilson Bull.*, 73:57–78.

Brackbill, H. 1959. An avian predator alarm of the American robin. *Bird-Banding*, 30:46–47.

Bremond, J. C. 1963. Acoustic behaviour of birds. In *Acoustic Behaviour of Animals*, ed. by R. G. Busnel: 709–750. Elsevier Publishing Company, Amsterdam.

Brown, W. L., Jr. and E. O. Wilson. 1956. Character displacement. *Syst. Zool.*, **5**:49–64.

Busnel, R. G. 1963. On certain aspects of animal acoustic signals. In *Acoustic Behaviour of Animals*, ed. by R. G. Busnel: 69–111. Elsevier Publishing Company, Amsterdam.

————, B. Dumortier, and M. C. Busnel. 1956. Recherches sur le comportement acoustique des Éphippigères (Orthoptéres, Tettigoniidae). *Bull. Biol.*, **90**:219–286.

Capranica, R. 1965. *The Evoked Vocal Response of the Bullfrog.* Massachusetts Institute of Technology Press, Cambridge.

Carpenter, C. R. 1940. A field study in Siam of the behavior and social relations of the gibbon (*Hylobates lar*). *Comp. Psychol. Monog.*, **16**(5):1–212.

Collias, N. E. 1963. A spectrographic analysis of the vocal repertoire of the African village weaverbird. *Condor.* **65**:517–527.

Craig, W. 1943. The song of the wood pewee, *Myiochanes virens* Linnaeus: a study of bird music. *N.Y. St. Mus. Bull.*, **334**:1–186.

Davis, J. 1958. Singing behavior and the gonad cycle of the rufous-sided towhee. *Condor,* **60**:308–336.

Davis, L. I. 1961. Songs of North American *Myiarchus*. *Tex. J. Sci.*, **13**:327–344.

Delco, E. A., Jr. 1960. Sound discrimination by males of two cyprinid fishes. *Tex. J. Sci.*, **12**:48–54.

Dilger, W. C. 1956. Hostile behavior and reproductive isolating mechanisms in the avian genera *Catharus* and *Hylocichla*. *Auk*, **73**:313–353.

Dixon, K. 1961. Habit distribution and niche relationships in North American species of *Parus*. In *Vertebrate Speciation*, ed. by W. F. Blair: 179–216. Texas University Press, Austin.

Dumortier, B. 1963a. Morphology of sound emission apparatus in Arthropoda. In *Acoustic Behaviour of Animals*, ed. by R. G. Busnel: 277–345. Elsevier Publishing Company, Amsterdam.

————. 1963b. The physical characteristics of sound emissions in Arthropoda. In *Acoustic Behaviour of Animals*, ed. by R. G. Busnel: 346–373. Elsevier Publishing Company, Amsterdam.

————. 1963c. Ethological and physiological study of sound emissions in Arthropoda. In *Acoustic Behaviour of Animals*, ed. by R. G. Busnel: 583–684. Elsevier Publishing Company, Amsterdam.

Eisenberg, J. 1963. The behavior of heteromyid rodents. *Univ. Calif. Publ. Zool.*, **69**:1–114.

Faber, A. 1953. Laut-und Gebärdensprache bei Insekten: Orthoptera (Geradflüger). *Mitt. st. Mus. Naturk. Stuttg.*, Nr. **287**:1–198.

Falls, J. B. 1963. Properties of bird song eliciting responses from territorial males. *Proc. 13th Int. Orn. Congr.*, Vol. 1:259–271.

Ficken, M. S. and R. W. Ficken. 1962. The comparative ethology of the wood warblers: a review. *The Living Bird*, **1**:103–122.

Frings, H. and M. Frings. 1957. Recorded calls of the eastern crow as attractants and repellents. *J. Wildl. Mgmt.*, **21**:91.

————, ————, B. Cox, and L. Peissner. 1955. Auditory and visual mechanisms in food-finding behavior of the herring gull. *Wilson Bull.*, **67**:155–170.

———— and J. Jumber. 1954. Preliminary studies on the use of a specific sound to repel starlings (*Sturnus vulgaris*) from objectionable roosts. *Science,* **119**:318–319.

Gompertz, T. 1961. The vocabulary of the great tit. *Brit. Birds,* **54**:369–394, 409–418.

Gray, G. A. and H. E. Winn. 1961. Reproductive ecology and sound production of the toadfish, *Opsanus tau. Ecology,* **42**:274–282.

Haddow, A. J. 1952. Field and laboratory studies on an African monkey, *Cercopithecus ascanius schmidti* Matschie. *Proc. Zool. Soc. Lond.*, **122**:297–394.

Hall, K. R. L. 1962. The sexual, agonistic and derived social behaviour patterns of the wild chacma baboon, *Papio ursinus. Proc. Zool. Soc. Lond.*, **139**:283–327.

————. and I. DeVore. 1965. Baboon social behavior. In *Primate Behavior*, ed. by I. DeVore: 53–110. Holt, Rinehart and Winston, New York.

Hall-Craggs, J. 1962. The development of song in the blackbird, *Turdus merula. Ibis*, **104**:277–300.

Hartshorne, C. 1958. Some biological principles applicable to song-behavior. *Wilson Bull.*, **70**:41–56.

Haskell, P. T. 1961. *Insect Sounds*. H. F. and G. Witherby, London.

Hill, W. C. O. and A. H. Booth. 1957. Voice and larynx in African and Asiatic Colobidae. *J. Bombay Nat. Hist. Soc.*, **54**:309–321.

Hinde, R. A. 1958. Alternative motor patterns in chaffinch song. *Brit. J. Anim. Behav.*, **6**:211–218.

Howard, E. 1920. *Territory in Bird Life.* John Murray (Publishers), London.

Hüchtker, R. and J. Schwartzkopff. 1958. Soziale Verhaltensweisen bei hörenden und gehörlosen Dompfaffen (*Pyrrhula pyrrhula* L.). *Experientia*, **14**:106–107.

Huxley, J. S. 1942. *Evolution: The Modern Synthesis.* George Allen and Unwin, London.

Isaac, D. and P. Marler. 1963. Ordering of sequences of singing behaviour of mistle thrushes in relationship to timing. *Anim. Behav.*, **11**:179–188.

Jay, P. 1965. The common langur of North India. In *Primate Behavior*, ed. by I. DeVore: 197–249. Holt, Rinehart and Winston, New York.

Johnson, N. K. 1963. Biosystematics of sibling species of flycatchers in the *Empidonax hammondii —oberholseri—wrightii* complex. *Univ. Calif. Publ. Zool.*, **66**:79–238.

Kellogg, P. P. and R. C. Stein. 1953. Audio-spectrographic analysis of the songs of the alder flycatcher. *Wilson Bull.*, **65**:75–80.

Konishi, M. 1963. The role of auditory feedback in the vocal behavior of the domestic fowl. *Z. Tierpsychol.*, **20**:249–367.

————. 1964. Song variation in a population of Oregon juncos. *Condor*, **66**:423–436.

————. 1965. Effects of deafening on song development in American robins and black-headed grosbeaks. *Z. Tierpsychol.*, **22**:584–599.

Lack, D. and H. N. Southern. 1949. Birds on Tenerife. *Ibis*, **91**:607–626.

Lanyon, W. E. 1957. The comparative biology of the meadowlarks (*Sturnella*) in Wisconsin. *Publ. Nuttall Orn. Club*, **1**:1–67.

————. 1960a. The middle American populations of the crested flycatcher, *Myiarchus tyrannulus. Condor*, **62**:341–350.

————. 1960b. Relationship of the house wren (*Troglodytes aedon*) of North America and the brown-throated wren (*Troglodytes brunneicollis*) of Mexico. *Proc. 12th Int. Orn. Congr.*, Vol. 1:450–458.

————. 1961. Specific limits and distribution of ash-throated and Nutting flycatchers. *Condor*, **63**:421–449.

————. 1962. Specific limits and distribution of meadowlarks of the desert grassland. *Auk*, **79**:183–207.

————. 1963. Experiments on species discrimination in *Myiarchus* flycatchers. *Amer. Mus. Novit.*, No. 2126:1–16.

———— and W. R. Fish. 1958. Geographical variation in the vocalizations of the western meadowlark. *Condor*, **60**:339–341.

Leston, D. and J. W. S. Pringle. 1963. Acoustical behaviour of Hemiptera. In *Acoustic Behaviour of Animals*, ed. by R. G. Busnel: 391–410. Elsevier Publishing Company, Amsterdam.

Liesenfeld, F. J. 1961. Über Leistung und Sitz des Erschütterungssinnes von Netzspinnen. *Biol. Zbl.*, **80**:465–475.

Littlejohn, M. J. 1959. Call differentiation in a complex of seven species of *Crinia* (Anura, Leptodactylidae). *Evolution*, **13**:452–468.

—— and T. C. Michaud. 1959. Mating call discrimination by females of Strecker's chorus frog (*Pseudacris streckeri*). *Tex. J. Sci.,* **11**:86–92.

Loher, W. 1957. Untersuchungen über den Aufbau und die Entstehung der Gesänge einiger Feldheuschreckenarten und den Einfluss von Lautzeichen auf das akustische Verhalten. *Z. vergl. Physiol.,* **39**:313–356.

Marler, P. 1952. Variation in the song of the chaffinch, *Fringilla coelebs*. *Ibis,* **94**:458–472.

——. 1955. Characteristics of some animal calls. *Nature,* **176**:6–8.

——. 1956. The voice of the chaffinch and its function as a language. *Ibis,* **98**:231–261.

——. 1957. Specific distinctiveness in the communication signals of birds. *Behaviour,* **11**:13–39.

——. 1959. Developments in the study of animal communication. In *Darwin's Biological Work,* ed. by P. R. Bell: 150–206. Cambridge University Press, Cambridge.

——. 1960. Bird songs and mate selection. In *Animal Sounds and Communication,* ed. by W. E. Lanyon and W. N. Tavolga: 348–367. American Institute of Biological Sciences, Washington, D.C.

——. 1965. Communication in monkeys and apes. In *Primate Behavior,* ed. by I. DeVore: 544–584. Holt, Rinehart and Winston, New York.

—— and D. J. Boatman. 1951. Observations on the birds of Pico, Azores. *Ibis,* **93**:90–99.

—— and D. Isaac. 1960a. Physical analysis of a simple bird song as exemplified by the chipping sparrow. *Condor,* **62**:124–135.

—— and ——. 1960b. Song variation in a population of brown towhees. *Condor,* **62**:272–283.

—— and ——. 1961. Song variation in a population of Mexican juncos. *Wilson Bull.,* **73**:193–206.

——, M. Kreith, and M. Tamura. 1962. Song development in hand-raised Oregon juncos. *Auk,* **79**:12–30.

—— and M. Tamura. 1962. Song 'dialects' in three populations of white-crowned sparrows. *Condor,* **64**:368–377.

—— and ——. 1964. Culturally transmitted patterns of vocal behavior in sparrows. *Science,* **146**:1483–1486.

Marshall, F. H. A. 1964. Voice in communication and relationships among brown towhees. *Condor,* **66**:345–356.

Martof, B. S. and E. F. Thompson, Jr. 1958. Reproductive behavior of the chorus frog, *Pseudacris nigrita. Behaviour,* **13**:243–258.

Mayr, E. 1942. *Systematics and the Origin of Species.* Columbia University Press, New York.

Messmer, E. and I. Messmer. 1956. Die Entwicklung der Lantäusserungen und einiger Verhaltensweisen der Amsel (*Turdus merula merula* L.) unter natürlichen Bedingungen und nach Einzelaufsucht in schalldichten Räumen. *Z. Tierpsychol.,* **13**:341–441.

Moulton, J. M. 1963. Acoustic behaviour of fishes. In *Acoustic Behaviour of Animals,* ed. by R. G. Busnel: 655–693. Elsevier Publishing Company, Amsterdam.

Mulligan, J. A. 1963. A description of song sparrow song based on instrumental analysis. *Proc. 13th Int. Orn. Congr.,* Vol. 1:272–284.

——. In press. Singing behavior and its ontogeny in the song sparrow, *Melospiza melodia. Univ. Calif. Publ. Zool.*

Nice, M. M. 1943. Studies in the life history of the song sparrow. II. The behavior of the song sparrow and other passerines. *Trans. Linn. Soc. N.Y.,* **6**:1–328.

Payne, R. S. 1962. How the barn owl locates prey by hearing. *The Living Bird,* **1**:151–159.

Perdeck, A. C. 1958. The isolating value of specific song patterns in two sibling species of grasshoppers (*Chorthippus brunneus* Thunb. and *C. biguttulus* L.). *Behaviour,* **12**:1–75.

Petter, J. J. 1965. The lemurs of Madagascar. In *Primate Behavior,* ed. by I. DeVore: 292–319. Holt, Rinehart and Winston, New York.

Poulsen, H. 1958. The calls of the chaffinch (*Fringilla coelebs* L.) in Denmark. *Dansk Orn. Foren. Tidsskr.,* **52**:89–105.

Promptoff, A. N. 1930. Die geographische Variabilität des Buchfinkenschlags (*Fringilla coelebs* L.) in Zusammenhang mit etlichen allgemeinen Fragen der Saisonvögelzüge. *Biol. Zbl.,* **50**:478–503.

Reynolds, V. and F. Reynolds. 1965. Chimpanzees of the Budongo forest. In *Primate Behavior,* ed. by I. DeVore: 368–424. Holt, Rinehart and Winston, New York.

Roth, L. M. 1948. A study of mosquito behavior. An experimental laboratory study of the sexual behavior of *Aedes aegypti* (Linnaeus). *Amer. Midl. Nat.,* **40**:265–352.

Rowell, T. E. 1962. Agonistic noises of the rhesus monkey (*Macaca mulatta*). *Symp. Zool. Soc. Lond.,* **8**:91–96.

——— and R. A. Hinde. 1962. Vocal communication by the rhesus monkey (*Macaca mulatta*). *Proc. Zool. Soc. Lond.,* **138**:279–294

Sauer, F. 1955. Über Variationen der Artgesänge bei Grasmücken. *J. Orn.,* **96**:129–146.

Schneider, H. 1961. Neuere Ergebnisse der Lautforschung bei Fischen. *Naturwissenschaften,* **48**: 513–518.

Schwartzkopff, J. 1950. Beitrag zum Problem des Richtungshörens bei Vögeln. *Z. vergl. Physiol.,* **32**:319–327.

———. 1955. On the hearing of birds. *Auk,* **72**:340–347.

Selander, R. K. and D. R. Giller. 1961. Analysis of sympatry of great-tailed and boat-tailed grackles. *Condor,* **63**:29–86.

Sibley, C. G. 1955. Behavioral mimicry in the titmice (Paridae) and certain other birds. *Wilson Bull.,* **67**:128–132.

———. 1957. The evolutionary and taxonomic significance of sexual dimorphism and hybridization in birds. *Condor,* **59**:166–191.

———. 1961. Hybridization and isolating mechanisms. In *Vertebrate Speciation,* ed. by W. F. Blair: 69–88. Texas University Press, Austin.

Smith, W. J. 1965. Message, meaning, and context in ethology. *Am. Nat.,* **99**:405–409.

Sotavalta, O. 1963. The flight-sounds of insects. In *Acoustic Behaviour of Animals,* ed. by R. G. Busnel: 374–390. Elsevier Publishing Company, Amsterdam.

Stein, R. C. 1956. A comparative study of "advertising song" in the *Hylocichla* thrushes. *Auk,* **73**:503–512.

———. 1958. The behavioral, ecological and morphological characteristics of two populations of the alder flycatcher, *Empidonax traillii* (Audubon). *N.Y. St. Mus. Sci. Serv.,* Bull. No. 371:1–63.

Stout, J. F. 1963. The significance of sound production during the reproductive behaviour of *Notropis analostanus* (Family Cyprinidae). *Anim. Behav.,* **11**:83–92.

Tavolga, W. N. 1956. Visual, chemical and sound stimuli as cues in the sex discriminatory behavior of gobiid fish *Bathygobius soporator. Zoologica,* **41**:49–64.

———. 1958. The significance of underwater sounds produced by males of the gobiid fish, *Bathygobius soporator. Physiol. Zool.,* **31**:259–271.

———. 1960. Sound production and underwater communication in fishes. In *Animal Sounds and Communication,* ed. by W. E. Lanyon and W. N. Tavolga: 93–136. American Institute of Biological Sciences, Washington, D.C.

———. 1964. Sonic characteristics and mechanisms in marine fishes. In *Marine Bio-Acoustics,* ed. by W. N. Tavolga: 195–211. The Macmillan Company, New York.

Tembrock, G. 1963. Acoustic behaviour of mammals. In *Acoustic Behaviour of Animals,* ed. by R. G. Busnel: 751–786. Elsevier Publishing Company, Amsterdam.

Thielcke, G. 1961. Stammesgeschichte und geographische Variation des Gesanges unserer Baumläufer (*Certhia familiaris* L. und *Certhia brachydactyla* Brehm). *Z. Tierpsychol.,* **18**: 188–204.

————. 1962. Versuche mit Klangattrappen zur Klärung der Verwandtschaft der Baumläufer *Certhia familiaris* L., *C. brachydactyla* Brehm und *C. americana* Bonaparte. *J. Orn.*, 103:266–271.

————. 1965. Gesangsgeographische Variation des Gartenbaumläufers (*Certhia brachydactyla*) im Hinblick auf das Artbildungsproblem. *Z. Tierpsychol.*, 22:542–566.

Thielcke-Poltz, H. and G. Thielcke. 1960. Akustisches Lernen verscheiden alter schallisolierter Amseln (*Turdus merula* L.) und die Entwicklung erlernter Motive ohne und mit künstlichem Einfluss von Testosteron. *Z. Tierpsychol.*, 17:211–244.

Thorpe, W. H. 1958. The learning of song patterns by birds, with especial reference to the song of the chaffinch, *Fringilla coelebs. Ibis*, 100:535–570.

————. 1961 *Bird Song: The Biology of Vocal Communication and Expression in Birds.* Cambridge University Press, Cambridge.

———— and D. R. Griffin. 1962. The lack of ultrasonic components in the flight noise of owls compared with other birds. *Ibis*, 104:256–257.

Tschanz, B. B. 1949. *Zur Brutbiologie der Trottelumme* (*Uria aalge aalge* Pont.). E. J. Brill, Publisher, Leiden.

Ullrich, W. 1961. Zur Biologie und Soziologie der Colobusaffen (*Colobus guereza caudatus* Thomas 1885). *Zool. Gart.*, 25:305–368.

Walcott, C. and W. G. Van der Kloot. 1959. The physiology of the spider vibration receptor. *J. Exp. Zool.*, 141:191–244.

Walker, T. J. 1957. Specificity in the response of female tree crickets (Orthoptera, Gryllidae, Oecanthinae) to calling songs of the males. *Ann. Ent. Soc. Amer.*, 50:626–636.

Weeden, J. S. and J. B. Falls. 1959. Differential responses of male ovenbirds to recorded songs of neighboring and more distant individuals. *Auk*, 76:343–351.

Weih, A. S. 1951. Untersuchungen über das Wechselsingen (*Anaphonie*) und über das angeborene Lautschema einiger Feldheuschrecken. *Z. Tierpsychol.*, 8:1–41.

White, G. 1789. *The Natural History and Antiquities of Selborne.* Benjamin White and Son, London.

Wilson, E. O. and W. H. Bossert. 1963. Chemical communication among animals. *Recent Prog. Hormone Res.*, 19:673–716.

Winn, H. E. 1964. The biological significance of fish sounds. In *Marine Bio-Acoustics,* ed. by W. N. Tavolga: 213–231. The Macmillan Company, New York.

Wishart, G. and D. F. Riordan. 1959. Flight responses to various sounds by adult males of *Aedes aegypti* (L.) (Diptera: Culicidae). *Can. Ent.*, 91:181–191.

thirteen

EMITTED-ENERGY ORIENTATION

The use of sounds in echolocation • Bat sounds • Morphology and behavior of echolocating bats • Theories of echolocation • Resistance to
jamming • Fish-catching bats • Echolocation in the sea • Orientation
by surface waves • Electrical orientation in fish.

For most organisms the sensory basis of directional orientation is passive in
the sense that it relies on the detection and utilization of environmental
energy, particularly celestial light. But in some environments, especially
those with little light, animals have developed active orientation mechanisms that depend on the emission of energy by the orienting animal.
This energy interacts with the environment in some way; the complete
or partial return of the signal provides the orienting information. By this
means dark environments have been penetrated effectively by several
groups of organisms. An obvious step, but one which few animals seem
to have taken, is to emit sufficient light for it to be reflected from the environment. Where light emission has developed it seldom seems powerful
enough to illuminate the environment for orientation purposes, and probably serves other functions such as social attraction and prey capture.

By contrast, the generation of sound waves as an orientation mechanism is widespread. This preference is related to the physical properties
of sound waves and the physiology of sound and light detection. The
absolute energy required to produce a physiologically detectable sound
echo is less than that required to obtain comparable amounts of information from an emitted-light source. The usefulness of sound and light in
water differs. A sound wave in water travels great distances, attenuating

less than in air. Light, on the other hand, scatters, and clear vision is possible only for short distances in any but the clearest water.

BAT ECHOLOCATION

◆ *Experimental Demonstration of Echolocation.* Spallanzani performed experiments between 1793 and 1794 that demonstrated the ability of blinded bats to find their way flying about a room. Jurine, one of Spallanzani's correspondents, repeated this experiment, with the additional and then startling discovery that if the ears of these blinded bats were plugged with wax this ability was lost (Spallanzani 1932, Dijkgraaf 1960). In 1941 Griffin and Galambos initiated intensive behavioral and physiological analysis of direction-finding in the little brown bat, *Myotis lucifugus.* They found that the little brown bat could effectively negotiate a line of fine (1.2 mm) wires spaced one foot apart if its ears and mouth were both unobstructed (Table 13-1). The wires were successfully evaded about 35% of the time by chance alone (Griffin 1958). Mouth and ears were

Table 13-1   Ability of Bats to Move Through a Wire Maze

Number of bats		Result		Control	
		Flights	Successful	Flights	Successful
28	Eyes covered, controls untreated	2016	76%	3201	70%
12	Ears covered, controls untreated	1047	35%	1297	66%
9	Ears and eyes covered, controls' eyes covered	654	31%	832	75%
8	Closed glass tubes in ears, controls with tubes open	580	36%	636	66%
12	Ears covered, controls with one ear covered	853	29%	560	38%
6	Eyes and one ear covered, controls with eyes covered	390	41%	590	70%
7	Mouth covered, controls with eyes covered or intact	549	35%	442	62%

From Griffin 1958.

necessary; the eyes were not. These experiments demonstrated the ability of flying bats to perform the delicate task of avoiding thin wires without vision. Hartridge's (1920) contention that the emitted sounds might somehow provide the significant orienting cues was supported. The next step was to analyze these sounds and to determine how bats detect their echos.

◆ *The Echolocating Call.* Based on observations made with the unaided ear Griffin and Galambos (1941) and Dijkgraaf (1943) reported audible clicks. Dijkgraaf concluded that echolocating bats were using sounds near the upper limit of his own hearing ability; in describing these sounds he noted that the clicking rate increased when the bat was required to make more difficult maneuvers. With the development of adequate electronic devices (Griffin 1958, Novick 1958a, b), the frequency and the intensity of the pulses of many species of bats have been measured. What the earlier experimenters had heard was the very small part of the energy of these pulses audible to man. The peak energies were far beyond man's hearing range.

The intensity of these ultrasonic cries, so faint to our ears, is astonishing.

It is interesting to compare the sound pressures generated by one of these typical insectivorous bats with those of familiar noises as they reach our ears. For example, the noise of a pneumatic drill breaking up the pavement on a city street strikes the ears of the sidewalk engineer at about 3 dynes/cm², a subway train rattles past the platform with a noise of about 10 dynes/cm², in a boiler shop the noise level may reach 25 dynes/cm², and the cabin of a noisy fighter airplane may contain sound pressure levels of roughly 100 dynes/cm². To be sure, the sound pressure of 60 dynes/cm² from a typical bat pulse is measured at two or three inches from the animal's mouth, and it is the peak-to-peak pressure of a very brief pulse of sound, while the comparative figures cited above are average levels commonly measured at the position of a listener who may be several feet from the source of the sound. Nevertheless the initial sound levels of bat pulses may equal those present in some of the noisiest environments to which men expose themselves for prolonged periods without risking damage to their ears. It is only because of the frequency limits of human hearing that these pulses are almost inaudible to us; to bats and other small mammals having good hearing at 20 to 80 kc they must be very loud indeed. Other bats of the family Vespertilionidae emit pulses with still higher intensities [Novick 1958b] but even these are virtually inaudible to human ears (Griffin 1958, p. 96).

The little brown bat modulates its pulses with a drop of 40 kc/sec in the course of each pulse. Peak intensities are reached near the middle of each pulse. These sounds are generally composed of short pulses lasting only a few thousandths of a second. When the big brown bat, *Eptesicus fuscus,* hunts flying insects it emits about ten comparatively long pulses

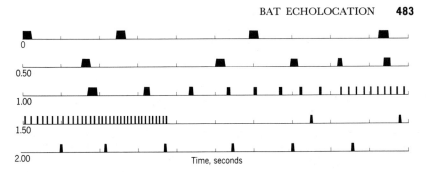

Figure 13-1   Diagram of the echolocation pulses of a big brown bat, *Eptesicus fuscus,* diving at a pebble thrown in front of it. Amplitude, here made equal for convenience, was not actually measured. The time scale is accurate. After Griffin 1958.

per second. But if a pebble is tossed in front of a hunting bat, the pulse rate increases immediately and the duration of the pulse drops sharply. The series of pulses shown in Figure 13-1 came from a bat hunting insects over a woodland stream. A pebble tossed into its path is quickly detected and approached.

Under laboratory conditions other vespertilionid bats show cruising pulse rates and durations not greatly different from those of *Eptesicus.* Möhres (1953) reported that the horseshoe bats, Rhinolophidae, emitted unmodulated pulses averaging 65 msec in duration. This discovery presented something of a dilemma, because these relatively long unmodulated pulses would result in the overlap of the emitted pulse with the returning echo when the bat was within detection range of insects. The bat would therefore be required to detect faint echoes while it was emitting intense vibrations at nearly the same frequencies. When Griffin (1962) reinvestigated these bats, however, he found that newly captured horseshoe bats were in fact emitting frequency-modulated pulses and that, given a difficult string grid to negotiate, these bats shortened pulse durations still further. It would appear, therefore, that the echolocation mechanism of rhinolophid bats is not as different from that of the vespertilionids as originally thought. The discrepancy between Möhres' (1953) findings and Griffin's later work appears to be based upon recording equipment differences and the fact that Möhres' bats were held in captivity for long periods before being tested.

Although the differences between the rhinolophid and vespertilionid pulses are not as great as originally thought, important differences remain. Rhinolophid pulses, for example, are at about 80 kc/sec for *Rhinolophus ferrum-equinum* (Möhres 1953; Griffin 1962) and 100 kc/sec in *Rhinolophus hipposideros* (Möhres 1953), well above the peak energies of vespertilionid pulses. The emission of sounds through the nose and the elaborate nose leaf are further evidence of the long period of independent evolution of rhinolophids and vespertilionids.

◆ *Prey Capture by Echolocation.* Griffin, Webster, and Michael (1960) discovered a method of inducing captive insectivorous bats to feed in flight. The experimental chamber was flooded with mosquitoes and fruit flies. High-speed motion picture records with simultaneous sound analysis showed the following phases of prey capture.

1. A searching phase during which frequency-modulated pulses sweep from 100 to 50 kc/sec every pulse. During this phase *Myotis* is alert and actively hunting. At any time the subsequent phases may lead to prey capture in less than half a second.

2. An approach phase initiated when the bat turns toward the prey and progressively shortens the interval between pulses and the duration of each pulse. Sound frequencies remain unchanged.

3. A terminal phase in which the frequency drops to 25 to 30 kc/sec. The pulse duration drops to 0.5 msec and the interval between pulses drops to 5 or 6 msec. The resulting sound produces an audible buzz. Novick (1963) has identified similar phases in the phyllostomid fruit bats, *Pteronotus davyi, Chilonycteris psilotis* (Novick 1965), and *Chilonycteris parnellii* (Novick and Vaisnys 1964). All 20 species studied, including *Rhinolophus,* give a buzz or marked increase in pulse repetition rate while insect catching, dodging a difficult object, or landing (Griffin in litt.).

◆ *Morphology and Behavior of Echolocating Bats.* Before discussing how bats analyze echoes it will be helpful to review certain morphological and behavioral peculiarities of these animals. Bats have a unique laryngeal specialization: the cricothyroid muscles that serve the larynx are developed enormously. The arytenoid cartilages are ossified and fused, precluding any possible participation in phonation. The ears are large, enormous in some species. A second 'ear,' the tragus, which generally repeats the contour of the ear, is present in some species. The role of this structure, presumably an additional specialization concerned with echolocation, has not been determined. In the auditory pathway, the cochlear nucleus is the first area which afferent fibers reach, followed by the inferior colliculus. Both areas are enormously enlarged in comparison with those of other mammals. The role of these structures has been the subject of intensive neurophysiological analyses (Grinnell 1963a, b, c, d; Griffin, McCue, and Grinnell 1963; Suga 1964a, b).

High-speed movies show that the mouth of vespertilionid bats is continuously open while they are in flight. The same is not true of the rhinolophids, which emit their cries through the nose. In flight rhinolophids show another peculiarity. Unlike the fixed ears of vespertilionids, rhinolophid ears are capable of continuous and independent rotation. In addition, the ears are moved rapidly back and forth at rates of up to 50 vibrations per second, the tip of the ear moving 8 to 10 mm. When the muscles that control these movements are denervated, the bats become disoriented, confirming the relevance of this unusual behavior to echolocation orientation. The echolocating megachiropteran, *Rousettus*, emits its cries through the corners of the closed mouth (Novick 1958). The demonstration that these movements are coordinated with the emitted calls (Griffin, Dunning, Cahlander, and Webster 1962; Pye, Flinn, and Pye 1962) further confirms the role of these movements in sonic orientation.

There are pronounced frequency and pulse duration differences between certain groups of bats. Intensity also varies, and these variations tell a good deal about the habits of these bats. The rhinolophid bats, for example, emit extremely intense sounds through the nostrils rather than the mouth (Dijkgraaf 1946). Immediately behind the nose is a peculiar epidermal modification, a sort of horn which probably directs the sound forward. The nostrils are spaced half a wavelength apart so that the sounds emitted from them interact to reinforce and interfere, amplifying the potential signal strength at the bat's ear. The nose leaf serves as a sort of megaphone, neatly adjusted to amplify and reinforce the 80- to 100-kc/sec frequencies which these bats emit (Möhres 1953). Perhaps because of the epidermal horn the sound level directly in front of these bats is considerably greater than that emitted by vespertilionids. Certainly it is more directional, for Möhres could detect no sound at all 45 degrees to the side of the facing position. By contrast Griffin found intensities of 20 percent or more 90 degrees to the side of the *Myotis* sound beam.

Many New World phyllostomid fruit bats have nose leaves that may serve a similar function, concentrating mouth-emitted sounds. But Grummon and Novick (1963) found no significant loss of ability to negotiate a wire grid when the nose leaf of the free-tailed bat, *Macrotus mexicanus*, was trimmed, covered, or masked.

The emitted pulses of a fruit bat, *Carollia*, are much fainter than those of the insectivorous vespertilionids. When these bats were first tested, Griffin and Novick (1955) could detect no sound at all. Were these bats relying on vision? Although this frugivorous species has larger eyes than typical vespertilionids, experiments showed sound-based obstacle avoidance. Only after better microphones had been developed could their faint pulses be detected. *Carollia* produces only one-thousandth of the sound energy of the smaller *Myotis*. Indeed, it seems to be the rule that species taking insects on the wing emit far more intense pulses than species feeding on fruit, pollen, or large prey as do vampires. Perhaps considerably more energy is required to detect and intercept a flying insect than to detect forest vegetation, fruit, or a sleeping mammal. The significance of these characteristics lies in the nature of the information provided by the echo, and of this we know very little. At what point does an insectivorous bat decide that a prey item is edible? What items are rejected? How complete is the 'sound picture' of the environment, and to what distances can this perception penetrate?

Novick (1965) has asked another intriguing question: Why haven't all species hit upon the same solution to the problem of efficient prey detection? This solution would lead to the same pulse duration, intensity, and range in all forms. The same question may be posed of many species differences and, of course, the answer sometimes lies in the historical probability of lighting on any particular strategy. Novick suggests that a part of the answer may be interspecific competition. Comparisons of echolocation calls have not been adequately related to hunting techniques. In part, such an analysis is dependent on a better understanding of the information that echoes provide.

The experimental evidence indicates that bats depend on sound echoes for their orientation. Further questions arise: (1) What is the nature of the echo? (2) What is the resolution capacity of the bat's sound analysis? (3) How is echo analysis achieved? (4) How does the bat avoid confusing the emitted signal and the returning echo? (5) What use is made of non-aural information in the oriented movements of bats?

◆ *Sound Echoes.* Sound echoes are faint when compared with the intense emitted pulses. Because sound energy drops with the square of the distance traveled, the amount of energy returning as an echo will be a minor fraction of the emitted pulse. The detection range of obstacles and prey thus becomes a critical measurement. When an object is thrown into the air, the bat changes direction if the object is not directly to the front. Using this response as an index to object detection, photographic measurements of the response of free-flying big brown bats to 1-cm pebbles indicate a maximal response distance of about 2 meters. Griffin and Grinnell (1956) and Grinnell and Griffin (1958) recorded the pulse of a little brown bat and its position simultaneously as it approached a wire grid. The rise in rate of pulse emission when an object is detected was used to measure detection distance. The little brown bat makes this response to wires 1.07 mm in diameter at about 2 meters, the same distance that Griffin had determined for responses to marble-sized pebbles. Measurements such as these permit a calculation of the intensity of the reflected echo. The estimates are based on the laboratory determination of emitted pulse intensities measured directly in front of the bat.

The exceptionally large ears of *Plecotus* apparently permit the use of fainter emitted pulses (Griffin 1958). Thus, with a pulse intensity of 59 to 65 decibels 10 cm from the mouth, *Plecotus* is able to negotiate a wire barrier more effectively than can a *Myotis* that emits 100-decibel sounds at a comparable distance.

What kind of information can the bat derive from echoes? Certainly bats are able to discriminate targets. Webster (1963) tested the ability of little brown bats to distinguish a variety of targets. Preliminary tests suggested inability to distinguish a rubber disk from a mealworm (Webster 1963). Re-examination of the situation, however, revealed that the tendency of the bat to approach anything, including a tennis ball, had confused the results. Actually a hungry bat was quite capable of distinguishing the rubber disk from mealworms (Webster 1963). The rejection of objects by echolocating bats could be determined by sudden decrease of the pulse rate that ordinarily increases until prey interception. Analysis of the species of insects taken shows that bats are somehow selective in their choice of prey, although this choice may be made after capture. Certainly size discrimination is possible, for Griffin found differential responses to objects of various sizes tossed in front of a flying big brown bat.

Intensity differences at the two ears, a result of the sound shadow of the head, give important directional differences to man. The bat's hornlike ear may serve this end. But the bat responds to considerably more than the direction of objects. Distance is important, especially in making the final approach to prey and roosting places. The ability to move through a fairly complex maze such as the interior of a cave speaks well for the ability to localize larger objects. But features may be responded to as they are encountered, and the bat may at any time obtain only a limited 'sound picture' of the overall features of its environment. The intensity of echoes will give information about the distance of the reflecting object as well as its direction.

Measurement of cochlear microphonics suggests that bats detect frequencies as high as 100 kc/sec (Galambos 1942). Recording action potentials in the inferior colliculus, Grinnell (1963a) determined frequency-intensity 'audiograms' for the little brown bat and big-eared bat, *Plecotus townsendi* (Figure 13-2). Neural sensitivity to frequencies of up to 150 to 200 kc/sec for the little brown bat and 100 to 110 kc/sec for the big-eared bat was established. Although the little brown bat is most sensitive to frequencies near the lower limits of its cruising pulses, the big-eared bat has two areas of maximal sensitivity, one slightly below the fundamental of the emitted pulse, the other corresponding to the second harmonic at a much higher frequency. Recordings with microelectrodes of smaller populations of cells which comprise the audiograms of Figure 13-2 show individual cells or cell groups with unique frequency response properties. Minimal auditory thresholds are especially significant to an animal that must detect a faint echo microseconds after emitting an intense cry. At the sensitive frequency, responsiveness to variations in intensity begins at very low sound pressures. It rises sharply to a maximum with additional sound pressures, reaching a plateau for greater intensities. Further increase in sound pressures results in a decrease in responsiveness or in no response at all. Here are the makings of a system for differential filtering of the emitted pulse and its echo.

Time differences may be important in direction analysis. Unless an echo starts from a position equidistant from both ears, the wave train will arrive at one ear before the other. Time comparisons will be facilitated if the sound is short and has abrupt beginnings and endings, or well-defined intensity maxima. These are salient characteristics of vespertilionid pulses.

If time measurements are to provide location cues, extremely rapid recovery is necessary for sufficiently accurate time discrimination. Neuro-

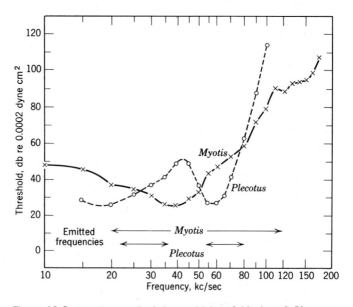

Figure 13-2 "Audiograms" of the sensitivity of *Myotis* and *Plecotus* to sounds of different frequencies. The range of emitted frequencies is also shown. After Grinnell 1963a.

physiological studies of the sensitivity of the colliculus of the little brown bat (Grinnell 1963b) show that this species is especially able to discriminate brief sounds. Recovery has already begun after 0.6 to 0.8 msec, and there is complete recovery or even supersensitivity after 1.0 to 1.5 msec.

The discussion of distance discrimination by an echolocating bat has been centered about two hypotheses. The time interval between the emitted pulse and its echo should provide sufficient information for distance discrimination (Hartridge 1945). If, in addition, the brief interval between the return to each ear can be resolved, directional information can also be perceived. Grinnell (1963b) again provides us with the neurophysiological background. He demonstrated several cellular response patterns that could permit accurate distance determinations based upon the direct detection of the echo. First, there is not the great problem of an echo following immediately after an intense cry; this will be discussed later. Second, populations of collicular nerve cells are specialized to respond to a second pulse which comes as soon as 0.6 msec after a preceding pulse. And finally, latency changes vary only slightly with intensity, which minimizes the problem of obtaining an accurate measurement of the temporal sequence of two signals of greatly differing intensities, i.e. the outgoing signal and the echo.

Several possibilities exist for directional localization of the source of sound echoes (Grinnell 1963c, Suga 1964a, b). The difference in phase of the echo at the two ears could provide directional information. But there is little support for such a suggestion from neurophysiological studies with bats. Direct time comparisons of arrival at the two ears is another possibility, but the short interval distance of 1.5 cm combined with what is known of the sensitivity of bats to sound intervals (Grinnell 1963b) seems to preclude such a mechanism. Bats are sensitive to brief time intervals, but angular discrimination remains a problem. The ability to make accurate angular discriminations, shown in behavioral studies (Griffin, Webster, and Michael 1960), has not yet been explained by physiological analysis. Instantaneous frequency comparisons of the signal received at the two ears could permit direction discrimination. But Grinnell (1963c), basing his opinion on neurophysiological evidence, thinks that the most compelling arguments favor direction determination by interaural intensity comparisons. He found different collicular sensitivity patterns related to the position of the stimulus. Since these threshold differences can be shown to be manifest before time comparisons could have been made, intensity comparisons are implicated.

◆ *Beat Theory of Bat Echo Analysis.* Pye (1960, 1961, 1963) and Kay (1962) have independently set forth related theories of echo analysis. They sug-

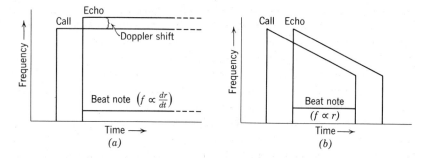

Figure 13-3 The beat note theory of bat echo analysis as applied to (*a*) rhinolophid echoes and pulses, (*b*) vespertilionids. The beat frequency *f* is directly proportional to the range *r* of the target in *b* and to relative velocities of bat and target *dr/dt* in *a*. After Pye 1961.

gest that what is important to the bat is not the echo itself but the interaction of the echo with emitted pulses. Consider a flying rhinolophid bat approaching the echo returning from objects in front of it (Figure 13-3*a*). The echo has a slightly higher frequency than the emitted pulse because of Doppler shift. Interaction between emitted and returning sound waves will produce beat notes of much lower frequency where they come into phase. The frequency of these beat notes is proportional to the relative velocity of the bat and the target, providing a possible basis for homing on the target. Responsiveness to low-frequency beat notes would have the potential advantage of minimizing masking by the much higher frequencies of the emitted sounds.

The vespertilionid bats, with a frequency-modulated pulse, could obtain distance information from beat notes originating in a different way. Here the beat frequency depends on the phase of the echo, which is a function of the distance of the target (Figure 13-3*b*). The frequency difference between call and echo, generating the beat note, decreases as the bat approaches the target. In the phyllostomid bats *Pteronotus* and *Chilonycteris,* with long pulses, there is evidence that the echo overlaps the pulse (Novick 1963, Novick and Vaisnys 1964, Novick 1965).

Pye suggests that the beat note hypothesis fits the observed facts for the rhinolophid type of echolocation. But there is some question about its potential applicability to the vespertilionids. The interpulse interval of the little brown bat is such that the returning echo of this vespertilionid either does not overlap the outgoing echo or, if it does, only for a fraction of a wave (Griffin, Webster, and Michael 1960). Other analyses of the little brown bat's pulses (Webster 1962) suggest that the bat is deliberately avoiding pulse overlap; as the echo return time shortens, pulses shorten and there appears to be no pulse overlap whatsoever. It is unlikely that the bat can derive useful information from overlap of only a part of a wavelength. Kay (1962) suggests that this difficulty could be overcome by supposing that the bat continuously hums the pulse to insure interaction with the echo.

Another objection to the beat note hypothesis is that jamming (Griffin, Webster, and Michael 1960, Griffin, McCue, and Grinnell 1963) has been effective only with high-frequency sounds. Yet if the beat note is what is detected by the bat, rather than the high-frequency emitted pulse, the lower frequencies should be more effective for jamming.

◆ *Resistance to Jamming.* Investigations of the ability of bats to avoid obstacles in the laboratory demonstrate a remarkable resistance to experimental attempts to jam their systems (Griffin, McCue, and Grinnell 1963, Grinnell 1963d). The evolutionary basis for this sensory capacity is the complex audio environment in which these night-flying creatures ply their trade. As Grinnell (1963d, p. 114) puts it,

Echolocating bats must not only hear and analyse echoes, or even a single echo following a louder emitted cry; in their native environment they must be able simultaneously to detect several objects at different distances, even in the presence of tens or hundreds of other bats. They show remarkable skill at discriminating the faint echo of an insect from the commonly louder background 'noise' of echoes from the ground, tree trunks or limbs, hazardously placed twigs, leaves, other insects, and perhaps rain-drops.

The first experiments with jamming sounds were performed by Spallanzani in 1794; he gathered together five redoubtable assistants who shouted as loud as they could and clapped hands. The ability of the bat seemed unimpaired (Dijkgraaf 1960). In the light of recent experiments this is no surprise.

One way to jam a bat is to present a large number of targets in an attempt to confuse it. Webster (1963) confused or intimidated a red bat, *Lasiurus borealis,* to the extent that it turned away from large clusters of mealworms tossed in the air. It turned away from a cluster of 25 mealworms but took one worm from a group of 15.

Tests of resistance to jamming with sounds have been made with bats flying through vertical wires. The probability of chance collision can be calculated (Figure 13-4, Griffin 1958, Griffin, McCue, and Grinnell 1963). As the bat flies at this grid of wires, two measures of the effectiveness of the jamming attempts are available: the number of collisions and the change in pulse rate of the bat's echolocating pulses as it approaches the line of wires. Little brown bats attempted to escape when jamming

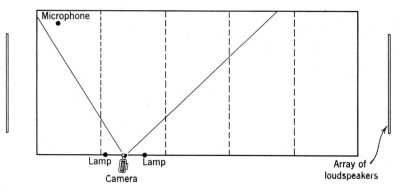

Figure 13-4   Experimental situation for testing the ability of bats to resist jamming by intense background noise. The obstacle planes, one meter apart, are marked by dotted lines. After Griffin, McCue, and Grinnell 1963.

sounds were directed directly at them. Yet when forced to fly through the wire grid, their performance did not suffer!

Another method of testing resistance to jamming was used by Griffin, Webster, and Michael (1960). Little brown bats, induced to hunt in a chamber flooded with large numbers of fruit flies, were subjected to intense noise at low (0.1 to 15 kc/sec) and high (20 to 100 kc/sec) frequencies. Most bats stopped hunting under both conditions, and no bats remained hunting during the high-frequency noise. In the low-frequency noise some bats persisted and continued to catch prey effectively. The reluctance of these bats to chase insects in the high-frequency noise has an equivocal interpretation. Since it is difficult to get bats to feed in flight in captivity in the first place, their failure to respond in the presence of any deterrent is not surprising. As Griffin et al. (1963) point out, an experimenter can force a bat to attempt to negotiate a grid but he cannot insist that it catch insects. *Plecotus,* which emits much fainter pulses, was also tested for resistance to jamming (Griffin, McCue, and Grinnell 1963). Subjected to noise and confronted with a wire grid (Figure 13-4), these bats intensified their calls and only lost their ability to avoid obstacles among the finest wires (Figure 13-5).

This species has a frequency-modulated pulse, dropping from 45 kc/sec to 25. If the frequency range of a masking sound is increased from 20 to 50 kc/sec up to 10 to 90 kc/sec, there is a drop in the ability to avoid wires. Evidently the harmonic of the fundamental plays a significant role in echo detection. A role for the second harmonic is also suggested by the auditory threshold which is essentially the same as that for the funda-

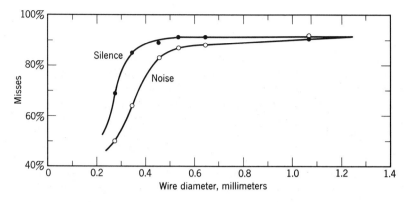

Figure 13-5 Average scores of four *Plecotus townsendii* flying through a wire maze in silence and in intense broad frequency noise. After Griffin 1958.

mental frequency. When the noise spectrum was expanded further to 120 kc/sec, no additional masking could be detected.

What is the effective signal-to-noise ratio that will mask an echo? Calculations provided the surprising answer that the echo signal energy was several decibels weaker than the ambient noise. Communications engineers have determined that an ideal detector will be effective 50 percent of the time if the signal is 10 decibels stronger than the noise. In the experiments the bat was 90 percent effective. The explanation for this apparent paradox may lie in the special directional sensitivity of bats to sounds.

In addition, the special temporal pattern of the pulse and, therefore, of the echo is likely to play a role in permitting the resolution of the proper signal in a noisy environment. It would be interesting to determine the effectiveness of patterned noise in echo masking. Griffin (1958), considering the observed frequency modulation of the pulse and referring to parallels in information theory, points out that a predictable and orderly pattern is essential to separate information from noise. The temporal pattern of pulse emission possesses this characteristic to a considerable degree. Detection of echoes of this pattern would be especially enhanced by some sort of neural template formulated in conjunction with the emitted train of pulses. We again have Grinnell (1963d) to thank for information about actual features of the nervous system that may do just this. In particular, the sensitization of populations of cells by the emitted pulse (Figure 13-6) furnishes the bat with the neural template suggested by Griffin.

This coding is short-term (5–10 msec) and takes the form of sensitization (by as much as 20 db) of a large population of cells to a sound of approximately the same frequency coming within that time. . . . Since the bat cries are swept in frequency, their entire range must be sensitized, while frequencies outside this range are not. Possibly the temporal relations of the sweep are important, too; i.e. cells might be facilitated to a given frequency only after others have responded to a slightly higher frequency a certain time before. Such a 'programmed' receiver could theoretically distinguish the correct (bat's own) frequency sweep from an 'unknown' one. To a degree, therefore, the bat's auditory receiver is 'programmed' after each pulse to respond most sensitively to a sound having the same characteristics as one which has just been heard, 1–10 msec earlier (Grinnell 1963d, p. 124).

These observations seem to explain why broadening the noise frequency spectrum into areas to which the bat can be shown to be sensitive (Galambos 1942, Grinnell 1963a) does not cause additional orientation problems (Griffin and Grinnell 1958).

The external ear is a highly directional receptor and may be oppor-

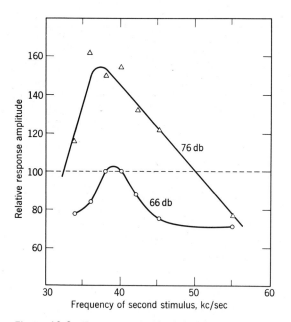

Figure 13-6 Frequency-specific facilitation is a possible coding mechanism in the auditory tract of *Myotis*. The first stimulus was at 38 kc/sec and 69 decibels. A louder second stimulus (76 decibels, upper curve) showed maximal sensitivity between 35 and 40 kc/sec. A weaker second stimulus (66 decibels, lower curve) is responded to only between 38 and 40 kc/sec. After Grinnell 1963d.

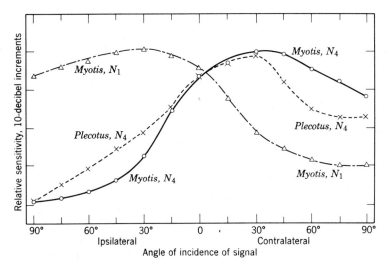

Figure 13-7 Average sensitivity of evoked collicular potentials as a function of the angle of incidence of a 40 kc/sec (or higher) pulse. After Grinnell 1963c.

tunely placed to mask the emitted pulse to a considerable degree. In addition, collicular recordings (Figure 13-7) demonstrate directional tuning of certain populations of receptors, the sensitivity changing according to the azimuth of the signal (Grinnell 1963c). Probably several of these mechanisms play contributing roles in masking the emitted pulse and in producing the remarkable ability to remain acoustically oriented in intense artificially induced thermal noise.

Neurophysiological mechanisms may also contribute to the lack of interference by the loud emitted pulse with the detection of the relatively faint echo. There is a relatively steep response curve from threshold of sensitivity to maximum response. At greater sound pressures responsiveness may decline or blank out, though these loud pulses may supersensitize the system to the next pulse (Grinnell 1963b). In addition, there is a sizable population of cochlear nerve fibers which may be sensitive only to faint sound pressures (Grinnell 1963a). If these cells were, in addition, sensitized by the outgoing and much louder sound, echo detection might actually be facilitated.

It has been suggested that the intra-aural reflex blanks the outgoing cry (Hartridge 1945). The intra-aural muscles are especially well developed and innervated in the bat (Henson 1961). The contraction of the stapedius muscle can damp incoming pulses at the cochlea to the extent of 20 decibels in *Tadarida*. The rate and phase of contraction are related to the pulse repetition rate. Contraction precedes pulse emission. Stapedius relaxation begins during the pulse, and it is complete during at least a part of the interpulse interval. Damping of the start of the pulse by stapedius contraction facilitates the monitoring of faint echoes a moment later. After the prey is located and during the approach phase, the stapedius remains continuously contracted (Henson 1964). At this stage circumstances apparently combine to produce a favorable signal-to-noise ratio which eliminates the need for relaxation of the stapedius damping mechanism (Novick 1965), thus permitting the use of more rapid pulses.

◆ *Fish-Catching Bats.* The blood-lapping habit of vampire bats is widely known, partly because man is sometimes a victim. But fish-eating bats are in some ways more spectacular. They include only four species, all vespertilionids, which seemingly differ from their insectivorous relatives mainly in the structure of the hindfeet. The toenails are enlarged and sharply curved to serve as gaffs. Only one species, *Noctilio leporinus,* has been studied extensively. Bloedel (1955) was successful in inducing captives to feed from a tray stocked with minnows. His observations and

Figure 13-8   A trained fish-eating bat, *Noctilio leporinus,* approaches a wire which marks a piece of fish. The bat learned to find the bait when it was marked with fine wires but did not learn to distinguish between the wires slanted in different directions as in this photograph. Courtesy Roderick A. Suthers.

photographs confirm the use of the gafflike claws in fish capture (Figure 13-8). As the claws strike the water surface the interfemoral membrane is raised, and if a fish is struck it is quickly shifted forward to the mouth.

How are fish detected beneath the water surface? Often the bats dropped their feet into the water briefly and at erratic intervals during flight. But sometimes Bloedel's captives dragged their feet through the water for considerable distances, perhaps trawling for prey at random. Bloedel's calculations on feeding efficiency show that random dipping may well be sufficient for satisfactory catch in nature. Surface disturbances do seem to attract these bats, however, and in the quiet lagoons and backwaters where they are prone to hunt, these cues could be quite important.

The problem was experimentally attacked by Suthers (1965) with captive fish-eating bats. Trained to trawl in a tub, these bats did not detect completely submerged pieces of fish or balloons. But when a 0.21-mm-diameter wire marked the location of food, the bats soon located the wire, taking the food 80 percent of the time when the wire protruded 5 mm above the surface and a significant number of times when only 1 mm of wire was exposed. Pieces of food were detected as long as they broke the surface, and hungry bats dipped at surface disturbances. Thus subsurface objects do not seem to be detected by fish-eating bats. Attempts to train these bats to distinguish between wires slanted in different directions failed. Complete darkness does not eliminate the ability to locate surface disturbances, ruling out the need for vision.

◆ *Evolution of Echolocation.* The role of sound intensities in the evolution of echolocation in the Megachiroptera, the flying foxes, has been investigated by Novick (1958). Of nine genera of these large-eyed bats investigated, only one, *Rousettus,* uses acoustic orientation. The others rely on vision. The choice of visual or auditory orientation for *Rousettus* depends on the circumstances. Pulses come from the corners of the closed mouth and are probably produced by tongue clicking. Novick (1958) argues convincingly that the development of echolocation is an original innovation for *Rousettus.* Its isolated occurrence in the group and the sizable eyes of related genera suggest that visual orientation was a starting point for all the Megachiroptera. With a history of echolocation in the group reduction in eye development would have been likely and a return to visual orientation would be improbable. Had echolocation been a part of the group's ancestry, its considerable advantage to a nocturnal group makes it unlikely that all vestiges would have been forsaken by descendants.

The number of bat species inhabiting a given region is often great, especially in tropical regions. Niche specialization and separation are at present poorly understood. Differences in niche structure may well be traced largely to behavioral adaptations that permit seemingly rather homogeneous food resources to be divided in many ways. The rhinolophids, for example, show a much more intense pulse than does *Myotis,* and the horn permits highly directional beaming of this intense pulse. Exploration off the main flight path, however, requires scanning movements of the head. Vespertilionids have less need for scanning. We might expect that certain insects will be caught more frequently by one method than by another. Comparative studies of three closely related species of phyllostomatid bats, *Pteronotus* (Novick 1963), *Chilonycteris parnellii* (Novick and Vaisnys 1964), and *Chilonycteris psilotis* (Novick 1965), reveal differences in their detection-range capabilities. *Chilonycteris parnellii* flies considerably faster than the other two species. Its pulse intensity and duration are greater. This is presumably why it detects fruit flies while more than 3 meters away, a greater range than the other species have.

We should not conclude our review of the echolocation mechanism in bats without pointing out the role of other sensory modalities in their orientation. At close distances and in a familiar environment a kinesthetic sense may be important. Griffin describes a revealing experiment with a big brown bat. A heavy screen was placed across a flight room where this bat was accustomed to fly. Simultaneous recordings indicated that this bat was emitting pulses when it started on the usual route. Yet it crashed into the screen two times in succession. Apparently it was relying on the kinesthetic sense and familiarity with the environment rather than the information derived from ultrasonic pulses.

Many species of bats are migratory, making journeys up to several hundred miles to habitats better suited for hibernation or feeding. The mechanisms for directional orientation of these journeys is a complete mystery today.

◆ *Responses of Insect Prey Species to Bat Sounds.* As in most instances in which continued predation pressures are operative, some prey species have developed countermeasures. Noctuid moths can detect and respond to sound pulses (Schaller and Timm 1950, Treat 1955). The echolocating cries of bats elicit discharge of the auditory nerve fibers in moths (Roeder and Treat 1961a, b, see page 406). At considerable distances from the bat the moth may simply turn and fly away from the source of the pulse. But at close range the response is bewilderingly complex, including power dives, passive falling, or erratic movement (Roeder 1962). To catch moths a bat must extrapolate a course that intercepts a ballistic track (Figure

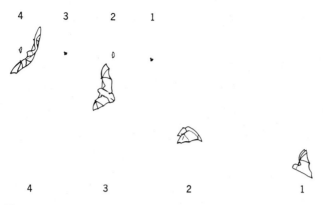

Figure 13-9   A free-flying wild red bat intersects the path of a moth. A bat may intercept a curved path as well. From photographs taken by Frederick A. Webster.

13-9). This erratic behavior must give the bat as much trouble in predicting the course as it gives us. Roeder and Treat (1961b) found that moths stoód a 40 percent greater chance of escape if they attempted evasive action when bats attacked than if they did not. Even the most intricate aerial maneuvers of bats (Figure 13-10) sometimes fail to capture insects.

In addition to overt escape some moths may be more active in their own defense. Certain arctiid moths produce ultrasonic sounds (Blest, Collett and Pye 1963). The ultrasonic pulses of the moth *Halisidonta* may be triggered by bat echolocation cries and are surely audible to hunting bats. Playback of recorded moth sounds will cause a bat to swerve away from a moth it is pursuing (Dunning and Roeder 1965). It would be surprising if moths could jam the echolocation system in view of the difficulty that experimenters have had in achieving this. A more likely possibility is that the moth is announcing identity. Sound production often seems to occur in moths which have chemical or other means of protection. For example, the moth *Halisidonta* has five spurs on the legs which may trouble the bat during capture.

◆ *Echolocation by Sea Animals.* The development of antisubmarine sound devices during World War II revealed that the depths of the sea are full of natural sounds (Schevill, Backus, and Hersey 1962). This environment is especially favorable for echolocation. Light levels fade sharply, and at great depths only biological light remains. Turbidity also contributes to light loss. Sound, however, is more effective in water than in air, attenuates less, and moves more rapidly.

A resting porpoise, at least under captive conditions, does not sleep. At intervals of 15 to 20 seconds it emits high-frequency pulses (Kellogg 1961). When a dead fish was quietly slipped into the water soon after one of these

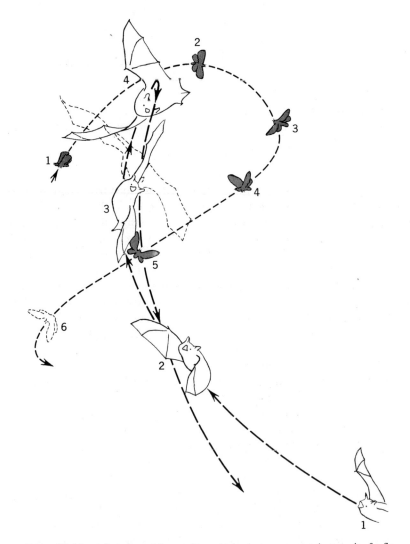

Figure 13-10 A little brown bat performs an intricate maneuver in pursuit of a flying moth. This diagram is drawn from multiple-exposure photographs that record simultaneously the position of predator and prey. From Webster 1963.

pulses, no apparent response appeared until *after* the next exploratory train of pulses. Then, as if the 'view' of the environment had been at this instant changed, the porpoise became alert and followed the exploratory pulse with a nearly continuous sound train. This continued during the approach and seizure of the fish. The fish was at the opposite end of a murky pool in which a brilliant disk was invisible to a man only a few centimeters away. Although the underwater vision of porpoises may be better than that of man, it is inconceivable that it could penetrate the distances at which objects can be detected.

Even when cruising in brilliantly clear water intermittent sound bursts persist, varying from one to six very short pulses. In other experiments Kellogg found that a trained porpoise effectively distinguished between two species of food fish and could select a preferred species on the basis of size.

The most conclusive evidence that sound echoes are the basis of this performance comes from another experiment performed by Kellogg with trained captive animals. A net barrier stretched across the pool had two sizable openings. When forced from one end of the pool to the other the porpoises quickly located openings in the net that could not have been visible to them (Figure 13-11). When one opening was covered with a sheet of clear plexiglass they were still 98 percent effective in avoiding the barrier and selecting the unobstructed opening (Kellogg 1961).

Porpoises have no vocal cords. Nevertheless, they are capable of producing high-frequency sounds, apparently by rapid movement of air from one nasal air sac to another through special valves. Thus there is no air

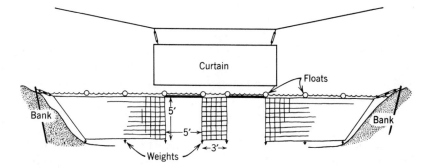

Figure 13-11   Experimental design in porpoise sonar experiments. A steel curtain with two openings is drawn across a pool, and the openings are blocked with a plastic curtain. In the critical experiments the curtain is raised and one opening is blocked with a sheet of clear plexiglass. After Kellogg 1961.

loss through the blowhole, even though they can make sounds by moving air past the flap of this orifice when they emerge from the water (Lawrence and Schevill 1954); in this case they emit a sound which has often been likened to a 'Bronx cheer.'

The porpoise can emit a frequency-modulated whistle starting at 7 kc/sec and ending around 15 kc/sec. More significant, however, are clicks of much shorter duration, with a spectrum ranging from 20 kc/sec up to more than 100 kc/sec. It is the echoes from clicks such as these that provide information about the location of objects. The higher frequencies have particular value in resolving the finer details of an object, but they attenuate rapidly with distance. Under such circumstances the lower frequencies are more useful until the range is reduced. There is no evidence that frequency structure can be modified at close range, but this possibility is worth pursuing further in new sonar studies both in porpoises and in sea lions (Poulter 1963).

WAVES ON THE WATER SURFACE

Whirligig beetles, *Gyrinus,* possess a unique active orientation system. They gather in traditional areas to swirl together at close quarters. Yet they avoid collisions with other individuals as long as they are moving. Animals at rest, however, may be crashed into, leading to the conclusion that the bow wave of other beetles is detected (de Wilde 1941). As the beetles whirl about on the water surface, the waves which spread out from them rebound from objects in contact with the water surface. The second antennal segment is remarkably modified for the detection of these returning wavelets. A set of fine brushes rests on the water surface. When the segment is trimmed away, denervated, or contacts only distilled water, the orientation fails. Surface tension thus seems to be a critical factor permitting the coupling of the antennae to the surface film (Eggers 1927). Even in darkness these beetles are able to guide themselves, and they avoid the walls of an aquarium as long as the normal antennal receptor system is intact.

Another example of response to disturbances of water surface occurs in the surface-dwelling fish, *Aplocheilus lineatus,* which uses surface waves to detect prey (Schwartz 1965). Modified lateral line organs (Figure 13-12) situated in shallow troughs on the top of the head are oriented in various directions. These localize the source of surface waves. Selective ablation of these several receptors reveals that cooperation of symmetrical receptors on each side of the head is necessary for direction orientation. The curvature of the wave front detected by the two forward groups apparently is the key to distance determination. This remarkable system undoubtedly had its beginnings in the sensitivity of the lateral line to displacement.

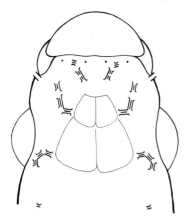

Figure 13-12   The surface-dwelling fish *Aplocheilus lineatus* has modified lateral line receptors on the top of its head which detect surface ripples made by potential prey. After a photograph in Schwartz 1965.

ELECTRICAL ORIENTATION

The great turbid river systems of Africa and South America are homes for two remarkably similar (Figure 13-13) but phyletically different families of fishes, the Mormyridae and Gymnotidae. In 1951 Lissmann began a series of investigations which revealed at least a partial explanation of why these groups are so similar in appearance. Consider the movements of an African mormyrid fish, *Gymnarchus*. It swims with equal facility backward or forward. Propulsion is largely by the undulatory movement of an elongate dorsal fin (Figure 13-13). When obstacles are encountered, fore or aft, they are avoided. Crevices are entered tail first.

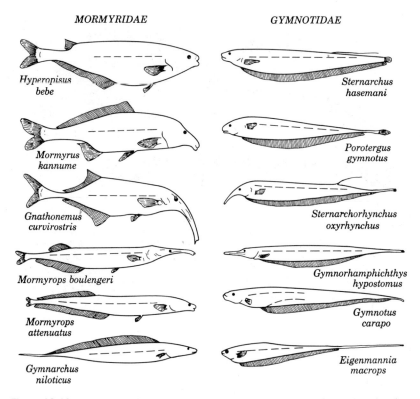

MORMYRIDAE   GYMNOTIDAE

Hyperopisus bebe

Sternarchus hasemani

Mormyrus kannume

Porotergus gymnotus

Gnathonemus curvirostris

Sternarchorhynchus oxyrhynchus

Mormyrops boulengeri

Gymnorhamphichthys hypostomus

Mormyrops attenuatus

Gymnotus carapo

Gymnarchus niloticus

Eigenmannia macrops

Figure 13-13   The Mormyrid fishes of Africa and the Gymnotids of South America show convergence not only in the development of electrical discharge but also in the reduction of tail fins, locomotion by undulatory movements of a long unpaired fin, and the development of long snouts. After Lissmann 1958.

Lissmann (1951) suggested that the unusual orientation ability of *Gymnarchus* might be based on the unique tail organ which was known to generate weak electrical pulses. He initiated experiments to test this hypothesis. When a piece of metal was placed in an aquarium with a *Gymnarchus*, the fish responded to it. When a rectangle of copper wire was placed around a small individual in a shallow vessel, it behaved as though trapped, backing away when it approached the wire. Pressed to escape, it finally crossed the wire on its side, as near the water surface as possible. A hidden magnet evoked a directed attack. One fish was led along the slate face of an aquarium with a magnet. Even the electrostatic charge of a plastic comb elicited a response.

A copper wire formed in a horseshoe induces a current flow when dipped just below the water surface. Such a weak current was immediately detected by *Gymnarchus,* for it showed vigorous responses when the circuit was closed. When the circuit was open there was no response unless the fish approached very close to the immersed tips.

The ability to respond to current was analyzed by conditioning to a food reward. A fixed magnet was mounted out of sight outside an aquarium so that it induced electrical currents in a fish swimming through the magnetic field. With this arrangement *Gymnotus carapo* readily learned to locate the current, at densities ranging up to 10^{-4} $\mu A/cm^2$. This is not the maximum calculated sensitivity of the mechanism, however. Current density could be reduced to 2×10^{-5} $\mu A/cm^2$, as calculated from the response distance to the horizontal movement of an electrostatic charge outside the aquarium.

All animals are sensitive to strong electric currents. Most often, however, the response is that of gross muscular contraction (Loukashkin and Grant 1954). Data gathered by various workers for several species of fish indicate responses only with currents many thousands of times as strong as the values effective in *Gymnotus.*

Using a similar conditioning technique and food reward, Lissmann (1958) was able to train *Gymnotus* and *Gymnarchus* to distinguish between conductors and nonconductors. These experiments were extended by Lissmann and Machin (1958) with the fish *Gymnarchus niloticus* required to distinguish various conductors inside closed porous pots (Figure 13-14). When these pots were well soaked in water they had little effect upon an electric field.

A pot filled with aquarium water was distinguished from a pot saturated and filled with paraffin, a distinction that persisted when either simultaneous or sequential comparisons were required. Distilled water was distinguished from aquarium water. But when an acid or salt electrolyte was added to the distilled water so that electric conductivity matched that of the water in the aquarium, the distinction could no longer be made. When distilled water was added to aquarium water, the diluted water could be distinguished when it contained only 25 percent distilled water, perhaps even as little as 12.5 percent! These experiments clearly indicate that electric conductivity is distinguished instead of chemical composition. When glass tubes were inserted into aquarium water contained in the pots, *Gymnarchus* distinguished between the pot with the glass

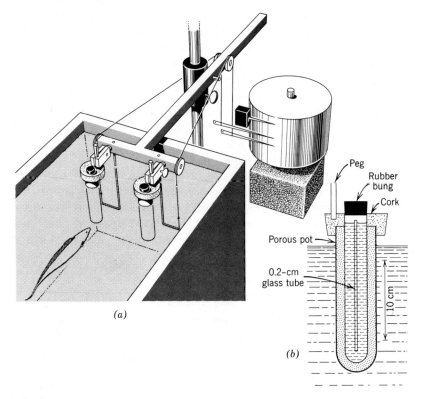

(a)

(b)

Peg
Rubber bung
Cork
Porous pot
0.2-cm glass tube
10 cm

Figure 13-14 Experimental arrangement for testing the ability of a fish to distinguish comparative conductivity of substances in identical closed pots. Inset shows a cross section of the porous test pots. After Lissmann and Machin 1958.

tube and that containing only water. A tube only 2 mm in diameter was detected in 203 out of 318 tests. The primary requirement, therefore, for an object to be detectable is that it be either more or less conductive than the surrounding water. Any object that meets this criterion and is at least 1 mm in diameter will distort the electric field surrounding the fish and hence can be detected (Lissmann 1963).

◆ *The Emitted Pulse.* In the predatory species, *Gymnarchus niloticus*, the characteristics of electric organ discharge vary with the individual and with temperature. Three specimens, 38, 42, and 52 cm long, produced voltages of 3, 7, and 4 volts respectively. The discharge frequency was unique to each individual. It averaged about 300 cycles/sec. At higher temperatures discharge frequencies usually increase. There is generally a resting level discharge which may rarely be 'turned off.' The emitted pulse is 1.3 msec in duration, the interval between pulses 2.3 msec.

Eigenmannia viridescens has a discharge rate of from 250 to 400 cycles/sec and, like the rate in *Gymnarchus,* it depends on temperature. But for each individual the discharge rate is remarkably constant, varying less than 0.2 percent (Hagiwara and Morita 1963). The discharge pattern of several gymnotid species is illustrated in Figure 13-15.

During discharge the tail, the site of the electric organ, becomes negative relative to the anterior end (Figure 13-16). Monitoring electrical activity in the lateral line nerve, Hagiwara et al. (1962) found discharges corresponding to pulses emitted from the electric organ. This nerve innervates mormyromasts, receptors that are located along the lateral line and concentrated at the head. The abundance of mormyromasts in electric fishes and the strong development of the cerebellum, with which they are connected, had earlier suggested to Lissmann (1958) that these might be the electric receptors. A conductor placed directly over one of these electroreceptors decreases the discharge rate, but the same conductor placed to the front or behind the receptor increases its discharge rate (Hagiwara et al. 1962). A dielectric in the same positions gives an opposite result.

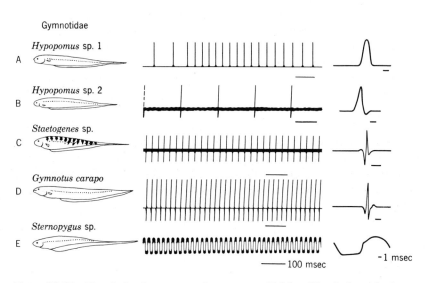

Figure 13-15   Electrical pulse patterns of some gymnotid fishes. The discharge in A was provoked. The remainder are from resting fishes. The column to the right shows pulse shape. After Hagiwara and Morita 1963.

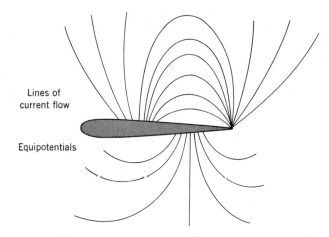

Lines of
current flow

Equipotentials

Figure 13-16 The electrical field of a weak electric fish. After Lissmann and Machin 1958.

◆ *Evolution of Electrical Systems in Fish.* The locomotion by undulations of fins so prominent in the teleost gymnotids and mormyrids is paralleled in the marine elasmobranch skates. These fin movements serve to keep the body axis straight, circumventing the lateral tail movements that would otherwise greatly distort the electric field. Detection of objects depends on electric field distortion. Rigidity of the poles is extremely important for accurate signal detection (Lissmann and Machin 1958). This necessity may explain the unique Gemminger's bones of the Mormyridae, which preserve symmetry along the longitudinal axis. In addition, they may strengthen the tail region, which has reduced musculature. Numerous additional morphological features of the Mormyridae and Gymnotidae are involved in the detection of electricity. These include changes in the epidermis, which may affect conductivity, and enormous enlargement of the cerebellum. Such modifications are of special interest when comparisons with elasmobranch electric fish are made. So far there is no behavioral evidence for perception of electric fields in this group. But the habit of feeding on clams raises doubts about the validity of earlier claims that these groups use electric organs only to stun prey.

Lissmann (1958) has suggested a possible route for the evolution of organs for perception of some electrical properties of the environment. This involves, first, the usurpation of the lateral line system which is sensitive to muscular action potentials. In deep water and muddy streams this sensitivity would have been advantageous. The muscular elements that generated current might then have developed into organs capable of more efficient electricity production. The ability to detect food objects would have been enhanced by the addition of more electric organs which can, in series, produce greater voltage. This greater voltage may in turn have been used by certain predatory forms to stun prey. The range of such a system would be further enhanced by increasing the distance between the poles, which has undoubtedly led to the unusual elongation of the body in these species (Figures 13-13, 13-15). Additional elongation may have placed additional importance upon stabilization of the body axis, leading to the distinctive mode of swimming that is so characteristic of these fish.

◆ *Social Significance of Electrical Discharges.* Among both weak and strong electric fishes casual observations suggest that the electrical discharge may have a social function. To date this aspect of the problem remains almost uninvestigated. Subsurface electrodes that emit the pulses of hand-held *Gymnarchus* or signals from a frequency generator are attacked when they are lowered into pools containing *Gymnarchus*. These attacks occur regardless of frequency. As Lissmann (1958) points out, these asocial fish must be less aggressive during the breeding season, if only briefly. It remains to be seen whether these signals permit individual and species recognition.

REFERENCES

Blest, A. D., T. S. Collett, and J. D. Pye. 1963. The generation of ultrasonic signals by a New World arctiid moth. *Proc. Roy. Soc. Lond., B,* **158**:196–207.

Bloedel, P. 1955. Hunting methods of fish-eating bats, particularly *Noctilio leporinus. J. Mammal.,* **36**:390–399.

Dijkgraaf, S. 1943. Over een merkwaardige functie van den gehoorzin bij vleermuizen. *Versl. Ned. Akad. Wetenschappen Afd. Natuurkunde,* **52**:622–627.

———. 1946. Die Sinneswelt der Fledermäuse. *Experientia,* **2**:438–448.

———. 1960. Spallanzani's unpublished experiments on the sensory basis of object perception in bats. *Isis,* **51**:9–20.

Dunning, D. C. and K. D. Roeder. 1965. Moth sounds and the insect-catching behavior of bats. *Science,* **147**:173–174.

Eggers, F. 1927. Nähere Mitteilungen über Johnstonsche Sinnesorgan und über das Ausweichvermögen der Taumelkäfer. *Zool. Anz.,* **71**:136–156.

Galambos, R. 1942. Cochlear potentials elicited from bats by supersonic sounds. *J. Acoust. Soc. Amer.,* **14**:41–49.

Griffin, D. R. 1958. *Listening in the Dark.* Yale University Press, New Haven.

———. 1962. Comparative studies of the orientation sounds of bats. *Symp. Zool. Soc. Lond.,* **7**:61–72.

————, D. C. Dunning, D. A. Cahlander, and F. A. Webster. 1962. Correlated orientation sounds and ear movements of horseshoe bats. *Nature* (London), **196**:1185–1186.

———— and R. Galambos. 1941. The sensory basis of obstacle avoidance by flying bats. *J. Exp. Zool.*, **86**:481–506.

———— and A. D. Grinnell. 1956. The sensitivity of echolocation in bats. *Anat. Rec.*, **125**:634.

———— and ————. 1958. The ability of bats to discriminate echoes from louder noise. *Science*, **128**:145–147.

————, J. J. G. McCue, and A. D. Grinnell. 1963. The resistance of bats to jamming. *J. Exp. Zool.*, **152**:229–250.

———— and A. Novick. 1955. Acoustic orientation of neotropical bats. *J. Exp. Zool.*, **130**:251–299.

————, F. A. Webster, and C. R. Michael. 1960. The echolocation of flying insects by bats. *Anim. Behav.*, **8**:141 154.

Grinnell, A. D. 1963a. The neurophysiology of audition in bats: intensity and frequency parameters. *J. Physiol.*, **167**:38–66.

————. 1963b. The neurophysiology of audition in bats: temporal parameters. *J. Physiol.*, **167**:67–96.

————. 1963c. The neurophysiology of audition in bats: directional localization and binaural interaction. *J. Physiol.*, **167**:97–113.

————. 1963d. The neurophysiology of audition in bats: resistance to interference. *J. Physiol.*, **167**:114–127.

———— and D. R. Griffin. 1958. The sensitivity of echolocation in bats. *Biol. Bull.*, **114**:10–22.

Grummon, R. A. and A. Novick. 1963. Obstacle avoidance in the bat, *Macrotus mexicanus*. *Physiol. Zool.*, **36**:361–369.

Hagiwara, S., K. Kusano, and K. Negishi. 1962. Physiological properties of electroreceptors of some gymnotids. *J. Neurophysiol.*, **25**:430–449.

———— and H. Morita. 1963. Coding mechanisms of electroreceptor fibers in some electric fish. *J. Neurophysiol.*, **26**:551–567.

Hartridge, H. 1920. The avoidance of objects by bats in their flight. *J. Physiol.*, **54**:54–57.

————. 1945. Acoustic control in the flight of bats. *Nature* (London), **156**:490–494.

Henson, O. W., Jr. 1961. Some morphological and functional aspects of certain structures of the middle ear in bats and insectivores. *Kans. Univ. Sci. Bull.*, **42**:151–255.

————. 1964. Echolocation and hearing in bats with special reference to the function of the middle ear muscles. Thesis, Yale University, New Haven.

Kay, L. 1962. A plausible explanation of the bat's echo-location acuity. *Anim. Behav.*, **10**:34–41.

Kellogg, W. N. 1961. *Porpoises and Sonar.* University of Chicago Press, Chicago.

Lawrence, B. and W. E. Schevill. 1954. *Tursiops* as an experimental subject. *J. Mammal.*, **35**:225–232.

Lissmann, H. W. 1951. Continuous electrical signals from the tail of a fish, *Gymnarchus niloticus*. *Nature* (London), **167**:201–202.

————. 1958. On the function and evolution of electric organs in fish. *J. Exp. Biol.*, **35**:156–191.

————. 1963. Electric location by fishes. *Sci. Amer.*, **208**(3):50–59.

———— and K. E. Machin. 1958. The mechanism of object location in *Gymnarchus niloticus* and similar fish. *J. Exp. Biol.*, **35**:451–486.

Loukashkin, A. S. and N. Grant. 1954. Further studies of the behavior of the Pacific sardine (*Sardinops caerulea*) in an electrical field. *Proc. Calif. Acad. Sci.*, **28**:323–337.

Möhres, F. P. 1953. Über die Ultraschallorientierung der Hufeisennasen (Chiroptera-Rhinolophinae). *Z. vergl. Physiol.*, **34**:547–588.

Novick, A. 1958a. Orientation in paleotropical bats II. Megachiroptera. *J. Exp. Zool.*, **137**:443–461.

———. 1958b. Orientation in paleotropical bats. I. Microchiroptera. *J. Exp. Zool.*, **138**:81–153.

———. 1963. Pulse duration in the echolocation of insects by the bat, *Pteronotus*. *Ergeb. Biol.*, **26**:21–26.

———. 1965. Echolocation of flying insects by the bat, *Chilonycteris psilotis*. *Biol Bull.*, **128**:297–314.

——— and J. R. Vaisnys. 1964. Echolocation of flying insects by the bat, *Chilonycteris parnellii*. *Biol. Bull.*, **127**:478–488.

Poulter, T. C. 1963. Sonar signals of the sea lion. *Science*, **139**:753–754.

Pye, J. D. 1960. A theory of echolocation by bats. *J. Laryng. Otol.*, **74**:718–729.

———. 1961. Echolocation by bats. *Endeavour*, **20**:101–111.

———. 1963. Mechanisms of echolocation. *Ergeb. Biol.*, **26**:12–20.

———, M. Flinn, and A. Pye. 1962. Correlated orientation sounds and ear movements of horseshoe bats. *Nature* (London), **196**:1186–1188.

Roeder, K. D. 1962. The behaviour of free flying moths in the presence of artificial ultrasonic pulses. *Anim. Behav.*, **10**:300–304.

——— and A. E. Treat. 1961a. The reception of bat cries by the tympanic organ of noctuid moths. In *Sensory Communication*, ed. by W. A. Rosenblith: 545–560. Massachusetts Institute of Technology Press, Cambridge.

——— and ———. 1961b. The detection and evasion of bats by moths. *Am. Scient.*, **49**(2):135–148.

Schaller, F. and C. Timm. 1950. Das Hörvermögen der Nachtschmetterlinge. *Z. vergl. Physiol.*, **32**:468–481.

Schevill, W. E., R. H. Backus, and J. B. Hersey. 1962. Sound production by marine animals. In *The Sea*, by M. N. Hill, Vol. I: 540–566. John Wiley and Sons, New York.

Schwartz, E. 1965. Bau und Funktzion der Seitenlinie des Streifenhechtlings (*Aplocheilus lineatus* Cuv. u. Val.). *Z. vergl. Physiol.*, **50**:55–87.

Spallanzini, L. 1932. Le Opere di Lazzaro Spallanzini. 5 Vols. Ulrico Hoepli, Milano.

Suga, N. 1964a. Recovery cycles and responses to frequency modulated tone pulses in auditory neurones of echo-locating bats. *J. Physiol.*, **175**:50–80.

———. 1964b. Single unit activity in cochlear nucleus and inferior colliculus of echo-locating bats. *J. Physiol.*, **172**:449–474.

Suthers, R. A. 1965. Acoustic orientation by fish-catching bats. *J. Exp. Zool.*, **158**:319–348.

Treat, A. E. 1955. The response to sound in certain Lepidoptera. *Ann. Ent. Soc. Amer.*, **48**:272–284.

Webster, F. A. 1962. Mobility without vision by living creatures other than man (with special reference to insectivorous bats). In *Proc. Mobility Res. Conf.* (New York), ed. by J. W. Linsner: 117–120. American Foundation for the Blind, New York.

———. 1963. Active energy radiating systems: the bat and ultrasonic principles II; acoustical control of airborne interceptions by bats. In *Proc. Internat. Cong. Technology and Blindness*, Vol. 1: 49–135. American Foundation for the Blind, New York.

Wilde, J. de. 1941. Contribution to the physiology of the Johnston organ and its part in the behaviour of the *Gyrinus*. *Arch. Néer. Physiol.*, **25**:381–400.

fourteen

ORIENTATION OF THE BODY

The force of gravity as a frame of reference • Structure and function of statocysts in Crustacea and other groups • The vertebrate labyrinth— are pressure or shearing forces involved? Headstander and tailstander fishes • Dorsal light reactions in vertebrates and invertebrates • Acceleration receptors • Gravity detection in insects.

A few organisms seem to move independently of the plane of gravity but for most it is a basic plane of reference. It is especially important to terrestrial organisms during locomotion. We find a diversity of mechanisms for detecting and maintaining position relative to gravity. The sensory equipment is by no means the same in different groups, but gravity translation devices all operate on the same principle. A free or attached particle or structure responds to gravity. This structure acts upon sensory cells by a shearing force or pressure, providing information for behavioral adjustment.

Some organisms make use of a completely different mechanism to tell up from down. In many environments light normally comes from the sun somewhere above the animal. The sun is used by a broad phyletic spectrum of species to orient to the vertical in so-called dorsal light reactions. There are other ways of identifying the gravitational plane, such as by reference to a horizon.

CRUSTACEAN STATOCYSTS

The gravity orientation responses of the Crustacea have been intensively studied. Many Crustacea have paired statocysts. These structures are

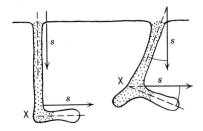

Figure 14-1 When a burrowing fiddler crab, *Uca pugilator,* is rotated 90° at point x, it resumes burrowing at the same angle with respect to gravity (*s*) that it was taking before the rotation. After Dembowski 1926 and Schöne 1961.

present only in the Decapoda and Syncarida, located at the bases of the antennules, and in the Mysidacea, located on the endopodite of the sixth abdominal appendage. Crustacean statocysts are hollow pits lined with sensory hairs. They contain statoliths, which for most decapods are sand grains and for mysids are calcareous (CaF_2) concretions. These statocysts are ectodermal in origin and their walls are molted regularly with the rest of the exoskeleton. Statocyst hairs and the statolith are also shed. The sensory hairs of the statocyst are of two types. Certain hairs respond to position; they actually touch the statolith. Another kind, thread hairs, are stimulated by movement of the statocyst fluid during angular acceleration. The floor of the statocyst is often tilted. In *Palaemon*, for example, it makes an angle of approximately 30 degrees with the horizontal.

The ensuing discussion is drawn mostly from experiments done with *Palaemonetes* and a few other crustaceans. But the basic pattern is apparently much the same in all statocyst-bearing Crustacea. The original demonstration of the role of crustacean statocysts in maintaining balance was made by Kreidl (1892). He took experimental advantage of the molt of the statocyst. The only replacement statoliths he provided were iron filings. These bits of iron were substituted by the experimental crayfish for the shed sand grains. When a magnetic field was applied the iron statoliths were attracted. The response of the crayfish was a change in body position that was the resultant of both magnetic and gravitational forces. Most earlier workers had emphasized the role of crustacean statocysts in hearing and had questioned their role in gravity detection. Therefore Kreidl's dramatic and conclusive experiments were of singular importance.

The role of statocysts in orienting crustacean body position has been demonstrated in many ways. Statocysts orient burrow digging in Crustacea. The isopod *Cyathura* cannot effectively dig burrows if the statocysts are removed (Langenbuch 1928). Orientation in directions other than the vertical may also be based on gravity. If a burrowing fiddler crab, *Uca pugilator,* is rotated 90 degrees (Figure 14-1), it resumes digging its hole with the same angular relationship to gravity as previously (Dembowski 1926).

◆ *Compensatory Eyestalk Movements.* The actions of Crustacea that have been exploited most frequently in measuring the effects of gravitational stimuli are the compensatory eyestalk and limb movements. They move in a direction opposite to bodily rotation. Thus an animal rotated along the longitudinal axis to the right moves its eyestalks to the left, and the legs on the left side are straightened and extended.

When statocyst hairs are deflected with a fine jet of water, the movements of the eyestalks are the same as the response of an intact animal to rotation about the longitudinal axis (Figure 14-2, Schöne 1951). The eyes must be covered or a blinded animal must be used in these experiments since the angle of incidence of light also contributes to the position of the body. If *Palaemonetes* is blinded and slowly rotated on the longitudinal axis, the maximum eyestalk deflection occurs at 90 degrees left or right. When the animal is upside down the eyestalks return to the normal horizontal resting position. But if one statocyst of this blinded *Palaemonetes*

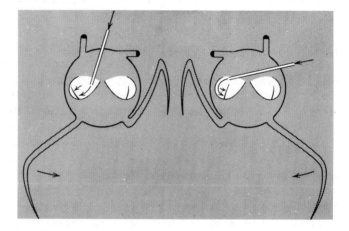

Figure 14-2 Compensatory eyestalk and limb movements of the crustacean *Astacus astacus* can be elicited by turning the body axis or, as in this illustration, by deflecting the statocyst hairs with a fine jet of water. The statolith has been removed. After Schöne 1951.

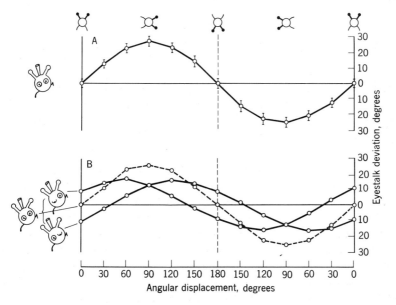

Figure 14-3 Compensatory eyestalk movements of a blinded shrimp, *Palaemonetes varians*, as it is rotated about the longitudinal axis. The sum of the responses of unilaterally statocystless individuals (dashed curve B) equals the performance of a normal animal (A, above). After Schöne 1954.

is removed, the maximum deflection takes place at 60 degrees inclination to that side or 120 degrees to the other (Figure 14-3). Because the floor of the statocyst is sloped 30 degrees in the resting position, these maxima coincide with the maximum inclination of the statolith with respect to the vertical. If the two response curves of Figure 14-3 are summed, they reproduce the response curve of the intact animal (Schöne 1951).

It therefore seems that in the intact animal each statocyst stimulates the animal to rotate on the longitudinal axis because of the inclination of the statocyst floor. In the normal dorsoventral position these stimuli are equal and opposite. But if the animal is rotated about the longitudinal axis, one statocyst provides a greater rotational stimulus than the other and recovery follows. With a pair of sloped statocysts the system is active in all positions.

The action of the statolith on its hair receptors is not the entire mechanism for position compensation. This can be demonstrated by removing one statocyst cup of a balanced animal after the statoliths have already been removed on both sides. Under these conditions balance is upset and the animal rotates continuously in the contralateral direction. Unlike the response to unilateral statolith ablation, however, the occurrence of rotation is independent of the animal's position in space. The animal continues to rotate toward the deficient side (Schöne 1951) until central compensatory mechanisms intervene. The animal acts as if positional information is being provided in the absence of statoliths. Like the information provided by the statolith, the information from each statocyst signals a turning movement equal to and opposite in sign from that signaled by the contralateral statocyst.

◆ *Central Compensation.* Statocyst hairs respond maximally to the greatest shearing force, that is, to the force exerted by the statolith parallel to the statocyst wall. Stimulation from both statocysts is treated vectorially by the central nervous system to produce the rotational response. When the statoliths are molted species that use sand grains as statoliths cannot replace them with exactly balanced statolith particles. So the animal initially experiences some imbalance. Before long, however, it resumes a normal horizontal position. Through other frames of reference, either tactile or visual, the imbalance is detected and compensated for.

The compensatory eyestalk movements correlated with unilateral statolith ablation are also fleeting. An animal deficient in one statolith (Figure 14-4, 2a) regains the ability to maintain normal posture (Figure 14-4, 2b). If the second statolith is now removed leaving only the statocyst hairs, the shrimp performs eyestalk movements in the opposite direction (Figure 14-4, 3a). Compensation for the original mutilation has produced a tendency to rotate equal to the rotating tendency from the intact side. The new ablation upsets the balance once more. This new balance is also compensated for in time (Figure 14-4, 3b). The same sequence of over-

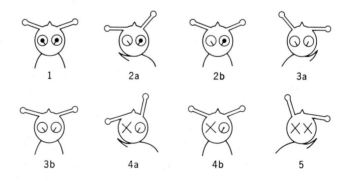

Figure 14-4   The removal of statoliths and whole statocysts results in compensatory movements (2a, 3a, 4a, 5), which are subsequently compensated for (2b, 3b, 4b). After Schöne 1954.

compensation followed by return to a normal posture results from the subsequent removal of the empty statocyst pockets (Figure 14-4, 4a, 4b, 5, Schöne 1954).

Another remarkable demonstration of the role of central compensation is made by placing a shrimp in a position with the dorsoventral axis vertical with respect to gravity. The shearing force of the statocyst is thus eliminated. In this situation an animal lacking either one or both statoliths shows no tendency to rotate. Nor does the intact animal rotate in this position. But if an animal such as 2b or 4b of Figure 14-4 is placed in this position, it rotates about the longitudinal axis, effectively demonstrating that the compensation mechanism is central and completely independent of spatial position. Here stimuli from the statolith play no role whatsoever!

◆ *Mechanisms of Statocyst Action.* Cohen's (1955, 1956, 1960) electrophysiological analysis of the statocyst of the lobster, *Homarus americanus,* confirms and elucidates the behavioral evidence. The nerve fibers innervating the hair receptors of the statocyst discharge when the lobster is in the normal resting position. When the statocyst fluid is drained the thread hairs flatten against the statocyst wall and the discharge frequency drops. In their normal fluid environment the resting thread hairs, uninfluenced by a shearing statolith force, remain erect regardless of position. The statolith hairs also discharge at a steady rate without adaptation.

When the lobster is rotated in the normal posture each individual statolith hair shows a bell-shaped response curve, with a maximum discharge rate at 90 degrees. If the rotation is performed with the animal upside down, a similar but slightly displaced curve is produced (Cohen 1955).

How can the position equidistant from the points of maximum response, the only unique point on the response curve, be determined by the animal? We know that such determinations are made by the animal without accessory cues because the compensatory reflexes persist in the absence of visual cues and a substrate. And since the response pattern of a single element provides ambiguous information, the animal must derive more information from other elements.

In the absence of the statolith the statolith hairs maintain a position deflected 40 degrees from the statocyst floor. Maximal discharge frequency is reached when this hair is lifted another 15 degrees. Further lifting toward the vertical results in a gradual decline in discharge frequency. In the intact animal, however, the irregular statolith will displace various individual statolith hairs by different amounts and in different directions. When Cohen deflected the intact statolith and recorded electrically from individual elements, he found different discharge frequencies. Because each statocyst is provided with 400 statolith hairs, each position produces unique patterns of statocyst discharge. The ambiguous information from a single element could thus conceivably be resolved by the central nervous system (Cohen 1960).

This interpretation implies an important role for the central nervous system, not only in unraveling the complex message from the 400 elements but also in setting the mechanism in the first place. No preset pattern of responsiveness is possible because the molting process makes properties of the statolith unpredictable. The central nervous system must first interpret the new pattern of stimulation in relation to other cues. Only then can the information from the statolith mechanism be interpreted in relation to a position defined by gravity.

There appear to be two different kinds of lobster statolith receptors. Type I receptors respond primarily to absolute position. The direction of rotation in approaching the position that induces them to respond does not influence the frequency of discharge. Type II receptors, however, discharge at rates that depend on the direction and rate of rotation in approaching their position of maximum discharge. This response pattern would seem to leave problems of interpretation since, unlike the response pattern of type I receptors, it does not include a way for position to be instantaneously distinguished. This ambiguity in positional information results from different rates of approach in any position. Thus at any position the type II receptors may discharge at different rates. The ambiguity cannot be resolved by relying on the adapted discharge level since it is not very different from the unadapted level. Furthermore, the adapted level is still based on the previous history, i.e. it represents a discharge rate that includes central compensation (Cohen 1955). The conclusion is therefore inescapable that the input message is interpreted continuously with respect to the temporal sequence of information provided to it by the receptor elements. Additional receptors are triggered by acceleration rather than absolute or relative position. Cohen (1955) cautions us not to be too rigid in applying the classification of type I and type II receptors. The type I receptors may also show discharge rate changes during rotation about the longitudinal axis.

The receptor elements of the crustacean statocyst respond to vibration as well as gravitation and acceleration stimuli. The same is true of the vertebrate otolith. Can these two quite different sources of stimulation be distinguished by the organism? Cohen (1960) suggests that they can, for the pattern of nervous activity that they generate is different.

◆ *Statocysts in Other Groups.* Statocysts are not a unique crustacean feature. They are a widespread gravity detection device, a group of similar receptor systems found from coelenterates to mammals. These organs have in common two basic elements which together provide the minimal components necessary for detection and response to gravity. One is a fluid-filled vessel, the other an inclusion with a specific gravity different from that of its surroundings. *Beroe,* a pelagic ctenophore, bases a rich repertoire of locomotory movements on a single apical statocyst. This radially symmetrical animal usually maintains a position with the longitudinal axis pointed upward. If it is tilted, righting is accomplished by the cessation of all movement except along one or two of its eight longitudinal cilia rows (Bauer 1910). Ctenophores are not restricted to a single orientation movement. Another ctenophore, *Pleurobranchia,* performs a complicated feeding maneuver involving a 360-degree turn through many positions (von Buddenbrock 1952).

The number of statocysts that an organism possesses is intimately related to its symmetry and manner of locomotion. The ctenophores which are, in terms of locomotion, radially symmetrical have a single apical statocyst. The radially symmetrical medusae of coelenterates have, by contrast, a ring of symmetrically arranged statocysts. When the medusa of *Cotylorhiza* is tilted from the vertical, the nerve net near the uppermost statocyst becomes excited, preventing complete relaxation of the neighboring muscles. The next stroke by the opposite muscles, which are completely relaxed, is stronger and soon brings the animal back to the vertical (Fraenkel 1925). Statocysts are required for the normal swimming pulsations of the contractile ring. Their ablation results in the termination of swimming movements in *Aurelia aurita* (Romanes 1885). The radially symmetrical sea cucumber, *Synapta,* possesses a ring of five statocysts (von Buddenbrock 1912). Starfish apparently rely on the shearing force of the body upon the tube feet; specialized structures for gravity detection have not been located (Kalmus 1929, Crozier 1935).

The vast majority of groups that depend on statocysts for orienting to gravity have paired statocysts. Paired statocysts are generally associated with bilateral symmetry, although the bilaterally symmetrical flatworms have a single statocyst. If a flatworm is cut in two, only the half that contains the statocyst continues to maintain a vertical gravitational response.

◆ *Gravity Responses of Protozoa.* The gravity responses of protozoa have not received recent attention. This is regrettable since earlier investigations relied completely on behavioral results to elucidate the mechanisms involved; the basis of coordination and the receptors are unknown. Penard (1917) described a row of statocyst-like structures in the ciliate *Lexodes* which may have been gravity receptors, but no evidence of their function was obtained. Paramecia in a test tube soon collect at the upper end and the response persists in an inverted U-shaped tube, effectively ruling out the surface as an orienting cue (Jennings 1906). The suggestion that position changes in paramecia are responses to stimulation of inclusions of varying densities (Lyon 1905) seems plausible. To test the hypothesis that inclusions have a statocyst-like action, Koehler (1922) fed paramecia iron powder and tested their response to a magnet. To eliminate passive transport by simple attraction of the iron and the paramecia along with it to the magnet, Koehler used a high concentration of carbon dioxide in the medium. In this situation most individuals reverse the negative gravity response. The paramecia should now be repelled by the magnet if the metallic inclusions have an effect on the receptor system, and this was indeed the result. Thus, although the vacuoles and inclusions of a *Paramecium* are not homologous to the statocysts of other groups, their method of operation may be analogous.

VERTEBRATE LABYRINTH

Morphologically the vertebrate labyrinth is divided into a pars superior, consisting of the semicircular canals and the utriculus, and a pars inferior, which includes the sacculus and lagena (Figure 14-5). The semicircular canals are primarily concerned with rotational acceleration

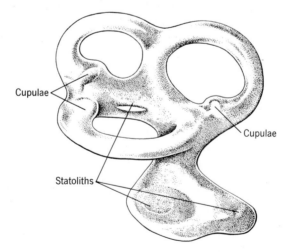

Figure 14-5 The labyrinth of a fish, showing the horizontal statoliths and the cupulae of the semicircular canals. After von Holst 1950a.

responses and the utriculus is a statocyst-like structure primarily involved in posture.

Cutting the nerves from the utriculi of a frog demonstrates a role for these elements in gravity and acceleration responses (McNally and Tait 1933, Tait and McNally 1934). Electrophysiological analyses of the frog confirmed the importance of the sacculus, but Ross (1936) also found that some gravity responses originate in the posterior labyrinth. The postural adjustments of the fins and eyes of most fishes seem unimpaired by ablation of the sacculus and lagena (Lowenstein 1957), but they fail when both utriculi are eliminated. This does not mean that sacculus and lagena play no role in the regulation of spatial position (MacNaughton and McNally 1946). Some righting responses persist with only the lagena intact (Schoen and von Holst 1950). Electrophysiological recordings from the sacculus show discharge patterns similar to those recorded from the utriculus (Lowenstein and Roberts 1950), though Lowenstein feels that information from the sacculus may be dispensable under natural conditions.

Like crustacean statocysts the otolith receptors of the elasmobranch skate, *Raja*, show a background discharge in all positions (Lowenstein and Sand 1940a, b). Against this background discharge there are receptors that show maximal activity in particular spatial positions. Still other receptor cells respond to position change regardless of direction. These 'out-of-position' receptors adapt to a base level rate of discharge regardless of the final resting position and show new discharge bursts with any change in position. Receptors in the horizontal semicircular canals discharge more rapidly during rotation about the vertical axis but are unaffected by rotation in the longitudinal axis (tilting to the left or right) and transverse axis (tilting forward or backward). These relationships and the responses of the vertical canal receptors are summarized in Figure 14-6.

The calcareous vertebrate otolith is part of a fairly rigid structure. Historically its mode of operation has been considered to depend on the pressure of the otolith on the macula (Quix 1925), or on the shearing action of the otolith on the sensory hairs (Magnus and de Kleijn 1926).

◆ *Shearing or Pressure Forces?* The question whether the shearing or pressure force of the otolith on the macular hairs is the effective physiological stimulus remained unanswered until von Holst (1950b) performed an ingenious series of experiments which were to yield an unequivocal answer. Von Holst chose familiar aquarium fish, the angel fish, *Pterophyllum*, and black tetra, *Gynocorymbus*, as experimental subjects because they are laterally compressed. This greatly facilitated measurement of the angle

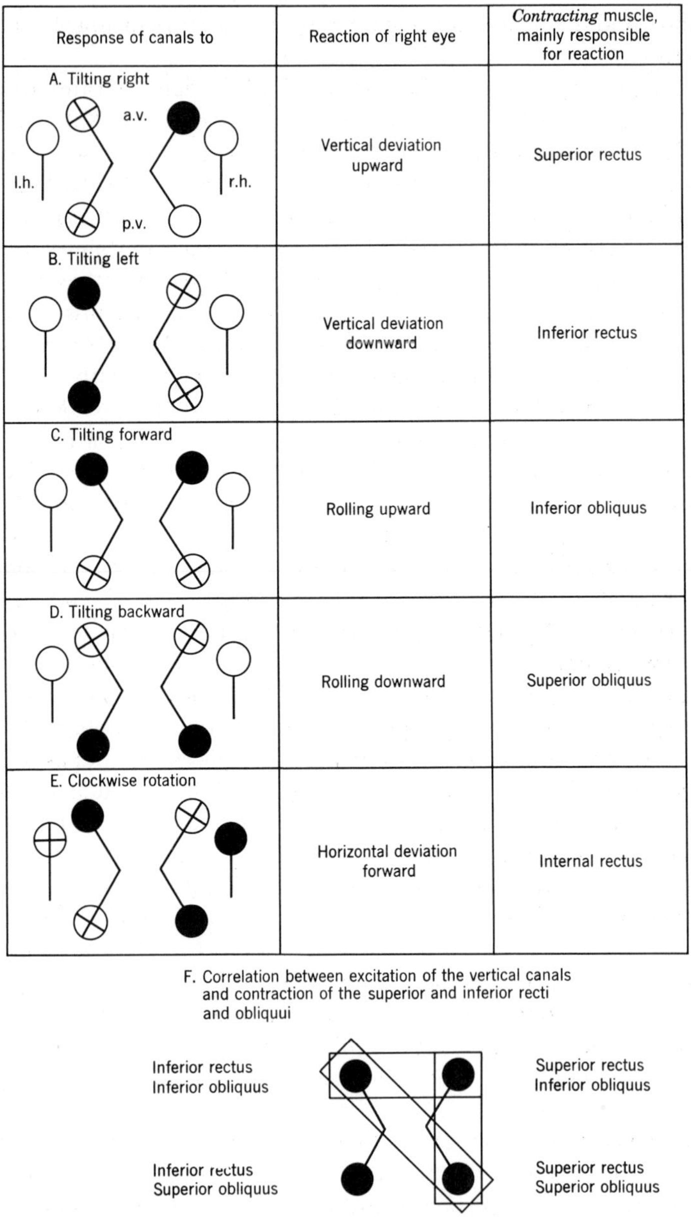

Response of canals to	Reaction of right eye	*Contracting* muscle, mainly responsible for reaction
A. Tilting right	Vertical deviation upward	Superior rectus
B. Tilting left	Vertical deviation downward	Inferior rectus
C. Tilting forward	Rolling upward	Inferior obliquus
D. Tilting backward	Rolling downward	Superior obliquus
E. Clockwise rotation	Horizontal deviation forward	Internal rectus

F. Correlation between excitation of the vertical canals and contraction of the superior and inferior recti and obliquui

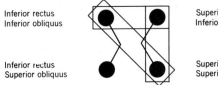

Inferior rectus
Inferior obliquus

Superior rectus
Inferior obliquus

Inferior rectus
Superior obliquus

Superior rectus
Superior obliquus

Figure 14-6 Responses of the semicircular canal receptors of the dogfish, *Scyllium canicula*, to angular displacement in different planes. Compensatory eye movements and their musculature correlates are also indicated. Excited ●, inhibited ⊕, unaffected ○, anterior vertical canals a.v., posterior vertical canals p.v., left horizontal canal l.h., right horizontal canal r.h. After Löwenstein and Sand 1940b.

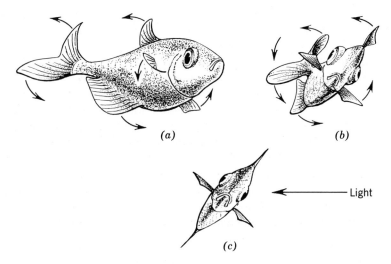

(a)   *(b)*

←——————— Light

(c)

Figure 14-7   A fish tilted about the longitudinal axis makes fin movements represented by arrows in (*a*) and (*b*) which will bring it back to the vertical position. These movements disappear when light is presented from the side (*c*). Now the tilted posture is the position of equilibrium. Note that the eyes are also compensating for the tilt in (*b*) but not in (*c*). After von Holst 1950a.

the fish assumed with respect to gravity. In these fish the otolith lies in the horizontal plane with respect to gravity (Figure 14-7).

The experimental plan was to increase the weight of the otolith by placing the fish and its aquarium in a centrifuge. This would increase both the shearing force and pressure upon the otolith, but not equally. To make meaningful measurements it was important to take into account the role of light.

These fish use an auxiliary positioning mechanism which relies on the incident angle of light. When the statoliths are intact the fish assumes an equilibrium position based on the light stimulus and gravity (Figure 14-7, van Holst 1950a).

The experiments were performed with light of constant intensity. The same incident angle of light was maintained throughout the experiments. The orientation of the fish to the vertical (Figure 14-8, angle α) is based on the light and gravity components. When the weight of the statolith is doubled, will the pressure or the shearing force be compensated for? The new position the fish took (Figures 14-8, 14-9) shows clearly that it is the shearing force which the statocyst mechanism measures.

➤ *Headstanders and Tailstanders.* Some species of fish have resting postures in which the head is held considerably below the tail (headstanders) or the tail is held below the head (tailstanders). Braemer and Braemer (1958a, b) have considered the role of the labyrinth in maintaining these postures. Their experiments were performed in a remarkable centrifuge which housed the experimental apparatus and the experimenter! Instead of maintaining light at a constant angle, diffuse light was used so that there would be no positional response to it. The penguin fish (*Thayeria*), a tailstander, does not change posture with an increase in gravity (Figure 14-10). This result suggests that the shearing force of the utricular statolith does not change with increased gravitational forces. This could hold true only if the statolith were horizontal in the normal tailstanding posture. Anatomical analysis confirmed that this is indeed the case.

Another tailstander, the pencil fish, *Poecilobrycon,* decreases the angle of inclination as the centrifuge is rotated more rapidly. This suggests that, unlike the statolith in the penguin fish, the statolith in the pencil fish is

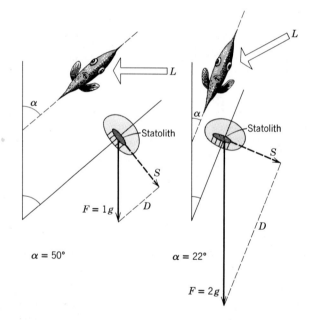

Figure 14-8   Experiments to decide whether pressure or shearing force is used by fish to detect gravity. The incident angle of light *L* is maintained constant while normal gravity, 1 *g,* is increased to 2 *g* in a centrifuge. When this is done the angle α that the fish maintains relative to gravity shows that the shearing force *S* is held constant even though pressure *D* may increase. It is thus the shearing force in the utriculus that contributes to the postural response of fish. After von Holst 1950b.

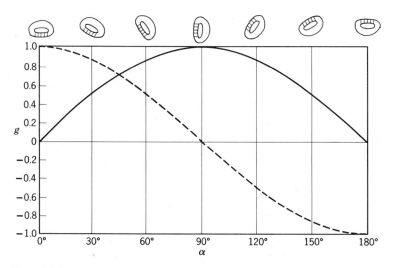

Figure 14-9 In a fish with a horizontal statolith the pressure of the statolith upon the sensory hairs (dotted curve) is greatest in the normal and inverted positions. The shearing component (solid curve) is least but changes most rapidly near the normal position. The abscissa is the position of the dorsoventral axis of the fish with respect to gravity. After von Holst 1950b.

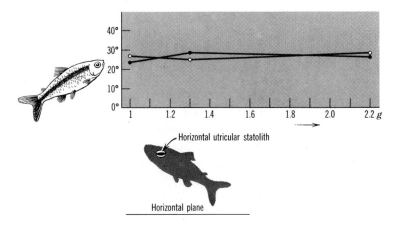

Figure 14-10 The angle of inclination of a tailstander fish, *Thayeria boehlkei*, is uninfluenced by gravity changes induced by centrifuging. The presence of a horizontal statolith in the normal resting position, together with the failure of the fish to respond to gravity changes by changing position, confirms the role of the shearing force rather than pressure as the effective stimulus. After Braemer and Braemer 1958a.

not horizontal in the normal resting posture, which ranges from over 70 degrees in young fish to about 45 degrees in mature specimens. Anatomical analysis again confirmed the prediction, with the actual statolith position lying nearly parallel with the long axis of the fish.

But in *Chilodus*, the only headstander studied, the interpretations based on actual statolith position and postural responses to gravity were not in full agreement. The Braemers suggested that the discrepancy may be caused by partial contributions of the lagena and sacculus statoliths to gravity orientation in this species.

DORSAL LIGHT REACTIONS

The experiments with shrimp and fish we have discussed were all made under carefully controlled lighting conditions. In von Holst's (1950b) experiments with fish the angular direction of incoming light was held constant (Figure 14-8). Braemer and Braemer (1958a, b) relied on diffuse lighting to negate the influence of directional light. In experiments with Crustacea the eyes are covered or removed or the light is kept at a constant angle. Otherwise the contribution of the statocyst to position responses cannot be evaluated.

Animals frequently use light in maintaining orientation to the vertical by ensuring that it falls upon the dorsal surface—the dorsal light reaction. The full effect is clear only when the statocysts have been removed. In this condition some fish respond solely to light and can be induced to swim in any position relative to the gravitational field.

◆ *Dorsal Light Reactions of Crustacea.* Many Crustacea exhibit dorsal light responses. For example, the brine shrimp, *Artemia,* usually swims with the dorsal surface toward light (Suffert 1932). The orientation may be abruptly changed by experimentally reversing the direction of incident light. When this is done the response depends on the state of the animal. If it is in a photopositive phase it will somersault backward when the lighting is reversed. If it is photonegative the correcting movement is a forward somersault, and if the light reaction status is indifferent the correction is a rolling movement.

When the statocysts of the shrimp *Palaemon* are removed, it makes no attempt to orient to gravity. Light alone serves as a positioning cue; the animal turns so that the dorsal surface is perpendicular to the plane of incident light. But when an animal without statocysts is placed on a horizontal surface and light is presented from the side, it turns about the

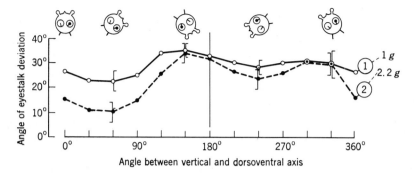

Figure 14-11 The angular eyestalk deviation caused by light varies according to the angular position of the shrimp, *Palaemonetes varians*, about its longitudinal axis. The tests were made with one eye covered and one statolith removed. When the weight of the remaining statolith is increased in a centrifuge (curve 2), this difference is emphasized. After Schöne 1961.

longitudinal axis for only about 45 degrees. Additional proprioceptive information is apparently received from the legs.

The role of light in the position reflexes relative to statocyst responses was determined by Schöne (1961) for *Palaemonetes varians*. If one eye is covered and one statolith removed, it is possible to determine the amount of compensatory movement that may be assigned to the light. This varies according to the position of the animal. In the positions with the greatest shearing force the role of light decreases (Figure 14-11).

The dorsal light reaction may be the sole positioning mechanism in some species. The crustacean *Processa canaliculata,* for example, has no statocysts and depends solely on the direction of incident light to maintain position (von Buddenbrock 1913). In other animals the importance of the dorsal light reaction may vary with the phase of the life cycle or the action pattern being performed.

◆ *Dorsal Light Responses of Insects.* When dragonflies, *Anax imperator,* alight they position themselves so that the sun's rays are perpendicular to their backs (Mittelstaedt 1950). Inverted flight is not aerodynamically possible for dragonflies, and when light is presented from below the dragonfly spirals downward and crashes.

Insects such as caterpillars that depend on countershading for protection must rely solely on a dorsal light response, at least in the normal resting posture (see page 359). The caterpillar of the butterfly *Colias edusa* is countershaded and while in the larval stage maintains a position with the dorsal surface exposed to light. The pupa is countershaded exactly opposite, and when it pupates a position is taken with the dorsal surface away from light (Suffert 1932). In these special situations light responses are particularly important in positioning the animal.

The direction of incidence of light does not provide complete information about the vertical unless the season and time of day are taken into account. The sun is rarely directly overhead. When accurate orientation to the vertical is required, some additional mechanism to allow for changes in sun declination is needed. So far none has been found. The sun compass mechanism is, except possibly in fish, adapted to allowing for the apparent azimuthal changes of the sun rather than changes in declination.

◆ *Water Strider Orientation to the Vertical.* Certain water striders have a remarkable tendency to head south under certain conditions, using a sun compass reaction (page 545). When an adult water strider, *Velia currens,* is placed on a vertical surface, it shows a gravity response that is, on the average, time-compensated (Birukow 1960). Its cyclic properties are typical of circadian rhythms—if the light-dark cycle is reversed the orientation rhythm reverses. And if the animal is kept in constant light the rhythm fades, to be replaced by a persistent negative geotaxis (Birukow and Oberdorfer 1959). These findings point to the possibility of gravity orientation mechanisms that compensate for the sun's position.

The dorsal light reaction may play an important role in making responses based upon gravity detection via statocysts more effective. For example, there may be ambiguity in resolving positions that produce equal shearing forces. The shearing force on statoliths is equal at numerous positions. Although the graphs that show the discharge rate of statocyst nerve fibers show two equal points, it must be recalled that these results were obtained in an experimental situation in which rotation was deliberately confined to a single plane. In water all planes of rotation are possible, and the situations in which ambiguous information would be provided are increased. The addition of a dorsal light reflex would effectively eliminate this ambiguity. Finally, a mechanism based solely on statocysts may respond too slowly to permit orientation of rapid swimming movements. If position is determined precisely by means of the statocyst mechanism and subsequent responses are based on light, considerable additional effectiveness might be achieved.

◆ *Dorsal Light Reactions of Fish.* The role of light in the positioning behavior of fish (Figure 14-7) was first elucidated by von Holst (1935). Only by taking responses to light into account was he later able to demonstrate that the shearing force is the physiologically effective stimulus in orienting to gravity (von Holst 1950a).

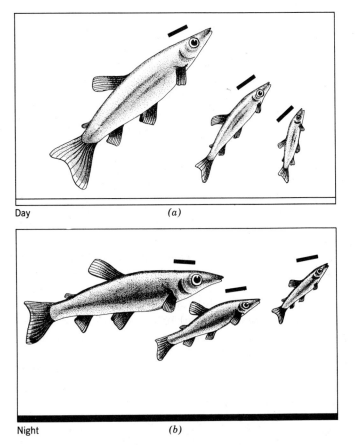

Day   (a)

Night   (b)

Figure 14-12   The position that the pencil fish, *Poecilobrycon eques* maintains with respect to gravity is with the statolith (*b*) nearly horizontal at
night and (*a*) tilted in light during the day. The position of the statolith
for each individual is indicated by the bar. Color changes accompany these
variations of posture. After Braemer and Braemer 1958a.

The receptor control of orientation varies to some extent with the state
of the fish. When a fish sleeps the labyrinth takes most responsibility for
maintaining position. The pencil fish, *Poecilobrycon*, rests near the surface
of the water at night with the utricular statolith nearly horizontal (Figure
14-12). During the day the position changes. This new posture is based
on light (Braemer and Braemer 1958a, b). An aroused fish depends more
on light. During active swimming and prey search there may be complete
control by vision. If the juice of food is added to water, the visual compo-

nent of these postural reflexes increases at the expense of the statocyst mechanism (von Holst 1950b).

Light plays a greater role in controlling the body position of fish after one utricular statolith has been removed (von Holst 1950b). When the force of gravity is doubled the attitude is the same as that of an intact fish in a normal gravitational field. Von Holst concluded from this finding that the contributions from the various sense organs used to detect the plane of gravity were added algebraically in the central nervous system.

Von Holst's concept of summation was further tested by Braemer and Braemer (1958a, b) in *Poecilobrycon* and *Chilodus*. They reasoned that in diffuse light the biased position which these headstander and tailstander fish took should increase following removal of one statolith. An increase in the angular deviation from the horizontal would increase the shearing force. If half of the sensory cells were destroyed, half of the afferent impulses would be eliminated. In a normal field of gravity an individual with one statolith would have to double the shearing force to reach an equilibrium equal to that of an intact individual. We should recall, however, that this would not involve a simple doubling of the angle of inclination. To double the angle of inclination is not to double the shearing force (Figure 14-8). The experimental results confirmed the importance of all sensory cells in maintaining an equilibrium posture (Figure 14-13). Nonetheless, the hypothetical expectation was not fully realized (Braemer and Braemer 1958a, b). The results suggest either that there is not simple summation or that the theory is correct but the experiment did not elimi-

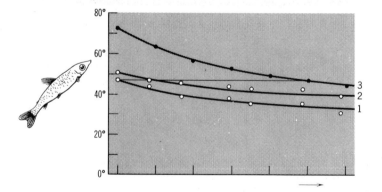

Figure 14-13   The angle of inclination of a tailstander fish, *Poecilobrycon*, as a function of the weight of the statolith. The posture of individuals which are intact (curve 1) or have one statolith removed (curve 2) are not in full agreement with the predicted experimental results (curve 3). For details see text. After Braemer and Braemer 1958a.

nate all positional information other than the statocysts. The deviation seems best interpreted for now by suggesting partial roles for other receptors, labyrinthine or otherwise.

ACCELERATION RECEPTORS

Most organisms are incapable of distinguishing acceleration from gravity. Responsiveness to angular and linear acceleration is closely related to gravity detection by statocysts. Vertebrates, however, and probably cephalopods as well (Young 1960), possess specialized organs for the detection of acceleration. As visual cues can substitute for gravity perception to some extent, so they can also give information about acceleration. But in some habitats, particularly aquatic ones, there are no such cues. The most elaborate acceleration detectors exist in aquatic groups, the fish and cephalopods.

➤ *Angular Acceleration.* The statolith hairs of crustaceans may not provide information enabling a crustacean to distinguish angular acceleration from gravity. In the statocyst organ, however, there are several distinct types of receptor elements which may allow for the resolution of these forces. Although statolith hairs are largely concerned with position reflexes, other statocyst hairs are unaffected by the shearing force of the statolith and are instead deflected by movements of the statocyst fluid.

The compensatory movement of the eyestalks is an effective measure of the response to acceleration (Dijkgraaf 1956). When a statocyst-bearing crustacean is rotated horizontally about the dorso-ventral axis, the eyestalk movement opposes the direction of rotation. After acceleration ends and a constant angular velocity is assumed, the eyestalks slowly return to the starting position. If the experimental turntable is braked sharply during acceleration or deceleration, rapid nystagmus movements similar to those of vertebrates appear. This is further evidence that, as in the semicircular canals of vertebrates, fluid movements are responsible (Cohen and Dijkgraaf 1961).

These compensatory movements are abolished by eliminating the thread hairs but are unaffected by denervation of the statocyst hairs. If the thread hairs of only one statocyst are removed, the acceleration responses remain qualitatively the same but the magnitude of the compensating movements may be lessened. Unlike positioning behavior based on the statolith hairs, the acceleration response that remains after unilateral statocyst hair denervation or ablation is the same for either ipsilateral or contralateral rotation.

In addition to the statocyst and statolith hairs of crabs, free hook hairs may be involved in the perception of rotation. Like the thread hairs these units respond to movement of the surrounding fluid and return to the vertical position when fluid flow stops. Their deflection is not as pronounced as that of the thread hairs, and they return more rapidly to the vertical position. Thus by their physical characteristics these hairs may serve to inhibit or control the rotational responses that depend on the thread hairs (Cohen and Dijkgraaf 1961). The function of these hairs is still uncertain. The rotational responses of cephalopods appear to operate on a remarkably similar principle. Compensatory movements during angular acceleration in *Octopus vulgaris* are abolished by bilateral statocyst removal (Dijkgraaf 1961).

The responses of the statocyst receptors of crustaceans and the semicircular canal receptors of vertebrates show remarkable similarities. These include (1) the interaction of paired receptor organs, (2) a resting discharge of component elements, (3) responses of a population of elements based on the direction of rotation, (4) differentiation of the response characteristics of component elements into discrete populations, each responding to rotation only in certain planes, and (5) depression of response characteristics as the apparent basis of differentiation of rotation in opposite directions.

◆ *Linear Acceleration.* Linear acceleration apparently is not detected by most crustaceans. If it is, there is no evidence that the statocyst mechanism is involved. It comes as no surprise to find that the statocyst mechanism does not include responses to linear acceleration, because the statocyst walls are rigid and linear acceleration induces no fluid movement that could stimulate the thread hairs (Cohen 1960).

INSECT GRAVITY DETECTION SYSTEMS

◆ *Diversity of Mechanisms.* The gravity receptors of insects are remarkably diverse and differ from the statocyst mechanisms of most organisms. An inclusion with a specific gravity different from that of the surrounding medium acts on sensory cells. Several genera of aquatic bugs use an air bubble as their equivalent to the statolith (Rabe 1953). The bubble is lighter than the water medium so the force is upward. This air bubble remains trapped between the antennae and the head. The receptors are apparently at the articulation joint between the first and second antennal segments. Disorientation induced by removal of the air bubble is corrected by an angular light response. The cooperation of these two sources of information in adjusting posture is an additional similarity to the positioning of fish and Crustacea.

◆ *Position Resolution by Flying Insects.* Perception of the plane of gravity is of great importance in the social communication of the honeybee (page 550). The receptors that detect gravity while the bees walk on the vertical face of the comb are hair tufts between the head and thorax. The effective stimulus is movement of the head relative to the thorax. The normal pendulum-like movement of the head on its axis provides positional information that is unique to each position. The role of these receptors in the dance of honeybees has been demonstrated clearly— dancing is inhibited and the directional component is disoriented when these tufts are denervated (Lindauer and Nedel 1959). The gravity orientation of ants is also disrupted by deinnervation of the hair tufts (Markl 1965).

Similar hair tufts in the head articulation of the dragonfly are thought by Mittelstaedt (1950) to be acceleration rather than gravity sensors. Here the inertia of the head relative to the thorax as the wings thrust the body forward stimulates these receptors. Instead of relying on these organs for gravity detection, position seems to be based primarily on the dorsal light reaction (Mittelstaedt 1950).

Flies have solved the evolutionary problem of in-flight balance in a unique way. The solution is unique not only in the morphological units used but also in its underlying principle. The organs are halteres, extremely modified hindwings. At the base of the halteres are campaniform sensillae. The halteres vibrate in synchrony with the wings but they move only up and down. When the halteres are cut off, stable flight is eliminated. Removal of one haltere does not greatly disturb flight unless the fly is also blinded (Faust 1952). But the deficiency of a single haltere is no impediment to flight for a fly that can see. Again the cooperation of sight and a position sensor is implicated in normal behavior.

The rapidly moving haltere apparently acts as a gyroscope. Movements in the yawing plane, that is, about the longitudinal axis, deform the cuticle and produce shearing forces which are detected by the sensillae (Pringle 1948). There has been some argument about which forces the halteres most effectively detect (Chadwick 1953). The haltere mechanism has received relatively little attention in recent years. What forces does the haltere generate, and what is the neuromuscular coordination? Are the members of a haltere pair always synchronized with one another or do phase comparisons play some part?

SOME COMMON GROUND

◆ *Two-Component Systems Resolve Gravity.* If we assume animal-like life on other planets, we can make predictions about the nature of their gravity sensors. Our own animals show a remarkable series of independently evolved solutions to the problem of sensing and responding to the plane of gravity. For the most part these operate on the same principle. There is a heavy inclusion or body part that is attached to or works against sensory end organs. We have seen that this inclusion or organ may be a sand grain or calcareous statolith within a crustacean statocyst, a statolith that is an integral part of a vertebrate statocyst, an air bubble as in certain aquatic insects, or any one of a series of other solutions. Frequently information on position is obtained from the exoskeleton, from the shell of a snail (Crozier and Navez 1930) or the cuticle of an insect.

◆ *Shearing Forces Resolve Gravity.* The theoretical curve in Figure 13-9 shows that there is a maximal shearing force change with position change when the shearing force is near 30-degree statolith inclination. This is the resting position of the shrimp *Palaemonetes.* Slight deviation from a horizontal statolith position results in little pressure change but considerable change in shearing force. Shearing forces are the effective stimuli in all groups that have been investigated. A probable evolutionary sequence for the development of the statocyst organ might start from a free statolith that was an inclusion, stimulating undifferentiated sensory hairs. If it were free, the initial statolith stimulation would have occurred in the horizontal position. When the statolith became attached, specialization of statolith hairs was possible and the point of attachment could rotate to a position other than the horizontal, maximizing the shearing force.

◆ *The Role of Light.* Throughout the animal kingdom statocysts and dorsal light responses make interacting and supporting contributions in maintaining postural equilibrium. In some groups one or the other of these components becomes more dominant. The relative roles also vary according to the activity being performed.

The point to emphasize is that the natural behavior is for most species dependent on several sources of information detected by different receptors. When we experiment with these mechanisms we deliberately eliminate part of the information, as by covering an eye or removing a statolith. The difference in performance after the experimental treatment may then be assigned not to the sensory system that has been eliminated but to the interaction of that system with all other systems that are involved in the performance these receptors mediate.

REFERENCES

Bauer, V. 1910. Über die anscheind nervöse Regulierung der Flimmerbewegung bei den Rippengvallen. *Z. allg. Physiol.,* **10**:231–248.

Birukow, G. 1960. Innate types of chronometry in insect orientation. *Cold Spr. Harb. Symp. Quant. Biol.,* **25**:403–412.

———— and H. Oberdorfer. 1959. Schwerkraftorientierung beim Wasserläufer *Velia currens* F. (Heteroptera) am Tage und zur Nachtzeit. *Z. Tierpsychol.,* **16**:693–705.

Braemer, W. and H. Braemer. 1958a. Orientation of fish to gravity. *Limnol. Oceanogr.,* **3**:362–372.

———— and ————. 1958b. Zur Gleichgewichtsorientierung Schrägstehender Fische. *Z. vergl. Physiol.,* **40**:529–542.

Buddenbrock, W. von. 1912. Über die Funktion der Statozysten im Sande grabender Meerestiere (*Arenicola* und *Synapta*). *Biol. Zbl.,* **32**:564–585.

————. 1913. Über die Funktion der Statozysten im Sande grabender Meerestiere. *Zool. Jahrb., Abt. Allg. Zool. Physiol.,* **33**:441–482.

————. 1952. *Vergleichende Physiologie.* Band 1. Sinnesphysiologie. Birkhäuser, Basel.

Chadwick, L. E. 1953. The motion of the wings. In *Insect Physiology,* ed. by K. D. Roeder:577–614. John Wiley and Sons, New York.

Cohen, M. J. 1955. The function of receptors in the statocyst of the lobster *Homarus americanus. J. Physiol.,* **130**:9–34.

————. 1956. Sensory and motor relationships of a crustacean central ganglion. *Biol. Bull.,* **111**:318.

————. 1960. The response patterns of single receptors in the crustacean statocyst. *Proc. Roy. Soc. Lond., B,* **152**:30–49.

———— and S. Dijkgraaf. 1961. Mechanoreception. In *The Physiology of Crustacea,* ed. by T. H. Waterman, Vol. 2:65–108. The Academic Press, New York.

Crozier, W. J. 1935. The geotropic response in Asterina. *J. Gen. Physiol.,* **18**:729–737.

———— and A. E. Navez. 1930. The geotropic orientation of gastropods. *J. Gen. Psychol.,* **3**:3–37.

Dembowski, J. B. 1926. Notes on the behavior of the fiddler crab. *Biol. Bull.,* **50**:179–201.

Dijkgraaf, S. 1956. Kompensatorische Augenstieldrehungen und ihre Auslösung bei der Languste (*Palinurus vulgaris*). *Z. vergl. Physiol.,* **38**:491–520.

————. 1961. The statocyst of *Octopus vulgaris* as a rotation receptor. *Pubbl. Staz. Zool. Napoli,* **32**:64–87.

Faust, R. 1952. Untersuchungen zum Halterenproblem. *Zool. Jahrb., Abt. Allg. Zool. Physiol.,* **63**:325–366.

Fraenkel, G. 1925. Die statische Sinn der Medusen. *Z. vergl. Physiol.,* **2**:658–690.

Holst, E. von. 1935. Über den Lichtrückenreflex bei Fischen. *Pubbl. Staz. Zool. Napoli,* **15**:143–158.

————. 1950a. Die Arbeitsweise des Statolithenapparates bei Fischen. *Z. vergl. Physiol.,* **32**:60–120.

————. 1950b. Quantitative Messung von Stimmungen im Verhalten der Fische. *Symp. Soc. Exp. Biol.,* **4**:143–172.

Jennings, H. S. 1906. *Behavior of the Lower Organisms.* Columbia University Press, New York.

Kalmus, H. 1929. Versuche über die Bewegungen der Seesterne besonders von *Asterina gibbosa. Z. vergl. Physiol.,* **9**:703–733.

Koehler, W. 1922. Über die Geotaxis von *Paramaecium. Arch. Protistenk.,* **45**:1–94.

Kreidl, A. 1892. Weitere Beiträge zur Physiologie des Ohrlabyrinths, II. Versuche an Krebsen. *S. B. Akad. Wiss. Wien,* **102**:149–174.

Langenbuch, R. 1928. Über die Statocysten einiger Crustaceen. *Zool. Jb., Abt. Allg. Zool. Physiol.,* **44**:576–622.

Lindauer, M. and J. O. Nedel. 1959. Ein Schweresinnesorgan der Honigbiene. *Z. vergl. Physiol.,* **42**:334–364.

Lowenstein, O. 1957. The acoustico-lateralis system. In *The Physiology of Fishes,* ed. by M. E. Brown, Vol. 2:155–186. The Academic Press, New York.

——— and T. D. M. Roberts. 1950. The equilibrium function of the otolith organs of the thornback ray *(Raja clavata). J. Physiol.,* **110**:392–415.

——— and A. Sand. 1940a. The mechanism of the semicircular canal. A study of the responses of single-fibre preparations to angular accelerations and to rotation at constant speed. *Proc. Roy. Soc. Lond., B,* **129**:256–275.

——— and ———. 1940b. The individual and integrated activity of the semicircular canals of the elasmobranch labyrinth. *J. Physiol.,* **99**:89–101.

Lyon, E. P. 1905. On the theory of geotropism in Paramoecium. *Amer. J. Physiol.,* **14**:421–432.

McNally, W. J. and J. Tait. 1933. Some results of section of particular nerve branches to the ampullae of the four vertical semicircular canals of the frog. *Quart. J. Exp. Physiol.,* **23**:147–196.

MacNaughton, I. P. J. and W. J. McNally. 1946. Some experiments which indicate that the frog's lagena has an equilibrial function. *J. Laryng. Otol.,* **61**:204–214.

Magnus, R. and A. de Kleijn. 1926. Funktion des Bogengangs—und Otolithenapparats bei Säugern. *Handb. Norm. Pathol. Physiol.,* **11**:868–908.

Markl, H. 1965. Wie orientieren sich Ameisen nach der Schwerkraft? *Umschau,* 1965:185–188.

Mittelstaedt, H. 1950. Physiologie des Gleichgewichtssinnes bei fliegenden Libellen. *Z. vergl. Physiol.,* **32**:422–463.

Penard, E. 1917. Le genre *Loxodes. Rev. Suisse Zool.,* **25**:453–489.

Pringle, J. W. S. 1948. The gyroscopic mechanism of the halteres of Diptera. *Phil. Trans. Roy. Soc. Lond., B,* **233**:347–384.

Quix, F. H. 1925. The function of the vestibular organ and the clinical examination of the otolithic apparatus. *J. Laryng. Otol.,* **40**:425–443, 493–511.

Rabe, W. 1953. Beiträge zum Orientierungsproblem der Wasserwanzen. *Z. vergl. Physiol.,* **35**:300–325.

Romanes, G. J. 1885. *Jelly-fish, Star-fish, and Sea-urchins.* Kegan Paul, Trench, Trubner and Company, London.

Ross, D. A. 1936. Electrical studies on the frog's labyrinth. *J. Physiol.,* **86**:117–146.

Schoen, L. and E. von Holst. 1950. Das Zusammenspiel von Lagena und Utriculus bei der Lageorientierung der Knochenfische. *Z. vergl. Physiol.,* **32**:552–571.

Schöne, H. 1951. Die statische Gleichgewichtsorientierung dekapoder Crustaceen. *Verh. Dtsch. Zool. Ges.,* **16**:157–162.

———. 1954. Statozystenfunktion und statische Lageorientierung bei dekapoden Krebsen. *Z. vergl. Physiol.,* **36**:241–260.

———. 1961. Complex behavior. In *The Physiology of Crustacea,* ed. by T. H. Waterman, Vol. 2:465–520. The Academic Press, New York.

Suffert, F. 1932. Phanomene visueller Anpassung, I, II and III. *Z. Morph. Ökol. Tiere,* **26**:147–316.

Tait, J. and W. J. McNally. 1934. Some features of the action of the utricular maculae (and of the associated action of the semicircular canals) of the frog. *Phil. Trans. Roy. Soc. Lond., B,* **224**:241–286.

Young, J. Z. 1960. The statocysts of *Octopus vulgaris. Proc. Roy. Soc. Lond., B,* **152**:3–29.

fifteen

SPATIAL ORIENTATION

Random and systematic search • Kineses • Sun compass orientation in
bees, fish, and birds • The role of learning in its development • Use of
landmarks in orientation • Movement in a fixed direction • Orientation
to the moon • Observations on protozoa.

Animals rely on many cues to orient their movements. In earlier chapters
we have reviewed the spatial and temporal characteristics of the information provided by light, sound, and chemicals. In this and the next chapter
we shall explore some of the mechanisms used to orient locomotion within
the particular spatial world of each organism. Navigation will be considered separately in Chapter 16.

RANDOM AND SYSTEMATIC SEARCH

➤ *Random Search in Bird Homing.* Orientation by random or systematic
search has been proposed to explain the homing of birds, bats, and other
animals. Griffin and Hock (1949) explored this possibility by following
gannets, *Morus bassanus,* with a light airplane. These birds had been displaced inland from their ocean cliff nests. Their plotted trails (Figure
15-1) showed that they often covered vast distances in incorrect directions
relative to home. Random or methodical search is certainly a conservative explanation of homing and even migration to a new area (Wilkinson
1952), and it has much to recommend it in terms of simplicity and general
applicability. But as with many aspects of the behavior of animals, sim-

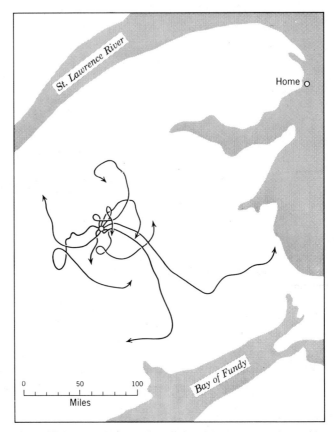

Figure 15-1   Courses followed by gannets, *Morus bassanus*, a large white seabird, taken from a nesting colony at the edge of the sea and released far inland in totally unfamiliar terrain. Their courses were followed by the experimenter from a light airplane overhead. After Griffin and Hock 1949.

plicity is not necessarily a good guide in predicting what sensory systems animals have evolved to orient locomotion in their environment. Nevertheless, the concept of a familiar area and some sort of organized search for it may have considerable applicability in attempts to explain the entire performance of homing and migrating animals. Systematic searching would imply that an animal methodically covers unfamiliar terrain, investigating new areas until it locates a familiar landmark- or goal-emitted cue. Once a cue from the goal or its vicinity is located, the systematic phase of the search, previously unguided by the goal, changes to a direct approach based upon new information (Figure 15-2).

Evidence of the existence of such search patterns is difficult to obtain,

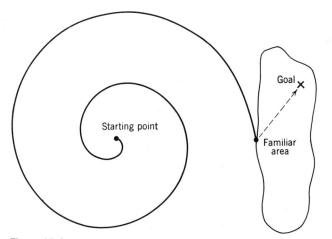

Figure 15-2   One of the search patterns suggested by Griffin (1955), based on the courses taken by birds released inland in Figure 15-1. When a bird reached a familiar zone it would reorient and fly directly to the goal. After Griffin 1955.

but the circuitous route taken by some animals in unfamiliar terrain favors such an interpretation. In another experiment pintail ducks, *Anas acuta,* were raised in a small enclosed pond and freed in the surrounding plains up to 90 miles away for their maiden free flight (Hamilton 1962a). The direction of most of these initial flights was extremely circuitous, but in spite of this a third of these birds actually returned to their natal cage and attempted to reenter it. A number of them also returned to the *release site* some time after they flew completely out of sight. Not withstanding their circuitous trail, they must have been learning about the terrain they traversed.

◆ *Kineses.* Many invertebrates respond to environmental conditions by movements proportional to the intensity of stimulation and independent of the spatial properties of the stimulus. These orientation movements have been called kineses. Let us consider, for example, the humidity kinesis of the wood louse, a small isopod living in the dampness beneath rocks, boards, and leaf litter. It cannot tolerate prolonged periods of dryness. In a chamber that provides a choice between moist and dry situations the lice soon gather in the more humid area. When they reach a moist area locomotion slows and some individuals may stop altogether (Gunn and Kennedy 1936, Edney 1954). Tests at different relative humidities show that more individuals are active at lower humidity levels. This combination leads to aggregation in the moist regions of the gradient, since activity in dry sections enhances the probability that animals will reach the moist area where reduction in rate of locomotion results in aggregation. A receptor for this form of orientation need only be capable of detecting variation in stimulus intensity.

The measurement used to detect variation in linear velocity by Gunn, Kennedy, and Pielou (1937) was the percent of the animals active at a given time and in given humidity conditions. Actual velocity was not measured. It remains uncertain, therefore, whether this kinesis is mediated through a change in actual velocity or a variation in the proportion of time during which the animal is actually moving.

The most frequently demonstrated kineses are controlled by light. Several flatworms characteristically found under rocks or in other dark places show kinetic responses at low light intensities. *Planaria gonocephala* crawls at an average rate of 57 mm/sec in total darkness. When a dim light is introduced the rate increases by 25 percent (Walter 1907). Another flatworm, *Plagiostomum,* raises its crawling rate 10 to 20 percent when the intensity of stimulation is changed from 7.5 to 1500 footcandles (Welsh 1933). Again, because actual measurements were indirect, we cannot be sure whether locomotion time or locomotion velocity was increased. In any event, the variable response to light leads to aggregation in dark places. Darkness then acts as a trap, slowing or stopping moving individuals.

The response of the ammocoete larva of the brook lamprey, *Lampetra planeri,* to light shows how important and effective kinetic responses to light may be in enabling even a vertebrate to select an environment. These larvae spend much of their time buried head downward in muddy streams or lake bottoms. When they are dug out and exposed to light they are continuously active, wriggling about with their heads pointed downward. The more intense the light the more active they become, at least after a certain threshold has been reached (Jones 1955). If a muddy substrate is provided, these downward-directed swimming movements become more active and the animal burrows. Burrowing persists until the very tip of the tail where the light receptor is located is no longer exposed to light. If the experimental aquarium is divided into lighted and darkened portions, the ammocoetes soon gather at the dark end. In the lighted area swimming is active and continuous, but when they pass to the darker end the movement is less vigorous and the animals usually become quiet unless disturbed. If by chance these low-intensity movements result in their return to the lighted area, the swimming movements again accelerate together with the rate of turning.

The *direction* of turning does not depend on the orientation of the light stimulus. If a larval ammocoete is placed in a narrow tube of flowing water and the light-sensitive part of the tail is lighted laterally by a focused beam, the initial movements of the head are equally likely to be away from or toward the direction of stimulation (Young 1935). The kinesis alone seems to be the mechanism for attaining the preferred degree of illumination.

Ullyott's (1936a, b) studies of *Dendrocoelum lacteum* show that, unlike planarians previously discussed, light intensity does not influence rate of movement. Yet in a gradient of diffuse light this species also aggregates in dark sectors. Ullyot found that a kinesis is involved, controlled not by the rate of locomotion but by the rate of turning.

In total darkness *Dendrocoelum* shows a basal rate of change of direction (RCD). Ullyott used the angle through which the animal turned as his measure of the RCD. Locomotion at increasing light intensities gave higher RCD values. If the animal is exposed to uniform diffuse light after being dark-adapted for some time, the RCD increases dramatically. But in time adaptation to the new condition weakens the response (Figure 15-3) to the base level RCD.

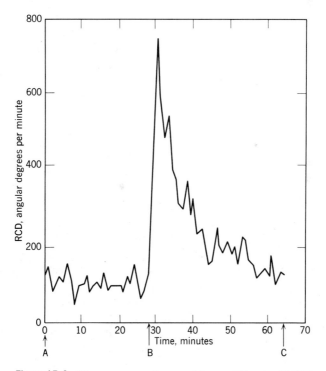

Figure 15-3 The average angular rate of change of direction (RCD) of fourteen planarians, *Dendrocoelum lacteum*, in darkness, A to B, and in light, B to C. After Ullyott 1936.

Adaptation thus suffices to lead the animal to the dark end of the gradient. Figure 15-4, taken from Ullyott's analysis of his results, suggests the mechanism. From A to B the intensity of incident light increases, resulting in an increased RCD. But in and around B adaptation will eventually lower the RCD to a basal level. If the animal turns toward the region of low light intensity, the lower basal RCD persists and the track to the region of lower light intensity B-C will be longer than A-B. When by chance the *Dendrocoelum* again turns toward the brighter end of the gradient (C to D), the RCD will once again increase, slowing the inappropriate progress (at D); adaptation will result, and the stage is again set for further progress down the gradient (D to E).

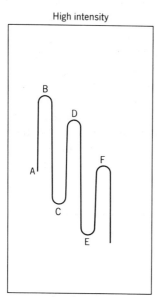

High intensity

Low intensity

Figure 15-4   Schematic diagram of an animal in an intensity gradient orienting by means of a kinesis. After Ullyott 1936.

Without adaptation, aggregation by variation of the RCD would not be possible. At any point in the light gradient the RCD would increase or decline, but there would be no overall direction to the movement. This can be demonstrated by making a very gentle gradient. On this gradient it takes longer for the animal to cross a given range of intensities. Adaptation occurs while the animal is crossing and the RCD returns to the basal rate. Therefore we do not expect *Dendrocoelum* to aggregate in the dark region of such a gradient. Ullyott found that they were still wandering throughout the length of such a light gradient after periods of over 10 hours. Without a basal RCD, adaptation is no longer an essential part of a kinesis. The animal will continue to approach the preferred environment as long as conditions improve.

The demonstration of a kinetic movement depends on the measurement of the track of moving animals. Ullyott's flatworms made slime trails on the glass substrate. With free-swimming animals such techniques are not feasible, and either photography or direct observation must be employed. Both of these methods are difficult at low light intensities, and it is thus not surprising to find that kineses have not been widely reported. Nevertheless, Jones (1955) believes that the ammocoete larva responds kinetically in a light gradient, and he reinterprets Hawes' (1945) analysis of the light responses of *Proteus,* a blind cave salamander, in the same way.

SUN COMPASS ORIENTATION

◆ *Sun Compass Orientation in Bees.* Two remarkable behavior patterns observed in a bird and an insect led to the discovery of the essential facts concerning sun compass orientation. Kramer (1949) found that captive starlings fluttered on a perch in the appropriate migratory direction. Von Frisch (1950) demonstrated communication of food direction in the honeybee.

The well-established ability of animals to determine a direction based on the sun and to maintain this direction by compensating for the cycle of solar directional change has been termed sun compass orientation. Where experimental evidence has been obtained the compensation has been found to be intimately related to the biological clock.

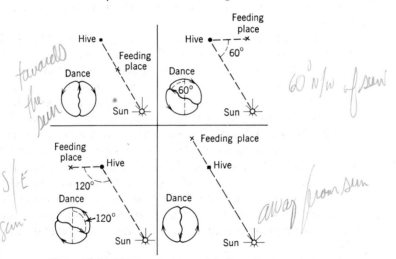

Figure 15-5 The waggle dance of the honeybee performed on the vertical face of combs inside the dark hive. The direction of the waggle run across the diameter of the circle conveys the direction of the food discovery. In the hive the direction is relative to the vertical, in flight relative to the sun. Thus a following bee must transpose the angle of the dance to the vertical to an angle relative to the sun when it sets out to locate the discovery that the scout has announced. After von Frisch 1953.

Von Frisch discovered that scout bees, having found a rich source of nectar, return with a full load of pollen or nectar to the hive to communicate accurately the location of their find. This they did by dancing in the dark hive on the vertical combs. The distances and directions of honey-water feeders were correlated with the dances of marked bees when they returned to the hive (Figure 15-5).

The angle between the waggle run and the vertical is determined by the position of the sun relative to the food. This angle changes during the day as the sun travels across the sky. Von Frisch and his co-workers demonstrated by observation and experimentation that bees can compensate for sun movement (1953). Lindauer (1961) studied the selection of new hive sites by swarming bees (Figure 15-6). He discovered that scout bees communicate the location of possible sites by the same dances that are used to announce food, except that they last much longer, sometimes several days. During the course of these persistent dances the relative direction of the sun changes and the orientation of the dance does so as well. Only when very few or no dissenting directional 'votes' are cast does the swarm move to the new hive site that they have agreed upon (Figure 15-6).

Persistent dances can also be induced by placing food inside the hives. When the scout bees dance under these circumstances they indicate the location of the most recent discovery outside the hive. Even if the sun and sky are not visible to them before they enter the darkened hive to dance, the waggle runs continue to indicate the correct direction of the previous site. Thus the orientation of the waggle run across the comb changes through the day, shifting counterclockwise relative to the vertical.

The bees' compensation for the sun's movement across the sky can be shown in another experiment. Foraging bees can be trapped at a food source away from the hive and imprisoned for several hours while the sun moves across the sky. When they are released in a similar field after having been displaced, they at once head in the compass direction of the hive in the original field, allowing for the displacement of the sun (Meder 1958).

Persistent dances by bees demonstrate the rhythmical nature of the sun compass. Bees that persist in dancing through the night continue to indicate the course which the sun would have taken had it been visible (Lindauer 1954). This is, of course, not functional in itself since the sun is never visible at night at the latitudes where these bees live. But it does serve to illustrate the persistence of the orientation rhythm. The sun compass mechanism is accurate at dawn because of a continuous process of adjustment (Lindauer 1957). The rhythmical nature of the sun compass in fish has also been emphasized (Schwassmann 1960, Braemer and Schwassmann 1963).

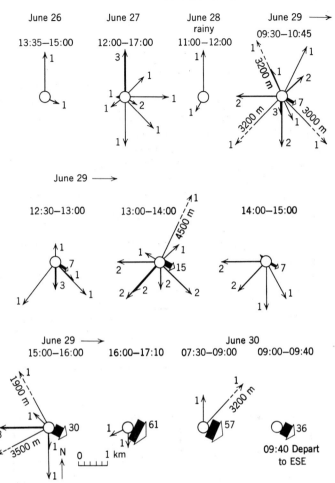

Figure 15-6 The dances of scout bees on a swarm indicating the location of new nest sites they have discovered. The direction and length of the arrows indicate the direction and distance of the sites; the numbers of dances in each direction are shown and are also represented by the width of the arrows. The final site agreed on was 350 meters southeast of the swarm. After Lindauer 1961.

A similar cyclic mechanism has been reported for the water strider, *Velia currens*, (Birukow 1956) and for the arthropod beach hopper, *Talitrus saltator* (Pardi and Papi 1952).

The relationship between the orientation of bee dances and the solar cycle has also been shown by translocation experiments (Renner 1960, see page 32) which demonstrate the interdependence of directional ability and the biological clock. Bees were trained on Long Island to go to food pots in a particular direction at a specific time of day. After the training was completed the hive was closed and transported overnight to Davis, California. Tests without a reward the following morning showed that the bees emerged almost exactly 24 hours after the training time. The direction of search had shifted, the amount of the shift reflecting the difference between the azimuth of the sun at Davis and that on Long Island (Figure 15-7). The training direction was not maintained relative to either true direction or the earth's magnetic field (Figure 15-7, theoretical curves 1 and 2). Nor was the course maintained with respect to the angle between the hive and sun at the training time (curve 3). The remaining alternatives are that the bees are actually able to compensate for the variable rate of apparent angular advance of the sun across the sky (curve 4), or that they are simply able to compensate for the average angular velocity of 15 degrees per hour (curve 5). The results demonstrated (curve 6) that the relationship between the orientation ability and the solar cycle is one of the latter alternatives, but the choice between them is not clear.

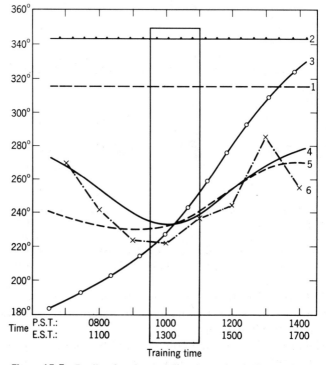

Figure 15-7 Predicted and actual directions taken by bees trained to a directional reward in New York and tested in California. After Renner 1959.

Distance communication in the bee dance is based on the energy expended in the *outward* flight to the nectar source (von Frisch 1948, Heran and Wanke 1952, Wenner 1962). If the bee encountered a head wind on the outgoing journey (von Frisch 1948, Wenner 1962) or was required to fly uphill (Heran and Wanke 1952), her dance indicated a greater distance than if she had been in still air or over level terrain. A bee can even be made to walk to a food source, and so may be induced to dance as though for a source of food at a considerable *flight* distance, even though it is actually only a few feet away (Bisetzky 1957). This explains why bees do not communicate about food discoveries the first time they return from them. The information for accurate communication is not available until the worker has made a direct flight to her discovery. By moving the feeding platform during the course of the experiment, Shaposhnikova (1958) was able to demonstrate that both distance and direction are based on the outward flight. This finding has been confirmed by Lindauer (1963) in another way. By requiring the bees to walk to a food source along a long gallery (Figure 15-8) the return flight distance can be manipulated; if the bee is freed after reaching the food reward rather than being required to crawl back along the gallery, it still communicates the distance of the outward journey (Lindauer 1963).

What features of the dance communicate distance? The tempo of the waggle run is correlated with the distance to the honey source (von Frisch and Jander 1957). But this parameter is in turn correlated with the time of each circling movement of the whole dance. In addition, during the straight part of the dance the bee makes a sound (Esch 1961, Wenner 1962, 1964). By attaching a magnet to the abdomen of a dancer, Esch was able to measure the electromotive force and thus the rate of waggling and compare it with the rate of sound production. Wenner

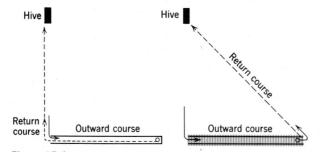

Figure 15-8   Experiment establishing the role of the energy expended in the outward flight as the basis of distance communication by the waggle dance of the honeybee. Whether the return course is long or short, dancing still indicates the same distance—that of the outward course. After Lindauer 1963.

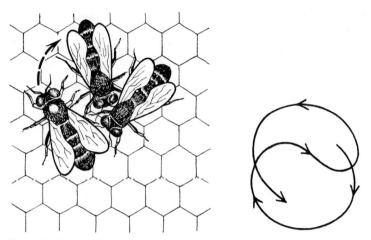

Figure 15-9   A worker honeybee performs a round dance on the vertical face of the hive comb. Her thorax has been marked with a dot of colored paint. The dance indicates that the food dish where she was marked is less than 85 meters away. The track of the dance, shown at the right, does not indicate the direction of the food source. After von Frisch 1953.

applied similar techniques, but he measured the waggle rate by placing a cellophane pane over the dancers. The pulse rate of the sound made is approximately 2.5 times as fast as the rate of waggling. Evaluation of these several parameters led Wenner (1962) to conclude that, of the mechanical features of the dance, the waggling time and the number of waggles produced during the straight run were most closely correlated with food source distance. But the pulse rate and duration of wing-produced sounds could also provide this information. The actual sensory modality involved in the transmission of information to the receptor bees is not known. Substrate vibrations may be as important as airborne sound waves. Steche's (1957) technique, using an artificial dancing bee with independently variable dance characteristics may provide the solution. Perhaps several parameters are responded to, insuring accurate directional information transfer.

At very short distances the method of signaling changes to a 'round' dance, and this particular pattern of dancing thus communicates distance (Figure 15-9). Species differences in distance communication have been investigated. The minimum distance communicated by a waggle dance varies from species to species and is closely correlated with their foraging habits (Figure 15-10). The slope of the dancing rate–distance curve also reflects the usual foraging range of each species. The dwarf bee, *Apis florea*, forages within 350 meters of the hive, and the slope of the dancing rate–distance curve is correspondingly steep. This permits more accurate

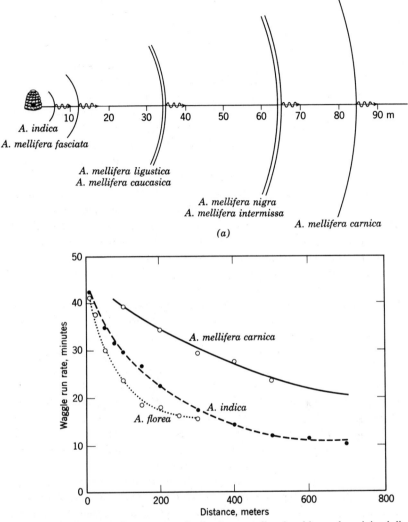

Figure 15-10 (*a*) Distance communication becomes directional beyond a minimal distance which varies according to the normal foraging range of the species. (*b*) The slope of the waggle dancing rate-distance curve is steeper for species that range closer to home in foraging flights. After Lindauer 1961.

distance communication at close range than is possible in the honeybee, *Apis mellifera*. The Indian bee, *Apis indica*, forages to 750 meters, and the change in rate of dancing with distance is less rapid than in the dwarf bee. Thus it sacrifices a certain amount of accuracy in communication at short ranges to extend the effective potential range of communication.

The honeybee, *Apis mellifera carnica,* shows the most gradual change of rate with distance, in agreement with its habit of foraging up to 2 km from the hive (Lindauer 1961).

Measurement of the horizontal direction of the sun is clearly basic to the communication of direction. What is known of the bees' capacity to detect the sun, make an angular measurement of its location, and relate this to gravity? The bee is able to persist in communicating direction of food even under complete overcast as a result of its keen sensitivity to ultraviolet light (von Frisch, Lindauer, and Schmeidler 1960). Bees can locate the sun when it is invisible to man. In addition, the bee can detect polarized light from blue sky and use this to determine the location of the sun, even though the sun itself is not visible (page 323). Complete overcast is often difficult to define operationally. In these experiments with bees it is used in the sense of complete cloud cover, but of course the ultraviolet wavelengths, effectively filtered by deep clouds, penetrate and are the basis of the orientation. Probably other controversial aspects of animal navigation can be clarified by establishing the actual energies, frequencies, and polarization planes of light that are available to the oriented or disoriented animal.

The ability of honeybees to make an angular determination of the sun's position was elucidated by taking advantage of the fact that in the tropics the sun passes directly overhead at certain seasons. Lindauer (1957) observed dancing bees during such an occasion. Normally the bees stopped dancing at local noon. However, Lindauer was able to induce dancing at this time by training bees to take a weak sugar solution in a particular direction. As noon approached he concentrated the solution. Now the bees were confronted with the dilemma of either ignoring this rich source or dancing. They chose to dance. Oriented dances persisted to within 19 minutes of local noon, when the sun was within 3 degrees of the zenith. When the sun did not pass directly overhead oriented dances persisted as long as the angle between the zenith and the sun was more than 2.5 degrees. This value agrees remarkably well with the ommatidial angle on the dorsal surface of the bee's compound eye, which is between 2 and 3 degrees.

One of the most remarkable features of the bee communication process is the transfer from the angle between the sun and the hive to the angle between vertical and the direction of waggle runs. What can we postulate as evolutionary antecedents of this remarkable transfer from sun orientation to gravity? Vowles (1954) approached this question by analyzing the orientation of ants. An ant running across a flat surface may base the direction of the run upon a light source. In the experiment the surface was quickly changed to the vertical as the light was turned out. Ants at once took up the orientation to gravity that they had had with respect to the light source. The starting point for this sensory transfer can be inferred from the identity of two elementary orientation mechanisms: a positive phototaxis, normally upward, which is often seen in disturbed arthropods including the honeybee, and a negative geotaxis, which is readily elicited from disturbed bees in the hive. Since a sun compass rhythm is well developed in many arthropods, it is not difficult to imagine the steps that might have led to the development of the bee dance. Birukow (1954) found essentially the same conversion process in the dung beetle, *Geotrupes silvaticus,* except that in this case a phototaxis is converted to a negative geotaxis.

Other possible antecedents of the bee dance have been discovered in arthropods. For example, blowflies, *Phormia regina,* perform what may be described as a crude dance after eating. The vigor and persistence of this dance are related to the distance that the fly has flown after eating (Dethier 1957). The moth *Automeris aurantiaca* performs rhythmical sway-ing movements following settling after any movement (Bastock and Blest 1958), and the number of oscillations is closely correlated with the dis-tance flown before settling (Blest 1958, 1959). Yet these moths have no social behavior with which these movements can be correlated.

◆ *Sun Compass Orientation in Starlings.* Kramer's original studies of the sun orientation mechanisms in starlings, *Sturnus vulgaris,* were made in a circular apparatus screened by a cylinder to limit the opportunity of the caged bird to see familiar landmarks. The measure of response was the heading of the bird while executing special fluttering movements that are characteristic only of individuals in migratory condition. Daytime fluttering movements during the migratory season were oriented in the migratory direction of this population. Accurate and seasonally appro-priate orientation was recorded in both the spring and autumnal migra-tory periods (Kramer 1949, 1950).

In a series of experiments Kramer demonstrated that (1) the birds oriented properly when the sun was visible, (2) the orientation failed under overcast, (3) clear blue skies without sun also eliminated the ori-ented response, (4) the response could be shifted by changing the apparent direction of the sun with mirrors, (5) magnetic fields did not upset the response, and (6) the orientation was maintained for periods of up to several hours (Kramer 1952). Hoffmann (1960) performed direction training experiments to clarify further the role of the sun in orientation. A starling was trained to seek a reward hidden in a food cup. The training was always at a particular time of day, and the food was always in the same true direction. Then unrewarded tests were made, both at the train-

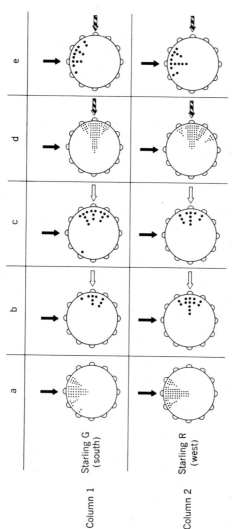

Figure 15-11 The sun-oriented directional choice of a trained starling is closely correlated with the phase of the sun or an artificially imposed light-dark cycle. In the circular diagrams each dot represents one unrewarded choice. In the upper five columns the solid inward arrows indicate the training direction. In the first two horizontal columns two birds (G and R) were trained to the south and west respectively (a). Then their light-dark schedule was delayed 6 hours and after 12 to 18 days they were tested (b). This new direction persisted even after 3 to 28 days of constant light (c). Then they were retrained during an artificial day (d), see the striped arrow, and again tested 8 to 17 days after they were returned to natural light (e). The shift of orientation after placing on an altered light-dark schedule is gradual (columns 3, 4, and 5). Here the light cycle is shifted 6 hours ahead. When starlings are held under constant conditions, the time of onset of activity shifts and with it the orientation of the trained choice (columns 6 through 8). After Hoffmann 1960.

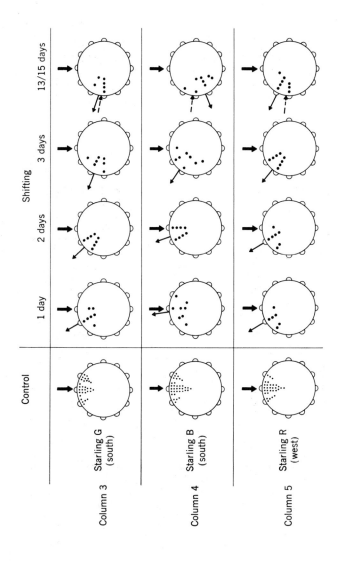

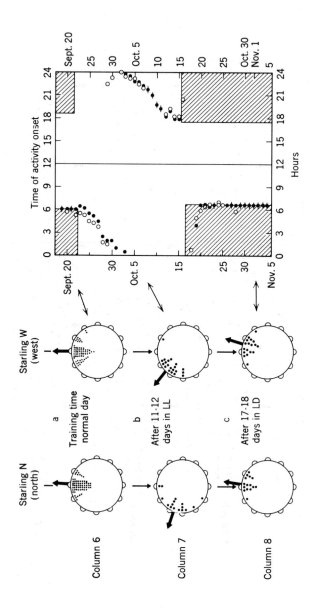

ing time and at other times of day, to evaluate the ability of the bird to allow for the apparent passage of the sun across the sky.

The role of an internal clock (page 35) in maintaining the orientation was easily demonstrated. When the trained bird was subjected to an altered light-dark schedule, inducing a shift in the phase of activity, there was a corresponding change in directional choice (Figure 15-11). In nature, of course, the clock is normally in phase with naturally recurring changes of night and day (Hoffmann 1960).

◆ *Sun Compass Orientation in Fish.* Like the beach amphipods of Italy and California (page 559), certain coastal fishes regularly range back and forth at right angles to the shoreline. Two such species, the parrot fishes *Scarus gaucamaia* and *S. coelestius,* range between offshore caves and feeding grounds near sandy tropical beaches. The orientation of these fish was tested by attaching small balloons to nylon cords which were hooked to the fish (Winn, Salmon, and Roberts 1964). When they were captured at their caves and displaced to unfamiliar shores, regardless of slope or hydrographical features, they headed southeast. Cloud cover, even a passing cumulus head, induced disorientation or stopped these escape runs. When the sky cleared the fish proceeded. These movements were interpreted as a response which normally would have led these fish back to their offshore caves, opposite the south coast of the island where they were captured. Additional experiments with other populations will be necessary to establish how and to what extent this orientation mechanism is adjusted to local conditions. Already there are indications that experience plays a role since young fish treated in the same way scattered.

The role of the sun was confirmed by shifting the light-dark schedule and testing orientation. The fish were held in large tanks and a 6-hour time shift was imposed. The shift resulted in an average deviation from south of 170 degrees. The controls remained unchanged. Thus the actual azimuthal change in the direction of the sun (165 degrees) rather than a simple 15 degrees per hour (90 degrees) seems to be the basis of the orientation mechanism of this species.

Similar experiments were carried out earlier with a lake species, the white bass (*Roccus chrysops*), which spawns in specific offshore areas of freshwater lakes. These fish possess a sun orientation mechanism (Hasler and Wisby 1958). Investigations were continued in the laboratory by Schwassmann (1960) and Braemer (1960). They found that the situation discovered by Kramer and Hoffmann for birds was in general applicable to fish. Oriented responses persisted only as long as a sun, real or artificial, was provided. Under overcast orientation failed.

The fish were trained to escape to a darkened crevice (Figure 15-12).

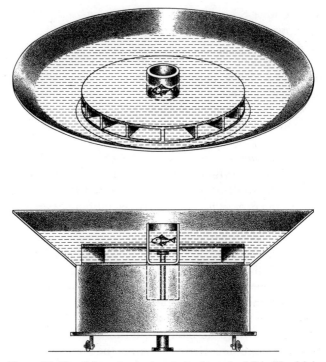

Figure 15-12   Orientation testing device for trained fish. The fish is
restrained in the center of an arena of shallow water. When the shield
is lowered the fish is free to select one of sixteen crevices at the end of
the platform as a hiding place. After Hasler and Schwassmann 1960.

They became directionally trained more readily than birds, and thus
provided an opportunity to test several features of the sun orientation
mechanism not dealt with in birds.

One of these is the matter of nocturnal orientation. Although night
orientation by the sun cannot occur outside polar regions, oriented responses could be obtained under laboratory conditions of continuous light.
Does the orientation rhythm unwind at night in fish as it does in the
honeybee? In the green sunfish, *Lepomis cyanellus,* a resetting of the rhythm
is accomplished by a reversal of the orientation angle relative to the sun
through the night (or period of continuous light), so that the setting is in
phase again by dawn (Schwassmann 1960). On the other hand, in a
tropical cichlid fish, *Cichlasoma facetum,* resetting is based on a continuation
of the change in the orientation angle through the night so that by dawn
the cycle has completed the 360-degree cycle without reversal (Braemer
1960). A functional explanation for this dichotomy is suggested by
Schwassmann (1960). He points out that in an equatorial species such as

a cichlid the amount of angular change of the sun which must be allowed for during daylight is half a sphere or approximately 180 degrees. It makes little difference whether the orientation rhythm which is the basis of the directional compensation operates by moving around to the starting point or resets by a reversal during the night. But an animal such as the green sunfish which has evolved in temperate regions must either greatly accelerate the rate of compensation through the night or retrace its pattern of compensation during the day at approximately the rate of the daytime compensation. This adjustment is necessary because the angle of horizontal movement of the sun through the day at these latitudes is considerably less than 180 degrees.

LEARNING AND COMPASS ORIENTATION

◆ *Bees Learn the Sun's Course.* When honeybees are moved to a new area the *local* features of the sun's path become the basis of the sun compass (Renner 1959, 1960, see page 545). How does this occur? In explaining this phenomenon Lindauer (1961) has exploited the special conditions that arise in crossing the equator. North of the equator the sun seems to move clockwise through the sky; to the south the apparent motion is counterclockwise. The honey dances of bees displaced from one region to the other remain confused for several weeks, perhaps for life. Only at the end of a generation span do appropriately oriented dances reappear. This finding seems to establish the fact that the local features of the sun's track are learned and that effects of the learning are not quickly extinguished. In one experiment bees were raised without the opportunity of seeing the sun. Then they were taken to an open field and directionally trained. When they were tested the following day at a new time and site, they failed to perform better than randomly in their search for the directional reward. An experienced group of foragers would have succeeded in this task. Evidently the single exposure to the sun during the one-hour training interval was not sufficient to permit the rapid development of the sun compass. In another experiment inexperienced bees were trained only in the afternoon. This training was continued for three afternoons, totaling about 300 flights per bee. When they were tested the following morning they indicated the reward direction incorrectly. Instead of communicating the proper direction they signaled a fixed angle with respect to the sun. This angle was appropriate for the afternoon training time. Finally, after five afternoons of experience, afternoon-trained bees began to signal correctly in the morning. Thus, although an appreciation of the movement of the sun's path across the sky can be shown to be

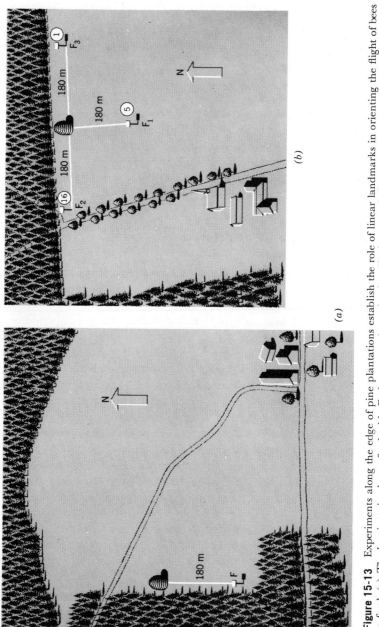

Figure 15-13 Experiments along the edge of pine plantations establish the role of linear landmarks in orienting the flight of bees to food. (a) The bee is trained to a food table F along a north-south edge, (b) then tested along an east-west edge. A few bees (5) fly away from the edge to maintain the southerly course, but most (16) fly along the edge to a food table. After Lindauer 1961.

learned by bees, this learning need not include the experience of even one complete cycle of the sun across the sky.

The situation is apparently much the same in the ant, *Formica rufa*. Only experienced individuals compensate appropriately for the local sun course. In the spring after hibernation this ability is lost. Jander (1957) suggests that these ants have forgotten the significant features of the sun and must relearn them.

There have been other observations of the failure of orientation mechanisms over winter. The wolf spider, *Arctosa*, scatters its sun compass orientation more widely in the spring than it did the previous fall before hibernation. The sun compass orientation of the beetle, *Padaerus rubrothoracicus*, disappears after hibernation (Jander 1957). Since there are numerous demonstrations of the failure of biological clocks when arthropods are cooled to near 0°C, it is perhaps not surprising that sun compass orientation should be disrupted by winter conditions.

◆ *Landmarks and Celestial Cues in Competition in Bee Orientation.* Experimental work with bees shows that cues other than the sun come into play in orientation. For example, von Frisch and Lindauer (1954) trained bees to a honey reward in a particular direction. In one experiment the training line was along the north-south edge of a pine plantation. Then the trained bees were tested the following day at the edge of a similar plantation. But this time the edge ran east-west. Most of the bees chose a westerly course; only a few left the edge to persist in a southerly course (Figure 15-13). When the experiment was repeated at a greater distance (210 meters) from the edge, the bees no longer relied on local landmarks but persisted in the training direction. In another experiment bees were trained near a large tree in an open field (Figure 15-14). The test, conducted this time near a small clump of trees, showed that the bees had not been directionally deceived. They persisted in the sun-based course. Additional experiments along streets and shorelines showed that landmarks have the most effect if they are linear and lead directly to the food.

◆ *'Setting' the Orientation Compass in Arthropods and Amphipods.* The role of learning in development of orientation of amphipods and spiders perpendicular to a local shoreline has been elucidated with a surprising result. In the case of *Talitrus saltator,* an amphipod, travel perpendicular to the shoreline brings them to a preferred zone on beaches above the pounding surf. The ability to orient to the beach is based on the sun or the polarization pattern of blue sky. When young animals were reared and tested in the laboratory away from the beach, their orientation directions did not differ from those of experienced individuals (Figure 15-15).

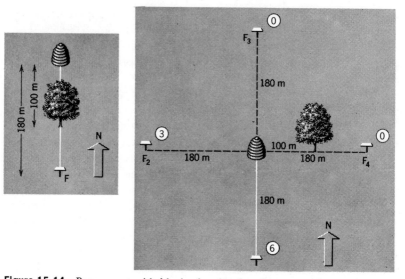

Figure 15-14   Bees are not misled by landmarks when they are not linear. Here bees were trained to fly south past a lone tree. When the hive was displaced and they were tested near a lone tree which this time was to the east, they usually chose the reward stand to the south. After Lindauer 1961.

The inexperienced individuals were more variable in their choice, however, suggesting that although the general orientation may be inherited each individual refines its ability as a result of experience (Pardi 1960).

The wolf spider, *Arctosa,* is another animal with a propensity to travel at right angles to shorelines, in this case the banks of freshwater streams. Like *Talitrus* the movement is guided by the sun. Where the creek edge is irregular or varies considerably with changing water levels, the orientation of the escape response is much more precise than along the straight banks of canals. Individual members of populations on small islets may orient in quite different directions (Tongiorgi 1962). Individuals living on opposite sides of the same stream have opposite directional tendencies.

Young wolf spiders were raised in the laboratory without exposure to a directional artificial shoreline. Yet they demonstrated a directional preference when first tested. However, this orientation did not conform with the typical escape direction of the population from which the parental stock was drawn (Papi and Tongiorgi 1963). Instead the movement was northward for all populations, and this tendency became increasingly prominent as these young spiders grew older. This northward orientation was altered by varying the light-dark cycle, demonstrating the role of a time-compensated sun orientation. Then these young spiders

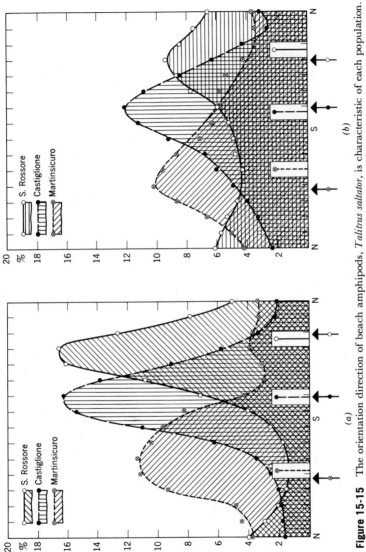

Figure 15-15 The orientation direction of beach amphipods, *Talitrus saltator*, is characteristic of each population. The frequency distribution of three populations with different theoretical lines of escape (TLE) is the same for (*a*) experienced and (*b*) inexperienced individuals from the same population, but the inexperienced individuals scatter more widely. After Pardi 1960.

were trained by hatching them in a laboratory aquarium provided with a 'shoreline' on one side and open water on the other. The northward tendency disappeared and they became oriented to the aquarium shoreline.

The female wolf spider carries her eggs in a cocoon attached to her spinnerets. When the eggs hatch the young climb onto the female's back and remain there several days. Papi and Tongiorgi (1963) tested the orientation responses of young that were leaving a wild female. They had not learned her escape direction—instead they headed north just as laboratory-reared young would do.

Can a new orientation direction be substituted for one already learned? Rigorous laboratory training in aquaria with *Arctosa cinerea,* another wolf spider, from a population which in nature headed east resulted in successful retraining to the west. Retraining to the south was incomplete within the limits of the experimental session, but an average shift of 31 degrees in the direction of south was noted. In another experiment populations from both banks of the Fiume River were marked and exchanged. Individuals that could be recovered several days later exhibited escape behavior in directions appropriate to their new shoreline.

SOCIAL ASPECTS OF ORIENTATION

Much experimental emphasis has been placed on the ability of inexperienced individual birds to orient properly and migrate successfully. During periods of migration large numbers of individuals, both experienced and inexperienced, are aloft at the same time. Some species seem more prone to flock than others.

One social species is the bobolink, *Dolichonyx oryzivorus.* Hamilton (1962b) found that the average orientation direction of spontaneous migratory fluttering of several individuals of this species corresponded with the normal course of the experimental population. However, these oriented movements, apparently based on the night sky, varied from individual to individual. Since these birds migrate in flocks it seems probable that they rely on the combined orientation preference of the flock to establish an accurate course.

The calls of migrating birds probably play a role in maintaining flock integrity at night. These calls may also form the night flocks, the sound serving to stimulate birds that are near migratory threshold to activity and perhaps to flight under natural conditions (Hamilton 1962d).

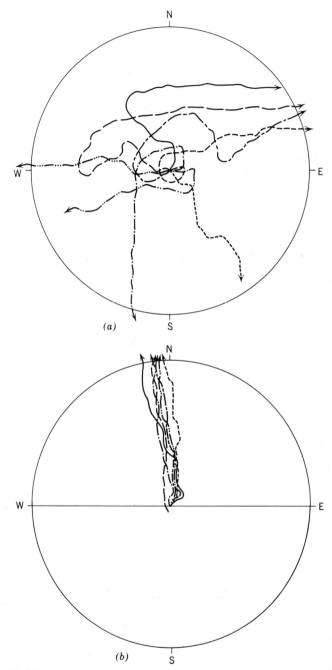

Figure 15-16 Orientation of mallard ducks released in unfamiliar terrain under (a) overcast and (b) clear skies. The diameter of the circles is 2 miles. After Bellrose 1958a.

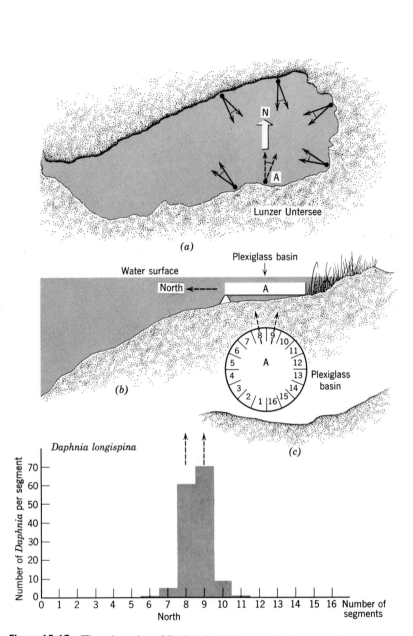

Figure 15-17 The orientation of *Daphnia longispina* in a plexiglass bowl is away from the shore. The double arrows in (*a*) represent the main swimming direction at several locations about the lake. A typical installation of the apparatus is shown in (*b*), and the result of this experiment is indicated by (*c*). After Siebeck 1964.

FIXED-DIRECTION ORIENTATION

◆ *Fixed-Direction Orientation in Mallards.* The alternative to testing the migratory fluttering of a single caged bird is to test birds in free flight. Bellrose 1958a, b) discovered that wild mallards, *Anas platyrhynchos,* headed north when released in unfamiliar terrain under clear daytime skies at any time of year. When the sky was overcast courses were erratic (Figure 15-16). By attaching small lights to these birds Bellrose showed that the northward trend persisted at night as long as the sky was clear. Matthews (1961) tested mallards in England in a similar fashion and found that they headed northwesterly. By shifting the light-dark schedule over a period of days, Matthews reset the internal clock of detained wild birds. The resetting could be demonstrated by the altered directional course which these birds took during the day. In this way directional deviations of up to 180 degrees were induced. But when these phase-shifted birds were tested at night the direction of the orientation remained unchanged (Matthews 1963). The birds steadfastly headed northwesterly. From this result Matthews argues that night orientation had a different basis than daytime orientation in this species. An internal clock does not seem to be a part of the nocturnal orientation mechanism, and the possibility of orientation by star patterns is suggested.

It should be noted that the results of the experiments with these ducks cannot be applied to the migratory orientation process, for these ducks were not heading toward migratory goals or a home. This prompted Matthews to term such performances "nonsense" orientation. The underlying mechanism of such performances may or may not be the same as for the migratory process.

◆ *The Orientation of Plankters: Fixed-Direction Orientation?* Small planktonic animals are not completely at the mercy of prevailing currents. Both vertical and horizontal movements occur. In a submerged vertical test tube the zooplankton collect at both ends. The proportion moving to the upper end increases with greater depth, but the response can be reversed by introducing light below the tube. Light is not the only basis of the behavior, however, since the sample of zooplankton separates to the ends of the tube even in total darkness (Hardy and Paton 1947), perhaps because of 'end' effects, i.e. the tendency to aggregate at the end of the vessel.

Lateral movement also takes place in zooplankton, such as the familiar *Daphnia, Cyclops,* and many other species (Bainbridge 1961). In lakes zooplankton may concentrate at night in littoral zones where they are uncommon in the daytime. The following morning, sampling reveals their return to deeper water (Ruttner 1914). Experimental orientation tests (Siebeck 1964) revealed that this migration is the result of oriented swimming movements. When collections of plankters are placed in a circular plexiglass basin, the movement is clearly perpendicular to the shoreline (Figure 15-17). This result seems to be correlated with field observations of swimming movements away from shorelines at dawn. Aggregation along the shore at night is presumably due to current drift and lack of orienting cues. But for some phases in the life cycle of certain species there is no offshore movement. The copepod nauplii of *Eudiaptomus gracilis,* for example, scatter in the test apparatus, which correlates well with the habit of the nauplii of this species of inhabiting the littoral zone.

Many planktonic organisms orient randomly in a light gradient (Cushing 1951), and aggregation at a certain light intensity seems to be based on a kinesis. Experimental studies of *Daphnia,* a freshwater cladoceran, indicate the importance of kineses at low light intensities. But with brighter lighting the movement is a direct, taxic response to the source of illumination (Harris and Wolfe 1955).

LUNAR ORIENTATION

The possibility of lunar orientation has received comparatively little attention (Papi 1960). The first demonstration of moon compass orientation was the report by Papi and Pardi (1953) on the beach hopper, *Talitrus saltator.* When these amphipods are placed in a cylindrical chamber they immediately respond with a phototactic orientation toward the moon. But when they are tested on a dry substrate they shift to a beachward orientation. Tests at night revealed a persistence of the geographically appropriate orientation as long as the moon was visible. When the moon was not visible, even though the sky was clear, directional orientation failed.

The lunar orientation emerges even after exposure to 24 hours of constant darkness before testing. Thus the orientation is apparently based on an ability to compensate for the movement of the moon across the sky (Papi and Pardi 1959) similar to the sun compensation mechanism. Papi and Pardi suggest that since the lunar orientation persists under these conditions, the ability to compensate for the 23.5-hour lunar cycle reflects an endogenous lunar rhythm independent of the sun compass orientation mechanism which has been demonstrated in this species (Pardi and Papi 1952). The conditions under which this orientation appears demonstrate again the importance of considering the motivational context of the response. When *Talitrus* is placed in an orientation chamber the immediate response is a phototactic orientation *toward* the moon. Only when tested on a dry substrate in a well-desiccated environment do these amphipods shift to the more sophisticated moon compass orientation.

Enright (1961) studied another amphipod, *Orchestoidea corniculata*, on the Pacific Coast of North America. He found that animals held in constant darkness before testing tend to maintain a fixed angle relative to the moon. Since a moon-compensated orientation appeared when these amphipods were pretreated by exposure to a natural day-night cycle, Enright suggested that orientation might be based on nightly rephasing of the compensation mechanism.

These considerations, if rigidly applied to Papi and Pardi's experiments, cast doubt on the conclusion that a separate free-running lunar rhythm has been demonstrated. In subsequent discussion of these discrepancies, Papi and Pardi (1963) suggest that the contrasting results might be caused by species differences; it is also possible that they are based on threshold differences in eliciting categories of orientation responses. Enright (1961) did not preheat his orientation chamber to obtain humidity comparable to that in which Papi and Pardi obtained a moon-compensated orientation.

So far the available evidence for birds, for both orientation cage experiments (Sauer 1957, Hamilton 1962a, b) and free-flying releases (Matthews 1963), suggests that at best the moon is ignored, at worst it is a hindrance to effective nocturnal orientation. In orientation cages spontaneous migratory fluttering is often directed toward either the moon or the lighted wall of the apparatus.

ORIENTATION OF PROTOZOA

The complexity and diversity of behavioral mechanisms in protozoa typify the diversity of solutions to the problem of orientation. Jennings' (1902) classic studies of the responses of *Stentor* to disturbance demonstrate

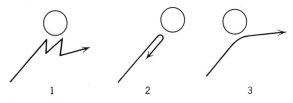

Figure 15-18 The angle of impact determines the reorientation of *Paramecium aurelia* in response to an obstacle. After Rose 1964.

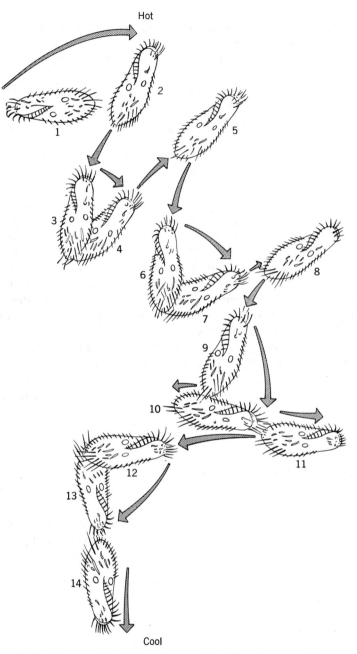

Figure 15-19 Response of *Oxytricha* to a heat gradient. There are repeated retreats and turns to the aboral side (1-12) until a course away from the heat source is achieved (13-14). After Jennings 1906.

the extent of individual plasticity in responsiveness. This same plasticity characterizes other free-living protozoa (Jennings 1906). The response of a *Paramecium* to an obstacle illustrates well the flexibility of responsiveness in protozoa. When a *Paramecium* strikes an impasse it stops, reverses the direction of ciliary movement, and backs away. After turning through an angle toward the aboral side it proceeds again (Jennings 1906). These movements are remarkably like a spring-driven toy depending on backing and turning to move about a room mechanically. Indeed, Loeb (1918) constructed such a toy and ascribed to it the characteristics of a behaving organism. Rose (1964) found more versatile obstacle reactions in *Paramecium*. The backing reaction of Jennings occurs only when the obstacle is met at an angle of between about 65 and 85 degrees. When an obstacle is met head on it somersaults on the transverse axis and rebounds (Figure 15-18), and when the angle of impact is more tangential the *Paramecium* turns to pass in a curve (Rose 1964).

These same behavior patterns enable ciliates to respond efficiently not only to obstacles but also to light, heat, and chemical gradients. The response of *Oxytricha* to excessive heat is an appropriate example (Figure 15-19). When *Oxytricha* moves into an excessively hot environment it stops, backs, turns aborally, and proceeds. If this direction again leads to excessive warmth the maneuver is repeated until an acceptable temperature is encountered. So the final course (from position 13, Figure 15-19) is a very direct one away from the heat. No additional turns are made while conditions remain the same or improve. Thus a series of avoidance responses are integrated into a very efficient overall mechanism for locating favorable conditions.

REFERENCES

Bainbridge, R. 1961. Migrations. In *The Physiology of Crustacea,* ed. by T. H. Waterman, Vol. 2: 431–463. The Academic Press, New York.

Bastock, M. and A. D. Blest. 1958. An analysis of behaviour sequences in *Automeris aurantiaca* Weym. (Lepidoptera). *Behaviour,* **12**:243–284.

Bellrose, F. C. 1958a. Celestial orientation by wild mallards. *Bird-Banding,* **29**:75–90.

———. 1958b. The orientation of displaced waterfowl in migration. *Wilson Bull.,* **70**:20–40.

Birukow, G. 1954. Photo-geomenotaxis bei *Geotrupes silvaticus Panz* und ihre zentralnervöse Koordination. *Z. vergl. Physiol.,* **36**:176–211.

———. 1956. Lichtkompassorientierung beim Wasserläufer *Velia currens* F. (Heteroptera) am Tage und zur Nachtzeit. I: Herbst-und Winterversuche. *Z. Tierpsychol.,* **13**:463–484.

Bisetzky, A. R. 1957. Die Tänze der Bienen nach einem Fussweg zum Futterplatz. *Z. vergl. Physiol.,* **40**:264–288.

Blest, A. D. 1958. Interaction between consecutive responses in a hemileucid moth, and the evolution of insect communication. *Nature,* **181**:1077–1078.

————. 1959. Central control of interactions between behaviour patterns in a hemileucine moth. *Nature*, **184**:1164–1165.

Braemer, W. 1960. A critical review of the sun-azimuth hypothesis. *Cold Spr. Harb. Symp. Quant. Biol.*, **25**:413–427.

———— and H. O. Schwassmann. 1963. Von Rhythmus der Sonnenorientierung am Äquator (bei Fischen). *Ergeb. Biol.*, **26**:182–201.

Cushing, D. H. 1951. The vertical migration of planktonic Crustacea. *Biol. Rev.*, **26**:158–192.

Dethier, V. G. 1957. Communication by insects: physiology of dancing. *Science*, **125**:331–336.

Edney, E. B. 1954. Woodlice and the land habitat. *Biol. Rev.*, **29**:185–219.

Enright, J. T. 1961. Lunar orientation of *Orchestoidea corniculata* Stout (Amphipoda). *Biol. Bull.*, **120**:148–156.

Esch, H. 1961. Über die Schallerzeugung beim Werbetanz der Honigbiene. *Z. vergl. Physiol.*, **45**:1–11.

Frisch, K. von. 1948. Gelöste und ungelöste Rätsel der Bienensprache. *Naturwissenschaften*, **35**:12–23, 38–43.

————. 1950. *Bees: Their Chemical Senses, Vision and Language*. Cornell University Press, Ithaca.

————. 1953. *The Dancing Bees*. Methuen and Company, London.

———— and R. Jander. 1957. Über den Schwänzeltanz der Bienen. *Z. vergl. Physiol.*, **40**:239–263.

———— and M. Lindauer. 1954. Himmel und Erde in Konkurrenz bei der Orientierung der Bienen. *Naturwissenschaften*, **41**:245–253.

————, ————, and F. Schmeidler. 1960. Wie erkennt die Biene den Sonnenstand bei geschlossenen Wolkendecke. *Naturw. Rdsh.* (Braunschweig or Stuttg.), **10**:1–7.

Griffin, D. R. 1955. Bird Navigation. In *Recent Studies in Avian Biology*, ed. by A. Wolfson: 154–197. University of Illinois Press, Urbana.

———— and R. J. Hock. 1949. Airplane observations of homing birds. *Ecology*, **30**:176–198.

Gunn, D. L. and J. S. Kennedy. 1936. Apparatus for investigating the reactions of land arthropods to humidity. *J. Exp. Biol.*, **13**:450–459.

————, ————, and D. P. Pielou. 1937. Classification of taxes and kineses. *Nature*, **140**:1064.

Hamilton, W. J., III. 1962a. Bobolink migratory pathways and their experimental analysis under night skies. *Auk*, **79**:208–233.

————. 1962b. Celestial orientation in juvenal waterfowl. *Condor*, **64**:19–33.

————. 1962c. Initial orientation and homing of inexperienced pintails. *Bird-Banding*, **33**:61–69.

————. 1962d. Evidence concerning the function of nocturnal call notes of migratory birds. *Condor*, **64**:390–401.

Hardy, A. C. and W. N. Paton. 1947. Experiments on the vertical migration of plankton animals. *J. Mar. Biol. Assn. United Kingdom*, **26**:467–526.

Harris, J. E. and U. K. Wolfe. 1955. A laboratory study of vertical migration. *Proc. Roy. Soc. Lond., B*, **144**:329–354.

Hasler, A. D. and H. O. Schwassmann. 1960. Sun orientation of fish at different latitudes. *Cold Spr. Harb. Symp. Quant. Biol.*, **25**:429–441.

———— and W. J. Wisby. 1958. The return of displaced largemouth bass and green sunfish to a "home" area. *Ecology*, **39**:289–293.

Hawes, R. S. 1945. On the eyes and reactions to light of *Proteus inquinus*. *Quart. J. Micr. Sci.*, **86**:1–53.

Heran, H. and L. Wanke. 1952. Beobachtungen über die Entfernungsmeldung der Sammelbienen. *Z. vergl. Physiol.*, **34**:383–393.

Hoffmann, K. 1960. Experimental manipulation of the orientational clock in birds. *Cold Spr. Harb. Symp. Quant. Biol.*, **25**:379–387.

Jander, R. 1957. Die optische Richtungsorientierung der Roten Waldameise (*Formica rufa* L.). *Z. vergl. Physiol.*, **40**:162–238.

Jennings, H. S. 1902. Studies on reactions to stimuli in unicellular organisms. IX. On the behavior of fixed infusoria (*Stentor* and *Vorticella*), with special reference to the modifiability of protozoan reactions. *Amer. J. Physiol.*, **8**:23–60.

——. 1906. *Behavior of the Lower Organisms*. Columbia University Press, New York.

Jones, F. R. H. 1955. Photo-kinesis in the ammocoete larva of the brook lamprey. *J. Exp. Biol.*, **32**:492–503.

Kramer, G. 1949. Über Richtungstendenzen bei der nächtlichen Zugunruhe gekäfigter Vögel. In *Ornithologie als biologische Wissenschaft*, ed. by E. Mayr and E. Schuz: 269–283. C. Winter, Heidelberg.

——. 1950. Orientierte Zugaktivität gekäfigter Singvögel. *Naturwissenschaften*, **37**:188.

——. 1952. Experiments on bird orientation. *Ibis*, **94**:265–285.

Lindauer, M. 1954. Dauertänze in Bienenstock und ihre Beziehung zur Sonnenbahn. *Naturwissenschaften*, **41**:506–507.

——. 1957. Sonnenorientierung der Bienen unter der Äquatorsonne und zur Nachtzeit. *Naturwissenschaften*, **44**:1–6, 360.

——. 1961. *Communication Among Social Bees*. Harvard University Press, Cambridge.

——. 1963. Kompassorientierung. *Ergeb. Biol.*, **26**:158–181.

Loeb, J. 1918. *Forced Movements, Tropisms, and Animal Conduct*. J. B. Lippincott Company, Philadelphia.

Matthews, G. V. T. 1961. "Nonsense" orientation in Mallard *Anas platyrhyncos* and its relation to experiments on bird navigation. *Ibis*, **103a**:211–230.

——. 1963. The astronomical bases of "nonsense" orientation. *Proc. 13th Int. Orn. Congr.*, Vol. 1:415–429.

Meder, E. 1958. Über die Einberechnung der Sonnenwanderung bei der Orientierung der Honigbiene. *Z. vergl. Physiol.*, **40**:610–641.

Papi, F. 1960. Orientation by night: the moon. *Cold Spr. Harb. Symp. Quant. Biol.*, **25**:475–480.

—— and L. Pardi. 1953. Ricerche sull'orientamento di *Talitrus saltator* (Montagu) (Crustacea-Amphipoda) II. Sui fattori che vegolano la variazone dell'angolo di orientamento nel corso del giorno. L'orientamento di notte. L'orientamento diurno di altre popolazioni. *Z. vergl. Physiol.*, **35**:490–518.

—— and ——. 1959. Nuovi reperti sull'orientamento lunare di *Talitrus saltator* Montagu (Crustacea Amphipoda). *Z. vergl. Physiol.*, **41**:583–596.

—— and ——. 1963. On the lunar orientation of sandhoppers (Amphipoda Talitridae). *Biol. Bull.*, **124**:97–105.

—— and P. Tongiorgi. 1963. Innate and learned components in the astronomical orientation of wolf spiders. *Ergeb. Biol.*, **26**:259–280.

Pardi, L. 1960. Innate components in the solar orientation of littoral amphipods. *Cold Spr. Harb. Symp. Quant. Biol.*, **25**:395–401.

—— and F. Papi. 1952. Die Sonne als Kompass bei *Talitrus saltator* (Montagu) (Amphipoda, Talitridae). *Naturwissenschaften*, **39**:262–263.

Renner, M. 1959. Über ein weiteres Versetzungsexperiment zur Analyse des Zeitsinnes und der Sonnenorientierung der Honigbiene. *Z. vergl. Physiol.*, **42**:449–483.

——. 1960. The contribution of the honey bee to the study of time-sense and astronomical orientation. *Cold Spr. Harb. Symp. Quant. Biol.*, **25**:361–367.

Rose, W. 1964. Versuchsfreie Beobachtungen des Verhaltens von *Paramecium aurelia*. *Z. Tierpsychol.*, **21**:257–278.

Ruttner, F, 1914. Die Verteilung des Planktons in Süsswasser. *Fortschr. Naturw. Forsch*, **10**:273–336.

Sauer, F. 1957. Die Sternenorientierung nächtlich ziehender Grasmücken (*Sylvia atricapilla, borin* und *curruca*). *Z. Tierpsychol.,* **14:**29–70.

Schwassmann, H. O. 1960. Environmental cues in the orientation rhythm of fish. *Cold Spr. Harb. Symp. Quant. Biol.,* **25:**443–450.

Shaposhnikova, N. G. 1958. The factors determining the formation of the recruitment signal in the honey bee, *Apis mellifera carnica. Ent. Rev.* (U.S.S.R.) (American Institute of Biological Sciences translation), **37:**473–481.

Siebeck, O. 1964. Researches on the behaviour of planktonic crustaceans in the littoral. *Internat. Vereinig. f. Limnologie,* Vol. 15, Part 2: 746–751.

Steche, W. 1957. Beitrage zur Analyse der Bienentanze (Teil I). *Insectes Sociaux,* **4:**305–318.

Tongiorgi, P. 1962. Sulle relazioni tra habitat ed orientamento astronomico in alcune specie del gen. *Arctosa.* (Araneae-Lycosidae). *Boll. Zool.,* **28:**683–689.

Ullyott, P. 1936a. The behaviour of *Dendrocoelum lacteum.* I. Responses at light-and-dark boundaries. *J. Exp. Biol.,* **13:**253–264.

———. 1936b. The behaviour of *Dendrocoelum lacteum.* II. Responses in non-directional gradients. *J. Exp. Biol.,* **13:**265–278.

Vowles, D. M. 1954. The orientation of ants. I. The substitution of stimuli. *J. Exp. Biol.,* **31:** 341–355.

Walter, H. E. 1907. The reactions of planarians to light. *J. Exp. Zool.,* **5:**35–162.

Welsh, J. H. 1933. Light intensity and the extent of activity of locomotor muscles as opposed to cilia. *Biol. Bull.,* **65:**168–174.

Wenner, A. M. 1962. Sound production during the waggle dance of the honey bee. *Anim. Behav.,* **10:**79–95.

———. 1964. Sound communication in honeybees. *Sci. Amer.,* **210**(4):116–124.

Wilkinson, D. H. 1952. The random element in bird 'navigation.' *J. Exp. Biol.,* **29:**532–560.

Winn, H. E., M. Salmon, and N. Roberts. 1964. Sun-compass orientation by parrot fishes. *Z. Tierpsychol.,* **21:**798–812.

Young, J. 1935. The photoreceptors of lampreys. I. Light-sensitive fibres in the lateral line nerves. *J. Exp. Biol.,* **12:**229–238.

sixteen

NAVIGATION AND HOMING

Requirements for homing • The sun-arc hypothesis • Homing in pigeons and turtles • Star orientation in birds • The earth's magnetic field • The role of experience in developing homing ability • Recognition of the goal • Migration and homing of bats.

The orientation of homing and migration often involves the maintenance or establishment of sensory contact with a goal. An animal that is out of direct sensory contact with its goal is not necessarily lost, however. The capacity to navigate, to establish a course toward a goal regardless of its direction, is frequently encountered among animals and is especially characteristic of vertebrates and arthropods with well-developed powers of locomotion.

HOMING BASED ON CELESTIAL CUES

The studies discussed in the last chapter deal with the ability of animals to determine compass direction. This ability is not necessarily related to the position of an animal on the surface of the earth except as experimental manipulation may take advantage of displacements to elucidate the characteristics of compass orientation. But many animals are able to account for position displacement by homing and make seasonal or daily migratory journeys, which implies an ability not only to determine direction but also to determine position. They can navigate.

◆ *Homing in Birds.* Shortly after Kramer reported his discoveries of the ability of starlings to orient by the sun, Matthews (1951, 1953) reported that pigeons use the sun as a cue in homing. Matthews (1955) demonstrated that pigeons released in unfamiliar areas were significantly oriented in the direction of home while they were still in sight of the experimenter and that this orientation failed when the sky was overcast. This discovery raised a fundamental question which is still very much the subject of active experimentation and debate. Is a bird capable of homing or correcting migratory courses using celestial cues alone, or does it require additional information used either in conjunction with the sun or independently of it?

The evidence that has been adduced to support various hypotheses about the direction finding of birds has come almost exclusively from experiments with captive birds trained to a directional reward and free-flying birds released in unfamiliar surroundings. In spite of the breakthrough achieved by the demonstration that migratory 'flight' can be witnessed in the laboratory, there has been no subsequent investigation of daytime migratory orientation based on this behavior, apparently because spontaneous migratory fluttering is restricted to the migratory season. Such experiments as are made at that time, however, have the distinct advantage of being directly related to migration, one of the natural phenomena which these investigations seek to explain.

Since Matthews made his initial discoveries several investigators have explored the basis of the appropriate initial homeward orientation. These experiments have shown that in pigeons (1) initial orientation varies significantly with location and is not always toward home (Wallraff 1959), (2) the direction of initial orientation can be changed by altering the light-dark cycle (Schmidt-Koeing 1960a, b), and (3) the initial flight direction is *less* accurate when releases are made relatively close to home than when they are made at a distance (Matthews 1955).

◆ *Sun-Arc Hypothesis.* These experiments led Matthews (1955) to hypothesize that bird navigation is based on the sun. He assumed that complete information about the location of home was derived from the sun by a displaced bird. Initial orientation failed to be goal-directed under complete overcast. Matthews suggested that a displaced bird actually sees the movement of the sun traveling across the sky and is able to extrapolate a partial or a complete arc that can then be compared with the familiar home arc. If the extrapolated noon position is higher than that at home, a northern hemisphere bird would be south of its home. East-west displacement is determined by the temporal schedule of the sun. If it is further along its arc than it would be at that time at home, the bird has

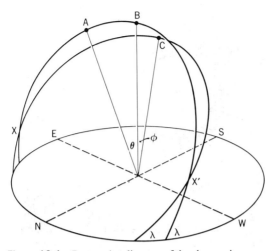

Figure 16-1   Perspective diagram of the changes in sun arc consequent on a move to the south and west, at noon (home time). The altitude of the highest point of the arc B is greater (by ϕ) than at home C. The inclination of the arc (λ) is also greater. The observed sun A has not moved so far round its arc (by θ) as it would have done at home. The bird is required to construct the 'foreign' arc by extrapolation of the observed movement of the sun at A, and to compare it with the memorized arc at home. Note the crossing over of the arcs at two points, X, X'. After Matthews 1955.

been displaced east; if it is not far enough, the displacement is westerly (Figure 16-1). Together with a time sense, the sun-arc could provide all the information needed to set a course for home. Matthews supported this theory by upsetting the internal clock of Manx shearwaters, *Procellaria puffinus* so disturbing their homeward orientation. Much discussion of this hypothesis ensued. A major question concerned the ability of a bird to make in less than a minute the extremely fine angular and temporal measurements that the theory requires (Adler 1963). A variation of the sun-arc hypothesis suggests that the bird measures the rate of change of altitude of the sun (Pennycuick 1960). This eliminates certain objections to the sun-arc hypothesis, but unequivocal experimental support is lacking.

◆ *The Internal Clock and Pigeon Homing.* The role of the biological clock in homing orientation has been examined by Schmidt-Koenig (1960b). In these experiments shifts of the light-dark schedule were successful in re-orienting initial headings in the predicted direction (Figure 16-2). This simple experiment, which demonstrates a time-dependent basis for hom-

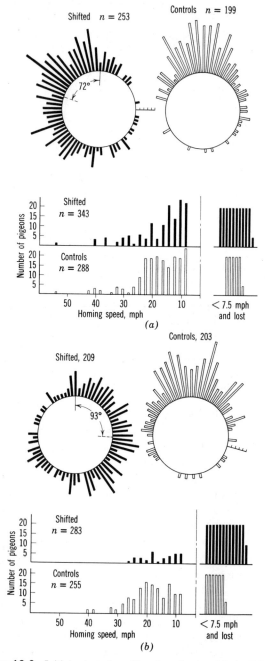

Figure 16-2 Initial orientation of homing pigeons with the light-dark schedule (*a*) advanced 6 hours, (*b*) delayed 6 hours, or (*c*) reversed by 12 hours. The orientation of controls in each of these experiments is shown at the right. After Schmidt-Koenig 1960b.

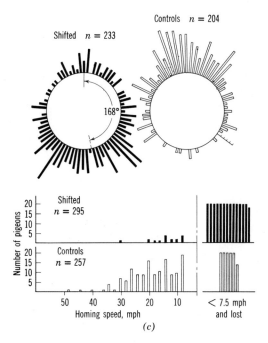

ing orientation in a natural environment, would seem to be a logical starting point in all analyses of homing. Yet to date Schmidt-Koenig's experiment seems to be unique in homing studies of animals.

The overwhelming problem which orientation studies of free-flying birds have so far not overcome is that the results comprise pooled data from numerous individuals. It is not possible to evaluate the accuracy of each individual bird by making successive tests under the same conditions. The range of individual variation cannot be separated from the population variation. Thus, within the range of performances of a large number of releases as demonstrated in Figure 16-2, a part of the scatter may be accounted for by individual differences in choice of direction. The problem may be overcome by training birds to indicate their homing preference without actual release. Several workers have attempted to do this and have failed. It is not sufficient to recover birds that home, recapture them, and release them again. Experience intervenes between the trials, so that they are not strictly comparable.

◆ *Turtle Homing.* Sea turtles perform some of the most remarkable of all migratory feats. They may travel over a thousand miles to a small island to breed. The entire population of the Atlantic ridley turtle, *Lepidochelys kempi,* apparently breeds on a small stretch of the Gulf Coast of Mexico

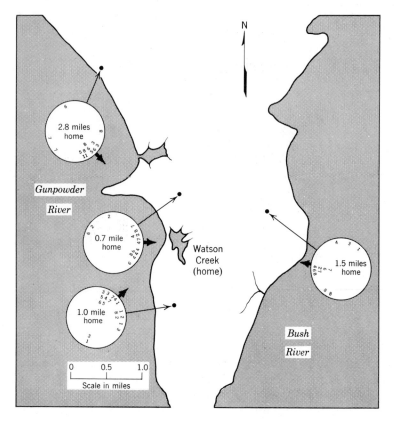

Figure 16-3 The overland initial orientation of eight painted turtles, *Chrysemys picta,* selected for homing ability and released near the home creek but in places where these largely aquatic turtles had probably never been. The numbers at the edge of the circles indicate the orientation of the numbered individuals. The location of the release site is indicated by the arrows from the orientation wheels. The dark arrow at the edge of each circle indicates the home direction. After Gould 1959.

(Carr 1963). So far there is no evidence on the sensory basis of these journeys.

Terrestrial and freshwater turtles have been the subject of some preliminary experiments. Gould (1957, 1959) released box turtles, *Terrapene carolina,* and painted turtles, *Chrysemys picta,* in open fields and golf courses short distances from their points of capture. As adults, they range over very short distances and were unlikely to have been familiar with the release site. Yet some individuals headed for home when released (Figure 16-3).

These performances improve upon the reported accuracy of pigeons, in heading toward the home from displacement distances of less than five miles, apparently without maintaining sensory contact with it. The orientation was effective only as long as a clear sky was visible; again the sun is implicated as at least a part of the basis of the orientation (Gould 1957). This orientation behavior, maintained at short range, is ideally suited for further experimentation.

STAR ORIENTATION IN BIRDS

◆ *Natural-Sky Experiments.* More birds migrate at night than during the day. Following the initial discovery that a caged bird will orient by reference to the sun, Kramer attempted to apply this method to night orientation. But nocturnal migrants such as the blackcap warbler, *Sylvia atricapilla,* performed inconsistently. Often they fluttered in the direction of city lights. Sauer (1957) subsequently investigated this problem with hand-and wild-raised garden warblers, *Sylvia borin.* A vertical screen restricted the view to less than 90 degrees of the sky (Figure 16-4). With the distracting city lights and city glow from the horizon effectively cut off, they oriented in the migration directions, southwest in the fall, northeasterly in the spring. When the sky was overcast the fluttering waned and they oriented randomly (Figure 16-4).

◆ *Artificial-Sky Experiments.* The orientation was reproducible under the artificial stars of a planetarium (Sauer 1957), affording an opportunity to investigate the effect of different star patterns. In a starless, lighted planetarium chamber the birds were disoriented. Under the artificial stars orientation varied according to the position of the bird relative to the central star projector. These variations, obtained with the same configuration of stars, were apparently due to parallax resulting from the displacement of the test apparatus to the side of the planetarium. The differences apparently caused the orientation of the bird to be displaced a number of degrees. All these responses were also obtained with hand-reared birds that had had no previous opportunity to see a natural sky.

Sauer (1957, Sauer and Sauer 1960) experimented with alterations of the artificial sky (Table 16-1). When the sky was shifted 6 to 11 hours clockwise or counterclockwise relative to local position and time, disorientation resulted. Orientation was analyzed with the sky seasonally out of phase, i.e. with the sky appropriate to the spring during fall and to the fall during spring. In these circumstances the birds fluttered both in the

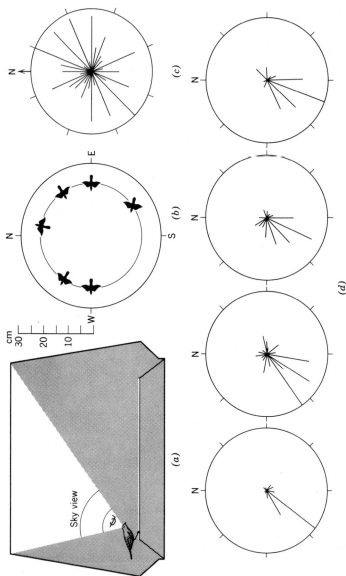

Figure 16-4 The orientation of birds provided with a view of only the natural night sky shows appropriate seasonal orientation. The bird stands on a circular perch (*a*) and the direction of fluttering movements (*b*) is recorded by an observer lying below and looking up through the glass bottom of the cage. The direction of fluttering (*d*) showed a southwesterly tendency during six nights during the autumn, the direction this population of birds would normally take in leaving Germany to reach the winter quarters. Under complete overcast movements are scattered (*c*) in all directions.

Table 16-1   Summary of Orientation Behavior of a Blackcap Warbler, *Sylvia atricapilla,* under the Artificial Sky of a Planetarium

Planetarium instrument setting	Response	Interpretation
Like natural sky	Southeast (as natural)	Sky is seasonally appropriate
Advance from local time 1 to 6 hours	Westward	Displacement east
Advance from local time 6 to 11 hours	Disoriented	Is not able to obtain directional information from stimulus pattern
Advance (retard) time 12 to 14 hours	Ambivalent orientation (see text)	Sky is not in phase with physiological state
Retard from local time 1 to 6 hours	Eastward	Displacement west
Retard from local time 6 to 11 hours	Disoriented	Is not able to obtain directional information from stimulus pattern

normal seasonal direction and in the direction appropriate to the season indicated by the experimentally presented sky. Over a period of days the balance between these alternate responses shifted to orientation appropriate to the presented sky.

The extent to which celestial configuration may be used in navigation is indicated by Sauer's suggestion that the latitudinal setting of the planetarium influences the directional choice. When the planetarium sky was shifted from the latitude of the native habitat to a setting equivalent to the eastern end of the Mediterranean, a directional alteration was induced. This shift is appropriate for direction changes which these birds make at the eastern end of the Mediterranean when they change their course to head into Africa (Figure 16-5). On the basis of these findings Sauer suggests that in these warblers the entire schedule of migratory movement as well as the directional component of migration may be under the control of optical stimuli from the night sky. However, the statistical validity of these experiments has been challenged by Wallraff (1960a, Figure 16-5) and Schmidt-Koenig (1964). Course changes do in fact take place in nature, and any alternative hypothesis to star navigation will have to take this into account.

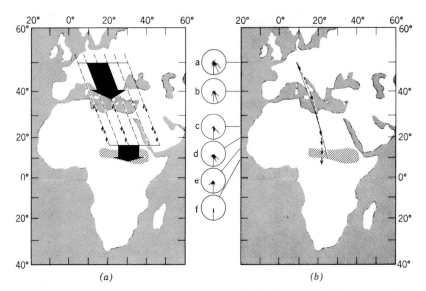

Figure 16-5   Alternate interpretations of the same data. (*a*) Sauer (1960) interprets his planetarium results as suggesting that the course change of warblers in migration observed in nature are based on the celestial configuration of the sky. (*b*) But Wallraff (1960a, b) suggests that the orientation is less dramatic and that there may be no significant deviation from a straight course. The actual data for the experiments are in the center. The matter remains unresolved.

The questions which critics of Sauer's interpretations raise point out the methodological problems challenging investigators of animal navigation. Any precise comparison of one performance with another, either by the same individual on two occasions or by different individuals in the same or altered circumstances, must have a solid statistical basis. Wallraff (1960a) has suggested that the entire result of each experiment, in this case the vector, be treated as a statistical unit (Figure 16-5). Although admittedly valid, such a procedure places heavy demands on experimental design and execution. Adequate numbers of experiments cannot always be performed to test the details of orientation mechanisms.

In an attempt to remedy this problem Hamilton (in press), working with American species of cuckoos, *Coccyzus americanus* and *C. erythropthalmus,* took time-lapse movies of birds fluttering at night on a circular perch similar to that used by Sauer (Figure 16-6). From these films a sample size (*N*) could be determined by comparing the difference between orientation directions at various time intervals. Analysis showed that the difference in direction of orientation continued to increase as the time interval was increased. When such comparisons are plotted (Figure 16-7) the curves are found to inflect at intervals which depend on the experimental conditions, the individual bird, the time of night, and the season. This inflection point determines the sample size—at this time interval, actions of the bird become independent of one another. Hamilton used these intervals to determine sample size and compare one oriented performance with another. This approach has the special advantage that all

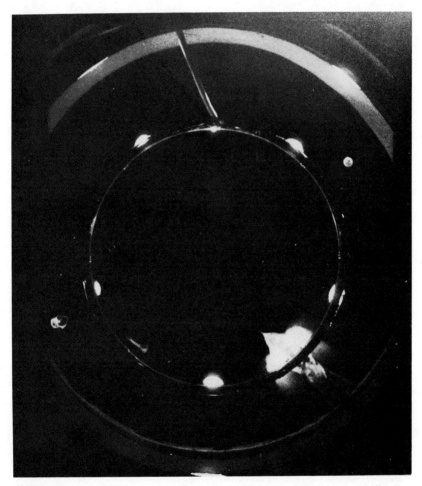

Figure 16-6 A black-billed cuckoo, *Coccyzus erythropthalmus,* flutters on a circular ring while pointing in the direction of migration. This behavior in a cage or orientation apparatus has been the basis of many studies of the temporal and directional aspects of migration. In addition, the performances of caged birds have been the subject of numerous physiological analyses.

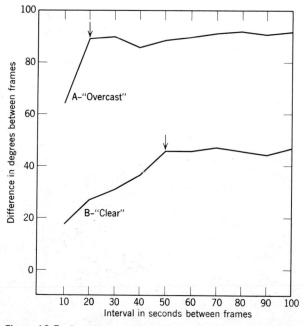

Figure 16-7 In A the curve for difference in orientation between successive frames flattens at about 50 seconds, in B at 30 seconds. Curve A is the orientation of a cuckoo under clear skies, B under overcast. For details see text. After Hamilton in press.

the usable data can be analyzed—the determination of N is neither conservative nor overly optimistic. Analyses such as these, which tailor the evaluation of experiments to the performance of each individual, circumvent one of the hazards of behavioral research epitomized by the discussion between Sauer and Wallraff.

Extensive experiments under natural skies showed that the fluttering of hand-raised cuckoos was oriented along the north-south axis during the first fall, but there was variation in individual orientation, and some individuals seemed incapable of any orientation. Orientation failed when there was an overcast. This conclusion could be confirmed by the fact that the inflection point of the curve representing differences between independent performances fell at 90 degrees, a result only to be expected when the performance is random.

In only one investigation so far have birds been trained to a directional reward at night (Hamilton 1962b). Young blue-winged teal, *Anas discors,* were raised in an experimental apparatus in which they could see only the rotatable walls of the apparatus and the sky above. In this situation they were trained to water which was available in only one of twelve identical compartments. Deprived of food, the birds were tested in pairs to determine their ability to locate the reward. Under clear skies during either day or night the teal could always accurately choose the compartment with the reward. As soon as the sun set below the artificial horizon of the apparatus, orientation failed until about that time at night when the experimenter was able to see the stars. When the sun struck the apparatus at an angle so that sharp shadows, quite visible to the bird when it was making choices, were formed on the walls of the apparatus, orientation also failed. Evidently a direct view of the sun or stars is necessary for accurate orientation in this circumstance.

Most experiments have dealt with the directional component of oriented behavior. The strength of the response may also be studied, but there are difficulties of interpretation. The persistence of migratory fluttering decreases under complete overcast in garden warblers (Sauer 1957) and bobolinks (Hamilton 1962a), probably partly because of the decrease of illumination. Wagner (1957) has shown, using thrushes in registration cages which measure the amount of movement, that maximal activity is closely correlated with normal nocturnal light intensities. Although the vigor of response may vary with the availability of orienting clues, it may also be affected by stimuli which are not directly related to orientation.

PERVASIVE CUES AS NAVIGATION AIDS

Animals traveling beyond the range in which the home or goal can be detected directly must either perform some kind of methodical or random search or orient by some cue that bears a constant or predictably changing relationship to the goal. These cues we categorize as pervasive. Nearly every known geophysical phenomenon that has a directional component has been suggested as a possible basis of oriented animal movement.

◆ *Perception of the Earth's Magnetic Field.* The belief that birds and other animals can detect the earth's magnetic field and orient by it during migration is widespread. This contention was supported by Yeagley (1947, 1951). He attempted to demonstrate that homing pigeons used a bicoordinate system consisting of the earth's magnetic field and the rotational force of the earth (Coriolis force) as an orientation system. Yeagley's interpretation was immediately challenged, both by reinterpretation of his data (Griffin 1955) and by new experiments which failed to support the original interpretation (Gordon 1948, Matthews 1951). There is at present no unequivocal experimental demonstration of the influence of magnetic forces on the behavior of birds.

Brown and his co-workers (Brown, Bennett, and Webb 1960) correlated the behavior of mud snails, *Nassarius,* with the force of weak magnetic fields. The orientation of these snails was tested by allowing them to glide down an inclined ramp. At the bottom they entered an artificial magnetic field stronger than the earth's field. The measure of response was the direction of free movement during the first three centimeters. Average orientation was either parallel or perpendicular to the experimental field. The experimental effect was slight but significant. Variations in the orientation of the response could be correlated with the time of day and phase of the moon. There has been no demonstration so far that these responses play any role in the normal behavior of these or any other species.

The possible use of the electric field of weakly electric fishes in position and direction orientation with respect to the earth's magnetic field remains only an area of conjecture, one worthy of experimental investigation.

ROLE OF EXPERIENCE IN NAVIGATION

Sauer's (1957) reports of accurate orientation by hand-reared garden warblers are of special interest. He reported that laboratory-raised birds respond directionally at once when they are given their first view of an artificial night sky. The ability to use the stars to tell direction seems to develop without earlier experience of star patterns. The potential ability to recognize and act upon the pertinent information of such a complex visual stimulus as the night sky has seemed to many critics to be impossible. It should be recalled, however, that we do not as yet know how directional information is derived from the night sky. Interpretation of this phenomenon must await the results of additional experiments.

◆ *Experience and Pigeon Homing.* The initial orientation of pigeons on release away from home is influenced by experience (Pratt and Thouless 1955, Matthews 1955, Wallraff 1959). Successive releases from the same site show a narrowing of dispersal, even after selection for successful homing has been accounted for. The way in which experience influences initial orientation has incidentally explained one of the mysterious variables, construed as evidence that a factor other than the sun is necessary for complete navigation. Wallraff (1959) felt the "position effect," i.e.

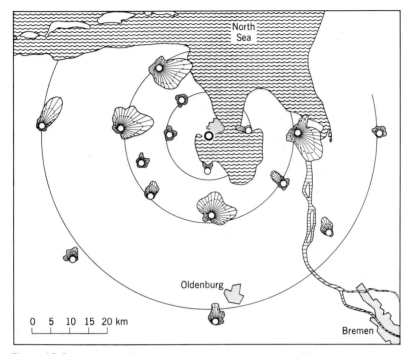

Figure 16-8   "Position effect" in pigeon homing experiments. The home loft is near Wilhelmshaven at the center of the concentric rings. The length of the radii is proportionate to the number of birds that flew in that direction. After Wallraff 1959.

the tendency of birds released at particular sites to fly in directions not precisely accurate, could be explained only by invoking a sensory capacity yet to be discovered. In Germany where Wallraff did his work, suitable release sites were limited primarily to the south. The loft, located on the North Sea, did not permit releases to the north (Figure 16-8). The tendency for "errors" from the precise home direction to be to the north side of the home direction supported this contention. Graue (1965) tested this hypothesis in a particularly ingenious experiment. A group of 50 experienced homing pigeons was divided into two lots. Release sites 10 miles from the loft were positioned symmetrically about the loft. The first lot was released one by one at the sites to the east of the loft, and the second lot was treated similarly at westerly release sites (Figure 16-9). In Figure 16-9 the arrows at each site indicate the *average* direction taken by the released pigeons while still in sight of the experimenter. The length of the arrows is a vector: the larger the vector, the less scattered the flight directions. Then the sequence of releases was repeated. The results of subsequent releases are indicated by numbers at the head of each arrow.

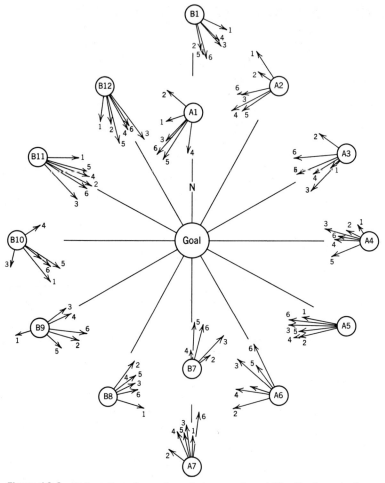

Figure 16-9   Orientation of experienced pigeons released 10 miles from the home loft (center circle). Birds were released individually in a programmed sequence in an A and B series in the following order; A3, A6, A2, A5, A1, A7, A4 and B9, B12, B8, B11, B7, B1 and B10. The result at each release site is summed by an arrow which indicates the angle and strength of the vector of the vanishing directions. The sequence of releases at each site is indicated by the numbers at each arrowhead. After Graue 1965.

By noting the sequence of releases and referring to Figure 16-9 it becomes clear that the birds were acting on a combination of two pieces of information: the direction of the home loft from the release site and the direction of the home loft from the previous release site. The partial role of these separate cues is of special interest. The flight was a vectorial summation of these directions. On the average the strength of the vector increased with subsequent testing and the direction of flight came to conform more and more closely with the home direction. These data confirm the role of experience in initial orientation of pigeons and seem to explain the "position effect" (Figure 16-8).

➤ *Locality Fixation in Birds.* In the course of replenishing depleted waterfowl populations which had disappeared from New York marshes, Foley (1954) introduced nestling pintails, *Anas acuta.* These ducks had hatched in Manitoba, over a thousand miles away. The following spring a few females returned to New York to nest. Experiments of this sort, involving thousands of ducklings, have shown that only the females return to the new areas to breed the following spring. None has been reported at the birthplace. These females apparently bring males attracted at the winter quarters, not the ones released with them. It has thus become the practice to use only females in these expensive restocking programs. In the spring females return to the vicinity of the region from which they took their maiden flight, and not necessarily from their birthplace.

Löhrl (1959) has provided the most complete study of locality fixation by wild animals. He hand-reared a large number of insectivorous pied flycatchers, *Ficedula albicollis.* They were divided into three groups for release 90 kilometers south of where they were reared. The first group was released shortly after fledging, the second two weeks before the period of natural migration, and the third following the first molt and during the period of natural migration. The result with the first two groups was essentially the same. About 20 percent of the males returned the following spring to the area where they were released. Allowing for natural winter mortality and the difficulty in locating birds that might have returned, these figures suggest that the majority of the males returned to the release site. None of the third group returned to the release area. Thus locality fixation in this species apparently develops just before molting.

How can these findings be related to migratory orientation? Perdeck (1958) trapped large numbers of wild starlings in Holland during their fall migration. A large group of juveniles were displaced to Switzerland, several hundred kilometers to the southeast, and there released (Figure 16-10). The subsequent recovery of 354 of these birds demonstrated (1) that adults subsequently reach the wintering area which they would normally have attained without displacement, (2) that juvenile, inexperienced birds winter farther south than usual to approximately the extent of the displacement, and (3) that young and adults separate when released together, confirming items 1 and 2. The course taken by the juvenile birds was parallel to the normal migratory route, whereas the

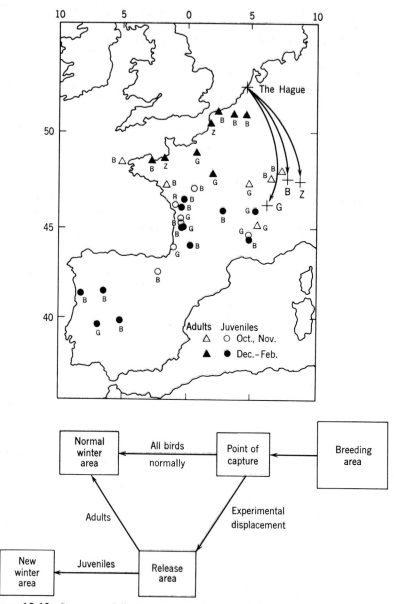

Figure 16-10 Summary of displacement experiments with Starlings, *Sturnus vulgaris*. Large numbers of transients were captured in Holland and displaced to Switzerland (localities G, B, Z). The subsequent reports of banded individuals show that displaced juveniles traveled farther than normal and parallel to the usual flight direction. Adults correct and reach the familiar winter quarters. These responses are indicated schematically in the diagram below. After Perdeck 1958.

course taken by the adults was corrected (Figure 16-9), implying some form of navigation. The following spring recoveries of banded young and adults alike were made in the breeding area where the experimental birds were obtained. The second winter all recoveries were of birds in the region where they had spent the previous winter.

The conclusion from this massive experiment is that each bird appears to be able to follow a path which parallels the normal migratory route without experience of it. Since it normally starts on this route it will usually be led in the direction of the normal wintering grounds. The area where the first winter is spent becomes the permanent wintering ground of that individual. Breeding grounds are the birthplace, and even with displacement during the first fall migration this area is retained as a place for breeding.

◆ *Homing Swallows.* The use of orientation cage techniques has been adopted to measure homing ability in only one investigation. Sargent (1962) studied the homing of the bank swallow, *Riparia riparia,* on displacement from nest cavities. When free-flying birds were released they were initially well oriented toward home at short distances (to 25 miles), scattered between 25 and 50 miles, and oriented randomly at greater distances. This finding, which contrasts with the results of homing releases of pigeons, suggests the importance of familiarity with the area near the nest. This conclusion is supported by the results of orientation cage studies. When the orientation cage provided a full view of the surrounding terrain, orientation was best near the nests. At 50 yards the orientation was precise. At increasing distances to 25 miles the accuracy of the orientation declined but some homeward orientation persisted. Beyond this range no homing was apparent. The most conclusive evidence comes from tests in which the view of surrounding terrain was precluded. Even at the short ranges there was no homeward orientation. These findings contrast with the results of investigations of other species of birds and emphasize the importance of considering the problem of orientation species by species.

RECOGNITION OF THE GOAL

How does a migrant bird identify its winter quarters? In some species such as geese, which travel in family groups, traditional wintering grounds may persist and be learned by successive generations (Hochbaum 1955). But other birds migrate in mixed groups and many probably travel alone. How do they know they have gone far enough?

◆ *Displacement Experiments with Caged Birds.* Sauer and Sauer (1959) asked this question of their garden warblers, which they had tested in orientation cages in Germany. Experiments using the same orientation cages (page 580) were carried out in Africa, the winter quarters of this species. Only a partial view of the night sky was permitted, with no view of the surrounding terrain. Yet these birds persisted in a southerly direction. The fluttering soon stopped, however, and the Sauers concluded that the celestial configuration of the sky in the southern hemisphere provided the cue to end the migration. These experiments were of a preliminary nature and should be repeated under more carefully controlled conditions.

◆ *Releases of Free-Flying Starlings.* An alternative mechanism for recognition of the winter quarters has been suggested. Perdeck (1964) evaluated the effect of displacing starlings to the south. These birds, young individuals trapped during their normal fall migration, were displaced south, some to hospitable and normal wintering quarters in Spain, others to Switzerland where few starlings can survive the winter. The effects of these manipulations upon the birds were measured by subsequent recoveries. When the experimental displacement is divided into early and late migrants, the result is clear. The early migrants, displaced to Spain, *continue* to migrate in spite of already being in suitable terrain. Late migrants taken to the same area scatter but do not move very far. For them the amount of migration is shortened. In the unfavorable environment of Switzerland there is a different result. Here the migration persists for both early and late migrants. The conclusion is that a young bird must perform a certain amount of migratory behavior before entering a phase of search for a suitable wintering habitat. The migration persists in the appropriate direction until suitable terrain is met.

This conclusion is in agreement with some other findings. Caged migratory birds of some species such as the garden warbler (Sauer 1957) and the yellow-billed cuckoo (Hamilton in press) initiate migratory restlessness as caged birds and persist for a few weeks, then desist, even though they have traveled nowhere. Could this amount of energy expenditure account for Perdeck's findings with starlings? If a bird were simply to fly in a given direction for a number of days, this would lead him approximately to the winter quarters. Surely following winds and head winds would cause confusion.

The ability of birds to home after displacement is well established, following experimental displacement from both the breeding grounds (Matthews 1955) and the winter quarters (Mewaldt 1965, Schwartz

1963). Thus once the winter quarters are attained they become fixed as a part of the personal migratory route of each individual. Subsequent movements take the bird back and forth along this line, probably in most cases to the same area of the previous visit.

OTHER NAVIGATION MECHANISMS

◆ *Orientation without Optical Cues: an Artifact?* Several authors have reported oriented migratory fluttering in birds in the apparent absence of directional optical cues. Merkel and Fromme (1958) and Fromme (1961) worked with the European robin, *Erithacus rubecula,* and the whitethroat *Sylvia communis.* Birds were evenly and faintly illuminated, but they had no view of the sky. Various experimental locations were used, the most restricted of these being the placement of the test apparatus in a cellar without windows. Here directional orientation persisted, even in a steel cylinder with airtight doors, as long as one of the doors remained open. The magnetic field of the earth at the cage was undisturbed. This finding contrasts with Sauer's demonstration that garden warblers became disoriented when placed in a diffusely lit planetarium or under natural overcast. The conditions and recording methods used by Merkel and Fromme (Figure 16-11) are different from those reported by Sauer, so that no direct comparison of results is possible.

Precht (1961) and Gerdes (1961, 1962) recorded the escape behavior of black-headed gulls, *Larus ridibundus,* displaced from their nests. These birds also maintained a significant orientation, heading toward home not only under overcast conditions but also in indoor rooms.

In all these experiments in which orientation has been demonstrated under apparently cueless conditions, the birds have not been as highly oriented as birds able to view the overhead sky. The problem was reinvestigated by Perdeck (1963), again with the European robin. Perdeck concentrated on methodological features. He showed that orientation was random under indoor conditions as long as the orientation device was rotated. When the device remained fixed during experiments, directional preferences not related to the migratory orientation of the species were expressed (Figure 16-12). In addition, Perdeck discovered that the presence of other robins in the same building provided directional auditory cues which influenced the test chamber responses.

◆ *Migration and Homing of Bats.* Bats taken from caves, barns, or buildings and displaced some distance often return. Sometimes the distances covered

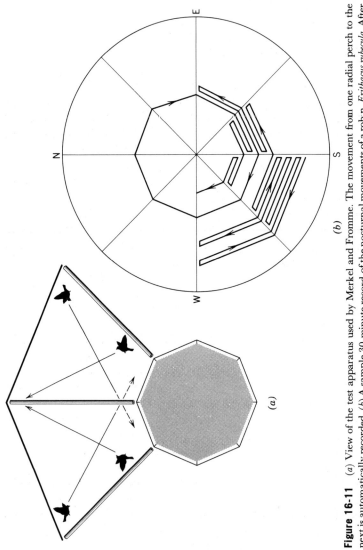

Figure 16-11 (*a*) View of the test apparatus used by Merkel and Fromme. The movement from one radial perch to the next is automatically recorded. (*b*) A sample 30-minute record of the nocturnal movements of a rob.n, *Erithacus rubecula*. After Fromme 1961.

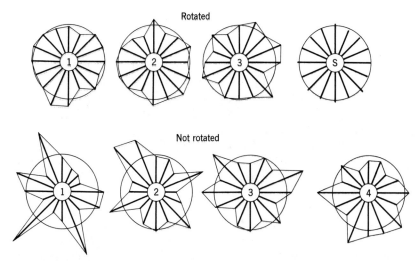

Figure 16-12   Orientation of the robin, *Erithacus rubecula*, in an experimental chamber lacking directional visual cues. The first row represents three individual experiments and the summary of thirteen such experiments. In the second row are four individual experiments which were performed without rotating the apparatus. After Perdeck 1963.

are great. A great deal is known about the homing of bats, but the difficulty of immediately recapturing them when they return and the possibility of missing many that do return make interpretations of the actual homing ability equivocal (Cockrum 1956).

Vision and familiar sounds at the home roost may provide terminal information detailing the precise location of the goal. But as in bird homing and migration, mechanisms involved in navigation may be different from those used in piloting. Determination of the initial directional course remains the primary unexplained phenomenon in bat homing. Preliminary experimental tests of the initial orientation of the fruit bat *Phyllostomus hastatus* seem to demonstrate accurate initial orientation at the release site (Griffin in litt.).

The possibility that search patterns provide an explanation of the orientation of migratory flights of bats can be dismissed. Direct migrations covering hundreds of miles have been recorded (Griffin 1958), and the seasonally appropriate directional flight of red bats, *Lasiurus borealis,* is a commonplace observation in the eastern United States. Yet it is remarkable that no author has suggested any explanation for how these travelers find their way! Bats often collide with towers in the same circumstances and often on the same nights as migrating birds do (Tordoff and Mengel 1956). Perhaps celestial orienting cues are a source of directional information for them.

CONCLUSIONS

There is a wealth of experimental data about celestial orientation mechanisms, particularly for arthropods and birds. The reason for the preeminence in this chapter of visual orientation systems may be found in the distinctive sort of information which celestial cues provide. Visual orientation relates the position of an animal to its home without direct sensory contact with a goal.

Nevertheless, we must recall that new studies continue to demonstrate the role of more than one type of stimulus in the complete orientation process, whether it is in the return of a bee to a hive or of a bird to its breeding grounds. This is not surprising, since the more information an animal acts on, the more reliable the outcome is likely to be. Bees use the sun to tell direction, and this may be important both during outward and homecoming journeys. But landmarks are also used. A bird in its migration to wintering grounds it has never seen acts on a host of variables. For some species the migration persists over the ocean, day and night. The sun during the day and the stars at night are implicated as orienting cues which set the course. But the bird also must account in some unexplained way for wind currents aloft. If it did not it would be blown off course. Landmarks play no role here, for the traveler has never experienced them. Some species travel in flocks, and the experience of older individuals probably contributes both to the setting of the course and its termination in these species. The urge to persist in migration is poorly understood, but its temporal pattern in some species suggests the prominent role of endogenous forces which motivate the bird to press on. Yet it is clear that the environment also plays a role in terminating migration; unless favorable terrain is encountered the migration persists.

So it is certainly a mistake to look for *the* mechanism of orientation in any species. A complete and accurate understanding of orientation will often depend on comprehending the role of supplemental information. To appreciate the actions of an animal in nature we must understand how various kinds of information interact in the fine adjustment of the orientation process. This approach may help to avoid controversy concerning the role of specific orientation mechanisms. Experiments are usually designed to deprive an animal of most of the information it would normally act upon, including especially the performance of other members of the same species. This approach is the only one that will allow us to define the operation of each sensory system in orientation. But ultimately the results must be related to the multisensory control system that prevails in most of the actions of an animal in nature.

REFERENCES

Adler, H. E. 1963. Psychophysical limits of celestial navigation hypotheses. *Ergeb. Biol.,* 26:235–252.

Brown, F. A., M. F. Bennett, and H. M. Webb. 1960. A magnetic compass response of an organism. *Biol Bull.,* 119:65–74.

Carr, A. 1963. Panspecific reproductive convergence in *Lepidochelys kempi. Ergeb. Biol.,* 26:298–303.

Cockrum, E. L., 1956. Homing, movements, and longevity of bats. *J. Mammal,* 37:48–57.

Foley, D. 1954. Survival and establishment of waterfowl released as ducklings. *N. Y. Fish Game J.,* January 1954:206–213.

Fromme, H. G. 1961. Untersuchungen über das Orientierungsvermögen nächtlich ziehender Kleinvögel (*Erithacus rubecula, Sylvia communis*). *Z. Tierpsychol.,* 18:205–220.

Gerdes, K. 1961. Über das Heimfindevermögen von Lachmöwen. *Verh. Dtsch. Zool. Ges., Zool. Anz.,* Suppl. 24:171–181.

———. 1962. Richtungstendenzen von Brutplatz verfrachteter Lachmöwen (*Larus ridibundus* L.) unter Ausschluss visueller Gelände-und Himmelsmarken. *Z. wiss. Zool.,* 166:352–410.

Gordon, D. A. 1948. Sensitivity of the homing pigeon to the magnetic field of the earth. *Science,* 108:710–711.

Gould, E. 1957. Orientation in box turtles, *Terrapene c. carolina* (Linnaeus). *Biol. Bull.,* 112:336–348.

———. 1959. Studies on the orientation of turtles. *Copeia,* 1959:174–176.

Graue, L. C. 1965. Experience effect on initial orientation in pigeon homing. *Anim. Behav.,* 13:149–153.

Griffin, D. R. 1955. Bird navigation. In *Recent Studies in Avian Biology,* ed. by A. Wolfson: 154–197. University of Illinois Press, Urbana.

———. 1958. *Listening in the Dark.* Yale University Press, New Haven.

Hamilton, W. J., III. 1962a. Bobolink migratory pathways and their experimental analysis under night skies. *Auk,* 79:208–233.

———. 1962b. Celestial orientation in juvenal waterfowl. *Condor,* 64:19–33.

———. In press. Analysis of bird navigation experiments.

Hochbaum, H. A. 1955. *Travels and Tradition of Waterfowl.* University of Minnesota Press, Minneapolis.

Löhrl, H. 1959. Zur Frage des Zeitpunktes einer Prägung auf die Heimatregion beim Halsbandschnäpper (*Ficedula albicollis*). *J. Orn.,* 100:132–140.

Matthews, G. V. T. 1951. The experimental investigation of navigation in homing pigeons. *J. Exp. Biol.,* 28:508–536.

———. 1953. Sun navigation in homing pigeons. *J. Exp. Biol.,* 30:243–267.

———. 1955. *Bird Navigation.* Cambridge University Press, London.

Merkel, F. W. and H. G. Fromme. 1958. Untersuchungen über das Orientierungsvermögen nächtlich ziehender Rotkehlchen (*Erithacus rubecula*). *Naturwissenschaften,* 45:499–500.

Mewaldt, L. R. 1965. California sparrows return from displacement to Maryland. *Science,* 146:941–942.

Pennycuick, C. J. 1960. The physical basis of astro-navigation in birds: theoretical considerations. *J. Exp. Biol.,* 37:573–593.

Perdeck, A. C. 1958. Two types of orientation in migrating starlings, *Sturnus vulgaris* L., and chaffinches, *Fringilla coelebs* L., as revealed by displacement experiments. *Ardea,* 46:1–37.

———. 1963. Does navigation without visual clues exist in robins? *Ardea,* 51:91–104.

———. 1964. An experiment on the ending of autumn migration in starlings. *Ardea,* 52:133–139.

Pratt, J. G. and R. H. Thouless. 1955. Homing orientation in pigeons in relation to opportunity to observe the sun before release. *J. Exp. Biol.*, **32**:140–157.

Precht, H. 1961. Über das Heimfindevermögen von Vögeln. *Psychol. Beitr.*, **6**:241–263.

Sargent, T. D. 1962. A study of homing in the bank swallow (*Riparia riparia*). *Auk*, **79**:234–246.

Sauer, E. G. F. 1957. Die Sternenorientierung nächtlich ziehender Grasmücken (*Sylvia atricapilla, borin* und *curruca*). *Z. Tierpsychol.*, **14**:29–70.

——— and E. M. Sauer. 1959. Nächtliche Zugorientierung europäischer Zugvögel in Sudwestafrika. *Vogelwarte*, **20**:4–31.

——— and ———. 1960. Star navigation of nocturnal migrating birds. *Cold Spr. Harb. Symp. Quant. Biol.*, **25**:463–473.

Schmidt-Koenig, K. 1960a. Internal clocks and homing. *Cold Spr. Harb. Symp. Quant. Biol.*, **25**:389–393.

———. 1960b. The sun azimuth compass: one factor in the orientation of homing pigeons. *Science*, **131**:826–828.

———. 1964. Über die Orientierung der Vögel; Experimente und Probleme. *Naturwissenschaften*, **18**:423–431.

Schwartz, P. 1963. Orientation experiments with northern waterthrushes wintering in Venezuela. *Proc. 13th Int. Orn. Congr.*, Vol. 1:481–484.

Tordoff, H. B. and R. M. Mengel. 1956. Studies of birds killed in nocturnal migration. *Univ. Kans. Publ. Mus. Nat. Hist.*, **10**(1):1–44.

Wagner, H. O. 1957. The technical basis of experimental research on migration. *Ibis*, **99**:191–195.

Wallraff, H. G. 1959. Örtlich und zeitlich bedingte Variabilität des Heimkehrverhaltens von Brieftauben. *Z. Tierpsychol.*, **16**:513–544.

———. 1960a. Können Grasmücken mit Hilfe des Sternenhimmels navigieren? *Z. Tierpsychol.*, **17**:165–177.

———. 1960b. Does celestial navigation exist in animals? *Cold Spr. Harb. Symp. Quant. Biol.*, **25**:451–463.

Yeagley, H. L. 1947. A preliminary study of a physical basis of bird navigation. *J. Appl. Phys.*, **18**:1035–1063.

———. 1951. A preliminary study of a physical basis of bird navigation. Part II. *J. Appl. Phys.*, **22**:746–760.

seventeen

THE EMBRYOLOGY OF BEHAVIOR

The embryonic behavior of fish • Developing behavior in amphibians • Behavior in chick embryos • Exogenous and endogenous factors in development • Mammalian embryos • Sex hormones and early development • Coghill's individuation principle.

BEHAVIOR OF EMBRYOS

Studies of the development of behavior in embryos of a variety of animals reveal that many acts appear in part or in full long before they assume functional significance. Inevitably we wonder about the relative contribution of exogenous and endogenous factors to their ontogeny. The course of development of many adult behavior patterns is related to the environment in which the animal grows up. To what extent do environmental factors influence very early stages of development?

Embryos are subject to various kinds of stimulation. However, the embryos of many species are insulated from variations in the external environment. Thus the embryological environment is often dominated not by the outside world but by the mother, an influence that can persist for varying periods after birth or laying of an egg. The embryo itself generates environmental variations in the course of its own growth. It is reasonable to suppose that environmental changes created by the embryo at one stage may influence the course of subsequent development. The interplay between these different external influences and the endogenous processes of growth leads to the development of structures that in turn determine behavior patterns. In the analysis of the mechanisms of behavioral development certain outstanding studies have been influential in shaping ideas.

◆ *Embryonic Behavior of Fish*. Building on the pioneer work of Preyer (1885) and others, Tracy (1926) described and experimented with developing behavior patterns in the embryo and larva of the toadfish, *Opsanus tao*. His results were presented in a framework closer to our present one than many subsequent studies. Movements of the eyes, heart, body, jaws, and branchial apparatus of the toadfish appear gradually in regular sequence. Experiments established that some of the movements could be elicited by the touch of a hair or by rotation of the body, particularly in the later developmental stages. The earliest movements seemed to occur spontaneously, however, without apparent triggering by the external environment.

Tracy concluded that the movements of the growing toadfish are first motivated from endogenous sources, originating in either the central nervous system or the viscera. The motor mechanisms develop first, their timing depending on the order in which new nervous connections are established. As the sensory connections become established and exteroceptors start to function, exogenous factors begin to play a part in behavioral control. The behavior of the mature adult is interpreted as a result of interaction between exogenous and endogenous factors.

Tracy was concerned mainly with the role of external stimuli in triggering and orienting behavioral responses. He gave little attention to the ontogenetic basis of the pattern of internal coordination of the acts themselves. Presumably he would have regarded them as genetically determined since he was impressed by the differences between the embryonic behavior of the four fish species he studied when raised under similar external conditions. "For each organism there appears to exist a specific motility type dependent on a specific organization pattern" (Tracy 1926).

Many of the earliest movements of the toadfish involve all muscles of the body. Localized movements of particular organs appear later.

The development of the tactile reactions, as well as the character of motility at its beginning, clearly indicates that in the toadfish, at least, the segmental reflexes are not the primitive components of behavior. The primitive response to touch is a response of the whole body musculature, and differs from the fully developed reaction only in its variability and incompleteness . . . and in the height of the threshold. . . . Hence the development of the responses through the afferent system does not occur by a fusion of segmental reflexes, but by completion of neurone connections with the motor column of the spinal cord as a whole which has already been welded into a functional unit. The afferent system in this way 'captures' the bilateral motor system and thus provides the mechanism by which changes in the external environment may determine the time incidence and spatial orientation of the activity of the motor system (Tracy 1926, p. 349).

◆ *Development of Behavior in Amphibians.* The sequence of early behavioral development in the tiger salamander, *Ambystoma tigrinum,* is similar to that in the toadfish in many respects (Coghill 1929). The earliest response to touch is flexion of the body; this response is soon elaborated to coiling, then to an S-shaped posture, and finally to a series of undulating movements that result in swimming. The first movements of the gills, forelimbs, and hindlimbs occur as part of the general body movement of swimming or walking. Only subsequently do they begin to perform independent movements of their own. Coghill concludes that "behavior develops from the beginning through the progressive expansion of a perfectly integrated total pattern, and the individuation within it of partial patterns which acquire various degrees of discreteness." He demonstrates that the ordering of development is a result of the gradual growth of nerve connections. Once again the patterns of motor coordination first develop endogenously, with external stimuli gradually assuming control of the orientation and timing of the movements.

There is no evidence that patterned external stimuli determine the motor coordinations. But experience of sensory feedback from pressure of the medium or substrate during movement might be necessary for full development of the pattern. Carmichael (1933) tested one such possibility. He raised embryos under chloretone anaesthesia which blocked all movement and compared their movements after emergence from anaesthesia with those of normal controls. He could detect no differences.

The studies of the salamander and toadfish suggest that endogenous factors are largely responsible for shaping embryonic patterns of behavior. External factors may play a permissive role and may trigger behavioral acts; sensory feedback may be involved, but there is no evidence at this level that patterns of behavior are acquired by exposure to similar patterns in the external environment.

Modifying Spemann's technique of transplanting parts of embryos, Weiss (1950) transplanted and reversed limb buds of amphibians in such a way that when the feet developed they pointed in the wrong direction. If sensory feedback from muscular activity were a major determinant of patterns of walking, we might expect the animal to adjust the movements of such reversed limbs to achieve normal forward locomotion. But there was never any sign of adjustment. An animal with all feet pointed backward consistently backed up in response to stimulation that would make a normal salamander walk forward. Similar experiments by Sperry

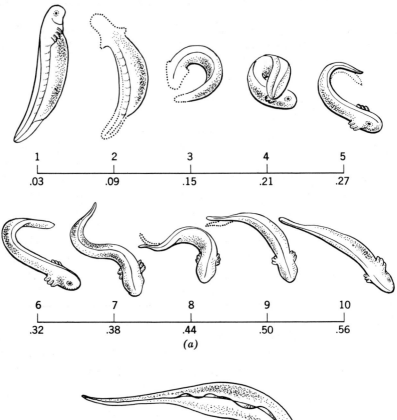

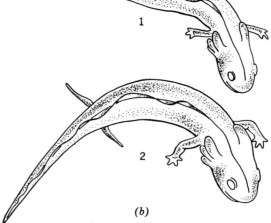

Figure 17-1 (*a*) Enlarged tracings from movie film of the early swimming movements of the tiger salamander, *Ambystoma tigrinum*. The series of actions 1 to 10, starts with a resting individual, 1, which moves the head and tail so rapidly that the film record (17 frames/sec) is blurred (2). In the third and fourth frames it completes a coil, with the anterior trunk straightening in 5 and 6. This is followed by a flexure to the right in 7 to 9 and a return to a resting position in 10. (*b*) An older larva, 1, initiates walking with forelimbs. A still older larva, 2, walks with all four limbs, although the hindlimbs are not yet capable of flexion and do not respond to local stimulation. After Coghill 1929.

(1951, 1958), who operated on the eyes of frogs and salamanders to change their orientation in the orbit, again produced abnormal behavior which the animals were never able to correct (Figures 17-2 and 17-3).

These experiments and others seem to imply that, at least under these rather drastically modified conditions, exogenous factors have little effect in determining the basic patterns of motor coordination in locomotion, optokinetic responses, and scratching (see page 662). Weiss (1939, p. 558) has summarized his interpretation of the situation in the following evocative way.

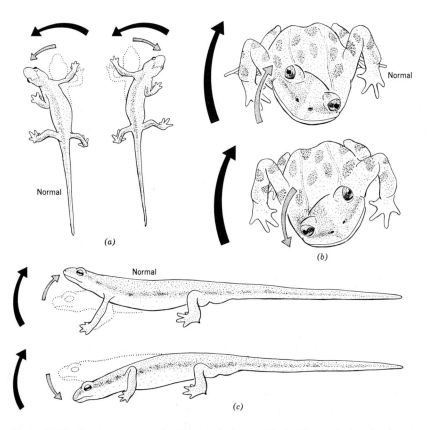

Figure 17-2 Sperry transplanted embryonic bud material, thereby producing disoriented structures and behavior. The outer dark arrows indicate the direction of an optokinetic visual stimulus. The normal controls are compared with experimentals in which the eyes have been 1, rotated 180 degrees; 2, 3, transplanted in the contralateral orbit and inverted either dorso-ventrally (2) or nasotemporally (3); or 4, in which the union of the optic nerves has been crossed. Treatments 1, 3, and 4 cause the reversal of response shown in (a); 1, 2, and 4 cause the reversal in (b); and 2 and 3 cause the reversal in (c). After Sperry 1951.

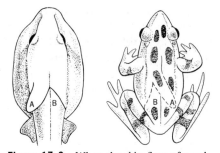

Figure 17-3   When the skin flaps of a tad-
pole are translocated contralaterally across the
midline of the back, the mature frog misdirects
wiping actions of the hindfoot when stimulated
on the transplanted flaps. A stimulus on the left
elicits wiping with the right foot directed at the
right flank. After Sperry 1951.

The nervous system reminds us of an industrial plant not only by the multiplicity
of cooperating agents and the harmonious coordination of their activities, but also
by the fact that the construction is completed in its main lines without the experience, and, in fact, even before the onset, of actual function. A ship at the time of its
launching represents best the state of the nervous system at the time when it first
engages in functional activities; though much remains to be perfected, it is able to
float, move and steer. Similarly, the nervous system, when for the first time called
upon to act, can already conduct and coordinate impulses and control the musculature, at least grossly.

It is well to remember some special aspects of the work we have discussed so far. It has been conducted mainly by embryologists and anat-
omists on the early behavior of fish and amphibians. The eggs of the
species selected hatch in water, and the young must perform swimming
actions at an early age. Swimming engages the whole body as well as the
limbs, so that the early appearance of coordinated movements of the
whole musculature has functional value in these species.

◆ *Development of Behavior in Chicken Embryos.* The growing embryo of a
bird can be observed while still in the egg by cutting a window in the
shell and making the inner shell membrane transparent with vaseline.
This method was the basis of one of the most thorough studies of behavioral development ever attempted (Kuo 1932a–e, 1933). A chicken
egg takes about 20 to 21 days from the beginning of incubation to hatch.
During embryonic development spontaneous activity is concentrated
between about the fourth and tenth days. This activity is followed by a
relatively quiet period before the intense activity of hatching. Move-

ments begin with the head and proceed backward during ontogeny. More or less extensive movements of the trunk then appear, involving the limbs to varying degrees. Finally separate movements of the limbs, tail, beak, and eyes are observed. Studies of the behavior of chicks removed from the egg at various ages confirmed Kuo's descriptions in most respects, although the first movements were seen at a somewhat later age (Orr and Windle 1934). There is a general parallel with other species in the occurrence of gross movements of the whole body musculature before independent movements of the extremities.

In addition to studies of the ordering of development of spontaneous actions within the undisturbed egg, Orr and Windle (1934) artificially stimulated embryos and recorded the development of responsiveness to various kinds of artificial stimuli. They found a different pattern of development from that of spontaneous movement. Independent movements of the wings can be induced by tactile stimuli at a stage when the spontaneous movements are more generalized. Thus the potential for local limb movement exists before the first independent movements within the confines of the egg actually occur.

Kuo devoted much attention to the question of spontaneity. Taking an extreme position, he concluded that "there is no such thing as 'spontaneous activity' any more than there is such a thing as 'spontaneous generation.'" He referred to the paradox that it is generally necessary to take account of external conditions before the characteristics of endogenous activity can be completely defined (see page 214). In particular, Kuo had in mind the influence of changing conditions within the egg in determining the timing of muscular activities.

The periods of maximal embryonic activity coincide with the most frequent movements of the amnion, which encloses the embryo and throws it into movement when it contracts (Figure 17-4). Kuo suggested that the amnion is primarily responsible for timing the onset of activity in the embryo, as a result of the mechanical disturbance it creates. There is no experimental proof of Kuo's idea, however. And Hamburger (1963) points out that there is no close synchrony between amniotic contractions and movements of the embryo.

The pattern of development of the nervous system determines the characteristics of behavioral ontogeny. Windle and Orr (1934) showed histologically that the motor side of the nervous system of the growing chick develops first. The sensory side becomes organized around the time of the first responses to extraneous stimuli, about four days after the first spontaneous movements. The time at which the different acts are first performed must be determined in large part as a consequence of nerve growth.

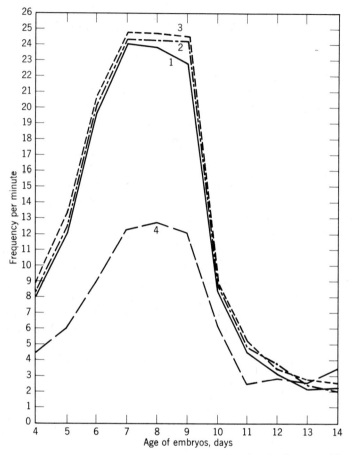

Figure 17-4   The actions of chicken egg embryos during development: (1) swinging movements, (2) yolk sac movements, (3) amnion contractions, and (4) general body activities. After Kuo 1932c.

Hamburger (1963) believes that endogenous rhythms of neural activity are also involved in the first activities. Careful study of the temporal organization of the spontaneous movements of chick embryos reveals a marked rhythmicity. There are regular phases of a minute or so of activity followed by a rather longer period of inactivity (Figure 17-5). Hamburger (1963) has studied the origin of this rhythmical pattern. He reasoned that if some rhythmical external stimulus is responsible, perhaps generated by the embryo itself in a previous cycle of activity, it should be possible to change the rhythm by external stimulation. Movements were elicited from chick embryos in the middle of inactive phases by touching with a hair. Comparison of the durations of active and inactive phases in

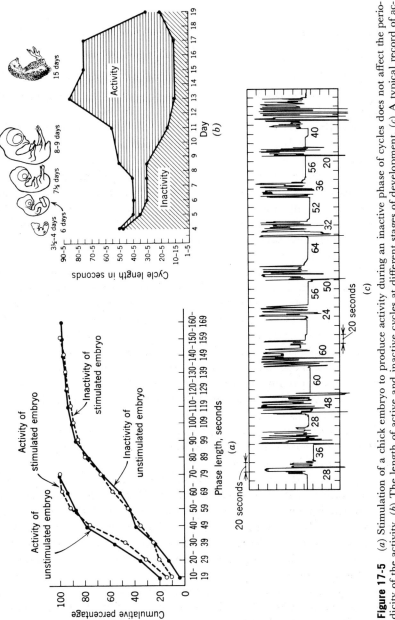

Figure 17-5 (a) Stimulation of a chick embryo to produce activity during an inactive phase of cycles does not affect the periodicity of the activity. (b) The length of active and inactive cycles at different stages of development. (c) A typical record of activity of a "stage 37 embryo." After Hamburger 1963 and Hamburger, Balaban, Oppenheim, and Wenger 1965.

animals stimulated in this way and in unstimulated controls revealed no differences (Figure 17-5). Hamburger concludes that sensory input probably plays no role in the triggering of overt embryonic activity at least up to eighteen days (i.e. up to about three days before hatching). Thus, although the elicitation of movement by external stimulation is possible after about seven and a half days of incubation, the potentiality is not realized until much later in the normal course of development.

The source of the rhythm is still unexplained. Is it neurally generated, or is there perhaps a cycle of oxygen or carbon dioxide levels that triggers cycles of activity, as Tracy believed? Hamburger (1963) sectioned the nerve cord of chick embryos at various places and compared activity cycles in the two parts (Figure 17-6). All isolated parts retained the capacity for spontaneous rhythmical activity. But whereas the movements of intact embryos are often coordinated, the activity cycles of isolated sections were now out of phase, which argues against a general metabolic trigger for activity such as carbon dioxide level. The cycles of movement suggest endogenous rhythms of neural activity.

Hamburger postulates centers of activation spreading over the spinal cord. There is evidence that the brain affects activity in other parts of the nervous system in the intact embryo, however. Activity cycles in parts of the embryo isolated from the brain involved 25 percent less activity in a given time. In eleven-day embryos, for example, decapitation lengthened the duration of the inactive phase but left the duration of the active phase unchanged (Figure 17-7). Evidently the brain is a source of tonic stimulation for the spinal centers, superimposing its effect on a pre-existent but slower rhythm of activity. A tonic effect of the brain upon spinal mechanisms was similarly indicated in studies of vertebrate and invertebrate locomotion (see page 221).

Thus present indications are that in the course of normal undisturbed development of the chick embryo endogenous factors are largely responsible for the initiation of movements.

In addition to the timing of development Kuo was interested in the shaping of the actual form of action patterns. He suggested that in several cases feedback relationships between different parts of the embryo and between the embryo and the egg play a role. For example, normal growth and function of the legs depend on adoption by the late embryo of a position in the egg with the legs beneath the body. This position allows extensor thrust to develop against the force of gravity. If this position is for some reason not achieved, the legs become deformed and locomotion is abnormal (Kuo 1932d). After the eleventh day with the embryo in the same position, the legs lie pressed against the breast beneath the yolk sac. At this time alternate leg movements begin. "Now in order to permit

Stage 11   Stage 30

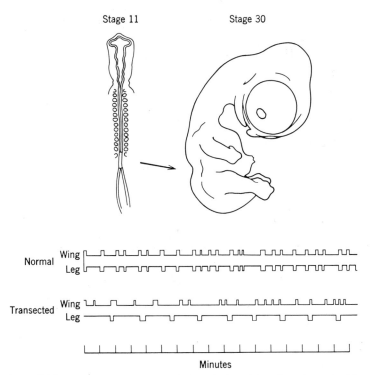

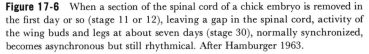

Minutes

Figure 17-6 When a section of the spinal cord of a chick embryo is removed in the first day or so (stage 11 or 12), leaving a gap in the spinal cord, activity of the wing buds and legs at about seven days (stage 30), normally synchronized, becomes asynchronous but still rhythmical. After Hamburger 1963.

movements, one of the legs has to push up the amnion and the yolk sac, thus lessening the pressure of the yolk sac on the other leg and allowing the latter more room for movements" (Kuo 1932e). The absence of such leg movements in embryos in which the yolk sac fails to orient properly in relation to the body suggested to Kuo that these alternating leg movements play a formative role in shaping the locomotory coordination.

By arguments such as these Kuo sought to emphasize that genetic information can be 'decoded' in a number of different ways, some involving an intimate relationship between the embryo and its environment. He felt it the task of developmental biologists to unravel the processes by which this decoding occurs. Many of Kuo's ideas still wait to be subjected to experimental testing, and it should not be forgotten that temporal correlations of the kind he established do not necessarily demonstrate a direct causal relationship.

The relationship of developing behavior to growth and the accom-

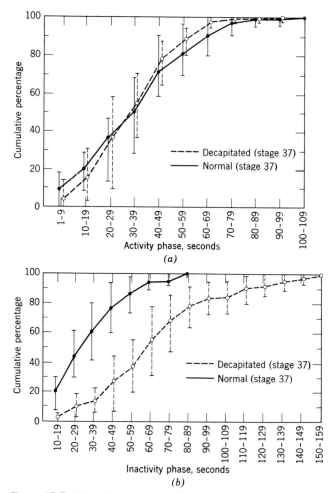

Figure 17-7   The effect of decapitation of an eleven-day-old chick embryo on the (a) active and (b) inactive phases of the behavior cycle. After Hamburger 1963.

panying changes in position of the embryo and its associated membranes help to determine subsequent behavior. This is clear at the time of hatching. Kuo (1932b) lists several stages which must be passed properly if hatching is to occur. In the course of extensive observations, many embryos that did not orient properly and failed to hatch were found. Permissive factors which do not shape the pattern of actions at hatching but are necessary for it to occur are involved.

One of the first acts after hatching is pecking. Several authors have experimented on the role of posthatching experience in the development of pecking. Much early work is reviewed by Maier and Schneirla (1964). The accuracy of the pecking of normal chicks improves during the first four or five days of life and then levels out. Is this improvement a result of practice? Chicks can be fed by hand, thus delaying the first opportunity to peck. If they are then allowed to peck, they begin with a somewhat better score than newly hatched chicks and reach a normal level of accuracy more rapidly (Figure 17-8). Growth and practice must both play a part in the improving accuracy of pecking in a normal chick.

If deprivation continues longer than five days, there is some inhibition of pecking, apparently because the birds become trained to hand feeding. Birds fed artificially for fourteen days failed to peck when given the opportunity (Maier and Schneirla 1964). Thus the opportunity to perform a motor activity may have a permissive role in maintaining its presence in the behavioral repertoire.

◆ *Mammalian Embryo Development.* The isolation of the young mammal in the mother's uterus makes it difficult to study behavioral development. Descriptions are made mainly of embryos after they have been removed

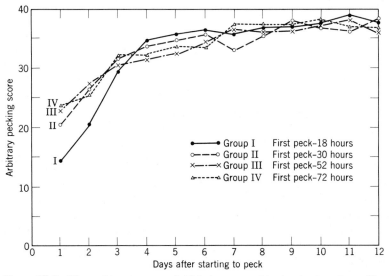

Figure 17-8 The pecking accuracy of chicks improves with experience and age. The two factors may be experimentally separated by feeding the chick without allowing it to peck for varying periods of time. In this graph the score of chicks is plotted from their first experience. A perfect score is 50. After Maier and Schneirla 1964.

from the mother. The conditions of observation are thus drastically different from their normal environment, and our knowledge of the nature and extent of spontaneous movements within the uterus is still scanty. What little evidence there is from transillumination in situ suggests that activity occurs infrequently, and certainly less often than after artificial separation from the mother. The following discussion refers only to actions of such separated embryos, the movement of which was often induced by active experimental stimulation.

Coghill's (1929) generalizations about the patterns of behavioral development in lower vertebrates led others to study a wide range of species including mammals. In rats, cats, and other species movements appeared earliest near the head and proceeded caudally (Table 17–1). Activity is most frequent near the middle of the gestation period and is inhibited as birth approaches. The first results obtained seemed to confirm that in rat and cat embryos the isolated movements of the extremities developed out of a series of generalized movements by a process which Coghill called in salamanders "individuation" (Angulo 1932, Coronios 1933).

Then a note of dissent was heard from such investigators as Windle (1940) working with rats and cats, Carmichael (1934) with guinea pigs, and Barcroft and Barron (1939) with sheep. They found individual movements of the extremities appearing at the same stage as mass movements of the embryo, or even earlier. As a result of the disagreement a major and often bitter controversy arose about whether the pattern of embryonic development in mammals conformed to Coghill's principle of individuation or not (Carmichael 1933, 1936, Hooker 1936, Barron 1941).

Subsequent work resolved the problem by showing that the differences in results were caused mainly by anoxia of the embryo in the early mammalian studies, which can favor the occurrence of mass movements (Windle 1950). With this factor under better control it became clear that the pattern of development in mammalian embryos is indeed different from that of lower vertebrates.

Organized movement in the mammal appears to commence not with co-ordinated movements of a myogenic character as in the fish, or indeed as neuro-muscular movements which are the expression of alterations in the Central Nervous System unprompted by afferent impulses—movements such as are seen in *Amblystoma* or the toadfish. Such movements may exist in the mammal, but rather as relics which appear at death than as the heralds of embryonic activity. The mechanism for their eclipse appears to be the chronological pushing forward of sensation relative to motion (Barcroft and Barron 1939, p. 150).

This temporal shift can perhaps in turn be related to the absence in these

Table 17-1 First Reflexogenous Zones Responding to Direct Stimulation

Animal	Foetal age	First reflexogenous zone	Movement
Rat	16th day	Side of snout	Later flexion of head away from stimulus
Rat	16th day	Corner of mouth, shoulder, and side	Involved neck and forelimbs
Rat	16th day	Snout	Lateral flexion and extension of head
Rabbit	15-16 days	Nose, head, and neck regions	Lateral flexion in the neck and upper trunk
Cat	23rd day	Head, shoulder, and paw	Reaction of foreleg
Cat	28th day	Nose and ears, to a lesser degree other points on the head	Extension, lateral flexion, and rotation of head
Guinea pig	31 days	Ear	Flexion of neck, raising of forelimb
Sheep	34th day	Face	Head extension
Man	8 weeks +	Face	Flexion of body, involving muscles of limb girdle

After Barron 1941 from various authors.

mammals of any early need for swimming, such as occurs in fishes and amphibia.

There is little or no information on the role of environmental factors in triggering the natural movements of mammalian embryos and in shaping their patterns. It is known that prenatal experience of the mother can change the thresholds for certain kinds of responses. If pregnant rats are subjected to situations calculated to generate anxiety, their young are more timid and emotional than normal, even when transferred to normal foster mothers at birth (Thompson 1957, Doyle and Yule 1959). We shall note later many parallel effects of postnatal experience.

SEX HORMONES AND DEVELOPMENT

The statement that sexuality has a genetic basis tells us little about how sexual characteristics actually develop. Experiments on the effects of sex hormones on mammalian development reveal that hormone production by the embryonic gonads is crucial in setting the stage for normal sexual behavior in adulthood (Young, Goy, and Phoenix 1964).

When female guinea pigs were treated with testosterone in the mother's uterus, they became masculinized as adults, both in genital structure and in behavior. They failed to come into heat and mounted other animals. The masculization effect was greatest with testosterone treatment at about halfway through pregnancy and did not occur with postnatal treatment. With female rats, which are less precocial than guinea pigs, testosterone treatment as late as the first day of life still has these masculinizing effects. Females so treated fail to show normal sexual behavior even if castrated and injected with estrogen and progesterone in dosages that reliably induce sexual receptivity in normal females.

Males treated at similar times with estrogen were feminized as adults, although still capable of mounting when given testosterone therapy (Levine and Mullins 1964, Whalen 1964, Young et al. 1964). A similar effect can be achieved by castrating newborn male rats (Harris 1964), indicating that estrogen probably affects the male infant by interfering with testosterone production. If a male rat, castrated in infancy, is treated with ovarian hormones in adulthood, it behaves like a female in encounters with sexually active males. The ovarian hormones have much less effect in feminizing a male rat castrated as an adult.

In addition to affecting the dominant patterns of sexual behavior, early hormone treatment also affects the cyclic properties. A female that has been masculinized by fetal or neonatal androgen treatment ceases to show estrous cycles. If a male rat feminized by neonatal castration is given an ovarian transplant, it shows cyclic activity approximating the estrous cycle of a normal female. There are no such cycles if a male castrated in adulthood is the recipient of the transplants (Harris 1964).

The evidence seems to indicate a key role for fetal and neonatal testosterone in organizing the parts of the central nervous system that control sexual behavior in mammals. Development in the absence of testosterone seems to lead to the female pattern of sexual receptivity and estrous cycling. Development with testosterone leads to hypertrophy of male genital characteristics, masculine sexual behavior, and a noncyclic organization of sexual behavior. The sensitive periods for these effects are well defined, and after their termination there seems little chance of reversal. In adult life the function of the sex hormones is to trigger a pattern of sexual behavior that is already preformed as a consequence of these early feedback effects of gonadal hormones on embryonic development.

CONCLUSIONS

The evidence indicates that environmental stimuli generally play a minimal role in directly determining the form and time of appearance of embryonic motor activities. Kuo's suggestion that sensory feedback is involved in the development of certain motor patterns in the chick embryo remains unproved although the effects of hormones on sexual development show how such feedback mechanisms can work. The emphasis is placed on endogenous processes. Hamburger (1963) concludes from his study of chicks that

there exists a *motor action system* with the following characteristics: (1) it is overt and spontaneous—that is, it discharges independently of reflexogenous stimulation; (2) it performs in motility cycles of regular periodicity, up to 13 days, and from then on almost continuously; and (3) it involves generalized motility of many or all parts that are capable of motility at a given stage. Independently of this system, there develops the *reflex apparatus* which begins to attain functional maturity 3 to 4 days after the onset of spontaneous motility. It differs from the latter in the following points: (1) it remains latent in the normal, undisturbed chick embryo, due to the absence of adequate stimuli; and (2) the response following experimental stimulation is more or less localized and of brief duration (Hamburger 1963, p. 351).

He is led to the conclusion that these two components are represented by different mechanisms within the central nervous system.

The spontaneous motor activity is not of course independent of environmental conditions. The circumstances must be such as to permit activity to occur. Movement of a chick embryo can be inhibited by exposure to a mixture of 10 percent CO_2 and 90 percent O_2. The actual timing of each phase of action and inaction seems to be determined endogenously, however. Only at birth does the interplay of sensory and motor mechanisms become a dominant factor in the development of new patterns of behavior in the chick.

Similar generalizations are probably valid for fish, salamanders, and other nonmammalian forms. The applicability to mammals is more tenuous. Sensory connections begin functioning at a relatively earlier stage than in lower forms. Nevertheless, Hamburger (1963) suggests that the main difference lies in the inhibition of spontaneous motility by the particular evironmental conditions in which mammalian embryos are placed. Only when the conditions are changed, as by reducing the oxygen supply to the embryo, do the movements appear. Thus the two components with similar characteristics, a motor action system and a reflex apparatus, may be present in mammalian embryonic development, although the capacity for movement is normally not overtly expressed.

What of the order in which different movements appear in the course of development? Coghill's model of integrated action patterns becoming individuated into localized movements in the course of development is valid for fish and amphibians. But it does not hold for birds and mammals where movements of individual limbs begin early in the developmental sequence. The integration of early movements in fish and salamanders seems in fact to be a characteristic that prepares the embryo for the actions of swimming after hatching.

REFERENCES

Angulo y González, A. W. 1932. The prenatal development of behavior in the albino rat. *J. Comp. Neurol.*, **55**:395–442.

Barcroft, J. and D. H. Barron. 1939. Movement in the mammalian foetus. *Ergeb. Physiol.*, **42**:107–152.

Barron, D. H. 1941. The functional development of some mammalian neuromuscular mechanisms. *Biol. Rev.*, **16**:1–33.

Carmichael, L. 1933. Origin and prenatal growth of behavior. In *A Handbook of Child Psychology*, ed. by C. A. Murchison: 31–159. Clark University Press, Worchester, Massachusetts.

———. 1934. An experimental study in the prenatal guinea-pig of the origin and development of reflexes and patterns of behavior in relation to the stimulation of specific receptor areas during the period of active fetal life. *Genet. Psychol. Monogr.*, **16**:337–491.

———. 1936. A re-evaluation of the concepts of maturation and learning as applied to the early development of behavior. *Psychol. Rev.*, **43**:450–470.

Coghill, G. E. 1929. *Anatomy and the Problem of Behaviour.* Cambridge University Press, Cambridge.

Coronios, J. D. 1933. The development of behavior in the fetal cat. *Genet. Psychol. Monogr.*, **14**:283–386.

Doyle, G. and E. P. Yule. 1959. Early experience and emotionality. I. The effects of prenatal maternal anxiety on the emotionality of albino rats. *S. Afr. J. Soc. Res.*, **10**:57–65.

Hamburger, V. 1963. Some aspects of the embryology of behavior. *Quart. Rev. Biol.*, **38**:342–365.

———, M. Balaban, R. Oppenheim, and E. Wenger. 1965. Periodic motility of normal and spinal chick embryos between 8 and 17 days of incubation. *J. Exp. Zool.*, **159**:1–14.

Harris, G. W. 1964. Female cycles of gonadotrophic secretion and female sexual behavior in adult male rats castrated at birth. *J. Physiol.*, **175**:75P–76P.

Hooker, D. 1936. Early fetal activity in mammals. *Yale J. Biol. Med.*, **8**:579–602.

Kuo, Z. Y. 1932a. Ontogeny of embryonic behavior in aves. I. The chronology and general nature of the behavior of the chick embryo. *J. Exp. Zool.*, **61**:395–430.

———. 1932b. Ontogeny of embryonic behavior in aves. II. The mechanical factors in the various stages leading to hatching. *J. Exp. Zool.*, **62**:453–487.

———. 1932c. Ontogeny of embryonic behavior in aves. III. The structural and environmental factors in embryonic behavior. *J. Comp. Psychol.*, **13**:245–271.

———. 1932d. Ontogeny of embryonic behavior in aves. IV. The influence of embryonic movements upon the behavior after hatching. *J. Comp. Psychol.*, **14**:109–121.

———. 1932e. Ontogeny of embryonic behavior in aves. V. The reflex concept in the light of embryonic behavior in birds. *Psychol. Rev.*, **39**:499–515.

————. 1933. Ontogeny of embryonic behavior in aves. VI. Relation between heart beat and the behavior of the avian embryo. *J. Comp. Psychol.*, **16**:379–384.

Levine, S. and R. Mullins, Jr. 1964. Estrogen administered neonatally affects adult sexual behavior in male and female rats. *Science*, **144**:185–187.

Maier, N. R. F. and T. C. Schneirla. 1964. *Principles of Animal Psychology.* Dover Publications, New York.

Orr, D. W. and W. F. Windle. 1934. The development of behavior in chick embryos: the appearance of somatic movements. *J. Comp. Neurol.*, **60**:271–285.

Preyer, W. 1885. *Specielle Physiologie des Embryo.* Grieben, Leipzig.

Sperry, R. W. 1951. Mechanisms of neural maturation. In *Handbook of Experimental Psychology*, ed. by S. S. Stevens: 236–280. John Wiley and Sons, New York.

————. 1958. Physiological plasticity and brain circuit theory. In *Biological and Biochemical Bases of Behavior*, ed. by H. F. Harlow and C. N. Woolsey: 401–424. Wisconsin University Press, Madison.

Thompson, W. R. 1957. Influence of prenatal maternal anxiety on emotionality in young rats. *Science*, **125**:698–699.

Tracy, H. C. 1926. The development of motility and behavior reactions in the toadfish (*Opsanus tau*). *J. Comp. Neurol.*, **40**:253–369.

Weiss, P. 1939. *Principles of Development.* Henry Holt and Company, New York.

————. 1950. Experimental analysis of co-ordination by the disarrangement of central-peripheral relations. *Symp. Soc. Exp. Biol.*, **4**:92–111.

Whalen, R. E. 1964. Hormone-induced changes in the organization of sexual behavior in the male rat. *J. comp. physiol. Psychol.*, **57**:175–182.

Windle, W. F. 1940. *Physiology of the Fetus: Origin and Extent of Function in Prenatal Life.* W. B. Saunders Company, Philadelphia.

————. 1950. Reflexes of mammalian embryos and fetuses. In *Genetic Neurology*, ed. by P. Weiss: 214–222. University of Chicago Press, Chicago.

———— and D. W. Orr. 1934. The development of behavior in chick embryos: spinal cord structure correlated with early somatic motility. *J. Comp. Neurol.*, **60**:287–307.

Young, W. C., R. W. Goy, and C. H. Phoenix. 1964. Hormones and sexual behavior. *Science*, **143**:212–218.

eighteen

BEHAVIORAL DEVELOPMENT:
SENSORY MECHANISMS

Use of the terms 'inherited' and 'learned' • Environmental influences on development • Genetic control • Responsiveness to external stimuli without previous exposure • Specific and unspecific effects of early sensory experience • Imprinting, conditioning, extinction, and habituation.

◆ *Use of the Terms 'Inherited' and 'Learned.'* Problems of nature and nurture have long been a major source of controversy in behavioral science. A particular bone of contention has been the validity of classifying behavioral acts as either 'instinctive' or 'learned.' This difficulty arises because the development of behavior, like the development of all characteristics of organisms, involves interaction between the genotype which the individual inherits and the environment within which it grows. This interaction is so intimate and complex that it is extraordinarily difficult to identify the effects of these two sources of influence which, between them, provide the information guiding the development of the organism (Lorenz 1961).

Viewing ontogeny in this light, many authors feel that it is meaningless to ask the age-old question of how much of a specific trait of an individual is caused by heredity and how much by environment. "Since no phenotypic trait is independent of either hereditary or environmental agents, an attempt to divide into two fractions the interrelation of two agents, neither of which alone can produce a phenotype, is futile" (Stern 1960, see Carmichael 1933, Haldane 1946, Dobzhansky 1950, Hebb 1953, Simpson, Pittendrigh, and Tiffany 1957, Lerner 1958, Fuller and Thompson 1960).

Such a statement may seem to imply that it is impractical to try to disentangle the roles of genetic and environmental influences in behavioral development. The reverse is actually true. This position stems from an appreciation of how the problem can be dealt with experimentally and from an understanding of the limitations of such investigations. The crucial point is epitomized by the preoccupation with a static 'specific trait of an *individual*.' When a geneticist speaks of an inherited trait he refers not to a characteristic of one individual but to the difference between two individuals or groups of individuals, or populations.

A population geneticist considers two sources of phenotypic variation within a population, genetic factors and environmental factors, and the processes of their interaction. The method of exploring the relative contributions of these factors to variation in the population is to hold either genotype or environment constant and observe the effect of systematically varying the other in experimental populations. Geneticists usually manipulate the genotype. Having established that a difference between two populations is genotypic, they proceed to explore the nature of the genetic mechanism by crossing and backcrossing experiments, gradually unraveling one aspect of the developmental process. At no point is the inference drawn that a particular trait in a given individual animal is inherited; rather a certain difference between the traits of the two individuals is shown to be inherited.

The same restrictions limit the inferences that can be drawn from experiments on the role of training in the development of a behavior pattern (Jensen 1961). The demonstration that a particular sequence of environmental stimuli is a prerequisite for development of a new behavior pattern in an individual animal shows that learning is crucial for the ontogeny of this particular act. But it does not prove that the act as such is learned. Learning inevitably involves interaction with the genotype. We can speak of the difference between the behavior of a trained and an untrained animal as learned, provided that their genotypes are similar, but the behavior of a single individual cannot be spoken of as learned. Again we find ourselves concerned with the recurring theme of interaction between the organism and its environment. This interaction itself is basic to the understanding of behavior.

◆ *Description.* Careful, thorough description of the development of behavior during the growth of individual animals is as important for the analysis of behavioral development as it is for any area of animal behavior. The interpretation of such descriptions, however, which we have found to be a fruitful source of information about the causal basis of a great deal of behavior, must be conducted with much greater caution in developmental studies. In descriptions of the behavior of adult animals which are moving freely in a varied environment, behavior in a range of different situations is recorded. In ontogenetic studies, on the other hand, particularly those concerned with juvenile or embryonic development, the environment is generally less variable. Here descriptions do not benefit from the natural experiments that occur when observations are made in a wide variety of external situations. Thus in investigations of behavioral development experimentation is especially important for deriving hypotheses about the causal mechanisms involved.

◆ *Types of Environmental Influences.* Experimental analysis of the ways in which genetic and environmental factors contribute to the processes of behavioral development is complicated by several different types of environmental influence. The major distinction lies between the part of the environment that the animal creates for itself and the part that is beyond its control. The division has theoretical as well as practical importance, because information that contributes to development by way of self-generated environmental changes may still derive ultimately from the genotype. Such changes have direct effects on growth processes. They can also involve various types of sensory feedback, a major factor in determining the course of development of some behavior patterns.

Sometimes the distinction between environmental influences that are self-generated and influences that are not is less clear. The environment in which development begins may be the outcome of chance events such as exposure to a particular current of wind or water. Often the situation is far from accidental, however. A developing animal which is motile may be able to select a particular range of environmental conditions. The choice may in turn have an impact on further development. Are the environmental factors that are selected self-generated? Clearly they are not, but neither are they random events.

The environment of the developing embryo may have been carefully selected by the mother at the time when the eggs were laid. She may tend the eggs and assume some positive control of the environment in which they develop, influencing such factors as temperature, humidity, and oxygen and carbon dioxide concentrations. Such control reaches its extreme in viviparous species. Similarly, after birth the environment in which the young animal finds itself is far from a random selection of available stimuli. Development may be greatly influenced by stimuli from parents and siblings, depending on the social system into which the young is born. Variations in behavior that arise in this way are clearly not genotypic. Nevertheless, genetic considerations are relevant. The services that the parent renders to the young, sometimes endangering its own survival, are a reflection of the close genetic relationship between parent and off-spring (Hamilton 1963).

These problems have considerable bearing on discussions of the evolution of patterns of behavioral development. But when the main concern is with the mechanisms of development, the distinction between genotypic and environmental influences generally remains clear.

◆ *Three Kinds of Effects on Behavioral Development.* The effects of manipulation of genetic and environmental variables on behavioral development include, first, permissive or triggering effects on a particular behavioral act or pattern of responsiveness. These cause either presence or absence without affecting the structure of behavior itself. Second, some variables have unspecific effects on behavior, changing the frequency of certain acts or shifting the thresholds of receptors without influencing the detailed structure of behavior. Third, some variables have specific effects on the structure of particular behavioral acts and systems of responsiveness. Distinctions between these categories are often relative and arbitrary. They denote only points on a continuum, but we shall nevertheless find them useful in the following discussions for avoiding some points of confusion.

External stimuli can have a variety of functions in the spatiotemporal control of established behavior patterns. They can provide an immediate trigger or they can inhibit an activity, they can lower or raise the threshold or otherwise modify the response to another stimulus, they can maintain or check an activity once it has begun, or they can orient or disorient the behavior in space. The specificity of the stimuli which have these different effects varies widely. How does the sensory equipment, peripheral and central, develop the properties required for these functions to be properly served? To what extent are species differences in the properties of sensory mechanisms under genetic control? How far can they be attributed to variations in the developmental environment? Or, focusing particularly on the part of the environment that is directly perceived by sense organs, what is the effect of past sensory experience on sensory function?

GENETIC CONTROL

A few studies have demonstrated genetic control of interindividual and interspecies differences in certain aspects of responsiveness to external stimuli (Fuller and Thompson 1960). Gross hereditary abnormalities in the structure of sense organs can affect behavioral function, resulting in blindness, deafness, or anosmia. We are more interested in subtler variations which are under genetic control.

The specificity of stimuli eliciting feeding behavior in some insects has been noted (page 231). The food plants of the larvae of two species of moth, *Callosamia promethea* and *C. angulifera,* are mostly different. Tests of hybrids between them showed that the *angulifera* genes were dominant in the choice of food, as well as in external morphology (Haskins and Haskins 1958).

In vertebrates, Rodgers and McClearn (1962) demonstrated in detail the genetic mechanism controlling a preference for ethyl alcohol in mice. In addition to breeding experiments, these workers also took the precaution of fostering young on mothers of different strains, confirming the genetic basis of differences. Another example of genetic control of sensory differences is the ability of humans to taste phenylthiocarbamide, a well-studied monofactorial recessive character (review in Fuller and Thompson 1960).

In such cases the control of sensory function is presumably a result of differences in the properties of the actual receptors and their afferent pathways. Influence may be less direct, as in the heritable difference in temperature preferences in certain inbred strains of mice. This is achieved by variations in the thermal insulation of the integument, including skin thickness and density of the fur which in turn affect the responsiveness of temperature receptors underneath (Herter 1936, 1938).

The examples considered so far demonstrate genetic control of the eliciting functions of external stimuli. Orienting effects may also be genetically controlled, as for example the geotactic and phototactic responses of *Drosophila* (Hirsch 1958, 1962). By selective breeding within a population which initially had a neutral orientation to gravity, Weiss (1959) developed one population that showed negative geotaxis in about 80 percent of its trials and another that was positive about 77 percent of the time. Hirsch and Boudreau (1958) achieved similar results with phototactic responses of *Drosophila* (Figure 18-1).

These studies of the genetic control of sensory mechanisms include (1) demonstrations of variation in sensory processes, (2) susceptibility to selective breeding (*Drosophila* taxes), and (3) analyses of the behavior of crosses between genetically dissimilar parents (food preferences of interspecific moth hybrids, man's ability to taste phenylthiocarbamide, alcohol preference in mice). The small number of examples reflects the limited amount of research directed at this problem. Nevertheless, these studies show the practicability of working out the genetic contribution to sensory

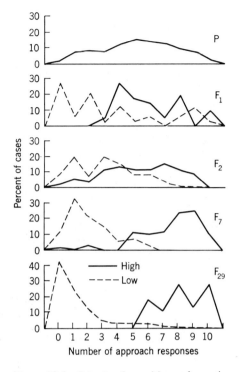

Figure 18-1   Selection for positive and negative phototactic responses in the fruit fly, *Drosophila melanogaster*. The graph is of approaches to the lighted side of a multiple Y-maze. After Hirsch and Boudreau 1958.

development. The feasibility depends in part on adoption of the level of statistical awareness that population studies of variable behavioral traits require. Hopefully, geneticists will soon begin exploring the developmental basis of responsiveness to some of the more complex eliciting and orienting stimuli that have such profound implications for survival under natural conditions.

RESPONSIVENESS TO SPECIFIC EXTERNAL STIMULI WITHOUT PREVIOUS EXPOSURE

There are many examples of response to a particular set of external stimuli on the first occasion that they are encountered. Although the developmental basis of such responsiveness remains unknown, it is clear

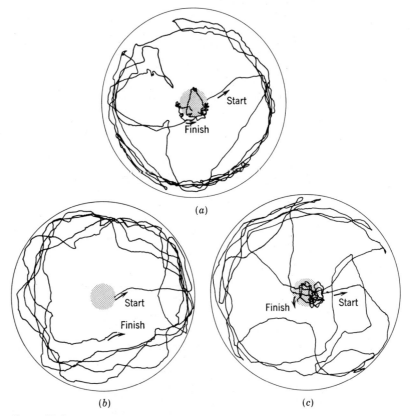

Figure 18-2 The paths followed by young cichlids, (a) *Tilapia mossambica*, (b) *Tilapia tholloni*, and (c) a hybrid, in a model experiment. The disk in the center shows the position of a spherical model. Young *mossambica* approach the sphere closely. Young *tholloni* keep more distance. The performance of the hybrid closely resembles that of *T. mossambica*, suggesting dominance of the genes regulating this behavior. Graphs (page 625) of the number and duration of contacts with the sphere show a similar relationship. After Peters 1963.

that response to certain stimulus properties does not depend on prior exposure to these same stimulus properties. This conclusion can be valid even when responsiveness to other properties of the same stimulus situation is found to be affected by prior sensory experience.

Some of the most persuasive demonstrations involve the behavior of young animals whose postnatal sensory experience has been experimentally controlled. For example, many young cichlid fishes have a strong bond with their parents. They can readily be persuaded to approach artificial models. The bright colors of the adults differ from species to

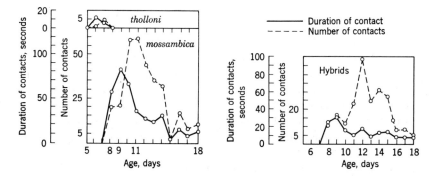

species. The newly hatched young of four cichlid species show an initial responsiveness to models that have the same dominant color as their parents, blue and violet in *Haplochromis multicolor* (Peters 1937), black, blue, and green in *Cichlasoma bimaculatus* and *C. biocellatum* (Noble and Curtis 1939, Baerends and Baerends-van Roon 1950, Kühme 1962), and red in *Hemichromis bimaculatus* (Noble and Curtis 1939, Peters 1941, Baerends and Baerends–van Roon 1950, Kühme 1962). The young of another fish, *Menidia*, raised in isolation, select young of their own species and school with them when first given a choice (Shaw 1961).

There is an interesting difference between the behavior of mouth-brooding and substrate-breeding cichlid fishes. Young mouth brooders are normally taken into the parents' mouth when danger threatens, and will readily approach and contact models exhibiting stimuli of appropriate color, size, and movement. Young substrate breeders approach models but keep a certain distance from them. Peters (1963) and his colleagues have shown that young hybrids between *Tilapia mossambica*, a mouth brooder, and *T. tholloni*, a substrate breeder, behave like mouth brooders, suggesting dominance of the genes controlling their behavior (Figure 18-2).

The pecking behavior of newly hatched gull chicks has been studied exhaustively. The chicks direct pecking movements at the parent's bill and in so doing strike food held in it. Experiments with models demonstrated that certain characteristics of color, size, shape, orientation, and movement of the parent's bill are significant in eliciting this response (see page 388). In the response of following the parents soon after hatching, the young of other species of birds, including ducks and chickens, are responsive to a particular configuration of size, color, shape, and movement (see page 635).

Among mammals, young rhesus monkeys have been tested with a

variety of 'surrogate mothers' in attempts to define the factors that establish the bond between mother and young (Harlow 1961, 1962). In addition to such elementary responses as the righting reflex and turning and suckling at something touching the cheek, there is a deep-rooted and lasting responsiveness to a surface with a particular texture, represented in these experiments by rough cloth. Young monkeys will cling to a 'cloth mother' in preference to a 'wire mother' even if they must lean over to the wire model to feed. Access to such a cloth mother surrogate is vitally important to the young monkey as a base from which to explore novel environments with confidence (Figure 18-3). A wire mother surrogate in strange surroundings is as inadequate as no mother at all. In such a situation the young rushes across the test room, throws itself face downward, and screams.

There are equally convincing examples of adult animals responding to external stimuli of which they have no experience. One of the most elegant comes from Drees' work on spiders (1952). The distinctive courtship behavior of the male jumping spider, *Epiblemum scenicum*, can be elicited by models. Drees found that males raised in isolation responded most strongly to models of a particular size and form having the black and white striped pattern characteristic of the female's abdomen. Similarly, the waving movements of the male's forelegs inhibit the prey-catching behavior of a female raised in isolation. A simple moving model had the same effect. In both males and females prey catching is elicited by a different set of visual stimuli.

Experiments with houseflies raised in isolation yielded similar results. Vogel (1957, see page 351) could identify no component of the stimulus situation eliciting male courtship that was modifiable by experience. The most effective models for eliciting courtship behavior actually departed from the pattern presented by female flies, with twice the surface area of the reacting male. Other critical features are a dark color, a broken silhouette, a flicker pattern, a certain length-to-width ratio, and movement away from the male. The courtship of various male butterflies can best be elicited by models colored like females of the species. In some cases, this is true of males confronted with such a stimulus for the first time (e.g. Ilse 1941, Crane 1955).

Two species of fish, a platyfish, *Xiphophorus maculatus,* and a cichlid, *Tilapia mossambica,* respond appropriately to conspecific members of the opposite sex after being raised in varying degrees of social isolation (Shaw 1962, Neil 1964). But Shaw's experiments also brought out the need to consider effects of different types of isolation. The responsiveness of platyfish raised alone in clear tanks from which they could see the outside environment, but no other fish, was much closer to the normal than that

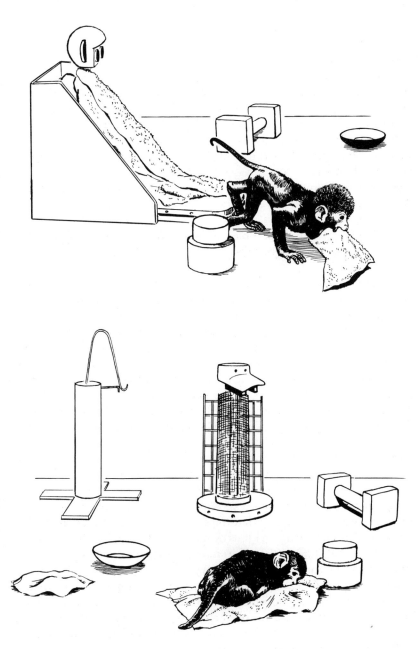

Figure 18-3 Above, a 150-day-old infant rhesus monkey explores a test arena with a surrogate mother as a base. Below, a wire mother is ignored in a similar situation. After photographs in Harlow 1961.

of fish raised alone in tanks with walls of ground glass. This result serves to remind us of the impracticability of placing an animal in complete sensory isolation. It is essential to describe the particular conditions used, since they can drastically affect the outcome of such an experiment.

Some birds respond to the visual stimuli presented by an owl at the first encounter. Song sparrows and chaffinches will mob an owl model the first time they see it (Nice and ter Pelkwijk 1941, Hinde 1954). The significant stimulus characteristics of an owl include general outline, the color pattern, a pair of forward-looking eyes, and a beak. In both experiments the birds were raised in isolation from adults of their species, but together with siblings. They thus experienced one kind of avian visual pattern. Schleidt (1961a, b) has shown that the alarm responses of birds to a hawk flying overhead may be based simply on the unfamiliarity of the silhouette. Thus it becomes necessary to check the possibility that in reacting to owls birds are responding to an unfamiliar avian configuration.

The responsiveness of inexperienced animals is not limited to visual stimuli. Young white-crowned sparrows learn the normal song pattern from older birds. Individuals raised in isolation from the age of three days and given sequences of two songs to listen to, one of their own species, one of another species, will select the conspecific song and learn it (Marler and Tamura 1964). Hamsters separated from their mothers between the fourth and tenth days and kept in isolation until adulthood responded normally when first exposed to the odor of other hamsters (Dieterlen 1959). Perhaps more remarkable is their strong alarm response to their first experience of the odor of material from the dens of a dog and a polecat.

In reviewing experiments on behavioral development in isolation, we should not forget their limitations. They cannot demonstrate the actual mechanism by which responsiveness develops, beyond establishing that it occurs normally without prior exposure to the particular environmental stimulus patterns. It is likely that the self-generated 'environment' which the isolated animal creates with its own body and behavior plays a crucial role (Shaw 1960, 1961, 1962). This may be particularly important in the development of auditory and olfactory responsiveness (see page 696). Unspecific effects of earlier sensory experience of a general nature also need to be taken into account, as we shall show in the next section. Nevertheless, demonstrations of unchanging developmental patterns in a varied environment are a first step toward establishing contributions of the genotype to sensory development.

◆ *Resistance to Environmental Control.* Demonstrations of an active resistance of sensory responsiveness to change by environmental influence are of special interest. Given a choice, the parasitic ichneumon wasp, *Nemeritis canescens,* will select the smell of larvae of the moth which is its normal host for oviposition, even if it has been raised on larvae of another species (Thorpe 1963). Some acquired responsiveness to the new host can be demonstrated, but only if competing stimuli from the normal host are absent (see page 640). The preexisting responsiveness to olfactory stimuli from the normal host, which is evident on the first occasion that *Nemeritis* encounters it, is not easily overridden by experience of different types of stimuli.

A quite different example is Harlow's (1961) demonstration that a young rhesus monkey's responsiveness to a cloth mother is difficult to eliminate. It persists even if the monkey has to go to a wire mother to feed, and even if each time it mounts the cloth mother it receives an unpleasant blast of air in the face. Such resistance to environmental change is clear evidence that responsiveness to certain types of external stimuli is sometimes deeply rooted. This persistence stands in striking contrast to the ease with which some types of responsiveness can be changed as a result of sensory experience.

UNSPECIFIC EFFECTS OF EARLY SENSORY EXPERIENCE

Early experience can influence sensory phenomena in a very general way. The development of normal perceptual abilities can be profoundly affected by sensory experience occurring at certain developmental stages. The studies of von Senden on the difficulties experienced by adult human subjects in acquiring normal visual abilities after the removal of congenital cataracts have been generalized by Hebb (1949) who noted the relevance of these findings to the behavior of animals and introduced a new approach to the study of perceptual development in both animals and man (e.g. Solomon et al. 1961). The best-known animal studies are those of Riesen (1958), who raised chimpanzees in darkness or in restricted visual conditions for varying periods of time. He then compared their performance in various tests of visual ability with that of animals raised under unrestricted visual conditions. The experimental treatments resulted in many abnormalities, including difficulty in fixation, inability to avoid obstacles, and drastic slowing in their learning of visual discriminations. Several studies on pigeons and other vertebrates show impairment of the ability to see after visual deprivation (Beach and Jaynes 1954).

Experiments involving sensory deprivation are complicated by several difficulties, including the possibility of neural and biochemical degeneration during the period of deprivation, a phenomenon that has been demonstrated in several animals reared in complete darkness (Beach and

Jaynes 1954, Riesen 1958, Eakin 1964, Wiesel and Hubel 1963, 1965a, b). There is also the possibility that compensatory means of behavioral control will develop during the deprivation period. It has been suggested that the abnormal tactual behavior of a chimpanzee raised as an infant with cardboard tubes over its hands and feet (Nissen, Chow, and Semmes 1951) might result in part from the development of reliance on other sensory modalities.

In spite of these reservations, there is a body of evidence which seems to indicate the importance of early visual experience upon subsequent perceptual abilities. The development of form vision seems to be the most profoundly affected. As Riesen (1958) views it, such development must await differential excitation from contours, corners, and edges. These ensure that certain loci in the retina, and hence certain cells in the projection areas, are maximally active while others remain relatively inactive. Normal form vision depends on the experience of consistency and repetition in the patterns of retinal stimulation. There is equally good evidence that prior experience is not required for normal form vision in other species, however (e.g. the rat, Hebb 1949, the cat, Hubel and Wiesel 1963).

Melzack (1962, 1965, Melzack and Scott 1957) has presented evidence of abnormal responses to nociceptive stimuli in dogs raised in social isolation under very restricted conditions. Other than this the role of early experience in the development of other sensory modalities has been little explored. Audition should be especially interesting to study from this point of view, since the dependence of some vocal behavior on auditory feedback (page 696) provides a ready indicator of any impairment of the sense of hearing.

Modifications of the early sensory environment that are less drastic than complete deprivation can have unspecific effects on subsequent sensory development. They can cause quantitative shifts in sensory thresholds. 'Emotionality' in rats has been studied for many years (e.g. Hall 1951). Animals are released in strange surroundings and the frequency of freezing, defecation, and exploration is noted. The score obtained in such tests, regarded as a measure of emotionality, is strongly affected by certain kinds of early experience (Denenberg 1962, Levine 1962).

Experimental handling such as removal from the cage, stroking, and a variety of noxious stimuli lower the level of emotionality in strange surroundings. Studies of associated changes in adrenal physiology and other phenomena, however, show that the situation is more complex than would appear at first sight. Animals given early noxious stimulation respond less strongly to general novel stimulation than untreated controls, but respond *more* strongly to further noxious stimulation. The untreated animals seem to require less extreme changes in the environment to elicit a physiological stress response, and in this sense they are hyper-reactors. The nonstimulated animals are hyper-reactors in another sense. These animals appear to show a more sustained response to chronic stress (Levine 1962). Thus early experience can raise the threshold of responsiveness to some stimuli but lower it to others.

◆ *Learning Ability.* Performance in various types of sensory learning tests can also be influenced by early experience. Rats that are handled or given noxious stimulation are often more successful than control animals in negative conditioning and other types of learning tests. The controls may freeze and show less exploration, or they may behave in an excited and erratic fashion, as Melzack (1962) found with dogs raised under restricted conditions. In either case their performance in conditioning tests suffers. Yet Denenberg (1962) has shown that excessive early stimulation can also cause a decline in learning performance, apparently because the animals become so phlegmatic that their motivation is deficient (see page 669).

The variety of sensory stimuli experienced in youth can also affect performance in learning tests. Rats raised in environments which provide a rich variety of sensory experience acquire new sensory discriminations more readily than animals raised in monotonous, restricted environments (review in Denenberg 1962), or the effects can be more specific. For example, rats learn to respond differentially to shapes more readily if they are able to see them from the home cage during infancy (Forgus 1956).

◆ *Genetic Contributions.* In considering the effects of such external factors on the early development of behavior, we should not forget that they result from interaction with the whole organism, including its genotypic manifestations. King and Eleftheriou (1959) obtained opposite effects of early handling on the subsequent rate of avoidance learning in two subspecies of deer mouse. There is ample evidence from inbred strains of mice for genetic control of differences in responsiveness (Hall 1951, McClearn 1959).

SPECIFIC EFFECTS OF EARLY SENSORY EXPERIENCE

◆ *'Learned' Behavior.* The term 'learned' hardly seems appropriate for the unspecific effects of early experience on emotionality. Moreover, there is some danger in allowing the concept of learning to become too broad and vague, or it may become as useless and diversionary as the term instinct. It is not easy to define the limits of sensory learning as a process, separate from the other kinds of effects of experience of the external environment. Thus the triggering of certain actions is one effect of the environment on behavior that needs to be distinguished from learning.

The idea of sensory learning usually involves the durable acquisition of responsiveness to a new pattern of environmental stimuli as a result of one or more experiences of a corresponding environmental pattern. The special spatio-temporal requirements which the experience must usually satisfy for learning to occur need not concern us for the moment. By definition, the consequences of sensory learning are rather specific in contrast with the kinds of environmental effects discussed in the previous section.

◆ *Imprinting.* Regarded in this way, learning is a prominent means of shaping the patterns of responsiveness to external stimuli in the young animal. The learning can take many forms. One kind is peculiarly characteristic of youth, namely 'imprinting.' Lorenz (1935) drew attention to the process by which young ducklings and goslings follow the parent soon after hatching and, in so doing, become responsive to the visual and auditory stimulus pattern that the parent presents. Subsequently, the response is elicited most strongly by this pattern, and in later life the same pattern often also elicits sexual behavior. The process is demonstrated strikingly if young are fostered to a parent of another species, establishing a durable bond with the foster species and excluding members of the bird's own kind. The bond is so lasting that Lorenz called the process which gives rise to it 'Prägung' or imprinting.

Although perhaps not different in kind from conditioning (Hinde 1962, Fabricius 1962, Sluckin 1962, 1965), imprinting has two characteristics of special interest for us. First, the growing animal is most readily imprinted at a certain stage of development, during a so-called critical period. Second, the patterns of external stimuli which result in successful imprinting cannot be randomly chosen but must possess certain well-defined properties. Imprinting thus illustrates the developmental interaction between exogenous factors, present here as the imprinting stimulus, and endogenous factors, represented by the critical period and by the restrictions on the stimuli which cause imprinting most effectively.

Fabricius (1951), Ramsay and Hess (1954), and many other workers have carried forward Lorenz's ideas, experimenting with a variety of subjects. This section concentrates on the studies of ducklings and domestic chicks, relying extensively on the reviews of Hess (1959a, b, c, 1964) and Moltz (1963).

The careful methods developed by Hess have been widely used by other workers. Ducklings are hatched in the dark and kept isolated until exposure to the test stimulus. Then they are released in a circular track and allowed to follow an object moving around the runway for a definite time or distance. The object also makes a sound. Later the ducklings are tested for effectiveness of the imprinting by releasing them between two models to see which is approached.

The pairs of models used in testing were designed to give a measure of the strength of the bond established. Ducklings trained with a model of a sound-producing drake mallard were then given four tests using the drake model and its artificial sound as one test object, and as the other, a model of a duck mallard producing the recorded call of a female calling to her young. Four test conditions followed each other in immediate succession: (1) both models stationary and silent; (2) both models stationary and calling; (3) both stationary, male silent and female calling; (4) male stationary and silent, female moving and calling. The four tests were judged to be in order of increasing difficulty and were scored accordingly. The response latency and the character of the call note (i.e. whether the duckling emitted pleasure tones or distress notes) were recorded. Scores were recorded as the percentage of positive responses by each animal. If the duckling responded positively in all four tests to the imprinting object, here the male decoy, imprinting was considered complete (Hess 1959b).

By using a scoring method of this type with ducklings exposed to the training situation at various ages, the existence of a sensitive period for imprinting can readily be demonstrated, peaking at about 13 to 16 hours

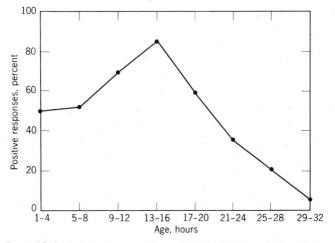

Figure 18-4   The critical period for mallard duckling imprinting. The curve shows the test score of ducklings imprinted at different ages. After Hess 1959a.

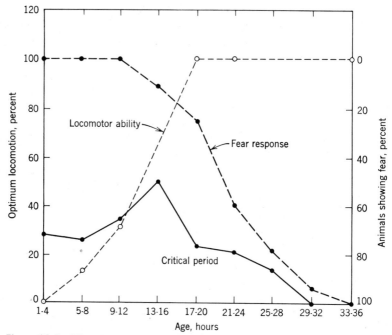

Figure 18-5   The critical period of following in chicks and mallard ducklings is apparently a result of the interaction between maturation of walking ability and the development of alarm responses to the imprinting object. After Hess 1959c.

(Figure 18-4). There is some variation. Certain birds can become imprinted at an earlier or later age than normal (Hess 1959b). Some variability can be ascribed to incubation conditions; reference to age since the start of incubation rather than age since hatching narrows the sensitive period appreciably (Gottlieb 1961, Klopfer and Gottlieb 1962).

Several workers have concluded that the timing of the sensitive period results from the interaction of two separate changes in the behavior of the growing chick (Hess 1959b). One is a gradual improvement in the ability to walk and follow the stimulus object, the other an increasing tendency to give alarm responses to the training object rather than to follow it (Salzen 1962, Figure 18-5). The developmental basis of the increasing fearfulness of strange objects needs to be worked out. Tranquilizing drugs promise to be valuable, although initial results are complex and somewhat contradictory (Hess 1957, 1959a, b). General experience of the environment also plays a part. Chicks were raised in a visually patterned environment and then given a moving object with a similar visual pattern to follow. They showed less avoidance of the model than did controls which lacked prior experience of the visual stimuli (Bateson 1964). Experience of the imprinting object may itself contribute to termination of the sensitive period. It may provide a familiar frame of reference against which other objects can be recognized as strange and thus as stimuli for avoidance (Salzen 1962, Sluckin 1962, 1965).

For imprinting to occur the duckling must either follow the stimulus object or at least fixate it. Hess (1959b) presented evidence that the strength of imprinting increases with the effort expended in following and is not related to time of exposure to the imprinting object. But Klopfer and Hailman (1964) found no significant correlation between the amount of initial and subsequent following.

The extent of general arousal at the time of following is also implicated, since experimental handling beforehand can increase the strength of imprinting on the object followed (Thompson and Dubanoski 1964). Mild electric shocks at certain stages of the imprinting procedure can also increase the strength of the learning (Hess 1964).

It is important to know what external stimuli arouse the strongest following response. Size of the object is significant. If it is too large ducklings will flee. If it is too small they will peck it (Fabricius and Boyd 1954). Color is a factor; for example, a blue object is more readily followed by chicks than a red one, which in turn is followed more than a yellow one (Hess 1959b, Figure 18-6). In experimenting with form, Hess found that the addition of stationary wings, tail, and head to a sphere reduces its effectiveness in eliciting following. According to Fabricius (1951), however, movement of the appendages is necessary to increase the probability of following in ducklings. Movement of the object away from the young bird is another important factor. And on-off stimulation from the object in the form of a flickering light or a dark sector rotating above a light ground also has been implicated (Smith 1962, Moltz 1963). Specific visual characters may also play a role. Klopfer and Hailman (1964) used plain and varicolored duck models. Although both models were followed equally well initially, ducklings imprinted to the more striking model were less inclined to switch when tested later.

In the process of imprinting the young chick or duckling acquires responsiveness to the whole visual aspect of the object presented. The possible range of effective objects is limited, however. In addition to the visual limitations we have discussed, sound may also be important. A silent object is less effective in eliciting following than one that makes sound. In chicks the structure of the sounds seems to be important; broken repetitive sounds are more effective than sustained ones (Collias 1952). Klopfer (1959) found little evidence of initial selectivity in the kinds of sound to

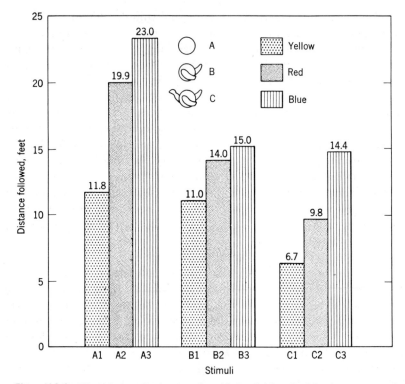

Figure 18-6   The relative effectiveness of models in eliciting the following response of chicks as a function of model complexity (A, B, C) and color. After Hess 1959a.

which the young of various ducks and geese would become imprinted, beyond a slight favoring of rhythmical sounds as compared with sustained ones. Gottlieb (1965), however, found that mallard ducklings more readily followed the sound of adult mallard calls than those of a wood ducks or a chicken. Domestic chicks also followed chicken sounds more freely.

Klopfer (1959) explored further the relationship between auditory and visual stimuli in eliciting the following response. When a visual stimulus is accompanied by a sound, there is imprinting on that particular sound pattern. The relative responsiveness to sight and sound of the model depends in part on the age at which the initial exposure takes place (Gottlieb and Klopfer 1962). Generally speaking, it was necessary for the sound to accompany visual stimuli. Most of the ducklings and goslings did not become imprinted on a sound alone. In ground-nesting water-fowl visual and auditory stimuli from the parent are normally experienced together by the young bird. Klopfer decided to experiment with a species in which the two kinds of stimuli are normally experienced separately.

Wood ducks nest in holes in trees, and the newly hatched young are called out of the hole by the parent. Here the opportunity for cooperation between visual and auditory stimuli is limited. Klopfer found that young wood ducks become imprinted on sound patterns presented without any accompanying visual stimuli, thus demonstrating a correlation between the mechanism of imprinting and the particular way of life of this species.

In addition to the immediate effects of imprinting on following behavior, Lorenz noted consequences for later life. Often ducks and geese became sexually fixated on objects or members of other species, even on Lorenz himself, after being imprinted on them in early youth (review in Thorpe 1963). This fixation may occur even if they are placed with members of their own species in later youth, indicating the durability of imprinting effects.

Experimental details on the sexual consequences of imprinting were slow in forthcoming. Chicks exposed to a distinctive model during the sensitive period demonstrated a transfer of sexual and aggressive responses to it at maturity or when injected with male hormone (Guiton 1961, 1962, Bambridge 1962).

The most extensive studies were carried out by Schutz (1965). He used mallard ducks and various other waterfowl. Ducklings were raised with an adult or a juvenile of another species for five or six weeks, starting at birth in some cases, and at one to three weeks of age in others. The latter were kept in individual isolation beforehand. After the exposure they were released onto a lake with many other waterfowl. Control birds were raised with a juvenile or an adult female of their own species and released in the same way.

As the birds became sexually mature they established pair bonds with birds of the opposite sex. The controls all paired with members of their own species. So did the females raised with another species. This was not true of a majority of the males raised with another species. They paired with a female of that species, though not the individual they were raised with. The results with males raised with an adult female of an alien species were more consistent than those with males raised with an alien sibling. Sexual imprinting of ducklings on ducks or geese was achieved more easily than imprinting on chickens or coots.

These experiments were not designed to identify the critical period for this effect of social experience on adult sexual behavior. But differences from imprinting of the following response are already obvious. Delay of the first experience of another species until three weeks of age, long after the sensitive period for following, did not hinder the transfer of male sexual responsiveness in adulthood. Thus imprinting of the following response and sexual imprinting may be distinct phenomena.

The lack of success in sexual imprinting of females is interesting. In most ducks males and females are very different in appearance. Females of many duck species look similar. The males are usually more conspicuous and most specifically distinct. It is conceivable that some female ducks inherit responsiveness to some properties of the pattern of the conspecific male. Schutz (1965) worked with one sexually monomorphic duck, the Chilean teal, *Anas flavirostris*. Both male and female are dully colored. This is the only duck in which females transferred their sexual attentions to members of another species when raised with them.

A parallel to imprinting of the following response is found in Hess's studies of the readiness of domestic chicks to peck at colored objects. Leghorn chicks pecking for the first time prefer red, orange, and blue objects over other colors. Ducklings and other strains of domestic chicks had a different preference (Hess 1956). Chicks also preferred circles to triangles. Hess set out to modify the initial preferences for a white circle on a blue background as compared with a white triangle on a green background by placing seeds behind the triangle on green (Hess 1962, 1964). The chicks quickly discovered the seeds and shifted their pecking to the triangle on green. After two hours of this rewarded pecking the seed was withdrawn. Their preferences were then tested on subsequent days without any seed being present. The result depended on the age at which the seeds were given. At three days the new preference for the triangle on green persisted. A lasting change in sensory organization was thus achieved. Birds given seed before or after this age quickly reverted to the initial preference for circles on blue (Figure 18-7).

As in the following response, there is a clearly defined critical period for modification of the sensory control of the pecking response. Modification again must begin with the presentation of stimuli which elicit pecking in the untrained chick. As a further parallel, the significance of which is uncertain, Schaefer and Hess (1959) have noted that in Vantress Broilers, another strain of domestic chickens, there is a close relationship between the color preferences of untrained chicks in pecking and in following. The pecking color preference in this strain is for yellow, with a low preference for blue and red. The color preference for following is precisely the reverse, high for blue and red and low for yellow, suggesting perhaps that the pecking and following preferences have a common sensory basis. It would be interesting to know the color preferences for following of Leghorn chicks, which prefer to peck orange and blue objects.

Our illustrations of imprinting have been drawn from the behavior of chickens, ducks, and geese, but similar processes are doubtless widespread

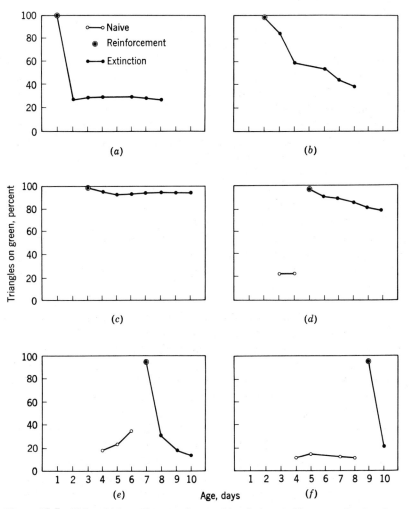

Figure 18-7 Naive chicks prefer to peck at a white circle on a blue ground rather than at a white triangle on a green ground. They are rewarded for pecking at a triangle on green by grain placed behind it. Reinforcement is given for one day only, either the first, second, third, fifth, seventh, or ninth. Only with reinforcement on the third day does the preference persist unchanged in the absence of a reward. The effects of reinforcement on chicks older or younger than three to five days extinguish rapidly. After Hess 1962.

in the animal kingdom, in other kinds of birds (Craig 1908, Goodwin 1948, Hinde, Thorpe, and Vince 1956, Nicolai 1956, Immelmann 1959, Klinghammer and Hess 1964), and perhaps in mammals as well (Collias and Collias 1956, Hess 1959a, Klopfer 1964).

Early olfactory experience can affect the choice of egg-laying sites in insects. In a series of experiments Thorpe and his colleagues (1963) showed that the ichneumonid wasp, *Nemeritis canescens,* which normally parasitizes larvae of the *Ephestia* moth, usually locates the host by smell. When the wasps are raised on new hosts, larvae of the moth *Meliphora* which is not normally parasitized, they acquire responsiveness to the smell of *Meliphora.* The new preference can be demonstrated in an olfactometer when the adults are ready for oviposition. The effect only occurs with exposure in the larval phase, at the time of emergence, or soon after. Experiments with *Drosophila* exposed to peppermint odor at various stages also reveal a sensitive period in the readiness to acquire responsiveness to the smell as an egg-laying adult (Thorpe 1938, 1939, Thorpe and Jones 1937, Thorpe and Caudle 1938). These results should not be taken to imply that olfactory responsiveness in these insects is entirely acquired. Thorpe and his colleagues also found *Nemeritis* responsive to the smell of the normal host, *Ephestia,* even when it has been raised on some other host. This initial selective responsiveness and the existence of a sensitive period remind us of imprinting, with which this olfactory conditioning has much in common.

◆ *Conditioning.* In addition to the special process of imprinting, development of new patterns of responsiveness may involve, to varying degrees, the more conventional types of learning. Often they play a vital role in the development of natural behavior. We cannot attempt a review of the huge literature on learning which has been authoritatively summarized by several authors (e.g. Hilgard and Marquis, revised by Kimble 1961, Thorpe 1963). Certain aspects of learning illuminate our general theme. The concept of conditioning developed by Pavlov (1927), Bekhterev (1928), and others is basic to the understanding of sensory learning. In essence it is very simple. An animal possesses a pattern of responsiveness such that a given external stimulus, the unconditioned stimulus, elicits a certain response. The prior history of the situation need not concern us. A new stimulus, previously neutral with respect to this response, is perceived repeatedly at about the same time as the unconditioned stimulus; subsequently it acquires the power to elicit the same response. For conditioning to occur, the temporal relationship between the unconditioned stimulus and the neutral stimulus is critical. Generally speaking, the neutral stimulus must occur a few moments before the unconditioned stimulus (Figure 18-8). The event to which conditioning occurs may be the onset of a stimulus or its ending. Conditioning is probably impossible to obtain when the neutral stimulus follows the unconditioned stimulus (Kimble 1961).

The timing as well as the ordering of the stimuli is critical. In a variety of situations the fastest conditioning has been obtained with a delay of about half a second between the neutral and the unconditioned stimulus. Conditioning is slower at longer or shorter intervals. The nature of the response usually evoked by the neutral stimulus also affects the rate of conditioning. If it usually elicits a response incompatible with that evoked by the unconditioned stimulus, alarm versus feeding for example, conditioning will be slow. If the neutral stimulus elicits an allied response, approach versus feeding, conditioning will be more rapid (Konorski 1950).

There are countless natural situations in which the criteria for rapid conditioning are satisfied. In the feeding behavior of many birds, for example, the simple stimuli which elicit pecking will be accompanied by other environmental stimuli characteristic of the situations in which food objects occur. Through conditioning such previously neutral stimuli can come to elicit feeding behavior.

In a different situation Lehrman (1955, 1956) has demonstrated that crop milk regurgitation in ring doves is initially elicited by the squab by tactile stimuli on the parent's breast over the engorged crop. As the naive parent raises its brood, a variety of other stimuli from the young become effective in eliciting regurgitation, presumably as a result of conditioning.

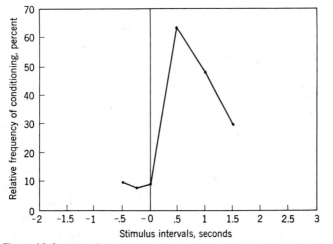

Figure 18-8   The effectiveness of conditioning the withdrawal of a finger from an electric shock to a buzz, with different temporal relationships between the two stimuli. Minus values indicate that the buzz followed the shock, positive values that the buzz preceded the shock. After Kimble 1961 from Spooner and Kellogg 1947.

The pecking response of young gulls, initially elicited by a relatively narrow set of external stimuli (page 388), also becomes evocable by new parental stimuli after a few days of experience, presumably as a result of conditioning (Hailman 1961, Klopfer 1962).

◆ *Extinction and Habituation.* If, after the process of conditioning is completed, the conditioned stimulus is presented repeatedly in the absence of the unconditioned stimulus, responsiveness to it will eventually wane. Pavlov's term for this waning was the "extinction" of a conditioned reflex. The special interest of extinction lies in the evidence that the animal does not revert to its original state and lose all trace of the conditioning effects.

The waning is not so much the result of a loss of the original effect as the consequence of an inhibitory process arising during presentation of the conditioned stimulus by itself. Spontaneous recovery can occur, if the animal is left unstimulated for a time after extinction and then given the conditioned stimulus once more. A sudden novel stimulus presented in the middle of an extinction session can bring responsiveness to the conditioned stimulus back to its original level, suggesting a release from inhibition, or "disinhibition" as Pavlov called it. The physiological processes underlying extinction are still poorly understood. There is, for example, argument about the role of new conditioning processes occurring during extinction. During repeated presentation the conditioned stimulus may become associated with a new set of responses incompatible with the previous one, hence the inhibition (Kimble 1961). A sudden alien stimulus would thus disrupt the new conditioning process, a result readily obtained in classical conditioning.

Extinction has much in common with what zoologists call 'habituation' (Thorpe 1963), a process which is vitally important for survival in many organisms. The elimination of existing patterns of responsiveness which fail to perform a useful function is as important as the acquisition of new patterns of responsiveness during the course of development. For example, many young animals give escape responses to a wide variety of unspecific stimuli (Thorpe 1944, 1950, 1963). As time passes many of these stimuli cease to be effective, evoking only an alerting reaction, or even no response at all. The effectiveness of other stimuli persists. Thus the specificity of responsiveness sharpens, focusing on stimuli that have been followed by more alarming consequences. The process by which responsiveness to innocuous stimuli becomes temporarily or permanently eliminated is known as habituation. The resemblance of the process to extinction of a conditioned reflex is obvious.

Although simple in conception, habituation is a complicated subject for experimentation. Habituation appears as the waning of responsive-

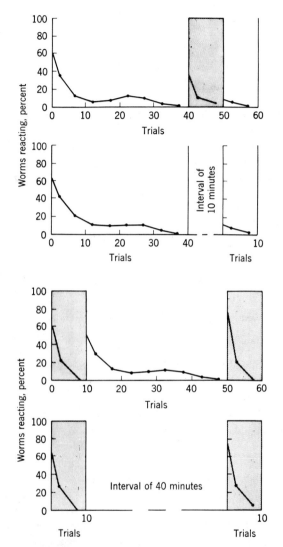

Figure 18-9 With repeated mechanical stimulation there is a decline in the number of worms giving withdrawal responses (unstippled). A moving shadow revives the response (stippled). Subsequent mechanical stimuli elicit the same proportion of responses as in control animals that have been resting in the interim. The same independence of habituation to mechanical shock and a moving shadow appears when they are presented in the reverse order, shadow–mechanical shock–shadow. After Clark 1960a.

ness to repetitions of a constant stimulus. This definition is inadequate to distinguish habituation from other causes of waning responsiveness such as fatigue or consummatory behavior. Confusion is reduced by specifying two other characteristics: (1) the extent to which the waning is response-specific, or stimulus-specific, and (2) the rate at which responsiveness recovers (Hinde 1954, Thorpe 1963).

These features are demonstrated by Clark's (1960a, b) study of waning of the withdrawal of the polychaete worm, *Nereis pelagica*, into its tube in response to mechanical and visual stimuli. The response to mechanical shock presented at 30-second intervals wanes rapidly after ten trials and disappears by the twentieth. The response to a passing shadow wanes at a similar rate. Preceding stimulation by the mechanical shock has no effect on responsiveness to a shadow and vice versa (Figure 18-9) thus demonstrating the stimulus specificity of the waning of responsiveness which is characteristic of habituation.

Some degree of stimulus specificity of habituation has been found in a variety of studies. There have been demonstrations of specificity to a sensory modality, as in Clark's study of *Nereis* (mechanical and visual) and in Prechtl's (1953) analysis of the begging response of nestling birds (mechanical, auditory, and visual). Specific waning of responsiveness to stimulus quality within the same modality has also been found. The gobbling of turkeys, elicited by a variety of sounds including pure tones, habituates to one sound frequency, but the turkey remains responsive to other frequencies (Schleidt 1955). Similarly, the mobbing response of a chaffinch to an owl habituates but revives in response to a stoat or a dog (Hinde 1954, 1960), demonstrating a degree of specificity of habituation to different visual configurations.

Habituation to a particular stimulus orientation can occur. Franzisket (1953) and Kuczka (1956) habituated the wiping response of a frog by stroking a certain point on the body and found renewed responsiveness at a new location. Eikmanns (1955) worked with the turning movement of a toad's head toward a visual stimulus preparatory to striking with the tongue. Responsiveness to a repeated stimulus in one part of the visual field eventually waned but was revived by stimulation elsewhere in the eye. A parallel study by Wolda (1961) of the backswimmer, *Notonecta glauca*, hanging on the water surface and turning toward a source of disturbance of the surface film, showed that after habituation of responsiveness to a stimulus from left-front, responsiveness on the right-front sector was unimpaired (Figure 18-10).

Although stimulus specificity of the waning of responsiveness is commonly found, it is often accompanied by some degree of stimulus generalization, as in the various studies of feeding and prey-catching

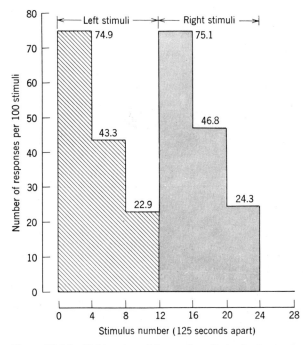

Figure 18-10   Habituation of the turning of a backswimmer to a disturbance on the left leaves responsiveness to a stimulus on the right unimpaired. After Wolda 1961.

behavior of jumping spiders (Drees 1952, Precht and Freytag 1958) and the mobbing behavior of chaffinches (Hinde 1954, 1960). In spite of these complications, the criterion of a *stimulus-specific response decrement* is valuable in distinguishing habituation from other types of response waning. This contrasts with the response-specific decrement that will result if repeated stimulation causes motor fatigue or consummatory behavior.

The definition of habituation can be further refined by referring to the recovery rate. Recovery from habituation usually takes minutes, hours, or days. Sensory adaptation of receptors as a result of repeated rapid stimulation, which can be confused with habituation, usually disappears within seconds (Thorpe 1963).

Having made this separation, we should not forget that waning of responsiveness seldom proves to be pure habituation, as defined earlier. A complex of processes is involved instead, some response-specific, others stimulus-specific, each accompanied by facilitating and inhibitory processes with different temporal characteristics (Hinde 1954, 1960). Repeated elicitation of the wiping reflex in spinal frogs can result in a lower-

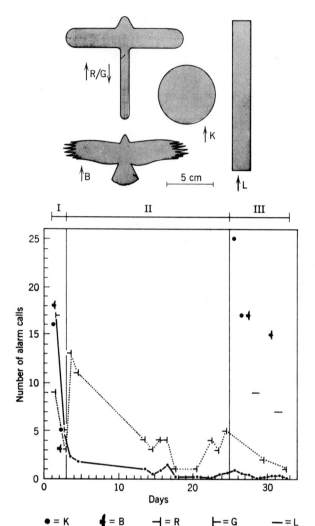

Figure 18-11   Number of alarm calls given by young turkeys to the various silhouettes moving above. On days 1 and 2 the birds were shown all four models. The responses to different models did not differ significantly. In the second part of the experiment, from days 3 to 25, the birds were shown in each trial model G ten times (solid line, averages) and model R once, placed at various stages of the stimulus sequence (dotted line). More calls were elicited by R than G. The effectiveness of both declined through the experiment. In the third phase, from days 26 to 34, the ten daily presentations of model G were accompanied by model R and sometimes by one of the other models. These new stimuli, whether a hawk model, a rectangle, or a simple disk, elicited a large number of alarm calls. After Schleidt 1961a.

ing of threshold rather than habituation under certain conditions (Franzisket 1963). The dominant effects seem to occur neither in the actual receptors nor in the effector musculature, but centrally. Electrophysiological studies are beginning to locate the organs involved and to identify the various processes responsible (e.g. Roberts 1962, Marsh, McCarthy, Sheatz, and Galambos 1961, Hernández-Peón and Brust-Carmona 1961, see page 421).

Habituation must be involved in shaping patterns of responsiveness in many natural situations critical for survival. Consider the responsiveness of many kinds of birds to a hawk. Several species respond to a moving hawk silhouette overhead (see page 247). How this response develops remained controversial until an elegant series of experiments by Schleidt (1961a, b) resolved the question in an unexpected way. Working with turkeys under carefully controlled conditions, he demonstrated that birds exposed to circles or rectangles overhead were at first alarmed, then became habituated. Such birds occasionally exposed to a hawk silhouette gave strong escape responses. Conversely, birds frequently exposed to a hawk silhouette became habituated. When presented with a circle they responded strongly. The initial response to the different models was not significantly different. Thus there is general unspecific responsiveness to objects of a certain apparent size and rate of movement (Figure 18-11). Schleidt concluded that response to a hawk silhouette in birds raised in a free environment results from their habituation to other types of birds flying overhead and from the relative rarity of hawks in the neighborhood. Thus habituation serves to achieve one of the most striking cases of response to a specific stimulus that has been demonstrated.

CONCLUSIONS ON THE ONTOGENY OF SENSORY MECHANISMS

The postnatal environment plays a vital role in shaping the sensory capacities of many animals. It exerts unspecific effects on the general properties of an entire sensory mode and on its potentialities for further development. It can modify responsiveness to certain situations in a highly specific fashion. At times the limits restricting potential changes are wide, so that differences in the environments in which individuals of the same species find themselves can result in very different patterns of responsiveness.

Sensory conditioning has an important role to play, often operating as a compound process, so that secondary and tertiary conditioning probably occurs. Habituation provides for change within narrower limits by eliminating some existing patterns of responsiveness and sharpening others. In imprinting the limits are still more restricted, not only in the stimulus properties responded to but also with reference to age. Critical periods confining the potential for change to a certain stage of development are particularly characteristic of imprinting. Other types of learning may also be influenced by critical periods, though they have been less intensively studied (Thorpe 1961, Scott 1962).

Finally, genetic factors also influence variations in the sensory mechanisms of animals, although they have hardly been explored at the intraspecific level. Our ignorance of this aspect should not distract us from the conclusion that, as in other aspects of behavior, the development of sensory mechanisms results from the interaction of endogenous and exogenous processes, and our understanding is bound to suffer if we explore one aspect to the neglect of the other.

REFERENCES

Baerends, G. P. and J. M. Baerends-van Roon. 1950. An introduction to the study of the ethology of cichlid fishes. *Behaviour Suppl.*, **1**:1–243.
Bambridge, R. 1962. Early experience and sexual behavior in the domestic chicken. *Science* **136**:259–260.
Bateson, P. P. G. 1964. Effect of similarity between rearing and testing conditions on chicks' following and avoidance responses. *J. comp. physiol. Psychol.*, **57**:100–103.
Beach, F. A. and J. Jaynes. 1954. Effects of early experience upon the behavior of animals. *Psychol. Bull.*, **51**:239–263.
Bekhterev, V. M. 1928. *General Principles of Human Reflexology* (translated by E. and W. Murphy). International Press, New York.
Carmichael, L. 1933. Origin and prenatal growth of behavior. In *A Handbook of Child Psychology*, ed. by C. A. Murchison: 31–159. Clark University Press, Worcester, Massachusetts.
Clark, R. B. 1960a. Habituation of the polychaete *Nereis* to sudden stimuli. 1. General properties of the habituation process. *Anim. Behav.*, **8**:82–91.
———. 1960b. Habituation of the polychaete *Nereis* to sudden stimuli. 2. Biological significance of habituation. *Anim. Behav.*, **8**:92–103.
Collias, N. E. 1952. The development of social behavior in birds. *Auk*, **69**:127–159.
——— and E. C. Collias. 1956. Some mechanisms of family integration in ducks. *Auk*, **73**:378–400.
Craig, W. 1908. The voices of pigeons regarded as a means of social control. *Amer. J. Sociol.*, **14**:86–100.
Crane, J. 1955. Imaginal behavior of a Trinidad butterfly, *Heliconius erato hydara* Hewitson, with special reference to the social use of color. *Zoologica*, **40**:167–196.
Denenberg, V. H. 1962. The effects of early experience. In *The Behaviour of Domestic Animals*, ed. by E. S. E. Hafez: 109–138. The Williams and Wilkins Company, Baltimore.
Dieterlen, F. 1959. Das Verhalten des syrischen Goldhamsters (*Mesocricetus auratus* Waterhouse). *Z. Tierpsychol.*, **16**:47–103.
Dobzhansky, T. 1950. Heredity, environment and evolution. *Science*, **111**:161–166.

Drees, O. 1952. Untersuchungen über die angeborenen Verhaltensweisen bei Springspinnen (*Salticidae*). *Z. Tierpsychol.*, 9:169–207.

Eakin, R. M. 1964. Is light required for the development and maintenance of rods and cones? (Abst.). *Amer. Zool.*, 4:317–318.

Eikmanns, K.-H. 1955. Verhaltensphysiologische Untersuchungen über den Beutefang und das Bewegungssehen der Erdkröte. *Z. Tierpsychol.*, 12:229–253.

Fabricius, E. 1951. Zur Ethologie junger Anatiden. *Acta Zool. Fenn.*, 68:1–178.

———. 1962. Some aspects of imprinting in birds. *Symp. Zool. Soc. Lond.*, 8:139–148.

——— and H. Boyd. 1954. Experiments on the following-reaction of ducklings. *Rep. Wildfowl Trust*, 6:84–89.

Forgus, R. H. 1956. Advantage of early over late perceptual experience in improving form discrimination. *Can. J. Psychol.*, 10:147–155.

Franzisket, L. 1953. Untersuchungen zur Spezifität und Kumulierung der Erregungsfähigkeit und zur Wirkung einer Ermüdung in der Afferenz bei Wischbewegungen des Ruckenmarksfrosches. *Z. vergl. Physiol.*, 34:525–538.

———. 1963. Characteristics of instinctive behaviour and learning in reflex activity of the frog. *Anim. Behav.*, 11:318–324.

Fuller, J. L. and W. R. Thompson. 1960. *Behavior Genetics*. John Wiley and Sons, New York.

Goodwin, D. 1948. Some abnormal sexual fixations in birds. *Ibis*, 90:45–48.

Gottlieb, G. 1961. Developmental age as a baseline for determination of the critical period in imprinting. *J. comp. physiol. Psychol.*, 54:422–427.

——— 1965. Imprinting in relation to parental and species identification by avian neonates. *J. comp. physiol. Psychol.*, 59:345–356.

——— and P. H. Klopfer. 1962. The relation of developmental age to auditory and visual imprinting. *J. comp. physiol. Psychol.*, 55:821–826.

Guiton, P. 1961. The influence of imprinting on the agonistic and courtship responses of the brown leghorn cock. *Anim. Behav.*, 9:167–177.

———. 1962. The development of sexual responses in the domestic fowl, in relation to the concept of imprinting. *Symp. Zool. Soc., Lond.*, 8:227–234.

Hailman, J. P. 1961. Why do gull chicks peck at visually contrasting spots? A suggestion concerning social learning of food-discrimination. *Am. Nat.*, 95:245–247.

Haldane, J. B. S. 1946. The interaction of nature and nurture. *Ann. Eugen.*, 13:197–205.

Hall, C. S. 1951. The genetics of behavior. In *Handbook of Experimental Psychology*, ed. by S. S. Stevens: 304–329. John Wiley and Sons, New York.

Hamilton, W. D. 1963. The evolution of altruistic behavior. *Am. Nat.*, 97:354–356.

Harlow, H. F. 1961. The development of affectional patterns in infant monkeys. In *Determinants of Infant Behaviour*, ed. by B. M. Foss: 75–88. John Wiley and Sons, New York.

———. 1962. Development of affection in primates. In *Roots of Behavior*, ed. by E. L. Bliss: 157–166. Harper and Row, New York.

Haskins, C. P. and E. F. Haskins. 1958. Note on the inheritance of behavior patterns for food selection and cocoon spinning in F_1 hybrids of *Callosamia promethea* × *C. angulifera*. *Behaviour*, 13:89–95.

Hebb, D. O. 1949. *The Organization of Behavior*. John Wiley and Sons, New York.

———. 1953. Heredity and environment in mammalian behaviour. *Brit. J. Anim. Behav.*, 1:43–47.

Hernández-Peón, R. and H. Brust-Carmona. 1961. Functional role of subcortical structures in habituation and conditioning. In *Brain Mechanisms and Learning*, ed. by J. F. Delafresnaye: 393–412. Council for International Organization of Medical Sciences Symposium, Oxford.

Herter, K. 1936. Das thermotaktische Optimum bei Nagetieren, ein mendelndes Art- und Rassenmerkmal. *Z. vergl. Physiol.*, 23:605–650.

————. 1938. Die Beziehungen zwischen Vorzugstemperatur und die Hautbeschaffenheit bei Mäusen. *Verh. Dtsch. Zool. Ges. Zool. Anz.* (Suppl.), **11**:48–55.

Hess, E. H. 1956. Natural preferences of chicks and ducklings for objects of different colors. *Psychol. Rep.,* **2**:477–483.

————. 1957. Effects of meprobamate on imprinting in waterfowl. *Ann. N.Y. Acad. Sci.,* **67**:724–732.

————. 1959a. Imprinting. *Science,* **130**:133–141.

————. 1959b. The relationship between imprinting and motivation. *Neb. Symp. Motiv.,* **7**:44–77.

———— 1959c. Two conditions limiting critical age for imprinting. *J. comp. physiol. Psychol.,* **52**: 515–518.

————. 1962. Imprinting and the "critical period" concept. In *Roots of Behavior,* ed. by E. L. Bliss: 254–263. Harper and Row, New York.

————. 1964. Imprinting in birds. *Science,* **146**:1128–1139.

Hinde, R. A. 1954. Factors governing the changes in strength of a partially inborn response, as shown by the mobbing behaviour of the chaffinch (*Fringilla coelebs*). I. The nature of the response, and an examination of its course. *Proc. Roy. Soc. Lond., B,* **142**:306–331.

————. 1960. Factors governing the changes in the strength of a partially inborn response, as shown by the mobbing behaviour of the chaffinch (*Fringilla coelebs*). III. The interaction of short-term and long-term incremental and decremental effects. *Proc. Roy. Soc. Lond., B,* **153**:398–420.

————. 1962. Some aspects of the imprinting problem. *Symp. Zool. Soc. Lond.,* **8**:129–138.

————, W. H. Thorpe, and M. A. Vince. 1956. The following response of young coots and moorhens. *Behaviour,* **9**:214–242.

Hirsch, J. 1958. Recent developments in behavior genetics and differential psychology. *Diseases Nerv. Sys.* (Monogr. Suppl.), **19**:17–24.

————. 1962. Individual differences in behavior and their genetic basis. In *Roots of Behavior,* ed. by E. L. Bliss: 3–23. Harper and Row, New York.

———— and J. C. Boudreau. 1958. Studies in experimental behavior genetics: I. The heritability of phototaxis in a population of *Drosophila melanogaster, J. comp. physiol. Psychol.,* **51**: 647–651.

Hubel, D. H. and T. N. Wiesel. 1963. Receptive fields of cells in striate cortex of very young, visually inexperienced kittens. *J. Neurophysiol.,* **26**:994–1002.

Ilse, D. 1941. The colour vision of insects. *Proc. Roy. Phil. Soc. Glasgow,* **65**:68–82.

Immelmann, K. 1959. Experimentelle Untersuchungen über die biologische Bedeutung artspezifischer Merkmale beim Zebrafinken (*Taeniopygia castanotis* Gould). *Zool. Jahrb., Abt. Syst. Ökol. Geogr.,* **86**:437–592.

Jensen, D. D. 1961. Operationism and the question "Is this behavior learned or innate?" *Behaviour,* **17**:1–8.

Kimble, G. A. 1961. *Hilgard and Marquis' Conditioning and Learning.* Appleton-Century-Crofts, New York.

King, J. A. and B. E. Eleftheriou. 1959. The effects of early handling upon adult behavior in two subspecies of deermice, *Peromyscus maniculatus. J. comp. physiol. Psychol.,* **52**:82–88.

Klinghammer, E. and E. H. Hess. 1964. Imprinting in an altricial bird: The blond ring dove *Streptopelia risoria. Science,* **146**:265–266.

Klopfer, P. 1959. An analysis of learning in young Anatidae. *Ecology,* **40**:90–102.

————. 1962. *Behavioral Aspects of Ecology.* Prentice-Hall, Englewood Cliffs.

————. 1964. Parameters of imprinting. *Am. Nat.,* **98**:173–182.

———— and G. Gottlieb. 1962. Imprinting and behavioral polymorphism: Auditory and visual imprinting in domestic ducks (*Anas platyrhynchos*) and the involvement of the critical period. *J. comp. physiol. Psychol.,* **55**:126–130.

——— and J. P. Hailman. 1964. Basic parameters of following and imprinting in precocial birds. *Z. Tierpsychol.*, **21**:755–762.

Konorski, J. 1950. Mechanisms of learning. *Symp. Soc. Exp. Biol.*, **4**:409–431.

Kuczka, H. 1956. Verhaltensphysiologische Untersuchungen über die Wischhandlung der Erdkröte (*Bufo bufo* L.). *Z. Tierpsychol.*, **13**:185–207.

Kühme, W. 1962. Das Schwarmverhalten elterngeführter Jungcichliden (Pisces). *Z. Tierpsychol.*, **19**:513–538.

Lehrman, D. S. 1955. The physiological basis of parental feeding behavior in the ring dove (*Streptopelia risoria*). *Behaviour*, **7**:241–286.

———. 1956. On the organization of maternal behavior and the problem of instinct. In *L'instinct dans le Comportement des Animaux et de l'homme:* 475–514. Fondation Singer-Polignac. Masson et Cie Éditeurs, Paris.

Lerner, I. M. 1958. *The Genetic Basis of Selection.* John Wiley and Sons, New York.

Levine, S. 1962. Psychophysiological effects of infantile stimulation. In *Roots of Behavior*, ed. by E. L. Bliss: 246–253. Harper and Row, New York.

Lorenz, K. Z., 1935, Der Kumpan in der Umwelt des Vogels. *J. Orn.*, **83**:137–213, 289–413.

———. 1961. Phylogenetische Anpassung und adaptive Modifikation des Verhaltens. *Z. Tierpsychol.*, **18**:139–187.

McClearn, C. E. 1959. The genetics of mouse behavior in novel situations. *J. comp. physiol. Psychol.*, **52**:62–67.

Marler, P. and M. Tamura. 1964. Culturally transmitted patterns of vocal behavior in sparrows. *Science*, **146**:1483–1486.

Marsh, J. T., D. A. McCarthy, G. Sheatz, and R. Galambos. 1961. Amplitude changes in evoked auditory potentials during habituation and conditioning. *Electroenceph. Clin. Neurophysiol.*, **13**:224–234.

Melzack, R. A. 1962. Effects of early perceptual restriction on simple visual discrimination. *Science*, **137**:978–979.

———.1965. Effects of early experience on behavior: experimental and conceptual considerations. In *Psychopathology of Perception:*271–299. Grune and Stratton, New York.

——— and T. H. Scott. 1957. The effects of early experience on the response to pain. *J. comp. physiol. Psychol.*, **50**:155–161.

Moltz, H. 1963. Imprinting: An epigenetic approach. *Psychol. Rev.*, **70**:123–138.

Neil, E. H. 1964. An analysis of color changes and social behavior of *Tilapia mossambica*. *Univ. Calif. Publ. Zool.*, **75**:1–58.

Nice, M. M. and J. ter Pelkwijk. 1941. Enemy recognition by the song sparrow. *Auk*, **58**:195–214.

Nicolai, J. 1956. Zur Biologie und Ethologie des Gimpels (*Pyrrhula pyrrhula* L.). *Z. Tierpsychol.*, **13**:93–132.

Nissen, H. W., K. L. Chow, and J. Semmes. 1951. Effects of restricted opportunity for tactual, kinesthetic, and manipulative experience on the behavior of a chimpanzee. *Amer. J. Psychol.*, **64**:485–507.

Noble, G. K. and B. Curtis. 1939. The social behavior of the jewel fish, *Hemichromis bimaculatus* Gill. *Bull. Amer. Mus. Nat. Hist.*, **76**:1–46.

Pavlov, I. P. 1927. *Conditioned Reflexes* (translated by G. V. Anrep). Oxford University Press, London.

Peters, H. M. 1937. Experimentelle Untersuchungen über die Brutpflege von *Haplochromis multicolor*, einem maulbrütenden Knochenfisch. *Z. Tierpsychol.*, **1**:201–218.

———. 1941. Fortpflanzungsbiologische und tiersoziologische Studien an Fischen. 1. *Hemichromis bimaculatus*. *Z. Morph. Ökol. Tiere.*, **37**:387–425.

———. 1963. Untersuchungen zum Problem des angeborenen Verhaltens. *Naturwissenschaften*, **50**:677–686.

Precht, H. and G. Freytag. 1958. Über Ermüdung und Hemmung angeborener Verhaltensweisen bei Springspinnen (Salticidae). Zugleich ein Beitrag zum Triebproblem. *Behaviour,* **13:**143–211.

Prechtl, H. F. R. 1953. Zur Physiologie der angeborenen auslösenden Mechanismen. I. Quantitative Untersuchungen über die Sperrbewegung junger Singvögel. *Behaviour,* **5:** 32–50.

Ramsay, A. O. and E. H. Hess. 1954. A laboratory approach to the study of imprinting. *Wilson Bull.,* **66:**196–206.

Riesen, A. H. 1958. Plasticity of behavior: Psychological aspects. In *Biological and Biochemical Bases of Behavior,* ed. by H. F. Harlow and C. N. Woolsey: 425–450. University of Wisconsin Press, Madison.

Roberts, M. B. V. 1962. The giant fibre reflex of the earthworm, *Lumbricus terrestris* L. *J. Exp. Biol.,* **39:**229–237.

Rodgers, D. A. and G. E. McClearn. 1962. Alcohol preference of mice. In *Roots of Behavior,* ed. by E. L. Bliss: 68–95. Harper and Row, New York.

Salzen, E. A. 1962. Imprinting and fear. *Symp. Zool. Soc. Lond.,* **8:**199–217.

Schaefer, H. H. and E. H. Hess. 1959. Color preferences in imprinting objects. *Z. Tierpsychol.,* **16:**161–172.

Schleidt, M. 1955. Untersuchungen über die Auslösung des Kollerns beim Truthahn (*Meleagris galopavo*). *Z. Tierpsychol.,* **11:**417–435.

Schleidt, W. 1961a. Über die Auslösung der Flucht vor Raubvögeln bei Truthühnern. *Naturwissenschaften,* **48:**141–142.

———. 1961b. Reaktionen von Truthühnern auf fliegende Raubvögel und Versuche zur Analyse ihrer AAM's. *Z. Tierpsychol.,* **18:**534–560.

Schutz, F. 1965. Sexuelle Prägung bei Anatiden. *Z. Tierpsychol.,* **22:**50–103.

Scott, J. P. 1962. Critical periods in behavioral development. *Science,* **138:**949–958.

Shaw, E. 1960. The development of schooling behavior in fishes. *Physiol. Zool.,* **33:**79–86.

———. 1961. The development of schooling in fishes. II. *Physiol. Zool.,* **34:**263–272.

———. 1962. Environmental conditions and the appearance of sexual behavior in the platyfish. In *Roots of Behavior,* ed. by E. L. Bliss: 123–141. Harper and Row, New York.

Simpson, G. G., C. S. Pittendrigh, and L. H. Tiffany. 1957. *Life.* Harcourt, Brace and Company, New York.

Sluckin, W. 1962. Perceptual and associative learning. *Symp. Zool. Soc. Lond.,* **8:**193–198.

———. 1965. *Imprinting and Early Learning.* Aldine Publishing Company, Chicago.

Smith, F. V. 1962. Perceptual aspects of imprinting. *Symp. Zool. Soc. Lond.,* **8:**171–191.

Solomon, P., P. E. Kubzansky, P. H. Leiderman, J. H. Mendelson, R. Trumbull, and D. Wexler. 1961. *Sensory Deprivation.* Harvard University Press, Cambridge.

Stern, C. 1960. *Principles of Human Genetics.* W. H. Freeman and Company, Publishers, San Francisco.

Thompson, W. R. and R. A. Dubanoski. 1964. Early arousal and imprinting in chicks. *Science,* **143:**1187–1188.

Thorpe, W. H. 1938. Further experiments on olfactory conditioning in a parasitic insect. The nature of the conditioning process. *Proc. Roy. Soc. Lond., B,* **126:**370–397.

———. 1939. Further experiments on pre-imaginal conditioning in insects. *Proc. Roy. Soc. Lond., B,* **127:**424–433.

———. 1944. Some problems of animal learning. *Proc. Linn. Soc. Lond.* (Zool.), **156:**70–83.

———. 1950. The concepts of learning and their relation to those of instinct. *Symp. Soc. Exp. Biol.,* **4:**387–408.

———. 1961. Sensitive periods in the learning of animals and men: a study of imprinting with special reference to the induction of cyclic behaviour. In *Current Problems in Animal Behav-*

iour, ed. by W. H. Thorpe and O. L. Zangwill: 194–224. Cambridge University Press, Cambridge.

———. 1963. *Learning and Instinct in Animals*. Harvard University Press, Cambridge.

——— and H. B. Caudle. 1938. A study of the olfactory responses of insect parasites to the food plant of their host. *Parasitology*, **30:**523–528.

——— and F. G. W. Jones. 1937. Olfactory conditioning in a parasitic insect and its relation to the problem of host selection. *Proc. Roy. Soc. Lond., B*, **124:**56–81.

Vogel, G. 1957. Verhaltensphysiologische Untersuchungen über die den Weibchenbesprung des Stubenfliegen—Männchens (*Musca domestica*) auslösenden optischen Faktoren. *Z. Tierpsychol.*, **14:**309–323.

Weiss, J. M. 1959. The hereditary determination of individual differences in geotaxis in a population of *Drosophila melanogaster*. Unpublished doctoral dissertation, Columbia University. Quoted in Hirsch 1962.

Wiesel, T. N. and D. H. Hubel. 1963. Effects of visual deprivation on morphology and physiology of cells in the cat's lateral geniculate body. *J. Neurophysiol.*, **26:**978–993.

——— and ———. 1965a. Comparison of the effects of unilateral and bilateral eye closure on cortical unit responses in kittens. *J. Neurophysiol.*, **28:**1029–1040.

——— and ———. 1965b. Extent of recovery from the effects of visual deprivation in kittens. *J. Neurophysiol.*, **28:**1060–1072.

Wolda, H. 1961. Response decrement in the prey-catching activity of *Notonecta glauca* L. (Hemiptera). *Arch. Néerl. Zool.*, **14:**61–89.

nineteen

THE DEVELOPMENT OF MOTOR PATTERNS

Relative stability of sensory and motor systems • Genetic control • Resistance to environmentally induced change • Practice • Changes in frequency and intensity • Reordering and reorientation of actions • Development of novel motor patterns • Sensory feedback and development.

During development sensory and motor mechanisms interact extensively. Nevertheless, we have chosen to discuss the developmental basis of motor patterns separately before considering the two together. In this way we hope to show that patterns of motor activity are more resistant to drastic reorganization by environmental influence than patterns of responsiveness to external stimuli.

THE RELATIVE STABILITY OF SENSORY AND MOTOR SYSTEMS

The contrast between the organization of sensory and motor development stems from differences in the underlying physiological mechanisms. Most sensory systems are relatively labile and free from constraint so that radical changes in the patterns of operation as a result of experience are often possible. The function of motor systems is to perform various kinds of mechanical work. The efficient performance of work imposes severe limits on the form of motor equipment (see page 204).

Intricate coordination of the characteristics of the skeletal, muscular, and neural systems is required, both static and dynamic, if appendages are to perform reliably such actions as locomotion or the acquisition of food. Changes in the form of such actions can often be accomplished only by growth of new tissues or elimination of existing ones. Such change can be vitally important in permitting adjustments, say, in the force exerted during an action. But the resulting modifications in the coordination of the motor behavior are necessarily minor. More extensive change would involve redesign of the entire motor equipment. Developmental adjustment of motor patterns in response to experience is thus restricted by the nature of the motor apparatus.

Weiss (1950) and Sperry (1951, 1958) have repeatedly reminded us that growth patterns of bones, muscles, and nerves seem to be closely controlled by endogenous processes (see page 601). In general, endogenous control seems to have a more direct and obvious influence on the patterns of motor activity than on sensory mechanisms, particularly when we consider the structure of individual acts. As a result genetic factors loom large in shaping variations in the form of motor activity.

In discussing environmental influences on the ontogeny of motor patterns we shall concern ourselves mainly with the more subtle changes in the order and timing of acts, shifts in their relative frequency, or modification of their orientation relative to the external environment. Only rarely, as in song development in birds or the development of new motor skills in some mammals, are there examples of drastic repatterning of motor activity by experience on the scale that is commonplace in sensory development.

GENETICALLY CONTROLLED MOTOR PATTERNS

Genetic control of motor patterns may be demonstrated either by selectively breeding for a particular behavioral trait or by crossing animals that are genetically dissimilar and studying the offspring (Fuller and Thompson 1960). Genetic influences on motor development may involve the structure of action patterns, or they may cause shifts in the relative thresholds of different acts so that some become more frequent and others more rare, while the actual patterns of action remain more or less unchanged.

Some of the most thorough studies of behavioral genetics deal with reproductive behavior. Separate, inbred lines of male guinea pigs, subjected to carefully quantified tests for mating activity, were found to differ in the frequency of mounting, intromission, ejaculation, and latency to ejaculation (Goy and Jakway 1962). Similarly, females may show strain differences in latency to estrus, duration of estrus, vigor of lordosis, frequency of mounting, and the temporal relationships between peak of mounting activity and peak of heat.

Breeding experiments showed that the genetic systems controlling the differences in male sexual behavior are relatively independent of those controlling female behavior. Moreover, it was possible to manipulate independently different behavioral elements in the same sex. In the male guinea pig, for example, there seem to be two genetic modes, one for motor activity and mounting, and one for intromission and ejaculation. This provides striking corroboration of Beach's conclusion from behavioral evidence that two mechanisms must be involved (page 96). In female guinea pigs there are at least three genetic factors controlling mating behavior (Goy and Jakway 1959).

Cockerels can be selectively bred for variations in the frequency and vigor of aggressive and sexual behavior (Guhl, Craig, and Mueller 1960, Wood-Gush 1960).

In the fruit fly, *Drosophila melanogaster,* Manning (1961) selectively bred for slow and fast mating speed during 25 generations. Differences in the time from introduction to copulation appeared remarkably quickly. Within seven generations one line had a mean mating latency of 80 minutes; for the other it was 3 minutes. Crosses between the lines produced individuals with intermediate mating speeds. The most obvious effect of selection was to raise the threshold for sexual activity in the 'slow' line, and to raise the threshold for general activity in the 'fast' line. Such threshold differences have also been found in the sexual behavior of other strains of *Drosophila melanogaster* (Bastock 1956). The sexual behavior of *Drosophila melanogaster* and *D. simulans* includes much the same set of action patterns, the differences between them lying mainly in the relative frequency with which they are used (Manning 1959a, b). Variation in thresholds may be responsible for many of the species-specific properties of *Drosophila* courtship (Spieth 1952).

Although much attention has been focused on reproductive behavior, it is equally easy to demonstrate genetic differences in the speed with which rats learn to run a maze (Tryon 1942), rates of wheel running in mice (Bruell 1962), the readiness of mice to explore an open field (McClearn 1959), and 'wildness' in turkeys and mice (Leopold 1944, Hall 1951). In general, selection can give rise to strains that differ strikingly in the frequency and vigor with which behavior patterns are performed in surprisingly few generations.

The distinction between motor and sensory control is by no means clear in threshold changes of this type. Increased frequencies of mating activity or avoidance could well result from changes on the sensory side, and in fact they have been considered in this context (see page 631). Alternatively, modification of central processes, which could be considered both sensory and motor, may be involved. We are again reminded that the separation of the two types of development is one of convenience in considering the overt behavioral changes during development. In the pursuit of the underlying physiological mechanisms the distinction may be better discarded in favor of a more unified approach, especially in borderline cases such as these.

Evidence for genetic control over the structure of action patterns stems not so much from selection studies as from the crossing of genetically dissimilar individuals from different strains or distinct species. Nonetheless, genetic selection for action patterns is assumed to be possible. This selection must have occurred countless times in the process of domestication, as Darwin (1859) demonstrated for the flight patterns of domestic descendants of the ring dove. Other examples are to be found in the crowing patterns of Japanese cockerels, the singing patterns of the roller canary, quantitative and qualitative variations in the behavior of domestic dogs (Scott 1954, Fuller 1962, Scott and Fuller 1965), and the many behavioral abnormalities of strains of domestic mice such as waltzing and circling (Grüneberg 1952).

The best examples of genetic control of the structure of action patterns come from birds and insects, which have large repertoires of stereotyped motor patterns. In the social behavior of F_1 hybrid finches Hinde (1956) found that differing action patterns of parents were intermediate in the hybrids. A hybrid between two thrushes, a male blackbird and a female American robin, showed an intermediate type of tail movement (Dilger 1959). The behavior of hybrid ducks may be intermediate between the two parent species. Sometimes they also apparently display an ancestral pattern or a recombination of parental elements in different temporal patterns (Lorenz cited in Dilger 1962).

The behavior of hybrids between the parrots *Agapornis roseicollis* and *A. fischeri* has been carefully studied (Dilger 1962). The nest-building behavior is of particular interest.

Females of *roseicollis* carry strips of nesting material (paper, bark, or leaves) tucked amidst the feathers of the lower back or rump. Several such strips are carried at a time, and if a strip is dropped for some reason before the bird reaches the nest cavity it is not picked up and retucked. On the other hand, *fischeri* females carry nesting material (strips of bark, paper, or leaves and more substantial items such as twigs) one piece at a time in the bill. Hybrid females almost always attempt, at least, to tuck nesting material in the feathers but are never successful in carrying in this way for several reasons: (1) Proper movements for tucking are made, but the bird seems unable to let go of the strip even after repeated attempts at tucking; (2) The strip is tucked but soon falls out—usually while the bird is busy cutting the next one;

(3) Tucking is attempted at locations other than the lower back and rump—a more "primitive" or ancestral pattern; (4) The strip is grasped somewhere other than at one end, making proper tucking impossible; (5) Tucking movements are begun; but the behavior gradually merges into preening movements, and the strip falls unnoticed to the ground; (6) Tucking-intention movements are made but not completed; (7) Inappropriate objects such as twigs are tucked; and (8) Sometimes the bird attempts to get its bill near its rump by running backward. These hybrids are only successful in carrying material in the mouth (Dilger 1962, pp. 41–42).

A majority of these patterns can be regarded as intermediate between the two parent species (1, 2, 4, and 7). Some may be a result of low motivation (2, 5) and one seems to be an ancestral character (3).

In a study of the songs of hybrid doves the relationship to vocalizations of the parents was found to vary from one species combination to another (Lade and Thorpe 1964). In some hybrids the song pattern of F_1's is intermediate, and in other crosses characteristics of one parent seem to be dominant. Occasionally the temporal pattern of the song breaks down altogether; then the hybrid songs lack any consistent rhythm, although the parent species may have markedly rhythmic song patterns. Disruption of genetically determined patterns of nervous activity, rather than change in syrinx structure, is probably responsible for the hybrid characteristics.

A study of the behavior of F_1, F_2, and backcross hybrids between platyfish and swordtails (Clark, Aronson, and Gordon 1954) revealed an intermediate condition in the F_1 for most characters. Blair (1956) and Bogert (1960) described calls of hybrid frogs and toads that are intermediate between those of the parents in some or all respects (Figure 19-1). Some calls of hybrid frogs and crickets are remarkably similar, as in crosses between two subspecies of *Nemobius fasciatus* (Fulton 1933), *Gryllus bimaculatus* and *G. campestris* (Hörmann-Heck 1957), and two species of *Acheta* (Bigelow 1960). The songs of the latter were intermediate between those of parental species in some respects and similar to those of one parent in others. Certain components of orthopteran songs such as rates of wingstroke and of chirping seem to be determined by different sets of genes. Perdeck (1958) analyzed the song in two species of short-horned grasshoppers. Hybrids have songs which are in many respects intermediate. Perdeck demonstrated the function of the specific differences in song patterns in reproductive isolation. In studies of insect behavior of other types, Caspari (1951) and Haskins and Haskins (1958) have found genetic contributions to patterns of silk-spinning behavior. Work on the sickle dances of hybrids between different strains of bees suggests genetic control (Baltzer 1952).

Thus there is ample evidence that genetic factors can control variations

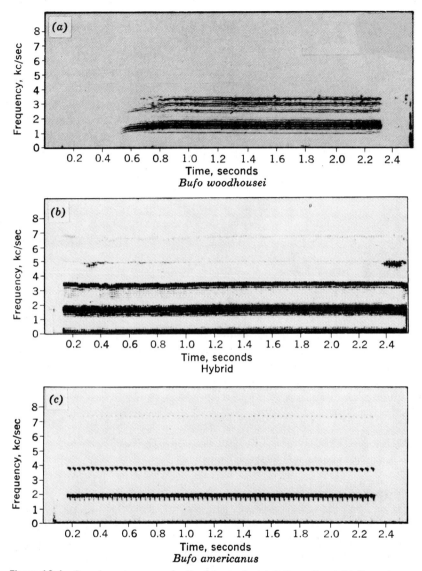

Figure 19-1 Sound spectrograms of calls of the toads, (a) *Bufo woodhousei*, (c) *B. americanus*, and (b) a hybrid. After Blair 1956.

in the coordination of action patterns as well as in their frequency and threshold. There are many pathways by which such effects can be exerted. The close dependence of motor activities on the muscular and skeletal equipment provides one way that genes can affect behavior. Davis (1957) has shown how differences in foraging behavior of brown and rufous-sided towhees are associated with differences in the weight and insertion of some of the muscles of the leg. Some characteristics of web-spinning behavior in spiders may be determined by variation in body weight or leg length (Witt and Reed 1965).

The singing behavior of crickets is closely dependent on variation in the number of teeth on the leg file, which is genetically controlled and tends to be intermediate in hybrids (Haskell 1961). Another factor is the rate of wing stroke, which seems to be controlled not by the mechanical properties of the singing organs but by neural mechanisms (Alexander 1962). Some independence from the morphology of the sound-producing organs is indicated in young crickets which perform appropriate movements for the production of species-specific sounds before the structures necessary for actual sound production develop (Weih 1951, Jacobs 1953). Frog calls are strongly dependent on the size and shape of the throat sacs, but here, too, the assumption that physical structure of the sound-producing organs dictates all the properties of the vocal patterns has been questioned (McAlister 1959).

Relatively unspecific effects of genetic factors on frequencies and thresholds of behavior seem to be achieved at least partly by changes in endocrine function or levels of autonomic activity. Modification of quite peripheral sensory structures can be responsible for genetic control, as for example in the vestibular dysfunction of the 'waltzing' mouse (Grüneberg 1952). We shall encounter this multiplicity of pathways for genetic influence on motor patterns again.

MOTOR PATTERNS WHICH DEVELOP WITHOUT EXPOSURE TO SIMILAR ENVIRONMENTAL PATTERNS

Direct analysis of the genetic basis of motor patterns requires breeding experiments. These are difficult or impossible in many animals. Another approach is to raise animals of the same species or stock under different environmental conditions and to see whether there are any variations in the behavior of the different groups. Such an approach is used in studying what effect varying the opportunity to perceive a motor pattern performed by other individuals has on the development of corresponding motor patterns. This is the basis of what is known in Germany as the Kaspar Hauser experiment after the nineteenth-century youth who, according to the legend, was kept in isolation for the first sixteen years of his life.

In isolation studies an animal is raised alone, or with a group of animals of similar age. The isolation from experienced animals of the same species begins very early, preferably from birth. The motor patterns that develop are compared with those of control animals raised in the company of adults. If a behavioral pattern develops normally in the absence of the example of an adult, the interpretation of the result is unambiguous. Whenever it can be shown that normal development occurs in the absence of a specific environmental influence, an advance has been made in understanding the developmental basis of that motor pattern. Such a pattern may then be a suitable subject for further analysis, genetic study for example.

But as Lorenz (1961) has pointed out, when behavior patterns develop abnormally in isolation, the results are much more difficult to interpret. The environments to which experimental and control animals are exposed contrast in a great many aspects, any of which might be responsible for the differences observed. The general health of animals is often impaired when they are deprived of normal parental care. Skill and patience in handling and caring for the animals are a prerequisite for such work. Another complication arises if the isolation conditions fail to provide appropriate stimuli for elicitation and performance of the motor pattern being studied. Only by eliminating deficiencies of this kind can the variations in behavior be attributed to more specific environmental effects on development.

Animals of widely different phyletic levels raised in isolation perform the normal motor patterns of sexual activity when first confronted with appropriate eliciting stimuli. Male jumping spiders have elaborate courtship patterns which appeared normally in Kaspar Hauser individuals (Drees 1952). Dieterlen (1959) raised ten young hamsters in isolation to adulthood, from ages ranging from four to ten days after birth. He found that although the intensity and timing of the behavior of the isolates differed in a number of ways from those of the controls, all their basic motor patterns appeared to be normal, including feeding and other types of maintenance behavior, territorial marking, and sexual and parental behavior. Eibl-Eibesfeldt (1961) has made similar observations in other rodents. Wilsson (in press) raised a number of beavers in isolation and found a wide range of motor patterns developing normally, including the complex movements used in felling trees and in constructing and maintaining dams. Thorpe (1963) has reviewed many other examples.

The amount of careful experimental information, coupled with meticulous description of the behavior of animals kept under controlled conditions, is still small. Nevertheless, it seems likely that many highly stereotyped action patterns of animals can indeed develop without the exposure to such patterns in the environment.

MOTOR PATTERNS RESISTANT TO ENVIRONMENTAL CHANGE

Attempts to divert the normal pattern of behavioral development by changing environmental factors are often successful. They are sometimes strikingly unsuccessful. We have already considered the experiments in which Weiss (1950) and Sperry (1958) rearranged muscle and nerve connections of amphibians and mammals, reversing the normal orientation of movement (Figure 19-2). In spite of exhaustive attempts at conditioning, no correction of these reversed movements was achieved. It would be difficult to find a more convincing demonstration of the relative lack of plasticity in certain types of motor organization.

In another experimental approach Hess (1956) fitted domestic chicks with a latex hood arranged to carry lenses or prisms in front of the eyes. Birds hatched in darkness were brought into the light and immediately

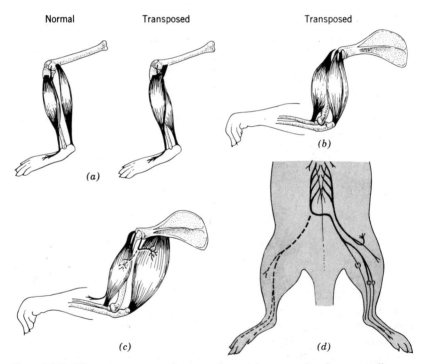

Figure 19-2 The rearrangement of nerve end organs in rats produced corresponding sensory and motor dysfunction that could not be corrected by retraining. (*a*) Transposition of opposing flexor and extensor muscles of hindlimb, (*b*) same in forelimb, (*c*) reinnervation of triceps extensor muscle by antagonist nerve from biceps flexor muscle, (*d*) contralateral crossed innervation of right foot by nerves from left foot. After Sperry 1958.

fitted with prisms which displaced the visual fields of both eyes 7 degrees to the right. Control birds were fitted with flat pieces of plastic. Hess was interested in the development of the coordination between eye and bill involved in pecking at grain. In particular, he sought to determine whether chicks learn to peck accurately by first making scattered pecks and then being rewarded by the capture of grain for pecking in a certain direction.

The results were unexpected and remarkable. The first pecks by the experimental birds were directed to the right of the target. After the chicks had a few days practice at pecking at grain, a comparison was made between experimentals and controls. Both were in one sense pecking more accurately. The pecks of both groups formed a much tighter cluster. But the pecks of the control birds were clustered around the target, and those of the experimentals were still 7 degrees to the right of it (Figure 19-3). Although they found some grain by accidental pecking, the birds with prisms soon became undernourished and some died. Thus the attempt at training failed to change the relationship between visual stimuli received from a target, and the orientation of pecking movements at that target.

Animal vocalizations provide other examples of the role of experience in the development of motor patterns. Among birds there is a general distinction between the song, which is a more or less complex vocal utterance, and the calls, which are shorter and simpler (page 442). There are several recent reviews of the developmental basis of these sounds (Lanyon 1960, Thielcke 1961, Thorpe 1961, Marler 1963). Most calls develop normally when birds are raised in isolation from conspecific adults, whether they are exposed to sounds of other species or not. Domestic chickens, for example, raised in an incubator vocalize normally (Schjelderup-Ebbe 1923). The same kind of experiment is more difficult to perform with small nidicolous passerines but has been accomplished with European whitethroats and blackbirds (Sauer 1954, Messmer and Messmer 1956, Thielcke-Poltz and Thielcke 1960). In both cases the calls developed normally. All 25 blackbird calls, for instance, matched those of wild members of the species.

Many more species of nidicolous passerines have been taken from the nest at various times between hatching and fledging, and raised by hand in varying degrees of isolation from their own and other species. It seems unlikely that experience of species-specific sounds during the pre-isolation period had a direct effect on the subsequent development of calls, though the possibility cannot be ruled out entirely. The calls of small passerines raised in this way, such as meadowlarks (Figure 19-4) and pied flycatchers (Lanyon 1957, Curio 1959), almost always develop normally. A wild

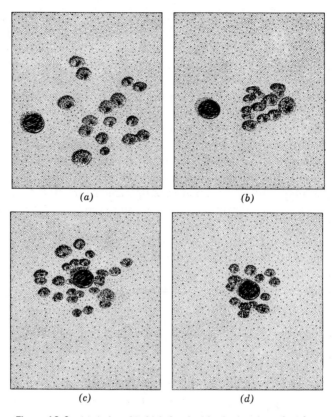

Figure 19-3   (*a*) A day-old chick fitted with plastic prisms that throw the apparent image 7 degrees to the right misses a brass nail by 7 degrees. (*b*) With experience a four-day-old chick clusters its strikes but the average score is still 7 degrees right. A control, fitted with flat windows, (*c*) strikes at the target from the start and (*d*) also becomes more accurate with experience. (*e*) A latex hood carries the lenses and prisms. After photographs in Hess 1956.

hybrid between pied and collared flycatchers developed an intermediate form of the one call that is distinctly different in the two species (Haartman and Löhrl 1950, Löhrl 1955). The calls of hand-raised song sparrows are normal, and the same is true of house finches and of all but one of the calls of the chaffinch (Miller 1921, Nice 1943, Marler 1956). On the basis of wide experience of hand-raising nestling birds, Heinroth (1924) concluded that generally the development of interspecific differences of birdcalls is relatively independent of acoustical influence from other birds.

Song development has been studied by similar experimental methods. Stadler (1929) suggests that differences between the songs of nonpasserine

(e)

birds develop normally in isolation, and the small amount of evidence available supports this conclusion. Incubator-raised domestic cockerels crow normally (Schjelderup-Ebbe 1923). Doves, such as species of *Streptopelia* and *Geopelia,* which were incubated and raised by another species developed normal patterns of cooing (Craig 1908, 1914, Lade and Thorpe 1964).

The songs of many passerine birds have been studied. Whitethroats and blackbirds raised in incubators developed more or less normal patterns of song (Sauer 1954, Messmer and Messmer 1956, Thielcke-Poltz and Thielcke 1960). Normal song development has been demonstrated in hand-raised nestlings of swallows and sand martins, European wrens, tree creepers, grackles, golden orioles, grasshopper warblers, reed and corn buntings, and bullfinches (reviewed in Heinroth 1924, Stadler 1929, Thorpe 1961, Marler 1963).

In addition to these examples of normal song development in isolation from conspecific adults, it is interesting to note the transformation of the

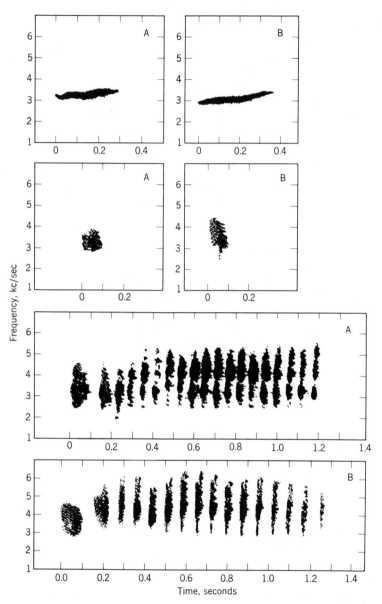

Figure 19-4 Some vocalizations of a hand-reared and isolated eastern meadowlark, *Sturnella magna* (A), are essentially the same as those of a free-living adult (B). After Lanyon 1960.

song of certain birds during domestication. The song of the roller canary is now very different from that of wild canaries as a result of direct selection for voice characters (Marler 1959). The distinctive 'tours' by which fanciers assess the quality of the song develop normally in males raised by a nonsinging female in a soundproof room (Metfessel 1935). Near the turn of the century a special form of domestic pigeon, the trumpeter pigeon, now extinct, was bred for an unusual type of cooing (Levi 1951). An ornamental strain of cockerels is bred in the Orient for a very attenuated crow. These cockerels are matched in crowing contests in much the same way as roller canaries are matched in singing contests in Europe and North America. A genetic analysis of these birds would be rewarding.

The information available on voice development in mammals other than man is sparse, even for primates. It seems likely that the sounds of subprimate mammals, and even of such primates as gibbons and orangutans, develop normally in isolation. Yet very few studies have been directed explicitly at this problem. Seitz (1955) raised a group of the small carnivore *Nyctereutes procyonoides* together in isolation and found that six calls and their variations developed normally. Two domestic cats raised in isolation developed normal calls (Weiss 1952). Among the Lagomorpha, the variety of calls of the pika develop normally in animals isolated after the first month of life (Severaid 1958).

Perhaps the most interesting of these examples is the observation by Boutan (1913) that all thirteen calls of a gibbon developed normally in a hand-raised animal, though it is not clear how familiar he was with the voice of wild individuals. This is a recurrent problem in primate studies. Hand-raised chimpanzees, for example, may develop as many as 32 distinguishable vocalizations (Yerkes and Learned 1925), but we have no information on how these compare with calls of wild animals. In spite of intensive efforts at training, there has been little or no success in inducing apes to utter new sounds including human speech (Furness 1916, Yerkes and Yerkes 1929). Again these vocal motor patterns are resistant to change by environmental influences.

In spite of the lack of information on many groups, it already seems probable that most animal vocalizations develop normally in isolation and are resistant to change in form by exposure to environmental sounds. This appears to be true of orthopterans, anurans and birds, and mammals including at least one primate. Vocal abnormalities in individuals raised out of hearing of their own kind are the exception. The extent of this vocabulary may range from a few sounds in orthopterans and anurans up to as many as 20 to 30 distinct vocalizations in some birds and mammals. The possibility that an animal's ability to hear its own voice may be important in development remains to be considered (see page 696).

DETAILED IMPROVEMENT BY 'PRACTICE'

In one famous experiment Grohmann (1938) reared pigeons in cardboard tubes that restricted wing movements. Controls were allowed normal wing-flapping movements in the nest. The experimental birds were released from the tubes, and their ability to fly was compared with the ability displayed in the maiden flights of controls of the same age. Grohmann could detect no difference between the two groups.

This experiment showed that the basic motor patterns of pigeon flight can develop without the normal experience of proprioceptive feedback that practice provides. Nevertheless, there can be little doubt that the motor patterns of flight and other types of locomotion are perfected as a result of practice (Tinbergen 1951, Thorpe 1963). Analysis of the subtle adjustments of such improvement is exceptionally difficult.

An example of how such an investigation might proceed is provided by Petersen, Lundgren, and Wilson (1957) who worked on the development of flight in *Pieris* butterflies. Newly emerged animals were released from the floor of a lighted arena to determine the height to which they would fly. With increasing age they flew higher and higher. To test the role of flight practice in this improvement three groups were allowed different amounts of flying time. One group (N) was tested from the first to the fifth day after emergence, four times a day at 20-minute intervals. A second group (M) was kept inactive for the first four days, by cooling, in darkness to a temperature of 18°C, and then given similar treatment on the fifth and tenth days after emergence. A third group (T) was given the same four trials per day, with an additional 20 'training' flights after each daily test on the first five days and the tenth day after emergence.

All groups showed a clear increase in the score with age, irrespective of amount of practice. A separate investigation revealed that this improvement was largely a result of stiffening of the wings. The heights achieved by all groups at equivalent ages were surprisingly similar, emphasizing that practice is not required for the basic movements of flying. Nevertheless, there was a slight but significantly more rapid increase in the T group as compared with the N group in the first two days of testing. The greater amount of flying experience of the T animals thus resulted in an increase in this measure of their flying efficiency.

Improvement in maternal behavior as a result of bearing previous offspring has been described in a few species (review in Lehrman 1961). These contrast with other well-documented cases of a similar degree of efficiency of maternal behavior in inexperienced and experienced mammalian mothers (e.g. Beach and Jaynes 1956). Successive nests of rabbits are constructed better (Ross, Denenberg, Sawin, and Meyer 1956).

The subtlety of such improvements as a result of practice makes accurate measurements difficult and explains the rarity of attempts to demonstrate the effects of practice. The slight modifications of the amplitude and timing of the components of the action pattern that result from sensory feedback from the body and the environment are difficult to detect. Yet a complete analysis of behavioral development must surely take them into account.

UNSPECIFIC ENVIRONMENTAL EFFECTS ON FREQUENCY AND INTENSITY OF MOTOR PATTERNS

There has been increasing interest in the effects of early experience on adult behavior in recent years. This interest is related in part to hypotheses about the role of infantile and childhood experience in shaping human behavior. A major contribution of such research has been to show how the frequency of some behavioral patterns in animals can be drastically and lastingly changed by certain kinds of early experience (Denenberg 1962, Levine 1962).

◆ *Emotionality.* To take a simple example first, the frequency of 'freezing,' urination, and defecation in rats and mice placed in strange surroundings are used as measures of emotionality (page 630). For a given strain of animals, raised and tested under the same conditions, the scores are fairly stable. Variations from the normal can readily be detected. Various kinds of rather unspecific environmental disturbances, including electric shock and handling by the experimenter ('gentling'), during the first few weeks of life have the effect of reducing emotionality. That is, rats and mice treated in these various ways and placed in strange surroundings defecate and urinate less than controls and are more active. Proprioceptive and kinesthetic experience may be important, particularly when induced by rather sudden, drastic external stimulation (Levine 1962).

There is a quantitative relationship such that, for example, rats stimulated for 20 days in infancy were less emotional than animals stimulated for 10 days, which in turn were less emotional than untreated controls (Denenberg 1962). There are also effects on performance in avoidance learning tests which can be attributed to the reduction of timidity in stimulated animals. Rats with an intermediate amount of stimulation in infancy, as determined by either the intensity or the number of days of stimulation, have the best learning scores. The controls do poorly as a result of excessive timidity; the least emotional animals do poorly because they are so phlegmatic that they respond only weakly to avoidance stimuli (Denenberg 1962).

More fundamental changes including accelerated growth, early myelination in the central nervous system, and various other physiological effects may be associated with these unspecific effects of early experience on adult rat behavior. Changes in adrenal function have special relevance. The production of steroids by the adrenal cortex, a response of the body to environmental stress, occurs more rapidly in stimulated animals. Adrenocortical activity also returns to the basic level sooner in stimulated rats than in animals which have not been stimulated. As a result the adrenal glands of unstimulated animals may ultimately reach a larger size than those of stimulated rats in response to adult stress (Christian 1963). In physiology as well as in behavior, the animals with the early experiences are more plastic, and as adults they are able to modulate their responses to varied situations more finely than unstimulated animals (Levine 1962).

◆ *Aggression.* Variations in social experience can affect behavior in adulthood. One pattern so influenced is aggressive behavior. Male mice were isolated from parents and siblings at weaning and placed with other males when adult. They were less aggressive than mice raised in groups, in the sense that they waited longer than the controls before starting a fight (King and Gurney 1954). Practice in fighting is not a crucial factor because mice that are isolated by a wire screen behave no differently from controls in adulthood. The long fighting latency of mice that were fully isolated in youth is an unspecific effect of early experience, probably resulting from a longer period of investigation of the opponent before starting a fight (King 1957). As in studies of emotionality, the age at which social contact occurs is important in determining whether the behavior will be normal. King found that ten days of contact immediately after weaning sufficed to cause normal aggressive behavior, whereas ten days in early adulthood did not.

In addition, the relative balance between aggressive and submissive behavior can be changed by early social experience. Dogs isolated as puppies often assumed a subordinate status in adult competition (Melzack and Thompson 1956). On the other hand, cats raised in isolation tended to be extremely aggressive as adults (Seitz 1959).

The specific experience of fighting can also affect later dominance behavior. Mice subjected to defeat in youth by exposure to a trained fighter tended to be subordinate to other mice as adults (Kahn 1951). Once more earlier experience had more effect than later exposure. Drastic effects, however, can also be demonstrated in adult mice and rats. Previous success tends to produce a dominant animal (Uhrich 1940, Ginsburg and Allee 1942, Seward 1945–1946, Scott and Fredericson 1951).

◆ *Sexual Behavior.* Early social experience may influence the quantitative properties of sexual behavior. The guinea pig has been thoroughly explored from this point of view (Young 1961, reviewed in Lehrman 1962). Males raised in isolation and then placed with estrous females had lower scores on number of mountings, intromissions, and ejaculations than males raised with males or females of the same age. As with mouse fighting, isolates having sensory access to other guinea pigs through a wire screen were normal in sexual behavior, which suggests that lack of practice of sexual mounting is not the prime factor responsible for the abnormalities of isolates (Gerall 1963). We shall note later some abnormalities in the sexual motor patterns of these animals which may contribute to the deficit in normal sexual scoring. Similarly, rhesus monkeys raised without siblings show both specific and unspecific deficits in their sexual behavior when compared with wild-caught controls (Figure 19-5, Mason 1960, 1965).

Shaw (1962) has shown with platyfish that variations of early experience of a nonsocial nature can have quantitative effects on the development of sexual patterns. The adult sexual behavior of individuals raised in isolation in tanks of clear glass providing a view of the surroundings resembled that of fish raised in groups under the same conditions. Fish isolated in tanks of frosted glass showed little or no sexual behavior in adult tests, however. Even grouped fish raised in such tanks had lower scores than members of groups in clear tanks. The surprising conclusion is that some aspect of early experience encountered in a tank of frosted

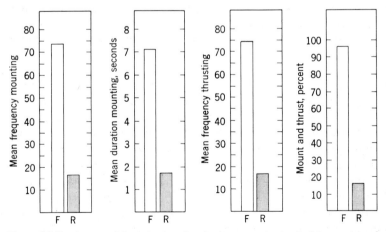

Figure 19-5 Aspects of the behavior of male rhesus monkeys raised in a restricted social environment (R) compared with the sexual behavior of wild-raised individuals (F). After Mason 1960.

glass alters later behavior. The significant elements of experience that so conspicuously modify adult sexual behavior remain an intriguing mystery.

◆ *Parent-Young Relationships.* A clear example of the effect of early experience on the subsequent frequency of a behavior pattern is found in the suckling of puppies. Puppies that are weaned early, before 10 days, show an abnormally large amount of 'non-nutritive' suckling at experimenters' fingers (Scott, Ross, and Fisher 1959). When the opportunity for suckling is varied by changing hole size of a milk bottle, puppies fed through extra-large holes finish the bottle quickly. They subsequently show much more non-nutritive sucking than the controls fed through nipples with small holes (Levy 1934). This work has been widely quoted as a parallel with thumb sucking in bottle-fed human babies, on the assumption that breast feeding takes longer and requires more sucking.

Care is needed in interpreting the results of experiments on the effects of early experience on adult behavior. For example, Riess (1954) raised rats with no opportunity to manipulate objects, giving them powdered food and even bobbing their tails. After mating they were placed in a new cage with nest material to give birth. They built poor nests and neglected their young by failing to retrieve them, and many of the young died. Riess inferred that lack of manipulative experience was responsible for the deficient maternal behavior. When Eibl-Eibesfeldt (1955) repeated the experiment, however, he found normal maternal behavior in females allowed to give birth in their home cages. A strange testing situation evidently disrupts maternal behavior. The result of this experiment emphasizes the importance of knowledge of the normal behavior in designing experiments of this type.

◆ *Feeding and Food Hoarding.* Many rodents carry food to the nest and hoard it there (e.g. pocket mice and kangaroo rats, Eisenberg 1963). Domestic rats hoard, and after early food deprivation hoarding becomes more frequent. Rats were fed for only short periods during the day for the fourth or fifth week of life for fifteen days; then they were given a continuous supply of food. They hoarded more in later life when hungry than controls raised without food restriction (Hunt 1941). Similar treatment of rats when two weeks older had no such effect. Both the rate of feeding and the schedule of feeding bouts may be affected by previous experience (Bindra 1959). There are strain differences in the frequency of hoarding. Generally, the more timid rats do the most hoarding (Bindra 1959). The rate of normal feeding behavior in dogs can also be affected by early food deprivation. Puppies given a reduced diet from the third to the seventh weeks subsequently ate faster than controls given ample food, although the total amount eaten was the same (Elliot and King 1960).

◆ *Conclusions.* Most examples of unspecific effects of environmental stimuli on the frequency of behavior patterns in later life seem to result from a change of the threshold for elicitation of the behavior. Thus exposure to various stimuli in youth can raise the threshold of the emotionality motor patterns of mice and rats. Food deprivation in youth lowers the threshold for subsequent hoarding in rats. Levine's (1962) work has shown that the changes in emotionality are associated with fundamental shifts in endocrine balance.

As with genetic effects of this type, the distinction between sensory and motor mechanisms breaks down. Lehrman (1961, 1962) found similar changes in doves. The induction of incubation behavior with injections of progesterone occurs more readily in experienced doves than in inexperienced ones (Lehrman and Wortis 1960). Thus an effect of previous experience on the threshold of responsiveness to hormones may help to explain some of the repercussions that early stimulation can have on the frequency of activities in later life.

REORDERING OF EXISTING MOTOR ACTIONS

One result of raising animals under experimentally controlled conditions is that they sometimes develop essentially normal action patterns but deliver them in an abnormal temporal or spatial sequence. The sexual behavior of rhesus monkeys is abnormal if they are raised with only a limited opportunity to contact and play with agemates or a mother. Isolated males with limited social contacts show some of the normal elements of adult sexual behavior during brief play periods. These include erection, mounting, and thrusting. But these movements are never integrated into the complete pattern. As a result male rhesus monkeys raised under such conditions never develop normal adult sexual behavior (Harlow 1961, 1962, Mason 1965).

Similar results have been obtained with chimpanzees. The inference drawn is that, at least in males, experience gained in play with siblings is essential for normal integration of sexual behavior (Mason 1960). The behavioral data thus corroborate physiological evidence that cerebral processes and the learning that they mediate are important in controlling the sexual behavior of male primates (see page 107).

Abnormalities have been noted in the sexual behavior of male guinea pigs raised in isolation. Once more all the basic elements are present in the behavior at a very young age. Play behavior is thought to be responsible not for achieving the proper sequence of actions but for disturbing it. The proper ordering of mating actions is apparently disrupted in animals raised in isolation by the intrusion of elements of play behavior which they have had little previous opportunity to express (Gerall 1963).

The reordering of existing motor patterns may play a part in the development of so-called 'string-pulling' behavior of birds discussed later (page 683). Although some species develop new motor patterns to solve this laboratory problem, other species already possess the necessary motor elements and need only to arrange them in the proper order to solve the puzzle (Thorpe 1963).

The examples of reordering of motor elements in the course of development are sporadic and imperfect. Nevertheless, it seems likely that such change is widespread in the environmental shaping of motor behavior. It will often be mixed with developmental changes of other types and may be difficult to separate from them.

ENVIRONMENTAL REORIENTATION OF EXISTING MOTOR PATTERNS

A more or less durable change in orientation is perhaps the most prevalent effect that past experience can have on the motor activities of animals. In its simplest form it can be seen in the development of attachments to certain localities. Insects such as digger wasps quickly learn the characteristics of the home area and are guided back to it repeatedly. Thorpe (1963) has reviewed in detail how wasps that return repeatedly to provision their burrows with prey for their young acquire a remarkable ability to orient to visual cues in the neighborhood. In addition to becoming responsive to stimuli close to the nest, some insects and spiders can also learn to use cues that only indirectly provide orientation, such as the sun or polarization patterns in the sky, in finding their way home (see page 557). The ability to acquire a new escape orientation in relation to the direction of the sun has been demonstrated in wolf spiders (Papi and Tongiorgi 1963).

The readiness of birds to orient by local landmarks is equally well known. So firmly learned are the characteristics of the territories of some migrant birds that they are able to return to them in subsequent years after migrations of thousands of miles between summer and winter quarters (Dorst 1962). Presumably the final phase of the return to the precise spot of previous nesting is based on visual recognition of the local environment. Perhaps more remarkable is the return of many young birds to nests close to the area where they were hatched (see page 589).

Young birds often travel with adults, and it is likely that orientation of migration routes is sometimes acquired in this way. In geese, for example,, the attachment of young to the parents is strong and the whole migration route seems to be maintained over many generations as a learned tradition. It may even persist after man has made certain areas unsuitable as a habitat by drainage or cultivation (Hochbaum 1955). In addition to such learning of landmarks, birds, like insects, are also able to acquire oriented responses to indirect clues from the sun and stars (Kramer 1952, Hoffmann 1953, 1954, Hamilton 1962). In the laboratory this can be achieved simply by rewarding them with food for movement in a particular compass direction.

The reorientation of such large-scale movements can take place in two ways. It may occur directly as the animal is rewarded for moving in one direction or another in the course of its own exploration of the environment. Or the environmental stimuli responsible may come from an animal, the observation of which leads another to perform actions with a similar orientation. These actions can occur either immediately or at some time in the future. The same alternatives recur in the acquisition of other types of reorientation, for example, in the solving of a maze or a puzzle box.

◆ *Detailed Orientation of Action Patterns.* We can discuss first the reorientation through experience of the separate elements of action patterns, such as occurs in the development of reproductive and feeding behavior. Consider the development of the motor patterns of feeding in a squirrel. Eibl-Eibesfeldt (1956a, 1961) raised European red squirrels by hand and give them varying opportunities to practice opening hazelnuts which are normally a staple part of their diet. Experienced adults open the nuts by cutting a furrow at the tip and springing apart the two halves (Figure 19-6). Eibl-Eibesfeldt found that the basic action patterns of gnawing, splitting, and turning the nut appeared the first time the inexperienced squirrels were given a nut. But initially the movements had no specific orientation on the nut and furrows were gnawed all over the surface. Only after opening several nuts did the movements become oriented in the natural manner so that the nut was opened with a minimum of effort.

Such improvement presumably takes place by trial and error. Kear (1962) has described a similar reorientation in the seed-husking actions of finches. Although young birds showed mandibulatory actions when

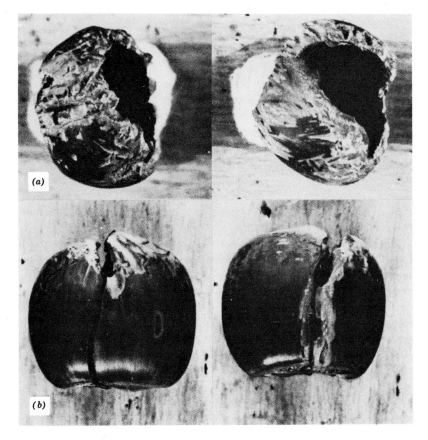

Figure 19-6   The European red squirrel makes appropriate chiseling movements in open-ing hazel nuts without previous experience or example. (*a*) The chiseling is scattered across the nut in a 76-day-old male that was given its first nut at 60 days. (*b*) Older individuals open the nut by chiseling at a certain point and springing the nut open. After photographs in Eibl-Eibesfeldt 1956a.

first pecking, many seeds were not husked successfully. Harder seeds were opened with normal facility only as the birds acquired the ability to orient them properly in the bill. Parallel changes have also been re-corded in the prey-catching techniques of polecats (Eibl-Eibesfeldt 1956b, 1961). The normal movements of pursuit, grasping the neck of a rodent, shaking it, and turning it over on its back, occur the first time an appro-priate object is presented. But the neck bite becomes properly oriented for quick killing of the prey only after several experiences.The sexual behavior of male rhesus monkeys raised in isolation is so disoriented that copulation is not possible (Mason 1960, 1965). Play with agemates seems to be necessary for the normal orientation to develop.

The behavioral patterns that are subject to reorientation through experience can themselves be dependent on prior experience for development. Playing with siblings, as an example, may contribute something to development of the elements of prey catching in polecats. (Eibl-Eibesfeldt 1961).

The ability of monkeys to solve what are known as 'instrumentation problems' (Harlow 1951, Riopelle 1960) provides another example of the role of experience in the development of motor patterns. Köhler (1925) developed the concept of 'insight' learning to explain the ability of chimpanzees, for example, to reach food attached to the ceiling by improvizations, such as making piles of boxes and jumping upon them, apparently without prior experimentation. Later workers (Bingham 1929, Birch 1945) found that previous experience with the implements used, boxes, hoes, and canes that fit together, is essential for the rapid solution of such problems. The apparently instantaneous solution of such problems is actually achieved largely by the reorientation of motor patterns already existing in the behavioral repertoire. Exploratory manipulation and play with the instruments are clearly crucial for their development. Schiller (1957), however, has emphasized that monkeys and apes embark upon play with an already well-formed repertoire of movements. Thus at the simplest level of organization genetic factors remain important (Riopelle 1960).

◆ *Reorientation by Observation of Other Animals.* A special case of the acquisition of new orientations for motor activity by individual experience occurs when the behavior of an animal is changed through observing another. One animal may follow another and so migrate along the same route or take the same course through a maze. Something similar is common in the feeding behavior of animals, in the phenomenon known as 'local enhancement' (Klopfer 1959, Thorpe 1963). An illustration from birds is the carefully documented spread in Great Britain of the habit among titmice of opening milk bottles (Fisher and Hinde 1949, Hinde and Fisher 1952). The motor patterns used were not new, for they resembled those used in opening nuts. What was novel, however, was the orientation toward milk bottle caps. This characteristic probably spread through the population as a result of some individuals observing others. Preference for berries of the shrub, *Daphne*, now characteristic of greenfinches throughout England, also appeared suddenly after starting in northern England (Petersson 1961).

In these examples the behavior patterns of actor and reactor often overlap in time, but they can be temporally separated with a similar result. When one animal is allowed to see another working the latch of a problem box, it may solve the problem more quickly when it is placed inside the box itself, apparently through concentrating its activity in the same place. Such 'observational learning' has been demonstrated in chicks, cats, and monkeys (Riopelle 1960).

In addition to acquiring a certain spatial orientation, an observing animal may learn to orient to a particular environmental stimulus, irrespective of where it is found. Some greenfinches were allowed to observe others learning to peck at seeds placed in front of one figure and to avoid those in front of another which was placed randomly to the right or left. They were then able to learn the discrimination more rapidly themselves (Klopfer 1959, 1961). Orientation *away from* a particular location can also be acquired in this way, as Klopfer (1957) demonstrated in ducks. Some were allowed to watch others being shocked when they touched a particular feeding dish. The observers subsequently avoided the dish in the absence of the trained birds without ever being shocked themselves, clearly demonstrating the efficacy of this process.

◆ *Reorientation through Individual Exploration.* The reorientation of motor activities may occur as a consequence of individual exploration of the environment. An example is found in the development of suckling behavior in young kittens (Ewer 1959, 1961, Rosenblatt, Turkewitz, and Schneirla 1961, Rosenblatt and Schneirla 1962). The newborn kitten moves around waving its head from side to side. If it strays too far from the mother she retrieves it. Eventually the kitten contacts the mother's body. It climbs up on to her body, periodically nuzzling in her fur, until it contacts a nipple. Then the nipple is grasped and suckling begins. After a few days the suckling of each kitten is largely restricted to one teat or pair of teats and continues so until about four weeks of age when the kittens begin to become independent of the mother. Apparently chemical characters are especially important in location of the teats. Fixation to a particular teat seems to develop gradually as a kitten discovers a nipple several times and becomes oriented to it more and more rigidly, at first testing other nipples and rejecting them until the proper one is located, and later moving directly to it.

This pattern of development has all the qualities of 'trial and error' learning (Thorndike 1911, Kimble 1961, Thorpe 1963), in which an animal performs motor actions varied in form or, as in the present case, varied in orientation. Some actions achieve nothing while others lead to food, water, warmth, social contact, or the avoidance of pain or alarm. Depending on the physiological state of the animal at the time, the consequent exposure to such external stimuli can result in persistence of the particular orientation which led to their experience. In this way the kitten acquires the ability to locate the mother's nipples, a rat finds the path through a maze to a food box, and a pigeon begins to peck at a key in a Skinner box to obtain food. In Skinner's (1938) terminology the process is one of "operant conditioning," so called because it is preceded by "operant" behavior. This is in contrast with "respondent" behavior, which depends on immediate eliciting external stimuli. Instrumental learning is another term for this process.

The literature on the processes underlying trial and error learning both in problem boxes and more particularly in mazes provides more information than we have for any other type of behavioral development. It has been reviewed by many authors (e.g. Munn 1950, Kimble 1961, Thorpe 1963). We shall do no more than comment on a few of the highlights.

Rats use many clues in finding their way through a maze. Visual, auditory, and olfactory stimuli may all be used, the particular emphasis depending on the nature of the runway. Vision is more important in orienting movement through an elevated maze than it is in an alley maze (Figure 18-9, Munn 1950). Experimental proof of multisensory control involves the manipulation of external stimuli and surgical interference with their perception. In addition to the distance receptors, the spatio-temporal integration of proprioceptive and tactile information has been shown to play a role in a number of cases (e.g. Figure 19-7). Apparently this integration occurs only after the course has first been established through other sensory modalities (Honzik 1936).

There has been considerable controversy about the temporal course of development of responsiveness to maze cues; the discussion has been focused around the issues of continuity and noncontinuity (Kimble 1961). A graph of the errors made by a group of rats in becoming oriented to the shortest path through a maze usually makes a more or less smooth curve. Taken at its face value, the curve seems to imply that the problem is solved by a gradual and continuous reduction in the number of errors. An examination of the performance of individual animals, however, suggests a discontinuous process.

Krechevsky (1938) points out the need to distinguish between the 'presolution' and 'solution' periods in trial and error learning. In the former stage of maze learning, a rat behaves in a fashion which is far from random trial and error. Rather it behaves as though it were testing out a series of what Krechevsky calls 'hypotheses.' For example, at each choice point in the maze it may first persist with right or with left turns. Then it may switch to the darker of the two alleys, and so on in a series of changes

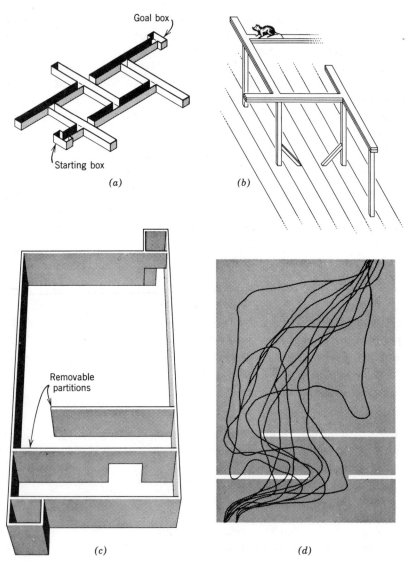

Figure 19-7   Mazes to test the learning ability of animals may take many forms. Here are illustrated a typical six-unit alley maze (*a*) and an elevated maze (*b*). The effect of removing partitions in another type of maze (*c*) is shown in (*d*); rats persist in following the same approximate trail. After Munn 1950 and Krech and Crutchfield 1958.

until the proper solution is found. The particular course of events varies with the individual and its previous history. Genetic factors are also implicated, one strain of rats starting off under visual control, the other under spatial control (Krechevsky 1933).

During the solution period many factors cooperate to determine the durability of the pattern of motor activity. These include the number of times it has been performed and whether it is the most recent pattern performed in the situation at the time a test is made. The behavioral consequences of properly oriented maneuvers are also important—whether they lead more quickly to food, for example, if the animal is hungry and whether the food is highly preferred or not. Consideration must also be given to whether food is obtained every time or not. Intermittent feeding results in a more durable pattern than feeding every time (Skinner 1938).

It is equally important to consider the consequences of movements which are not properly oriented in the maze such as those leading into blind alleys. Just as the finding of food by a hungry animal favors the orientation of movement that has led to it, so experience of a blind alley will discourage the orientation that led to it. As a result a rat can learn a great deal about the path through a maze simply by running through it, without any positive reward for the correct orientation (Figure 19-8).

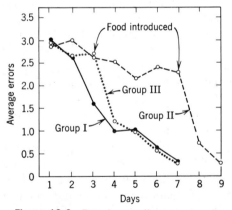

Figure 19-8   Rats in an alley maze were rewarded with food when they reached a box (group I). Group II received food only after the sixth day in the maze and group III only after the second day. The steeper slope of the performance curves for groups II and III after the initiation of food rewards shows that the rats learned some of the features of the maze without any association with feeding. After Krech and Crutchfield 1958 from Blodgett 1929.

Learning of this type must be constantly occurring as animals explore their natural environments, even though the effects may not become manifest until some emergency occurs; hence the term 'latent learning' is sometimes applied to it (Kimble 1961, Thorpe 1963).

The difficulty of distinguishing between learning and its manifestation in actual behavioral performance is a major issue in comparative psychology. It raises questions about which of the many possible measures of performance are to be adopted in a given experiment and what kinds of underlying processes are reflected by each of them. While some correlate with each other, others do not (Kimble 1961). The problem of unitary concepts arises here in much the same form as in motivation studies (Hinde 1959, see page 120) and seems to be just as far from solution.

LOSS OF SOME MOTOR PATTERNS AND EMPHASIS OF OTHERS

The types of change in motor activity that occur during development are usually mingled so that we seldom see any one in a pure form. This is particularly true of the dropping out of some patterns and the emphasis of others. Most of our examples are also discussed under other headings, but for the sake of completeness we have set up a separate category for this particular mode of behavioral development. Under the unspecific effects of early experience, we have considered the reduction in emotionality in rats that results from early noxious stimulation. It is associated with a reduced frequency of urination, defecation, and freezing in certain situations.

Such changes can take a more specific form, as in the adjustment of the orientation of motor patterns in maze running by the elimination of movements oriented toward blind alleys. Such effects are a major factor in the process of trial and error learning, whether it occurs in oriented locomotion or in the more intricate motor patterns used in opening problem boxes and working with mechanical toys and tools (review in Thorpe 1963). The dropping out of certain patterns of behavior plays a part in the generation of new sequences of action patterns by the piecing together of portions of existing patterns (see page 673). A similar process has been recorded in the development of the vocal patterns of song in certain birds (see page 695).

There has been little systematic study of the loss of motor patterns except in the special case of extinction of motor patterns which have themselves been acquired through trial and error learning (Kimble 1961). As in the extinction of conditioned reflexes studied by Pavlov, there is good reason to postulate an active inhibitory process in the loss of such activities. Interference by actions which are positively favored under the particular set of conditions is again difficult to separate, however (see page 642). There is much to learn about this important and neglected aspect of motor development.

DEVELOPMENT OF NEW MOTOR PATTERNS

The environment can affect motor actions very dramatically by giving rise to the development of new patterns of motor coordination. Most information on this subject comes from accounts of circus training, problem solving, and vocal learning in birds, and painting by chimpanzees. There is no sharp line between the kinds of changes in ordering or orientation of motor elements that we have considered in previous sections and those that we shall discuss now. By selectively rewarding actions which are rarely performed or are elicited only in special circumstances, it is possible for an experimenter or circus trainer to establish a new sequence of actions which gradually becomes performed as a unit. The novelty of such a pattern is only partial, for the elements of which it is made up must occur before they can be incorporated in the pattern. Nevertheless, the final result can be dramatic, as Thorpe (1963) and Vince (1956, 1958, 1961) have shown in the so-called string-pulling behavior of birds.

◆ *String Pulling in Birds.* Confronted with a piece of food on a string hanging from a perch down into a glass tube, a number of birds develop methods to draw the food up. The most skillful species, such as titmice and certain finches, solve the problem quickly by drawing up loops of string and catching them under one foot. There are somewhat similar coordinated movements of beak and foot occurring in normal feeding. The novel situation calls for little more than a reorientation or reordering of patterns that already exist.

Some species develop quite new motor patterns to solve the problem, however. The greenfinch, for example, does not use the beak and foot coordination in normal feeding, and it solves the problem more slowly than species that do. Nevertheless, young greenfinches in particular can develop string-pulling methods. The variety of methods that different birds employ is interesting. Of twelve birds tested, only one used the loop and foot method. Eight drew the string up gradually by working it between the mandibles and tongue, apparently making use of action patterns employed in husking seeds. Of the other five birds—

One method was to lift the string again and again until it caught on the perch or the top of the glass cylinder and the bait could be reached. A variant of this was to lift the string and flick the bait on to the perch or top of the cylinder, or to push the string over one or the other; in one case the bird developed a fairly stereotyped method which consisted of lifting the loop high above the perch, then hopping round and round thus twisting up the string until the bait was lifted out of the cylinder (Vince 1961, p. 109).

The new actions must have arisen in several different ways, even though none of them is complex enough to be far removed from pre-existing motor patterns.

Circus trainers make extensive use of what Hediger (1955) calls "putting it through the action" by forcing animals into desired postures or movements. As he describes it, the purest form of putting it through is used in training elephants. Here the "forcing of passive movements is seen at its most striking, since human strength is often so insufficient that pulleys have to be used, or the help of already trained elephants must be sought. If an untrained elephant has to learn to sit down, there is no alternative except to force it down gently on to a barrel that serves as a stool and then raise up its front legs" (Hediger 1955). Hafez, Williams, and Wierzbowski (1962) have described similar techniques used for training horses.

◆ *Copying of Environmental Sounds by Birds.* The advantage of studying sound production in animals is that, with the aid of electronic methods of analysis, an accurate picture can be obtained, reflecting in detail the pattern of motor actions by which the sounds are generated. We have already shown that some sound patterns are genetically controlled and that others are resistant to acoustical influence in the course of development (page 663). Some bird sounds, however, are known to be drastically and specifically influenced by previous auditory experience. In some young birds imitation of the vocal patterns of adults of their species is the normal means of developing certain of the natural vocalizations. Under wild and captive conditions some birds will imitate sounds of other species. The effects of environmental factors on the patterns of vocal behavior in birds are more dramatic than with any other kind of motor activity in animals (Thorpe 1961, Armstrong 1963, Marler 1963).

A male European chaffinch develops a song that is abnormal in several respects if it is taken into the laboratory as a nestling and raised in acoustical isolation (Poulsen 1951, Thorpe 1958, 1961). When a recording of a natural song is played into the soundproof room through a loudspeaker, the singing behavior of such a bird changes to match the pattern of the recording. A similar process of imitation can be observed under natural conditions, so that young males develop song patterns which resemble those of their adult neighbors (Figure 19-9).

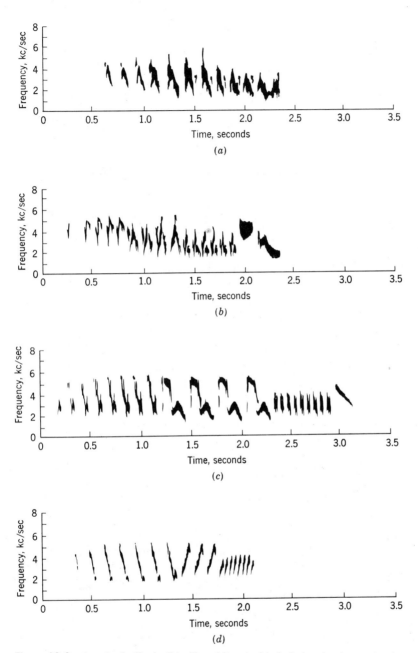

Figure 19-9 A male chaffinch, *Fringilla coelebs*, raised in isolation develops a simpler song pattern (*a*) than one that is allowed to hear other chaffinches singing (*b*). The song of a tree pipit, *Anthus trivialis*, resembles chaffinch song (*c*). If played to a chaffinch raised in isolation, some characteristics of a tree pipit song may be acquired (*d*). After Thorpe 1961.

This copying is restricted to about the first year of life. Most of the details of natural song are acquired at the start of the first breeding season of the young male, which begins at an age of about nine months. This

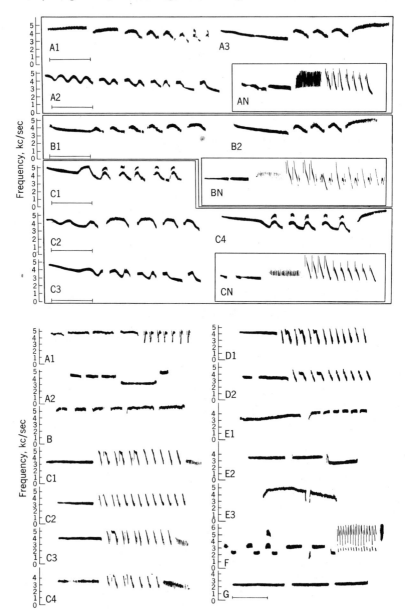

behavior pattern results in development of dialects in the natural song because males tend to breed in the same area year after year. Once this critical period has passed the song patterns are no longer affected by sounds heard, whether the birds have grown up under natural conditions or in isolation (Thorpe 1958).

In addition to these temporal restrictions there are constraints on the sounds that are copied and incorporated into the song. Attempts to induce chaffinches to utter the songs of other species have been generally unsuccessful, except for a tree pipit song, which is very similar to that of the chaffinch (Figure 19-9, Thorpe 1958).

In the song of male white-crowned sparrows in California dialects are very clearly marked, so that separate populations can be characterized by certain properties of the pattern as revealed in sound spectrograms (Marler and Tamura 1962). Full song develops at about 200 to 250 days of age. If young birds are captured in the area where they were born at an age of one to three months and placed in acoustical isolation, they develop the normal song dialect. When they are taken from the nest at an age of three to fourteen days, raised by hand, and kept in acoustical isolation, they still come into full song at the appropriate time. But the songs are abnormal in several respects, and characteristics of the local dialect are lacking (Marler and Tamura 1964).

When hand-raised birds are placed alone in acoustically insulated chambers and given experience of a normal white-crowned sparrow song through a loudspeaker, they subsequently produce a fair copy of it (Figure 19-10). This occurs if they are presented with eight minutes of singing per day for three weeks between the ages of about two weeks to two months. Exposure to a normal song between the third and eighth days,

Figure 19-10 Top, songs of nine male white-crowned sparrows, *Zonotrichia leucophrys*, from three areas in California raised together in isolation. (A1 to A3) Songs of birds born at Inspiration Point, 3 km northeast of Berkeley. (B1 and B2) Songs of individuals born at Sunset Beach. (C1 to C4) Songs of individuals born in Berkeley. The inserts (AN, BN, and CN) show the home dialect of each group. Bottom, songs of twelve males raised under various experimental conditions. (A1 and A2) Birds raised in individual isolation. (B) Male from Sunset Beach trained with Marin song (see Figure 12-21) from the third to the eighth day of age. (C1 to C4) Marin birds brought into the laboratory at the age of 30 to 100 days. (C1) Untrained. (C2 to C4) Trained with Sunset Beach songs; (C2) at about 100 days of age, (C3) at 200 days, (C4) at 300 days. (D1) Bird from Sunset Beach trained with Marin white-crowned sparrow song and a Harris's sparrow song (see G) from the age of 35 to 56 days. (D2) Marin bird trained with Marin white-crowned sparrow song and a song sparrow song (see F) from the age of 6 to 28 days. (E1 to E3) Two birds from Sunset Beach and one from Berkeley trained with song sparrow song from the age of 7 to 28 days. (F) A song sparrow training song for D2 and E1 to E3. (G) A Harris's sparrow training song for D1. After Marler and Tamura 1964.

while young birds are still in the nestling phase, does not result in copying of the song dialect. Thus auditory experience during the early nestling phase does not seem to have any specific effects on subsequent development of song dialects. There may be unspecific effects on more general aspects of vocal development which remain to be explored.

Isolated males exposed to two song dialects, one dialect at an early age (up to two months) and one later (three to ten months), copy only the first. Only if the second song is heard between three and four months is there a slight modification of the copy of the first song. Beyond this and on into subsequent years of life there is no further effect on the dialect. As in the chaffinch the development of new vocal patterns can only occur at a certain phase in the life cycle.

Some experiments have been conducted on the effects of exposure to songs of other species. No interspecific learning has yet been demonstrated. If white-crowned sparrows are given two songs in alternation during the training period, one a white-crowned sparrow song, the other a song of another species such as a Harris' sparrow, *Zonotrichia querula*, or a song sparrow, *Melospiza melodia*, the conspecific song is subsequently reproduced (Marler and Tamura 1964).

Like chaffinches, white-crowned sparrows thus have a predisposition to reproduce song patterns of their own species. They do this even in preference to songs of a close relative such as Harris' sparrow which has a very similar tonal quality. This same choice method has been used to search for any predisposition to learn the home dialect versus the dialect of another region. Limited results show no evidence of preference for the home dialect. Thus all evidence supports the interpretation that the dialect characteristics of white-crowned sparrow songs are phenotypic, transmitted by tradition from the adults of one generation to young of the next.

Although male white-crowned sparrows must often acquire the song patterns of their fathers, there is no specific mechanism for achieving this. In contrast, young male European bullfinches remain in the family group for several months after hatching and acquire the particular song pattern of their father (Nicolai 1956, 1959). Unlike chaffinches and white-crowned sparrows, young captive bullfinches can readily acquire a wide variety of sounds from other species. It was once a pastime in Germany to teach them tunes on the flageolet (Thorpe 1955). If birds that have acquired artificial song patterns such as a canary song or a tune whistled by the human foster parent are bred, their sons acquire the tune even though wild-type songs can be heard nearby. Among Nicolai's birds one such pattern was transmitted through three generations.

The constraints on the choice of sounds to be copied are narrow in some bird species, such as chaffinches and white-crowned sparrows, and are much wider in others, such as the bullfinch. When sounds of other species are copied, the novelty of the motor patterns which develop is all the more striking. Lanyon (1957, 1960) has shown that eastern and western meadowlarks copy the songs of other species (Figure 19-11). Juvenile meadowlarks are able to acquire song patterns from older birds from five weeks of age and on through the first winter. After this song patterns do not change, either in wild or captive birds. It is during this period that they will copy the songs of other species. An individual may acquire several distinct patterns. In nature, eastern meadowlarks have about twice as many song patterns in the individual repertoire as the western species. The same contrast appears in captive birds, even though the repertoire is built of copies of alien songs.

Some birds are mimics in the wild state, developing their natural songs by the incorporation and rearrangement of portions of the songs of different species of birds and other animals. They may even copy sounds from the inanimate environment, such as the twanging of a wire fence (Marshall 1950, 1954, Armstrong 1963). The renderings of human speech by the Indian hill myna correspond with the original in remarkable detail (Figure 19-12). It would be difficult to find a more dramatic example of environmental control of the development of motor patterns which are novel to the previous motor repertoire in almost every respect.

The ability to copy environmental sounds, which is common among birds, is rare in other organisms except man. Some dogs are said to imitate a few words of human speech, but more study is needed to confirm this claim. Exhaustive attempts to teach subhuman primates to speak have met with only limited success. The few so-called 'words' produced may already have existed in the vocal repertoire and been preferentially rewarded by the experimenters (Furness 1916, Yerkes and Yerkes 1929, Hayes and Hayes 1951). Although their larynges look adequate for the task of producing at least crude imitations of speech, they seem to lack the predisposition to copy environmental sounds.

◆ *The 'Invention' of New Motor Patterns.* The inadequacy of a simple classification of behavior into inherited and learned components is nowhere more evident than in motor patterns whose development involves an element of 'invention' or 'improvisation.' Let us consider chimpanzees. We have already noted that their vocal behavior is relatively stable and resistant to environmental change (Kellogg and Kellogg 1933, Hayes and Hayes 1951). Some of their behavior is acutely susceptible to change in response to the visual environment. The imitation of such human actions as sharpening a pencil or prying lids off cans with a screwdriver by a home-raised chimpanzee (Hayes and Hayes 1952) provides a rare ex-

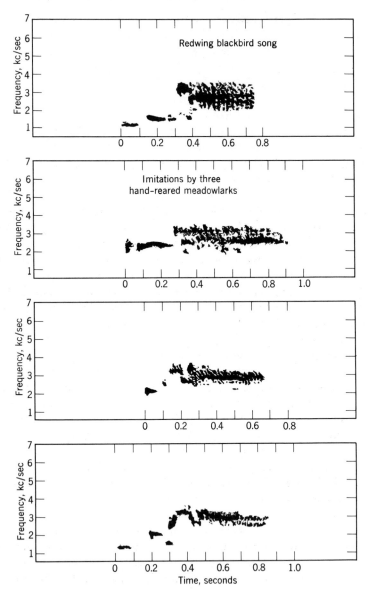

Figure 19-11   Hand-raised meadowlarks will acquire song patterns of other species they are exposed to, including the redwing blackbird, *Agelaius phoeniceus*, the wood pewee, *Contopus virens*, and the yellowthroat, *Geothlypis trichas*. Meadowlarks do not usually mimic other species in nature. After Lanyon 1960.

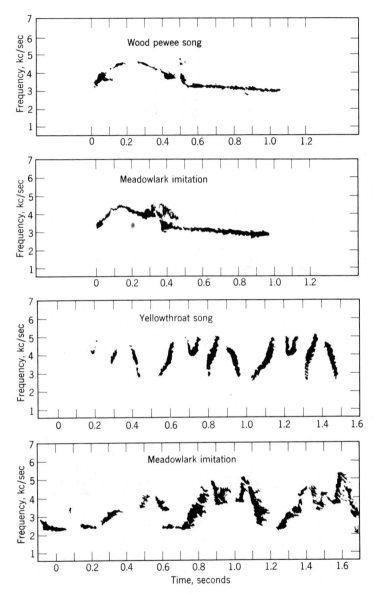

Time, seconds

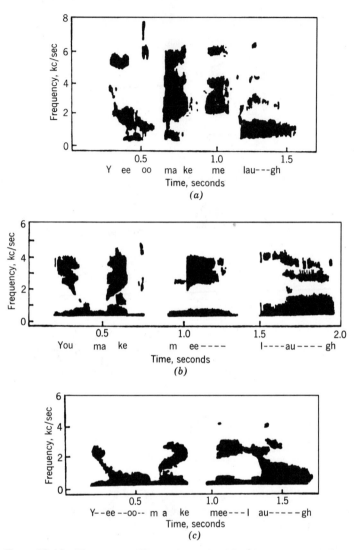

Figure 19-12 The sentence "You make me laugh" spoken by an (*a*) Indian hill mynah, (*b*) adult human male, New Jersey, and (*c*) adult human female, New England. After Thorpe 1958.

ample of the development of virtually new motor patterns through visual imitation (Figure 19-13). Actions involving the hands are especially labile in this respect but can be difficult to record.

One good measure is provided by giving the animal a pencil or a brush and allowing it to draw or paint. Morris (1962) studied chimpanzee paintings, with results that are fascinating to artists and biologists alike. There are many signs of a primitive aesthetic visual sense, as Rensch (1957, 1958) has also concluded from studies in various animals of preference for figures with a certain type of structure. Of special interest to us is the evidence for what Morris calls "thematic variation." Having developed a new "theme," the chimpanzee will repeat it, gradually introducing variations. "Sometimes the basic theme would itself be completely replaced, but more often he would simply find some way of making a slight enough change to produce a variation without completely obscuring the original theme on which it was based" (Figure 19-14). Such variations obviously depend on visual control. But they are not simply copies of environmental patterns. They seem to be the result of individual experimentation, something more than a recombination of existing components. There is an element of creative invention in such improvisations on a theme.

Close parallels can be found in the vocal behavior of birds. Inventiveness plays a role in the development of syllable diversity in songs of the Oregon junco (Marler, Kreith, and Tamura 1962). The best-documented example is the European blackbird. The complex motor patterns of blackbird song have been studied both in the laboratory (Messmer and Mess-

Figure 19-13   A chimpanzee will ape human actions and so develop new motor patterns. After Hayes and Hayes 1951.

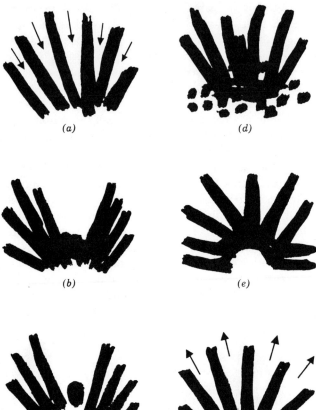

Figure 19-14   A chimpanzee, Congo, draws variations on a theme. (*a* to *e*) The fans are drawn from the edge to the center. (*f*) The strokes are away from the center. After Morris 1962.

mer 1956, Thielcke-Poltz and Thielcke 1960) and in the field (Hall-Craggs 1962). Song patterns with many natural elements develop in isolated birds and even in birds that have been deafened by removal of the cochlea. Deaf, isolated, and wild birds all recombine the parts of the song in different ways to produce a large number of different patterns. Some of these are stable while others persist for a time and then change, so that new sound sequences appear repeatedly during the life of an individual male (Messmer and Messmer 1956). Birds that can hear older blackbirds singing as they grow up develop a much larger number of sound patterns than isolated birds. Many of these are acquired as copies of adult blackbirds or of other species. The periods when such imitation occurs most frequently have been determined. A remarkably small number of exposures suffices for copying to occur (e.g. twelve times on a single day in one case, Thielcke-Poltz and Thielcke 1960). The copies vary in precision and subsequently undergo much fragmentation and recombination.

Hall-Craggs (1962) followed the development of song patterns in a wild male blackbird through one season. Starting with 26 "phrases" at the beginning of the season, she was able to demonstrate gradual transformations as a result of recombination, loss or repetition of elements, or the addition of new material. Some of the changes are reminiscent of variations on a theme in the painting of chimpanzees (Figure 19-15), and once more the invention of novel motor patterns seems to be implied. Apart from their interest as evidence for the generation of new motor pat-

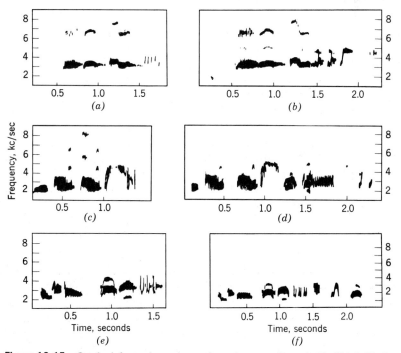

Figure 19-15 On the left are three phrases from the song of a male blackbird, *Turdus merula*. On the right are versions of these phrases, modified by the addition of new material, given about one to six weeks later. Phrase (*b*) replaced phrase (*a*) altogether. Phrases (*c*) and (*e*) and their derivatives persisted throughout the season. After Hall-Craggs 1962.

terns, they can also be viewed as examples of aesthetic exercise. Both blackbird song and the painting by chimpanzees have something in common with processes of aesthetic creation in man (Craig 1943, Hartshorne 1958, Hall-Craggs 1962, Morris 1962, Armstrong 1963, Thorpe 1963).

THE RELATIONSHIP BETWEEN SENSORY AND MOTOR DEVELOPMENT

Although we have considered the development of sensory mechanisms and motor patterns separately, they are obviously closely related. The unspecific effects of the environment on the frequency and intensity of such motor patterns as aggression or emotionality involve changes in the level of responsiveness to the external eliciting stimuli. The reorientation of motor activity by experience is mediated by a change in the external stimuli which control the spatial characteristics of the response.

The interconnection is especially close with proprioceptive and other sensory systems which participate in feedback relationships with motor activity. These are often directly involved in many aspects of motor control in both invertebrate and vertebrate animals. Mittelstaedt (1953, 1957, 1962, von Holst and Mittelstaedt 1950) has shown how proprioceptive feedback plays a variety of roles in controlling the patterning and orientation of motor actions.

A special case of such feedback occurs in vocal behavior where the ability to hear sounds produced is important both in maintenance and development. Deaf children have obvious difficulty in learning to speak, although their speech is reasonably stable once established. The speech patterns of adults with normal hearing are badly disturbed by auditory feedback from the voice delayed by about a tenth of a second (Zangwill 1960).

◆ *Auditory Feedback and Birdsong.* Konishi (1963a, b, 1964, 1965a, b) studied the role of auditory feedback in control of vocal behavior in several species of birds. In chickens deafening has some unspecific effects; certain calls become much less frequent. But the action patterns themselves are not affected. In some other birds deafening causes marked changes in vocalizations. Male black-headed grosbeaks, deafened in early youth, developed calls that were normal but a song that was different from the natural pattern. Birds raised in isolation from adults developed more or less normal songs, but evidently the development rested on the ability of the bird to hear its own voice.

Male American robins raised in isolation develop song patterns which differ from the wild form in several respects but have some normal properties. The songs of birds deafened in youth bear still less resemblance to the natural pattern. The songs of deaf robins have an unusually shrill or sibilant quality which is not evident in intact, isolated birds—a characteristic also noted by Messmer and Messmer (1956) in a deaf European blackbird. Evidently these species must hear themselves for sounds with a normal tonal quality to develop (Konishi 1965a).

Oregon juncos, deafened in youth, developed songs which resembled the natural form in overall pattern in some respects, but again there were some differences. The syllables of the deaf birds' songs were irregular in form and had many frequency inflections. Successive syllables of natural songs are repeated with great precision. In deaf birds repetitions are variable, and the song never becomes fully crystallized (Konishi 1964). It is almost as though the deaf birds were unable to proceed beyond one of the intermediate stages of normal development, before variable singing patterns become fully stereotyped (Figure 1916). Auditory feedback is thus necessary for some of the processes of normal motor development.

The effects of deafening on the song of white-crowned sparrows varies

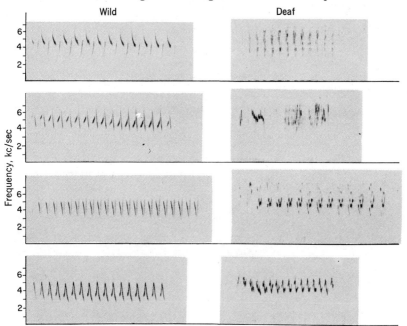

Figure 19-16   Song patterns of eight male Oregon juncos, four normal and four deaf. Note the variable syllables in the deaf males. After Konishi 1963a.

with the time of the operation (Konishi 1963a, 1965b). We have already noted that males raised in isolation from adults of their species develop songs which lack the distinctive characters of the dialect in the home area (see page 687). These are normally acquired during the first two months of life. Although the songs of isolated birds lack the characteristics of the local dialect, they do share some of the properties of the normal song, including the long whistles which are part of the introduction to natural pattern. Birds that are deafened in early youth fail to develop the home dialect. Their songs also lack the long whistles, consisting instead of a series of short irregular notes and fluctuating tones (Figure 19-17 and 19-18). As in deaf juncos, successive renderings of a song type vary more in deaf white-crowns than in intact individuals (Figure 19-18). Thus their pattern is even more abnormal than that of isolated birds.

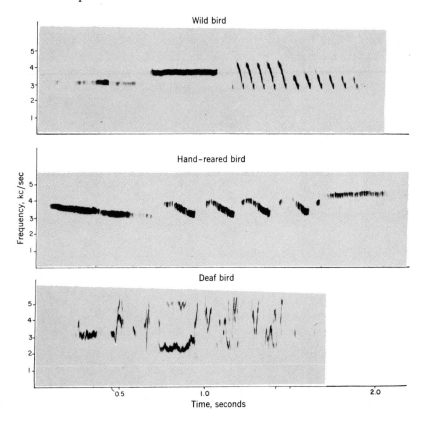

Figure 19-17 Songs of three male white-crowned sparrows, one a wild bird, one a male raised in isolation from adults, and one deafened in early youth. After Konishi 1963a.

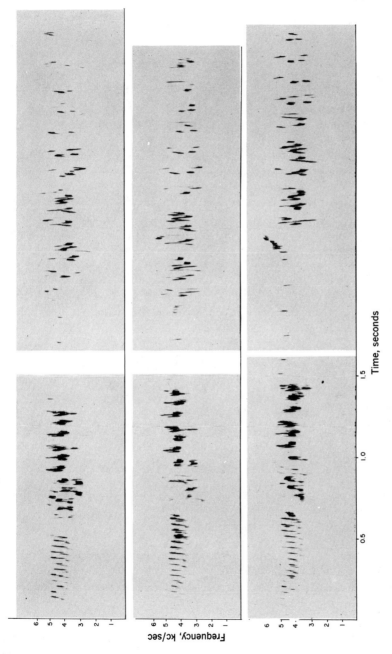

Figure 19-18 Three successive songs of two male white-crowned sparrows deafened in youth showing the variation from one rendering to another. After Konishi 1963a.

Frequency, kc/sec

Time, seconds

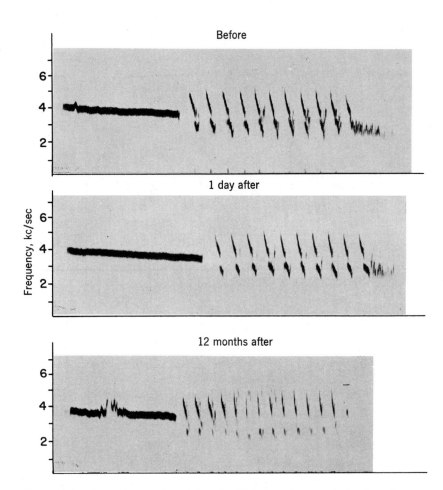

Figure 19-19 Typical songs of an adult male white-crowned sparrow before deafening, one day after the operation, and a year later. After Konishi 1963a.

Here too some of the processes of normal development depend on the occurrence of auditory feedback.

In white-crowned sparrows raised in the laboratory there is a lapse of some months between the period when the song patterns are acquired and the onset of full song. Konishi has shown that birds exposed to an adult song during the sensitive period and then deafened develop the same type of highly abnormal song as birds deafened before training. Thus a trained bird needs to be able to hear itself if it is to refer back to the acquired pattern and translate it into full song.

Deafening can also be postponed until either isolated or trained birds have come into full song. At this stage the immediate effects of deafening are almost negligible. Only after some weeks or months does the form of the song drift gradually away from the original pattern (Figure 19-19). Even so, it is never as poorly developed as the songs of birds deafened in youth. Thus auditory feedback is more important for the development of song patterns than for their maintenance, at least over the short term. Either nonauditory feedback or some central motor mechanism must assume control once the full pattern has appeared (Konishi 1965b).

Motor patterns of this type are intimately related to sensory mechanisms for development and, in some cases, for maintenance as well. Auditory control of vocal behavior is relatively easy to explore. But we can assume that sensory feedback control based on other sensory modes will be found once the methods for their analysis are developed. The distinction between sensory and motor development, which is sometimes unclear at the behavioral level, breaks down altogether when we analyze the underlying physiological mechanisms.

CONCLUSIONS ON BEHAVIORAL DEVELOPMENT

The main effort of this discussion has been to analyze behavioral development in terms of ontogenetic change. This has been done within a framework of the types of change induced in the actual behavior by variation in either genetic or environmental variables at the hands of the experimenter. It is striking that genetic and environmental controls achieve much the same range of behavioral consequences. Unspecific shifts in the frequency of motor actions, or in the thresholds and general functioning of sensory systems, can result both from changes in the genetic constitution and from changes in environmental factors. Both types of mechanisms can cause change in the more specific aspects of behavior, the detailed patterns of motor activity and specific eliciting external stimuli.

This overlap in the effects of changing genetic and environmental variables may be more than coincidental. The shifts in endocrine balance that are involved in unspecific behavioral changes seem to be accessible to both genetic and environmental control. Studies on brain chemistry suggest that the same may be true of the capacities for learning (Rosenzweig, Krech, and Bennett 1958, Bennett, Diamond, Krech, and Rosenzweig 1964). Thus, although genetic and environmental sources of developmental information are distinct, the mechanisms by which they actually shape behavioral ontogeny may be more similar than has been suspected. By the same logic, analysis of genetic mechanisms may in turn illuminate the less accessible problems of environmental control and mechanisms of learning.

Another recurring theme has been the interaction of exogenous and endogenous factors in behavioral development. As Kuo emphasized, this is central to the understanding of both genetic and environmental mechanisms. The issue is seen clearly in both embryological and postnatal development: the time at which stimulation occurs in the life cycle is crucial in determining the effect of exogenous factors. Similar principles emerge whether we are considering the development of organisms, organs, or cells (Scott 1962). The timing of these 'sensitive periods' may be determined in different ways. Sometimes they are a function of endogenous changes. Sometimes they are clearly controlled by the previous environmental experience of the animal (e.g. Schneirla and Rosenblatt 1963). In either case, their existence has important effects on the development of behavior. The clearly defined sensitive periods for imprinting make this process especially worthwhile for detailed analysis. There are further constraints on the sensory side which also need more study.

Although the data are quite limited we are still able to make the general point that sensory development is less subject to endogenous constraints than motor development, which is profoundly affected by the limitations of design of the motor equipment. Only in certain special cases, such as the vocal output of birds and the manual skills of primates, is the motor equipment versatile enough to permit the kind of developmental plasticity that is commonplace in sensory mechanisms. Yet even here both exogenous and endogenous factors must be considered if the underlying processes are to be fully accounted for, for it is the interaction between them that constitutes the process of development.

Finally, we should recall that identifying a factor which influences development as endogenous is only a first step in understanding how that factor operates. Endogeneity in this case implies no more than that the change in behavior so effected is a function, not of present environmental events but of events in the organism's past. The nature of these past events, and the interplay of genetic and environmental factors in their determination, still remains to be established.

REFERENCES

Alexander, R. D. 1962. Evolutionary change in cricket acoustical communication. *Evolution,* **16**:443–467.

Armstrong, E. A. 1963. *A Study of Bird Song.* Oxford University Press, London.

Baltzer, F. 1952. Einige Beobachtungen über Sicheltänze bei Bienvölkern verschiedener Herkunft. *Arch. Julius Klaus-Stiftung,* **27**:197–206.

Bastock, M. 1956. A gene mutation which changes a behavior pattern. *Evolution,* **10**:421–439.

Beach, F. A. and J. Jaynes. 1956. Studies of maternal retrieving in rats: II. Effects of practice and previous parturitions. *Am. Nat.,* **90**:103–109.

Bennett, E. L., M. C. Diamond, D. Krech, and M. R. Rosenzweig. 1964. Chemical and anatomical plasticity of brain. *Science,* **146**:610–619.

Bigelow, R. S. 1960. Interspecific hybrids and speciation in the genus *Acheta* (Orthoptera, Gryllidae). *Can. J. Zool.,* **38**:509–524.

Bindra, D. 1959. *Motivation. A Systematic Reinterpretation.* The Ronald Press Company, New York.

Bingham, H. C. 1929. Chimpanzee translocation by means of boxes. *Comp. Psychol. Monogr.,* **5**(3):1–91.

Birch, H. G. 1945. The relation of previous experience to insightful problem-solving. *J. Comp. Psychol.,* **38**:367–383.

Blair, W. F. 1956. The mating calls of hybrid toads. *Tex. J. Sci.,* **8**:350–355.

Bogert, C. M. 1960. The influence of sound on the behavior of amphibians and reptiles. In *Animal Sounds and Communication,* ed. by W. E. Lanyon and W. N. Tavolga: 137–320. American Institute of Biological Sciences, Washington, D.C.

Boutan, L. 1913. Le Pseudo-language. Observations effectuées sur un anthropoïde: Le Gibbon (*Hylobates leucogenys*—Ogilby). *Act. Soc. Linn. Bordeaux,* **67**:5–80.

Bruell, J. H. 1962. Dominance and segregation in the inheritance of quantitative behavior in mice. In *Roots of Behavior,* ed. by E. L. Bliss: 48–67. Harper and Row, New York.

Caspari, E. 1951. On the biological basis of adaptedness. *Am. Scient.,* **39**:441–451.

Christian, J. J. 1963. Endocrine adaptive mechanisms and the physiologic regulation of population growth. In *Physiological Mammalogy,* ed. by M. V. Mayer and R. G. Van Gelder, Vol. 1:189–353. The Academic Press, New York.

Clark, E., L. R. Aronson, and M. Gordon. 1954. Mating behavior patterns in two sympatric species of Xiphophorin fishes: their inheritance and significance in sexual isolation. *Bull. Amer. Mus. Nat. Hist.,* **103**:135–226.

Craig, W. 1908. The voices of pigeons regarded as a means of social control. *Amer. J. Sociol.,* **14**:86–100.

———. 1914. Male doves reared in isolation. *J. Anim. Behav.,* **4**:121–133.

———. 1943. The song of the wood pewee *Myiochanes virens* Linnaeus: a study of bird music. *N.Y. St. Mus. Bull.,* **334**:1–186.

Curio, E. 1959. Verhaltensstudien am Trauerschnäpper. *Z. Tierpsychol.* (Suppl.), **3**:1–110.

Darwin, C. 1859. *The Origin of Species.* John Murray (Publishers), London.

Davis, J. 1957. Comparative foraging behavior of the spotted and brown towhees. *Auk,* **74**:129–166.

Denenberg, V. H. 1962. The effects of early experience. In *The Behaviour of Domestic Animals,* ed. by E. S. E. Hafez: 109–138. The Williams and Wilkins Company, Baltimore.

Dieterlen, F. 1959. Das Verhalten des syrischen Goldhamsters (*Mesocricetus auratus* Waterhouse). *Z. Tierpsychol.,* **16**:47–103.

Dilger, W. C. 1959. Notes on a hybrid thrush (male blackbird × female American robin) and notes on a male American robin paired with a female song thrush. *Avicul. Mag.,* **65**:125–131.

———. 1962. Behavior and genetics. In *Roots of Behavior*, ed. by E. L. Bliss: 35–47. Harper and Row, New York.

Dorst, J. 1962. *The Migrations of Birds* (translated by D. D. Sherman). Houghton Mifflin Company, Boston.

Drees, O. 1952. Untersuchungen über die angeborenen Verhaltensweisen bei Springspinnen (*Salticidae*). *Z. Tierpsychol.*, 9:169–207.

Eibl-Eibesfeldt, I. 1955. Angeborenes und Erworbenes im Nestbauverhalten der Wanderratte. *Naturwissenschaften*, 42:633–634.

———. 1956a. Über die ontogenetische Entwicklung der Technik des Nüsseöffnens vom Eichhörnchen (*Sciurus vulgaris* L.). *Z. Säugetierk.*, 21:132–134.

———. 1956b. Angeborenes und Erworbenes in der Technik des Beutetötens (Versuche am Iltis, *Putorius putorius* L.). *Z. Säugetierk.*, 21:135–137.

———. 1961. The interactions of unlearned behaviour patterns and learning in mammals. In *Brain Mechanisms and Learning*, ed. by J. F. Delafresnaye: 53–73. Council for International Organizations of Medical Sciences Symposium, Oxford.

Eisenberg, J. 1963. The behavior of heteromyid rodents. *Univ. Calif. Publ. Zool.*, 69:1–114.

Elliot, O. and J. A. King. 1960. Effect of early food deprivation upon later consummatory behavior in puppies. *Psychol. Rep.*, 6:391–400.

Ewer, R. F. 1959. Suckling behaviour in kittens. *Behaviour*, 15:146–162.

———. 1961. Further observations on suckling behaviour in kittens, together with some general considerations of the interrelations of innate and acquired responses. *Behaviour*, 17:247–260.

Fisher, J. and R. A. Hinde. 1949. The opening of milk bottles by birds. *Brit. Birds*, 42:347–357.

Fuller, J. L. 1962. The genetics of behaviour. In *The Behaviour of Domestic Animals*, ed. by E. S. E. Hafez: 57–81. The Williams and Wilkins Company, Baltimore.

——— and W. R. Thompson. 1960. *Behavior Genetics*. John Wiley and Sons, New York.

Fulton, B. B. 1933. Inheritance of song in hybrids of two subspecies of *Nemobius fasciatus* (Orthoptera). *Ann. Ent. Soc. Amer.*, 26:368–376.

Furness, W. H. 1916. Observations on the mentality of chimpanzees and orang-utans. *Proc. Amer. Phil. Soc.*, 55:281–290.

Gerall, A. A. 1963. An exploratory study of the effect of social isolation variables on the sexual behaviour of male guinea pigs. *Anim. Behav.*, 11:274–282.

Ginsburg, B. and W. C. Allee. 1942. Some effects of conditioning on social dominance and subordination in inbred strains of mice. *Physiol. Zool.*, 15:485–506.

Goy, R. W. and J. S. Jakway. 1959. The inheritance of patterns of sexual behaviour in female guinea pigs. *Anim. Behav.*, 7:142–149.

——— and ———. 1962. Role of inheritance in determination of sexual behavior patterns. In *Roots of Behavior*, ed. by E. L. Bliss:96–112. Harper and Row, New York.

Grohmann, J. 1938. Modifikation oder Funktionsreifung? Ein Beitrag zur Klärung der wechselseitigen Beziehungen zwischen Instinkthandlung und Erfahrung. *Z. Tierpsychol.*, 2:132–144.

Grüneberg, H. 1952. *The Genetics of the Mouse* (2nd edition). Nijhoff, The Hague.

Guhl, A. M., J. V. Craig, and C. D. Mueller. 1960. Selective breeding for aggressiveness in chickens. *Poult. Sci.*, 39:970–980.

Haartman, L. von and H. Löhrl. 1950. Die Lautäusserungen des Trauer—und Halsband—fliegenschnäppers, *Muscicapa h. hypoleuca* (Pall.) und *M. a. albicollis* Temminck. *Ornis Fenn.*, 27:85–97.

Hafez, E. S. E., M. Williams, and S. Wierzbowski. 1962. The behaviour of horses. In *The*

Behaviour of Domestic Animals, ed. by E. S. E. Hafez: 370–396. The Williams and Wilkins Company, Baltimore.

Hall-Craggs, J. 1962. The development of song in the blackbird *Turdus merula. Ibis,* **104:**277–300.

Hall, C. S. 1951. The genetics of behavior. In *Handbook of Experimental Psychology,* ed. by S. S. Stevens: 304–329. John Wiley and Sons, New York.

Hamilton, W. J. III. 1962. Celestial orientation in juvenal waterfowl. *Condor,* **64:**19–33.

Harlow, H. F. 1951. Primate learning. In *Comparative Psychology,* ed. by C. P. Stone: 183–238. Prentice-Hall, New York.

———. 1961. The development of affectional patterns in infant monkeys. In *Determinants of Infant Behaviour,* ed. by B. M. Foss: 75–88. John Wiley and Sons, New York.

———. 1962. Development of affection in primates. In *Roots of Behavior,* ed. by E. L. Bliss: 157–166. Harper and Row, New York.

Hartshorne, C. 1958. The relation of bird song to music. *Ibis,* **100:**421–445.

Haskins, C. P. and E. F. Haskins. 1958. Note on the inheritance of behavior patterns for food selection and cocoon spinning in F_1 hybrids of *Callosamia promethea* $\times$ *C. angulifera. Behaviour,* **13:**89–95.

Haskell, P. T. 1961. *Insect Sounds.* H. F. and G. Witherby, London.

Hayes, K. J. and C. Hayes. 1951. The intellectual development of a home-raised chimpanzee. *Proc. Amer. Phil. Soc.,* **95:**105–109.

——— and ———. 1952. Imitation in a home-raised chimpanzee. *J. comp. physiol. Psychol.,* **45:**450–459.

Hediger, H. 1955. *Studies of the Psychology and Behavior of Captive Animals in Zoos and Circuses.* Butterworth and Company (Publishers), London.

Heinroth, O. 1924. Lautäusserungen der Vögel. *J. Orn.,* **72:**223–244.

Hess, E. H. 1956. Space perception in the chick. *Sci. Amer.,* **195**(1):71–80.

Hinde, R. A. 1956. The behaviour of certain Cardueline F_1 inter-species hybrids. *Behaviour,* **9:**202–213.

———. 1959. Unitary drives. *Anim. Behav.,* **7:**130–141.

——— and J. Fisher. 1952. Further observations on the opening of milk bottles by birds. *Brit. Birds,* **44:**393–396.

Hochbaum, H. A. 1955. *Travels and Traditions of Waterfowl.* University of Minnesota Press, Minneapolis.

Hoffmann, K. 1953. Die Einrechnung der Sonnenwanderung bei der Richtungsweisung des sonnenlos aufgezogenen Stares. *Naturwissenschaften,* **40:**148.

———. 1954. Versuche zu der im Richtungsfinden der Vögel enthaltenen Zeitschätzung. *Z. Tierpsychol.,* **11:**453–475.

Holst, E. von and H. Mittelstaedt. 1950. Das Reafferenzprinzip. (Wechselwirkungen zwischen Zentalnervensystem und Peripherie.) *Naturwissenschaften,* **37:**464–476.

Honzik, C. H. 1936. The sensory basis of maze learning in rats. *Comp. Psychol. Monog.,* **13**(4): 1–113.

Hörmann-Heck, S. von. 1957. Untersuchungen über den Erbgang einiger Verhaltensweisen bei Grillenbastarden (*Gryllus campestris* L. ∞ *Gryllus bimaculatus* de Geer). *Z. Tierpsychol.,* **14:**137–183.

Hunt, J. McV. 1941. The effects of infant feeding-frustration upon adult hoarding in the albino rat. *J. Abnorm. (Soc.) Psychol.,* **36:**338–360.

Jacobs, W. 1953. Verhaltensbiologische Studien an Feldheuschrecken. *Z. Tierpsychol.* (Suppl.), **1:**1–228.

Kahn, M. W. 1951. The effect of severe defeat at various age levels on the aggressive behavior of mice. *J. Genet. Psychol.,* **79:**117–130.

Kear, J. 1962. Food selection in finches with special reference to interspecific differences. *Proc. Zool. Soc. Lond.,* **138**:163–204.

Kellogg, W. N. and L. A. Kellogg. 1933. *The Ape and the Child.* McGraw-Hill Book Company, New York.

Kimble, G. A. 1961. *Hilgard and Marquis' Conditioning and Learning.* Appleton-Century-Crofts, New York.

King, J. A. 1957. Relationships between early social experience and adult aggressive behavior in inbred mice. *J. Genet. Psychol.,* **90**:151–166.

——— and N. L. Gurney. 1954. Effects of early social experience on adult aggressive behavior in C57BL/10 mice. *J. comp. physiol. Psychol.,* **47**:326–330.

Klopfer, P. 1957. An experiment on empathic learning in ducks. *Am. Nat.,* **91**:61–63.

———. 1959. Social interactions in discrimination learning with special reference to feeding behavior in birds. *Behaviour,* **14**:282–299.

———. 1961. Observational learning in birds: the establishment of behavioral modes. *Behaviour,* **17**:71–80.

Köhler, W. 1925. *The Mentality of Apes.* Harcourt, Brace and Company, New York.

Konishi, M. 1963a. The role of audition in the development and maintenance of avian vocal behavior. Ph.D. dissertation, University of California, Berkeley.

———. 1963b. The role of auditory feedback in the vocal behavior of the domestic fowl. *Z. Tierpsychol.,* **20**:249–367.

———. 1964. Effects of deafening on song development in two species of juncos. *Condor* **66**:85–102.

———. 1965a. Effects of deafening on song development in American robins and black-headed grosbeaks. *Z. Tierpsychol.,* **22**:584–599.

———. 1965b. The role of auditory feedback in the control of vocalization in the white-crowned sparrow. *Z. Tierpsychol.,* **22**:770–783.

Kramer, G. 1952. Experiments on bird orientation. *Ibis,* **94**:265–285.

Krech, D. and R. S. Crutchfield. 1958. *Elements of Psychology.* Alfred A. Knopf, New York.

Krechevsky, I. 1933. Hereditary nature of "hypotheses." *J. Comp. Psychol.,* **16**:99–116.

———. 1938. A study of the continuity of the problem-solving process. *Psychol. Rev.,* **45**:107–133.

Lade, B. I. and W. H. Thorpe. 1964. Dove songs as innately coded patterns of specific behaviour. *Nature,* **202**:366–368.

Lanyon, W. E. 1957. The comparative biology of the meadowlarks (*Sturnella*) in Wisconsin. *Publ. Nuttall Orn. Club,* **1**:1–67.

———. 1960. The ontogeny of vocalizations in birds. In *Animal Sounds and Communication,* ed. by W. E. Lanyon and W. N. Tavolga: 321–347. American Institute of Biological Sciences, Washington, D.C.

Lehrman, D. S. 1961. Hormonal regulation of parental behavior in birds and infrahuman mammals. In *Sex and Internal Secretions,* ed. by W. C. Young, Vol. 2:1268–1382. The Williams and Wilkins Company, Baltimore.

———. 1962. Interaction of hormonal and experiential influences on development of behavior. In *Roots of Behavior,* ed. by E. L. Bliss: 142–156. Harper and Row, New York.

——— and R. P. Wortis. 1960. Previous breeding experience and hormone-induced incubation behavior in the ring dove. *Science,* **132**:1667–1668.

Leopold, A. S. 1944. The nature of heritable wildness in turkeys. *Condor,* **46**:133–197.

Levi, W. M. 1951. *The Pigeon* (2nd edition). Brian, Columbia, South Carolina.

Levine, S. 1962. Psychophysiological effects of infantile stimulation. In *Roots of Behavior,* ed. by E. L. Bliss: 246–253. Harper and Row, New York.

Levy, D. M. 1934. Experiments on the sucking reflex and social behavior of dogs. *Amer. J. Orthopsychiat.,* **4:**203–224.

Löhrl, H. 1955. Beziehungen zwischen Halsband—und Trauerfliegenschnäpper (*Muscicapa albicollis* und *M. hypoleuca*) in demselben Brutgebiet. *Proc. 11th Int. Orn. Congr.* (1954): 333–336.

Lorenz, K. Z. 1961. Phylogenetische Anpassung und adaptive Modifikation des Verhaltens. *Z. Tierpsychol.,* **18:**139–187.

McAlister, W. H. 1959. The vocal structures and method of call production in the genus *Scaphiopus* Holbrook. *Tex. J. Sci.,* **11:**60–77.

McClearn, G. E. 1959. The genetics of mouse behavior in novel situations. *J. comp. physiol. Psychol.,* **52:**62–67.

Manning, A. 1959a. The sexual behaviour of two sibling *Drosophila* species. *Behaviour,* **15:**123–145.

————. 1959b. The sexual isolation between *Drosophila melanogaster* and *Drosophila simulans. Anim. Behav.,* **7:**60–65.

————. 1961. The effects of artificial selection for mating speed in *Drosophila melanogaster. Anim. Behav.,* **9:**82–92.

Marler, P. 1956. The voice of the chaffinch and its function as a language. *Ibis,* **98:**231–261.

————. 1959. Developments in the study of animal communication. In *Darwin's Biological Work,* ed. by P. R. Bell: 150–206. Cambridge University Press, Cambridge.

————. 1963. Inheritance and learning in the development of animal vocalizations. In *Acoustic Behaviour of Animals,* ed. by R. G. Busnel: 228–243, 794–797. Elsevier Publishing Company, Amsterdam.

————, M. Kreith, and M. Tamura. 1962. Song development in hand-raised Oregon juncos. *Auk,* **79:**12–30.

———— and M. Tamura. 1962. Song 'dialects' in three populations of white-crowned sparrows. *Condor,* **64:**368–377.

———— and ————. 1964. Culturally transmitted patterns of vocal behavior in sparrows. *Science,* **146:**1483–1486.

Marshall, A. J. 1950. The function of vocal mimicry in birds. *Emu,* **50:**5–16.

————. 1954. *Bower-birds.* Oxford University Press, London.

Mason, W. A. 1960. The effects of social restriction on the behavior of rhesus monkeys: I. Free social behavior. *J. comp. physiol. Psychol.,* **53:**582–589.

————. 1965. The social development of monkeys and apes. In *Primate Behavior,* ed. by I. DeVore: 514–543. Holt, Rinehart and Winston, New York.

Melzack, R. A. and W. R. Thompson. 1956. Effects of early experience on social behaviour. *Can. J. Psychol.,* **10:**82–90.

Messmer, E. and I. Messmer. 1956. Die Entwicklung der Lautäusserungen und einiger Verhaltensweisen der Amsel (*Turdus merula merula* L.) unter natürlichen Bedingungen und nach Einzelaufzucht in schalldichten Räumen. *Z. Tierpsychol.,* **13:**341–441.

Metfessel, M. 1935. Roller canary song produced without learning from external sources. *Science,* **81:**470.

Miller, L. 1921. The biography of Nip and Tuck. A study of instincts in birds. *Condor,* **23:**41–47.

Mittelstaedt, H. 1953. Über den Beutefangmechanismus der Mantiden. *Verh. Dtsch. Zool. Ges., Zool. Anz.* (Suppl.), **17:**102–106.

————. 1957. Prey capture in mantids. In *Recent Advances in Invertebrate Physiology,* ed. by B. T. Scheer: 51–71. University of Oregon Publications, Oregon.

————. 1962. Control systems of orientation in insects. *Ann. Rev. Ent.,* **7:**177–198.

Morris, D. 1962. *The Biology of Art.* Methuen and Company, London.

Munn, N. L. 1950. *Handbook of Psychological Research on the Rat.* Houghton Mifflin Company, Boston.

Nice, M. M. 1943. Studies in the life history of the song sparrow. II. The behavior of the song sparrow and other passerines. *Trans. Linn. Soc. N.Y.,* **6**:1–328.

Nicolai, J. 1956. Zur Biologie und Ethologie des Gimpels (*Pyrrhula pyrrhula* L.). *Z. Tierpsychol.,* **13**:93–132.

————. 1959. Familientradition in der Gesangsentwicklung des Gimpels (*Pyrrhula pyrrhula* L.). *J. Orn.,* **100**:39–46.

Papi, F. and P. Tongiorgi. 1963. Innate and learned components in the astronomical orientation of wolf spiders. *Ergeb. Biol.,* **26**:259–280.

Perdeck, A. C. 1958. The isolating value of specific song patterns in two sibling species of grasshoppers (*Chorthippus brunneus* Thunb. and *C. biguttulus* L.). *Behaviour,* **12**:1–75.

Petersen, B., L. Lundgren, and L. Wilson. 1957. The development of flight capacity in a butterfly. *Behaviour,* **10**:324–339.

Petersson, M. 1961. The nature and spread of *Daphne*-eating in the greenfinch, and the spread of some other habits. *Anim. Behav.,* **9**:114.

Poulsen, H. 1951. Inheritance and learning in the song of the chaffinch (*Fringilla coelebs*). *Behaviour,* **3**:216–228.

Rensch, B. 1957. Ästhetische Faktoren bei Farb—und Formbevorzugungen von Affen. *Z. Tierpsychol.,* **14**:71–99.

————. 1958. Die Wirksamkeit ästhetischer Faktoren bei Wirbeltieren. *Z. Tierpsychol.,* **15**: 447–461.

Riess, B. F. 1954. The effect of altered environment and of age in mother-young relationships among animals. *Ann. N.Y. Acad. Sci.,* **57**:606–610.

Riopelle, A. J. 1960. Complex processes. In *Principles of Comparative Psychology,* ed. by R. H. Waters, D. A. Rethlingshafer, and W. E. Caldwell: 208–249. McGraw-Hill Book Company, New York.

Rosenblatt, J. S. and T. C. Schneirla. 1962. The behaviour of cats. In *The Behaviour of Domestic Animals,* ed. by E. S. E. Hafez: 453–488. The Williams and Wilkins Company, Baltimore.

————, G. Turkewitz, and T. C. Schneirla. 1961. Early socialization in the domestic cat as based on feeding and other relationships between female and young. In *Determinants of Infant Behaviour,* ed. by B. M. Foss: 51–74. John Wiley and Sons, New York.

Rosenzweig, M. R., D. Krech, and E. L. Bennett. 1958. Brain chemistry and adaptive behavior. In *Biologocial and Biochemical Bases of Behavior,* ed. by H. F. Harlow and C. N. Woolsey: 367–400. Wisconsin University Press, Madison.

Ross, S., V. H. Denenberg, P. B. Sawin, and P. Meyer. 1956. Changes in nest building behaviour in multiparous rabbits. *Brit. J. Anim. Behav.,* **4**:69–74.

Sauer, F. 1954. Die 'Entwicklung der Lautäusserungen vom Ei ab Schalldicht gehaltener Dorngrasmücken (*Sylvia c. communis.* Latham) im Vergleich mit später isolierten und mit wildlebenden Artgenossen. *Z. Tierpsychol.,* **11**:10–93.

Schiller, P. H. 1957. Innate motor action as a basis of learning. In *Instinctive Behavior,* ed. by C. H. Schiller: 264–287. International University Press, New York.

Schjelderup-Ebbe, T. 1923. Weitere Beiträge zur Sozial-und Individualpsychologie des Haushuhns. *Z. Psychol.,* **92**:60–87.

Schneirla, T. C. and J. S. Rosenblatt. 1963. "Critical periods" in the development of behavior. *Science,* **139**:1110–1115.

Scott, J. P. 1954. The effects of selection and domestication upon the behavior of the dog. *J. Nat. Cancer Inst.,* **15**:739–758.

————. 1962. Critical periods in behavioral development. *Science,* **138**:949–958.

———— and E. Fredericson. 1951. The causes of fighting in mice and rats. *Physiol. Zool.*, **24**: 273–309.

———— and J. L. Fuller. 1965. *Genetics and the Social Behavior of the Dog.* University of Chicago Press, Chicago.

————, S. Ross, and A. E. Fisher. 1959. The effects of early enforced weaning on sucking behavior of puppies. *J. Genet. Psychol.*, **95**:261–281.

Seitz, A. 1955. Untersuchungen über angeborene Verhaltensweisen bei Caniden. III. Beobachtungen an Marderhunden (*Nyctereutes procyonoides* Gray). *Z. Tierpsychol.*, **12**:463–489.

Seitz, P. F. D. 1959. Infantile experience and adult behavior in animal subjects. II. Age of separation from the mother and adult behavior in the cat. *Psychosom. Med.*, **21**:353–378.

Severaid, J. H. 1958. The natural history of the pikas (mammalian genus *Ochotona*). Ph.D. dissertation, University of California, Berkeley.

Seward, J. P. 1945–1946. Aggressive behaviour in the rat, I–IV. *J. Comp. Psychol.*, **38**:175–197, 213–224, 225–238, **39**:51–76.

Shaw, E. 1962. Environmental conditions and the appearance of sexual behavior in the platyfish. In *Roots of Behavior*, ed. by E. L. Bliss: 123–141. Harper and Row, New York.

Skinner, B. F. 1938. *The Behavior of Organisms.* D. Appleton-Century Company, New York.

Sperry, R. W. 1951. Mechanisms of neural maturation. In *Handbook of Experimental Psychology*, ed. by S. S. Stevens: 236–280. John Wiley and Sons, New York.

————. 1958. Physiological plasticity and brain circuit theory. In *Biological and Biochemical Bases of Behavior*, ed. by H. F. Harlow and C. N. Woolsey: 401–424. Wisconsin University Press, Madison.

Spieth, H. T. 1952. Mating behavior within the genus *Drosophila* (Diptera). *Bull. Amer. Mus Nat. Hist.*, **99**:395–474.

Stadler, H. 1929. Die Vogelstimmenforschung als Wissenschaft. *Proc. 6th Int. Orn. Congr.* (1926):338–357.

Thielcke, G. 1961. Ergebnisse der Vogelstimmen-Analyse. *J. Orn.*, **102**:285–300.

Thielcke-Poltz, H. and G. Thielcke. 1960. Akustisches Lernen verscheiden alter schallisolierter Amseln (*Turdus merula* L.) und die Entwicklung erlernter Motive ohne und mit künstlichem Einfluss von Testosteron. *Z. Tierpsychol.*, **17**:211–244.

Thorndike, E. L. 1911. *Animal Intelligence. Experimental Studies.* The Macmillian Company, New York.

Thorpe, W. H. 1955. Comments on 'The Bird Fancyer's Delight': together with notes on imitation in the sub-song of the chaffinch. *Ibis.* **97**:247–251.

————. 1958. The learning of song patterns by birds, with especial reference to the song of the chaffinch, *Fringilla coelebs. Ibis*, **100**:535–570.

————. 1959. Talking birds and the mode of action of the vocal apparatus of birds. *Proc. Zool. Soc. Lond.*, **132**:441–455.

————. 1961. *Bird Song: The Biology of Vocal Communication and Expression in Birds.* Cambridge University Press, Cambridge.

————. 1963. *Learning and Instinct in Animals.* Harvard University Press, Cambridge.

Tinbergen, N. 1951. *The Study of Instinct.* Oxford University Press, London.

Tryon, R. C. 1942. Individual differences. In *Comparative Psychology*, ed. by F. A. Moss: 330–365. Prentice-Hall, New York.

Uhrich, J. 1940. The effect of experience on fighting behavior of albino mice. *Ecology*, **21**:100–101.

Vince, M. A. 1956. "String-pulling" in birds. I. Individual differences in wild adult great tits. *Brit. J. Anim. Behav.*, **4**:111–116.

710   THE DEVELOPMENT OF MOTOR PATTERNS

————. 1958. "String-pulling" in birds. II. Differences related to age in greenfinches, chaffinches and canaries. *Brit. J. Anim. Behav.*, **6**:53–59.

————. 1961. "String-pulling" in birds. III. The successful response in greenfinches and canaries. *Behaviour*, **17**:103–129.

Weih, A. S. 1951. Untersuchungen über das Wechselsingen (*Anaphonie*) und über das angeborene Lautschema einiger Feldheuschrecken. *Z. Tierpsychol.*, **8**:1–41.

Weiss, G. 1952. Beobachtungen an zwei isoliert aufgezogenen Hauskatzen. *Z. Tierpsychol.*, **9**:451–462.

Weiss, P. 1950. Experimental analysis of co-ordination by the disarrangement of central-peripheral relations. *Symp. Soc. Exp. Biol.*, **4**:92–111.

Wilsson, L. In press.

Witt, P. N. and C. F. Reed. 1965. Spider-web building. *Science*, **149**:1190–1197.

Wood-Gush, D. G. M. 1960. A study of sex drive of two strains of cockerels through three generations. *Anim. Behav.*, **8**:43–53.

Yerkes, R. M. and B. W. Learned. 1925. *Chimpanzee Intelligence and Its Vocal Expressions*. The Williams and Wilkins Company, Baltimore.

———— and A. W. Yerkes. 1929. *The Great Apes*. Yale University Press, New Haven.

Zangwill, O. L. 1960. Speech. In *Handbook of Physiology*, ed. by J. Field, Sec. 1, Vol. 3:1709–1722. American Physiological Society, Washington, D. C.

twenty

DESCRIPTION IN SPACE AND TIME

The process of selective description • Behavioral stereotypy and action
patterns • The temporal organization of action patterns • Appetitive
and consummatory behavior • Measures of behavioral intensity • The
relation between description and causal analysis.

Most people would agree that description is fundamental to the scientific
method. It may thus seem contrary that a discussion of it should occur at
the end of a book rather than at the beginning. Yet the process of description is less easy to embark upon than some would have us believe. In a
penetrating essay on "the relationship between observation and experimentation in the field study of behavior," which deserves reading by all
concerned with practical or theoretical problems of behavioral analysis,
Schneirla (1950) points out the close relationship between observation
and hypothesis.

SELECTIVE DESCRIPTION

An observer is seldom if ever a passive instrument translating information to data automatically. Neither observer nor instrument can
record a complete description of a behavior sequence. As with any physical phenomenon, the number of direct and indirect ways by which a
description can be prepared is infinite. The process of observation inevitably involves the selection of some aspects of the situation for close
attention while others are neglected.

711

There is no more crucial phase of an investigation than this initial selection of the aspects of the situation that are to be recorded. Whether by choice or not, an element of hypothesis is introduced at the outset (Altmann 1962). The potential fruitfulness of the study stands or falls by the effectiveness of the selection made. Any reliable observation makes some contribution to knowledge. But the success of scientific investigations is usually judged both by the questions which they answer and by the new hypotheses to which they give rise. It is with respect to these criteria that the process of selection of what is to be recorded has important consequences.

If initial selection is so critical, the investigator who tries to approach a project with a completely open mind is less likely to be successful than one who attempts to formulate the questions he wishes to answer. Yet it is in the very nature of progress to discover new questions in the process of answering old ones. So the framework of investigation should be flexible enough to allow detection of the unforeseen yet rigid enough to insure adequate preappraisal.

Behavioral research ramifies so widely that it may seem invidious even to attempt suggestions for the kinds of description that may be most appropriate. It is often by breaking away from current traditions that new discoveries are made. What follows is therefore intended as no more than a suggestion of some possibilities as seen from one point of view.

The areas of investigation of animal behavior fall into five broad categories: motivation, ecology, social communication, phylogeny, and ontogeny. The first is concerned with the causation of behavior in the individual. Motivational analysis is likely to involve special emphasis on changes in behavior on the one hand and environmental changes either preceding the behavior or concomitant with it on the other. Ecologists more often approach behavioral analysis to ascertain the *consequences* of behavioral interaction with the physical and biological environment, particularly as they relate to the flow of energy. The study of social communication poses questions about information transfer, and in many cases this may involve phenomena of interest to the ecologist as well. The two come particularly close in the investigation of demographic problems. Phylogenetic study involves the comparison of related forms, requiring broad surveys which often preclude the more extended descriptive studies of a single species demanded by other types of investigation. Finally, the analysis of cause and effect in the processes of behavioral development places a special burden on the observer, as necessary preparation for the kind of experimental treatment which is essential in ontogenetic study (see page 619). This is true whether the work concerns the maturing juvenile or the appearance of new behavior in the adult.

Consider the problems of observation in studies of the motivation of behavior. Experimental approaches to these questions have been emphasized, perhaps to the neglect of direct observation. Our concern with the temporal organization of behavior suggests one aspect that may be worthy of careful attention in motivational studies. Particularly when dealing with rhythmically recurring behavior, simultaneous observation of changes in the environment and behavior are required. Recorded in a way that elucidates temporal correlations between the two types of events, these data can be a fruitful source of hypotheses concerning questions of exogenous and endogenous control or the varying effects of external stimuli on behavior.

The plea for analysis of the temporal patterning of behavior is equally relevant to the description of social behavior, where the central problem of communication can be appraised by considering the temporal relations between the behavior of different individuals. At a finer level, the internal timing of communicatory behavior may reveal properties important for the performance of their function (page 467). This type of analysis seems equally relevant to ontogenetic studies and ecology. Only in phylogenetic investigations, where the time-consuming methods needed for temporal analysis may be prohibitive, does such an approach seem less appropriate. Thus in selecting characteristics for behavioral description temporal patterns can be fruitful sources of new hypotheses. It follows that such analysis must be *quantitative,* for there is no other acceptable way to examine temporal patterns. It is nevertheless important to note qualitative aspects of behavior as well, especially in the early phases of a study, when we are trying to define the minimal units on which to base a description.

BEHAVIORAL STEREOTYPY AND FIXED ACTION PATTERNS

◆ *Levels of Description.* Behavioral activity can be described at several levels. At one extreme, for example, the locomotor behavior of a horse may be considered as a pattern of activity in particular muscles as Weiss has regarded the locomotion of amphibia (Weiss 1941, 1950, Figure 20–1). Patterns of walking, trotting, or galloping are at another level. Gray (1953) and Kruger (1958) described them by the particular temporal pattern in which whole limbs are moved. In another dimension, swimming, flying, and climbing can be contrasted with movement on a level

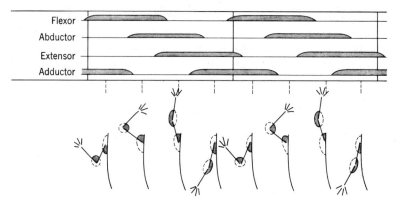

Figure 20-1   The sequence of muscle contractions of the left forelimb of a salamander during locomotion. After Weiss 1950.

surface. They all fall under the rubric of locomotion, including movements in all media and in all planes.

The selection made between the various types of description will depend on the purpose of the investigation. If we are trying to assemble an 'ethogram' of a species, the aim will be to select descriptive categories which are large enough to apply to an extensive study in a practical manner and yet sufficiently restricted to distinguish between functionally different forms of behavior. The judgment is a relative one since even the slightest variations in a motor pattern are likely to have some functional significance. The choice would be more difficult but for the fact that much natural behavior falls into categories which are ideally suited for our purpose.

The concept of the fixed action pattern, developed by Lorenz and Tinbergen, draws attention to the stereotyped nature of many natural motor coordinations, notwithstanding the variation in the orientation with which they are given. It is relatively rare for the behavior of a species to vary continuously in a wide variety of forms. Usually the variations are grouped around a series of modes, with few intermediates, so that basic patterns can be distinguished by what Altmann (in press) calls sequential demarcation. There are exceptions to this rule, but it applies sufficiently widely to serve as a useful point of departure in describing behavior.

Thus in describing locomotion in horses the most useful basic categories might be walking, trotting, and galloping. We can then proceed either to a finer analysis of variations within these relatively fixed categories or to a broader analysis of their place in the overall behavior of the animal.

◆ *Identification of Fixed Action Patterns.* If the identification of action patterns is the aim of a descriptive study of behavior, how is an investigator to proceed in dealing with a species not already familiar to him? Many practical hints are suggested by Calhoun, Carpenter, Emlen, Schneirla, Scott, and others in a symposium on methodology and technique in the study of animal societies (Scott 1950). Contact with the subject should be as intimate and sustained as possible. Great advantages may be gained by keeping animals in captivity under seminatural conditions.

Perhaps the most important point is the essential role of induction in setting up initial descriptive categories. Observation must begin by taking constant notes in categories which are empirical, yet sufficiently plastic to allow for extensive change. Many early notes prove to have limited value in themselves. But they play a role in the perfection of observational techniques. In time, what seemed at first to be an infinitely variable series of events begins to fall into a pattern as the observer makes an unconscious statistical assessment of the modal patterns about which the behavior is grouped.

Schneirla (1950) emphasizes the importance of this process of initiation into a descriptive problem. "With reasonably good qualifications at the start as concerns sensitivity, intelligence, and motivation in particular, the observer's technique as a skilled perceiver, reasoner, and manipulator of his subject matter may be advanced through experience to a high degree of scientific reliability and control."

Fraser Darling (1937) studied the behavior of red deer in Scotland and emphasized the subtle mental discipline that was required.

It takes time for the eye to become accustomed to recognize differences, and once that has occurred the nature of the differences has to be defined in the mind by careful self-interrogation if the matter is to be set down on paper. . . . The fact remains that an observer has to go through a period of conditioning of a most subtle kind. . . . The observer must empty his mind and be receptive only of the deer and the signs of the country. This is quite severe discipline, calling for time and practice. . . . It is necessary intellectually to soak in the environmental complex of the animal to be studied until you have a facility with it which keeps you as it were one move ahead. You must become *intimate* with the animal. . . . In this state the observer learns more than he realizes (Darling 1937, pp. 24–26).

In what terms should these action patterns be described? Needless to say they should be objective. Anthropomorphisms should be rigorously excluded. Rather than using terms such as 'afraid' and 'angry' which involve both observation and interpretation, every effort should be made to record the spatial coordination of limbs and body from which the action pattern is constructed. Sounds may be recorded or noted onomatopoetically, odors by analogy with other odors. To complete the basic description the temporal organization of these elements should also be noted.

The process of description is intimately involved with naming, and here too a degree of discipline is called for. Studies of communicatory behavior in animals have often included in their primary descriptions such terms as domination and subordination behavior, inferiority and superiority postures, intimidation, distraction, threat, and appeasement displays. These terms are liable to prejudge the function of behavior. At the same time they fail to provide a sound empirical description that can be the basis of further work not only by the investigator but also by other workers. Altmann draws attention to the same point. "While the justification for including any particular pattern in the catalogue is to be found in the social context in which the pattern occurs," in his account of a field study of the behavior of rhesus monkeys, "this social context is never part of the definition of the pattern" (Altmann 1962).

In studies of social behavior in the fish, *Tilapia macrocephala*, Aronson (1949) used terms such as *throat-puff, body-quiver, tail-slap,* and *head-nod.* This clear separation of description from function is desirable, especially when similar behavior patterns are shared by different species or when they occur in the same species at different times. There should be a maximal reliance on intrinsic properties of the behavior and a minimum of interpretation. Such terms, for example, as "head-up, tail-up," "nod-swimming," and "grunt-whistle," used in describing action patterns in the social behavior of ducks (Lorenz 1941), are preferable to 'courtship posture' or 'aggressive posture' for the initial description. Furthermore, "no important term should be kept in use without frequent careful examination, for the unchallenged crystallization of a key concept in a much used verbal expression may prevent the observer from ever noticing exceptions to its chief implications" (Schneirla 1950).

The difficulties of assembling a catalogue of action patterns should not be underestimated. It is often hard to decide when variants on a motor pattern should be lumped in one category and when they should be split (Altmann 1965, in press). Sometimes the extent of variation is so great and so close to continuous that divisions along it become arbitrary. Yet our inclination to quantize continuously varying phenomena almost seems to require that divisions be made. The possibility that such divisions are arbitrary rather than empirical should never be overlooked. Apart from the difficulties generated in communicating results to other workers and in permitting observations to be repeated, appreciation of the continuously varying nature of some motor patterns can give a direct insight into the function that they serve (see page 469).

Once the basic action patterns are established, there are several directions in which to proceed. Certain action patterns may be subjected to a finer analysis. Their variation may be studied, perhaps ultimately leading to a neurophysiological analysis. Alternatively, the approach may expand to include the sequences in which the action patterns occur. These in turn can be arranged in broad temporal groupings, introducing a new level of organization. Thus the action patterns can be arranged in successively broader classifications.

At this stage a given action pattern can also be described by the behavioral context in which it typically occurs (Altmann 1962, 1965). The characteristics of the environment may also be encompassed by the description, so that action patterns can be further defined by their environmental contexts. A logical next step is to embark on manipulation of the environment or of the physiological state of the animal to open up the experimental manipulation of behavior. Thus "the observation-selective method" prepares the ground for "direct-manipulative control of behavior" (Schneirla 1950). As we proceed from one to the other, interpretation becomes a more and more explicit part of the process of investigation. Whatever the direction of further exploration, the chances of success will be greatest if there is a sound basis of empirical description from which to proceed.

QUANTIFICATION OF OBSERVATIONS

Observations should be recorded systematically to permit statistical treatment as the study proceeds. To this extent elementary quantification is essential to the observational method and leads to the setting up of the 'qualitative' categories, for example, action patterns upon which further study will be based. The process of induction involves a somewhat parallel method, largely at a subconscious level. There is much to be gained by making the quantitative aspects explicit, once the basic descriptive categories have been selected. At the same time it is important to maintain a balanced perspective. A description does not acquire scientific respectability just because it is based on something that has been counted. Highly quantified descriptions based on irrelevant parameters of a situation can be more barren than observations which are not quantified at all.

There is no limit to the methods available for quantifying observations of behavior. Various instrumental aids can be used and are valuable if used with care, ranging from the direct recording of behavior with still and movie photography and tape recorders to the various indirect methods of actographs and Skinner boxes. Large samples of data are often needed if records of variable behavior are to be meaningful, although extensive qualitative observations can also provide an independent and sometimes more economical means of assessing the significance of small samples. Denenberg and Banks (1962) have many suggestions on observational and experimental aids and statistical methods.

By connecting a manual keyboard to a multichannel recorder with a continuously moving paper tape and by coding the keys to particular action patterns, a practiced observer can make a continuous record of a large number of different acts. Once recorded, the data can provide a wide variety of measures for quantification, especially if some of the more arduous calculations can be performed by a computer. In studies of the motivation of behavior, for which temporal patterning has a special significance, such continuous records may be an invaluable and even indispensable source of data.

◆ *Conclusions on Behavioral Description.* What generalizations can be drawn from this brief discussion of descriptive methods? Description is perhaps the most important phase in behavioral study. Its consequences can make or mar the remainder of the investigation, whether it continues to be observational or proceeds to an experimental level. The description may well begin on a broad inductive basis, as an aid in identifying the basic action patterns in which the motor behavior is organized. Once the descriptive categories are established the data can be quantified, with environmental changes included in the record as well. Finally the stage is set for experimental manipulation and perhaps for physiological analysis as well. In some circumstances it is possible to bypass part of this sequence, especially if the behavior has already been well described. In other cases the study may never proceed beyond the inductive phase. This is true of some comparative studies for which a very large array of material needs to be covered. All approaches have scientific validity if appropriate questions are asked of the data and if we do not draw conclusions that require a different kind of data for their verification.

CLUSTERS OF ACTION PATTERNS

Suppose that the observer assembles representative samples of the sequence of action patterns of a species covering a variety of different situations. One of the first points likely to emerge is that many activities tend to be grouped in time. Just as a sea anemone deprived of food performs a group of activities—elongation of the column, extension and waving of the tentacles, and expansion of the oral disk—so a hungry rat performs a series of alternative activities while searching for food and eating it—such as scratching at the ground, digging, sniffing, grasping, and biting. These activities tend to form a group which occurs for a given period of time and then ceases, to be replaced by a different group, perhaps grooming, nest building, or sleeping. In all animals some grouping of activities occurs. This point is readily appreciated intuitively and often forms a basis for such general categories as feeding or sexual behavior.

Some behavior patterns are not restricted to one type of temporal grouping. Certain elementary acts are repeated in many different groups of activities in much the same form. Movements preparing birds for flight recur in many different situations (Daanje 1950, Marler 1956). The act of biting can recur in eating, fighting, and perhaps in the preparation of nest material. At a more complex level, social behavior sometimes appears in more than one behavioral group. The cluster of acts that makes up the mutual grooming of deer mice, for example, is likely to occur both in aggressive encounters and in sequences leading to copulation (Eisenberg 1962). The same is true of the posture of primates which in females is the normal prelude to copulation. It recurs in aggressive situations and in males as well as females (Nissen 1951).

Some behavior patterns can hardly be ascribed to any particular behavioral group at all. They are likely to occur as single acts at any time in the animal's waking hours. Such acts as scratch reflexes and the various adjustments of posture which are continuously being made are included here. A sea anemone's nematocysts are liable to discharge at any time the tentacles are exposed. Certain patterns of locomotion may fall in this category as well. However, some reservations may still be necessary with respect to such patterns, for although it can be difficult to assign such behavior patterns to particular groups, there may be negative correlations. They may be rare or absent when certain other activities are being performed, such as resting or sleeping. Other acts which occur widely may be more frequent within some behavioral groups than in others. A special case is provided by 'displacement activities,' giving an impression of functional irrelevance in some of the alternative groups in which they occur (Tinbergen 1952). In a formal sense their temporal patterning may be little different from behavior patterns occurring in more than one behavioral group whose functional significance is more obvious.

Thus the temporal grouping of activities is only relative. Some behavior patterns are strictly confined to one group. Others occur in several, whereas some are difficult to assign to particular behavioral groups. Even in the latter case some temporal patterning may be imposed by other behavioral groups which exclude them. The extreme case is sleep, which precludes most other activities. There may also be more specific inhibitory or facilitatory relationships between particular patterns of behavior.

The temporal clustering of certain activities can be regarded from two points of view, proximity in time and the sequence of occurrence. Records of time intervals should show that behavioral activities belonging to one temporal grouping are likely to occur at about the same time, separated from each other by time intervals which are shorter, on the average, than those separating them from other temporal groupings. As a result of their temporal proximity actions are more likely to be immediately preceded or followed by members of the same grouping than by members of another group.

It is a prerequisite for survival that the different acts in the behavioral repertoire of an animal appear not in a random sequence but in definite temporal patterns. If it were otherwise the result would be chaos. The elements in a sequence often have an obvious functional relationship. We readily find ourselves classifying them together as elements of, for example, feeding or sexual behavior. Such categories are often set up intuitively. It is important to note that the temporal grouping of behavior patterns can be derived from purely empirical data. Moreover, even though temporally grouped activities are surely functionally related to each other in most cases, there are puzzling exceptions. We are better able to identify and to discuss these if we make the temporal grouping our primary concern and relegate functional considerations to the next stage of analysis.

The number of temporal behavioral groups in the natural behavior of most animals is probably fairly small. It must be admitted that there is little data on which such a judgment can be based. In describing the behavior of rodents, Eisenberg (1962, 1963) used such categories as locomotion, sleeping and associated activities, care of the body surface, feeding, drinking, defecation, urination, nest building, food hoarding, and various kinds of social behavior, including fighting, mating, and parental behavior. The finer subdivisions within these categories, especially the social behavior, need not concern us here. The point is that, with interruptions by such occasional acts as exploration and avoidance, behavior within this limited number of behavioral groupings occupies most of the animal's time. The list may not be exhaustive, but it cannot be much longer.

A similar list would serve for most of the behavioral activity of some birds, such as great tits (Hinde 1952) or chaffinches (Marler 1956). A few changes would be needed such as the removal of food hoarding and the addition of some further categories such as singing behavior. The component activities with each group would of course be quite different.

But the groups as a whole satisfy much the same kind of biological requirements in a mouse and a bird.

In animals with different ways of life the categories included will vary. In aquatic air-breathing animals, for example, respiration takes on the characteristics of a behavioral grouping (Spurway and Haldane 1954, see page 152) whereas in terrestrial vertebrates it is continuous. Feeding behavior is a characteristically grouped activity of most animals, but it may be virtually continuous in some plankton feeders and parasites. Drinking and elimination may also be continuous. The temporal characteristics of locomotion vary from an almost continuous activity, as for example in certain fishes and even aerial animals such as the swift (Lack 1956), through a condition in which it is intermittent and associated with several behavioral groups, to the situation in some sessile animals such as sea anemones where it tends to be a more strictly grouped activity. The predominant patterns also vary in different phases of the life cycle of the same animal.

It is clear that the subject of the temporal grouping of action patterns is complex. Difficulties are further compounded by the lack of careful quantitative studies. Although sequences of gross activity have been thoroughly investigated in relation to circadian rhythms, the entire spectrum of behavior has rarely been studied over periods of time. Such an analysis is difficult, often requiring considerable automation (e.g. Kavanau 1963). Even the behavior patterns which, as Richter (1927) has shown, can be recorded by automatic devices are seldom subjected to long-term study.

Although some birds have been investigated, the most thorough studies of temporal patterning of behavior have been conducted with fish. Of all the animals which can be studied in captivity over long periods of time, small aquatic animals are perhaps the least affected by the artificial conditions of the laboratory. A pioneer analysis was made by Baerends, Brouwer, and Waterbolk (1955) of the complex courtship behavior of the male guppy. They established the temporal ordering of the actions and demonstrated correlations with the elaborate and shifting patterns of coloration on the male's fins and body. Wiepkema (1961) made a similar study of another species of fish, the bitterling, *Rhodeus amarus*, with somewhat simpler behavior patterns than those of the guppy.

ORGANIZATION WITHIN A SEQUENCE

The organization of behavior patterns within a sequence of related activities is often complex and varied. It is difficult to generalize, especially when there are so few data to consider. Often the ordering seems to have little pattern. In some cases at least a series of acts can be discerned, one succeeding the other in a predictable manner. Orderly sequences can often be seen in sexual behavior.

The courtship of pigeons includes many different actions, giving a somewhat chaotic first impression. Fabricius and Jansson (1963) found that sequences of actions can nevertheless be discerned (Table 20-1).

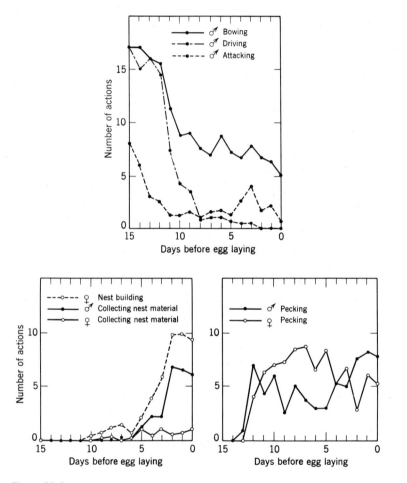

Figure 20-2   The frequency of some actions in the reproductive behavior of pigeons at various phases of the cycle. Here they are expressed as mean values (number of 2-minute periods with action per 34-minute session) for observations of six cycles in three pairs of birds. They are plotted against the time of laying of the first egg. After Fabricius and Jansson 1963.

Table 20-1 Relative Frequency with Which Actions of Pigeons Followed One Another, Expressed as Percentages

Male

	Subsequent behavior															
	Bw	Dr	A	Pe	Ea	Pr	Nd	Ni	Mo	Ps	Pem	Cm	D	Bi	M	Co
Bw	—	40.4	7.5	7.3	2.8	2.0	11.2	0.2	1.7	0	2.5	0.6	23.5	0.3	0	0
Dr	92.4	—	4.4	0.6	0.3	0	1.0	0	0	0	0	0	1.0	0	0.3	0
A	73.0	11.5	—	1.6	0.8	0	2.5	1.6	2.5	0	0.8	0.8	4.9	0	0	0
Pe	6.9	4.0	0.9	—	26.1	12.0	14.9	2.0	2.9	0	15.8	3.4	10.6	0.6	0	0
Ea	10.2	3.0	0.6	24.6	—	14.4	14.4	0	3.0	0	7.2	4.2	15.0	3.0	0.6	0
Pr	5.7	0.4	1.8	24.9	6.1	—	8.7	3.1	4.4	0	21.1	5.2	16.6	1.3	0	0
Nd	6.7	0.6	6.9	7.4	2.7	2.0	—	14.1	3.9	2.5	43.7	0.4	6.9	2.2	0	0
Ni	4.7	0	1.4	7.4	2.7	6.8	21.0	—	0	2.7	23.7	2.0	6.1	21.6	0	0
Mo	1.6	0	0	4.9	0	5.7	46.3	0.8	—	0.8	39.0	0	0	0.8	0	0
Ps	0	0	0	0	0	0	100	0	0	—	0	0	0	0	0	0
Pem	2.4	0	1.6	14.8	2.0	9.1	28.8	7.7	9.1	0	—	22.1	2.4	0.2	0	0
Cm	4.3	0	0	12.3	1.2	7.4	3.1	1.2	2.5	0	68.1	—	0	0	0	0
D	5.9	0	0.3	9.6	3.5	16.2	8.5	0.8	1.3	0	2.1	0.5	—	43.6	7.5	0
Bi	2.7	0	0.9	0.9	0.9	0.4	8.9	7.6	0.9	0	0.4	0.4	66.2	—	9.8	0
M	0	0	0	0	0	0	0	0	0	0	0	0	1.9	0	—	98.1
Co	51.9	0	0	3.9	0	3.9	25.0	0	5.8	0	5.7	0	3.9	0	0	—

Female

	Subsequent behavior															
	Bw	A	Pe	Ea	Pr	Nd	Ni	Mo	Ps	Pem	Cm	D	Bg	Bi	Sq	Co
Bw	—	13.6	27.3	0	4.5	4.5	4.5	0	0	4.5	0	27.3	9.1	0	4.5	0
A	11.1	—	0	0	11.1	18.5	40.7	0	0	3.7	0	11.1	0	0	3.7	0
Pe	0	0	—	30.1	17.9	7.8	13.9	2.4	7.1	6.4	0.3	7.4	4.7	1.7	0.3	0
Ea	0	0	38.1	—	4.8	9.5	19.0	2.0	7.5	4.8	0.7	4.8	7.5	0.7	0.7	0
Pr	0	2.4	28.9	7.6	—	9.0	18.0	3.4	2.8	6.6	0.5	12.3	7.6	0.5	0.5	0
Nd	0	1.4	7.8	1.4	4.2	—	11.9	6.6	15.9	38.4	0.3	38.4	6.0	3.2	0	0
Ni	0	0.4	14.1	2.0	8.2	42.4	—	2.0	16.5	9.4	0	0.8	0.4	3.9	0	0
Mo	0	0	5.8	2.3	5.3	42.7	1.8	—	1.8	36.3	0.6	1.2	2.3	0	0	0
Ps	0	0	0	0	0	100	0	0	—	0	0	0	0	0	0	0
Pem	0	0	5.9	0.8	3.1	51.3	4.4	25.8	3.4	—	1.8	0.5	2.1	1.0	0	0
Cm	0	0	0	0	7.1	7.1	14.3	21.4	21.4	28.6	—	0	0	0	0	0
D	0	2.5	10.5	1.5	22.5	3.0	4.5	0.5	1.5	0.5	0	—	23.0	12.0	18.0	0
Bg	0	0	4.4	1.7	2.2	2.8	1.1	0.6	0.6	0.6	0	7.2	—	78.5	0.6	0
Bi	0	0	13.1	2.8	3.3	6.1	4.2	0.5	1.4	0.9	0	34.7	18.8	—	14.1	0
Sq	0	1.4	1.4	0	0	0	0	0	0	1.4	0	20.8	1.4	4.2	—	69.4
Co	4	4	14	0	46	6	12	0	0	4	0	10	0	0	0	—

The data are based on four normal reproductive cycles of four pigeon pairs. Bw represents bowing, Dr driving, A attacking, Pe pecking, Ea eating, Pr preening, Nd nest demonstrating, Ni nibbling, Mo moulding, Ps pushing, Pem pecking at nest material, Cm collecting nest material, D displacement preening, Bi billing, M mounting, Co copulation, Bg begging, Sq squatting. After Fabricius and Jansson 1963.

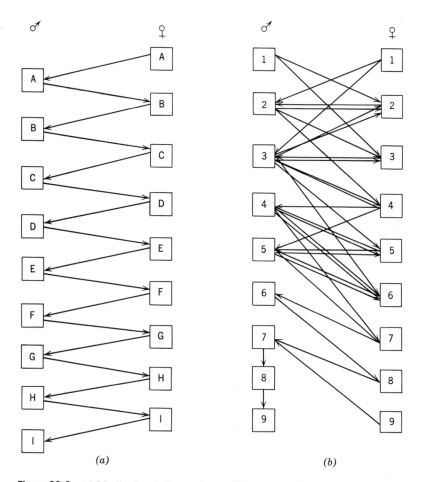

Figure 20-3   (*a*) Idealized and (*b*) actual courtship sequences in the ten-spined stickleback *Pygosteus pungitius*. After Morris 1958.

There seem to be two dominant activity chains in the male, one leading to copulation through displacement preening and billing, and another leading to nibbling and collecting of nest material via nest demonstration. . . . The same two dominating activity chains are present in the female, but the behaviour of the male often seems to determine which alternative will occur . . . the first behaviour shown by the male is almost always bowing, and to this the female reacts by pecking. If the male turns to nest demonstration, the female responds by nibbling and this may, through several alternative ways, develop into nest demonstration, pushing, and collecting of nest material. If the male continues bowing or turns to displacement preening, the female usually indulges in a series of activities which may lead to squatting, either through displacement preening or through begging and billing (Fabricius and Jansson 1963, p. 542).

Thus the sequence of actions in the individual varies with the external stimuli which are present, particularly the communication signals received from the mate. It also varies with the bird's physiological condition, so that the dominant sequence patterns vary at different phases of the cycle of courtship, nest building and egg laying (Figure 20-2).

In the sexual behavior of some fish there is an alternating sequence in the behavior of male and female (Figure 20-3). The main sequence is by no means obligatory. Many alternatives are possible, but the sequences are not random (Baerends et al. 1955, Morris 1958). The ordering varies with the external situation as, for example, in the courtship of the bitterling (Figure 20-4). In the cichlid fish, *Tilapia mossambica*, the male digs a

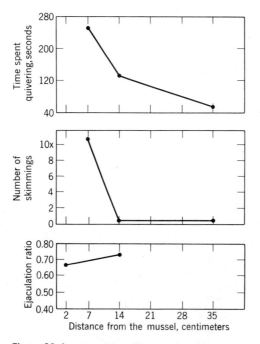

Figure 20-4   The relationship between frequency of certain movements of male bitterlings and the distance of the female from the host mussel. The ejaculation ratio is the proportion of fertilization acts to the number of skimming acts without ejection of milt (see page 732). After Wiepkema 1961.

pit and goes through an elaborate series of acts when a gravid female approaches (Neil 1964). A sequence often leads the female to spawn in the pit. Then the male fertilizes the eggs. The early behavior of the male varies according to the proximity of the female to the nesting pit (Figure 20-5). If she is more than 15 centimeters away the acts of *leading* and

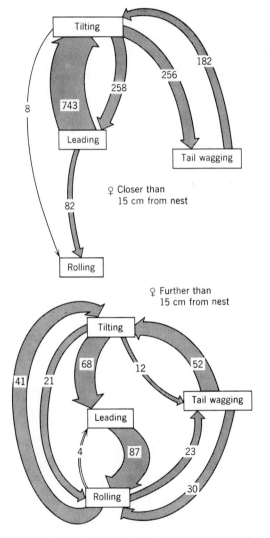

Figure 20-5 The courtship responses of territorial male cichlid fishes, *Tilapia mossambica*, to females more and less than 15 cm from the nest. After Neil 1964.

tilting predominate. Closer to the nest *rolling* becomes more prominent and may be followed by the other acts leading to spawning.

Within such a sequence as this we can distinguish two types of behavior patterns. Some, like leading and rolling, are preparatory or introductory to others, such as spawning, which occur later in the sequence. Such introductory patterns are often described as appetitive, to distinguish them from the consummatory behavior which follows. This distinction has implications for the pattern in time as well as for function.

APPETITIVE AND CONSUMMATORY BEHAVIOR

The great physiologist Sherrington (1906) distinguished "anticipatory" or "precurrent" reactions from "final" or "consummatory" reactions. The distinction is well illustrated in feeding behavior, in which movements of transferring food into the mouth are appetitive. These are steps toward final adjustments such as chewing and swallowing, which are terminal or consummatory.

Sherrington went on to define some of the general properties of these two kinds of behavior. He pointed out the relatively flexible nature of precurrent behavior compared with the more stereotyped consummatory reactions. His main point, however, was that the temporal patterning of the two types of behavior is different. One maintains activity within a bout, the other tends to terminate it. Some years later Wallace Craig (1918) made a similar distinction, using the term "appetitive" rather than "precurrent." His usage has persisted.

Craig's illustrations were drawn from the behavior of doves:

A good example of appetitive behavior is seen in the way in which a young male dove locates a nesting site for the first time. The first thing the observer sees is that the dove, while standing on his perch, spontaneously assumes the nest-calling attitude, his body tilted forward, head down, as if his neck and breast were already touching the hollow of a nest (incipient consummatory action), and in this attitude he sounds the nest-call. But he shows dissatisfaction, as if the bare perch were not a comfortable situation for this nest-dedicating attitude. He shifts about until he finds a corner which more or less fits his body while in the tilted posture; he is seldom satisfied with his first corner, but tries another and another. If now an appropriate nest-box or a ready-made nest is put into his cage, this inexperienced dove does not recognize it as a nest, but sooner or later he tries it, as he has tried all other places, for nest-calling, and in such a trial the nest evidently gives him a strong and satisfying stimulation (the appeted stimulus) which no other situation has given him. In the nest his attitude becomes extreme; he abandons himself to an orgy of nest-calling (complete consummatory action), turning now this way and now that in the hollow, palpating the straws with his feet, wings, breast, neck, and beak, and rioting in the wealth of new, luxurious stimuli. He no longer wanders restlessly in search of new nesting situations, but remains satisfied with his present highly stimulating nest (Craig 1918, pp. 97–98).

◆ *Characteristics of Consummatory and Appetitive Behavior.* In this example and others, Craig points to several phenomena associated with appetitive and consummatory behavior. Some relate to the increased responsiveness of the animal to certain external stimuli and decreased responsiveness to others during the course of appetitive behavior. Another is the greater readiness to perform certain motor acts. Appetitive behavior is less stereotyped and its orientation is more variable, particularly as compared with consummatory behavior. As with the other criteria which are used, the separation is not absolute nor is it always applicable (Lorenz 1950, Hinde 1953). This point should be borne in mind, but it does not invalidate the usefulness of the distinction.

Most significant for the present purpose is the fact that the appetitive behavior is associated with sustained restless activity, whereas consummatory behavior is terminal and followed by a relative state of rest. Thus the temporal patterning of these two types of behavior should be quite different. A typical behavioral series might be occupied mainly by appetitive actions and terminated by consummatory behavior.

Before going further we should eliminate uncertainty about two points. What exactly is supposed to be terminated by consummatory behavior, and is the termination effected by one occurrence of a consummatory behavior pattern or by several?

A single occurrence of a consummatory behavior pattern within a sequence seldom seems to terminate it. Thus, if we return to Sherrington's example, the act of food swallowing is repeated many times before a feeding sequence ends. The same applies to drinking. In the copulatory behavior of domestic rats the male mounts the female many times and ejaculates up to ten times before a sequence is terminated (Beach 1956, Larsson 1956, Table 20-2). The same is true of a bird such as the chaffinch, where a sequence of copulatory behavior, separated from other sequences by intervals of 30 to 60 minutes of other activities, may involve as many as six copulations (Marler 1956).

Thus consummatory behavior may be repeated, each time preceded by appetitive behavior, before a sequence comes to an end. Evidently such consummatory behavior does not simply terminate a given sequence of behavior. It is more accurate to say that the probability of a sequence ending increases rapidly with repetition of consummatory behavior patterns. Furthermore, since the distinction from appetitive behavior is a relative one, we should include the fact that the rate at which the probability of ending a sequence increases with repeated actions is greater in consummatory behavior.

Occasionally a bout may be terminated by appetitive behavior. A hungry animal, for example, may fail to find food and change to some other kind of activity. Nevertheless, it may be statistically true that bouts of feeding behavior are terminated by a certain number of feeding acts. Thus the distinction between appetitive and consummatory behavior should be empirically derivable from the analysis of temporal patterns. In the absence of quantitative treatment, these two categories of behavior should be used with care. The subjective impression of finality associated with some so-called consummatory behavior can be deceptive.

What does consummatory behavior terminate? It can end the particular sequence of appetitive behavior which precedes it. It can also contribute to the probability of eventual termination of the whole session of the behavioral grouping. In either case it is consummatory only in relation to other specific patterns of behavior (Nelson 1964a). If the sequence of actions of two individuals are considered together, the behavior of one may have consummatory consequences for the behavior of the partner. We should thus be wary of defining behavior as consummatory and of failing to state to what it is consummatory.

A given behavior pattern can be consummatory in relation to certain behavioral groups and not to others. This may occur with actions that belong to several temporal groupings. Locomotion, for example, can probably assume both roles in different situations. There is even some evidence for a dual role within the same pattern of activity, according to the position occupied in the sequence. For example, the presentation of a morsel of food to a hungry rat may have the initial effect of intensifying activity rather than reducing it (Morgan 1957). Eating is associated both with facilitating and inhibiting effects on feeding behavior. The inhibitory consequences come to predominate, as acts of feeding are repeated, and finally result in termination.

◆ *Consummatory Behavior in Fish.* The need to specify what is terminated by consummatory action is exemplified by some of the fish studies. In the breeding season, each male bitterling defends an area around one or more freshwater mussels against other males. Sexual behavior patterns of the male bitterling induce a gravid female to approach the mussel where she lays her eggs. In general, the sexual behavior of the male ceases once the eggs are in the mantle cavity of the mussel. Considering the actions of male and female together, the act of egg laying is terminal and therefore consummatory for the sexual activities of the male. The male subsequently becomes aggressive and chases the female away.

Table 20-2 Individual Records of the Sexual Behavior of Two Male Rats

Time, min-utes	Number 1			Number 2		
	Complete intro-missions	At-tempts	Beginning and end of the intro-mission series	Complete intro-missions	At-tempts	Beginning and end of the intro-mission series
1	4	1	010 (i.e. 0.10 min)	6		004 (i.e. 0.04 min)
2	3		↑	3		↑
3	3		│	4	2	│
4	1	2	↓	3		↓
5	1		434 ejaculation			450 ejaculation
6						
7				4		690
8						773 ejaculation
9						
10						
11	3		1038			
12			1074 ejaculation	2	1	1164
13				3	1	↕
14						1305 ejaculation
15						
16						
17	1	3	1698			
18	3		↕			1796
19	1		1830 ejaculation	3	2	↕
20				1		1907 ejaculation
21						
22						
23						
24						
25	1		2460			
26	1	2	↑	2	2	2510
27	3		↓	1		2654 ejaculation
28			2726 ejaculation			
29						
30						
31						
32						
33						

Table 20-2 Individual Records of the Sexual Behavior of Two Male Rats

Time, minutes	Number 1			Number 2		
	Complete intromissions	Attempts	Beginning and end of the intromission series	Complete intromissions	Attempts	Beginning and end of the intromission series
34				2		3300
35	1		3450 ejaculation	3	3	↕
36	1	1			2	3525 ejaculation
37		3				
38	1	1				
39						
40	1	1				
41		2				
42	2	3				
43				1	1	4235
44	1	1		1	3	↑
45	1	1		1	2	
46	1	1		1	3	↓
47		2			3	4665 ejaculation
48						
49						
50		2				
51						
52		2				
53		2				
54		1				
55	1	1		1	2	5425
56				1		↑
57		1		1		↓
58					1	5730 ejaculation
59		2				
60		1	End			
						7515 intromission End

Temporal record of the copulatory behavior of two male rats with estrous females. The first rat, for example, achieved the initial ejaculation in 4.34 minutes after twelve complete and three attempted intromissions. The first male ejaculated four times in the session, the second eight times. The intervals between the intromission series gradually increased during the sequence. After Larsson 1956.

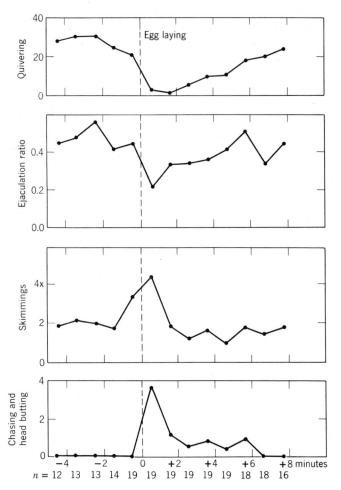

Figure 20-6 The frequency of certain movements of a territorial male bitterling in the minutes before and after egg laying: n = number of trials. See Figure 20–4 for explanation of the ejaculation ratio. After Wiepkema 1961.

There is one male sexual movement that continues after egg laying (Figure 20-6). This is 'skimming,' which occurs as part of the introductory courtship and is clearly a member of the temporally associated cluster of sexual activities. The same movement occurs later as the male ejects milt and fertilizes the eggs, after egg laying is completed. With respect to skimming and various aggressive activities, egg laying seems to have a facilitating effect rather than an inhibiting one (Wiepkema 1961). Thus the same action of the mate in this case may have opposite effects on the probability of different patterns occurring within the same behavioral group.

In the bitterling the act of sperm ejection seems to have no consummatory consequences. The same is true of the three-spined stickleback, at least in the short term. Again a female act, the laying of eggs in the nest, seems to terminate a sequence of male courtship (van Iersel 1953, Bol 1959, Sevenster-Bol 1962). If eggs are placed in the nest the sequence is likely to end. The termination is still more marked if the male is also allowed to 'quiver' with a female beforehand. Sperm ejection is not responsible. Other male courtship acts or perhaps presence of the female at the nest may be. Thus several actions in stickleback courtship seem to have consummatory consequences.

In the bitterling and stickleback fertilization is external. The relatively orderly sequences of male and female courtship activities in these species may be related to the need for precise physiological synchronization of actions in the two sexes. Certain characid fishes are internally fertilized, and the eggs are laid at some time in the distant future. Here there is less need for synchrony of the reproductive physiology. The sequential patterning of courtship is correspondingly less well organized (Nelson 1964a, b). Instead the male subjects the female to a repeated barrage of signals, which follow one another in no obvious order. In Nelson's study "female responses were rare and sporadic in occurrence and appeared to depend on the cumulative effect of male courtship activities."

When there is so little sequential ordering of activities, the concepts of appetitive and consummatory behavior can hardly be applied in their usual form. Some simplification is needed. The essential idea is that occurrence of some actions influences the probability that others will follow. Nelson (1964a) has shown how this possibility can be tested. Preceding and following actions are assembled in a contingency table. Each row is subjected to a chi-square test for a chance distribution of entries. The results show that in the courtship behavior of the male characid fish, *Corynopoma*, different action patterns do not occur independently of one another.

By defining the problem in this way the timing of actions is also brought into prominence. "It is reasonable to suppose that events which are further apart in time should be 'more independent' of one another than are events closely juxtaposed" (Nelson 1964a). The next step was to divide the data into several contingency tables of actions separated by different intervals of time: more than 5 seconds, more than 10 seconds, and so on up to more than 40 seconds. The application of chi-square and p-tests to these tables showed the time that must elapse after a given type of action before the occurrence of other actions became statistically independent of it. The result varied with different actions of the male, ranging from 10 seconds to as long as 40 seconds for one action. Here then is a method for extending the notions underlying appetitive and consummatory behavior in a different way. In particular, it focuses attention on the need for considering the actual time that elapses between different actions.

In a simpler fashion the same kind of relationship can be seen in bird-songs. The sequential pattern of syllables in the song of the mistle thrush becomes less determinate as the interval between syllables increases (Isaac and Marler 1963). It seems reasonable that at least in some situations the longer the time that lapses after an action, the less effect it will have on what follows. However, it is of special interest to show, as Nelson has done, that the effects of a lapse in time vary with different kinds of preceding activities. In this way it may be possible to probe more deeply into the central problem posed by appetitive and consummatory behavior, namely the facilitatory and inhibitory consequences of the performance of certain actions.

This discussion concerns the descriptive aspects of appetitive and consummatory behavior. The underlying physiological mechanisms may be many and varied. An action can take the animal into a new external stimulus situation, which in turn favors a different behavior pattern. The new situation may be generated by another animal. The effect on the male of egg laying by the female stickleback is a case in point. A chain of consecutive communication signals may be exchanged between individuals. An action may also generate sensory changes within the body, as when food is eaten. The repeated exposure to external stimuli which elicit an action may result in adaptation or habituation, changing the probability of recurrence of the action. We have seen examples in the feeding of flies and in mammalian sexual behavior (see page 97). The interplay of endogenous mechanisms can also play a part as in the control of respiratory rhythms in mammals (see page 150).

The diversity of mechanisms involved underlines the importance of distinguishing between the temporal organization of behavior, in which similar patterns recur in widely different organisms, and the physiological basis of such patterns, which may vary greatly in different organisms.

◆ *Preening in Terns.* The distinction between appetitive and consummatory behavior has little obvious application in behavior concerned with care of the body surface. Such is the case with the preening behavior of birds. Nevertheless, the actions do not appear in a random sequence. In terns, for example, the earliest movements to occur in preening after bathing are head shaking and breast, shoulder, and back preening. There is a second series which is lacking or infrequent in the early part of the preening bout but is common later. It includes preening of the wing, tail and pinions, and head rubbing. A third group, comprising shaking and preening of the shoulder, wing bow, and wing, comes somewhere between (van Iersel and Bol 1958). Thus the different activities in a bout of preening after bathing occur in an orderly fashion.

The sequential occurrence of these movements is related to their timing during the course of the sequence. The rate of performance of acts increases rapidly to a maximum soon after the sequence starts. Then it declines to the end with only minor fluctuations. As the frequency changes, different activities become dominant.

A possible interpretation of this pattern is that each of the behavior patterns in a bout of preening after bathing has a different threshold in relation to the total frequency of preening actions. When the frequency of preening acts is high, many different behavior patterns may occur; but those with the highest thresholds such as head rubbing and pinion preening predominate. Later in the bout, as the frequency declines, activities with lower thresholds become dominant. This continues until only those with the lowest thresholds of all, like head shaking and breast preening, are left at the end.

The main difference between this way of organizing a series of activities and the appetitive-consummatory system lies in the consequences of performance of the early actions in the sequence. Instead of facilitating further action in a specific way, the early acts may have a general facilitating effect on the whole class of preening activities. As a consequence the rate of preening increases, and as it does so, actions with higher and higher thresholds appear until the rate declines again. So there is a progression through the various activities that are necessary for proper care of the body surface.

FREQUENCY, VIGOR, AND COMPLETENESS OF BEHAVIOR

Changes in the frequency of actions occur in sequences of many types of behavior. A sequence of owl-mobbing acts by chaffinches varies in frequency, first rising to a maximum and then, with fluctuations, declining. Some actions are confined to the middle of the bout where the frequency is the greatest; others occur at the beginning, the end, or throughout (Hinde 1954, Figure 20-7).

The example of owl mobbing raises the question of measures other than

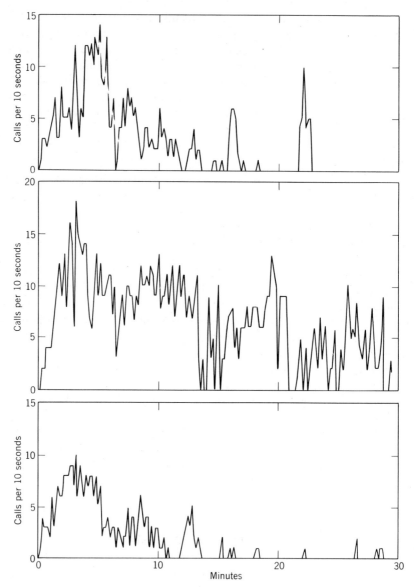

Figure 20-7 Three examples of buildup and waning of the rate of owl-mobbing calls by a chaffinch, *Fringilla coelebs*, measured as number of calls per 10-second interval. After Hinde 1954.

frequency which might be used as an index of 'intensity.' Hinde (1954, 1960b) points out that there are also changes in the vigor and completeness of the behavior patterns during the course of the bout. At the start, mobbing behavior is represented only by movements of the chaffinch's head. Later, movements of the body and tail are added to those of the head. The movements become more vigorous, and the bird begins calling. Once the peak rate of calling is passed, the vigor and completeness of the movements decline until mobbing stops. Tinbergen (1951) found variations in the completeness of sand digging used in territorial defense by the three-spined stickleback (Figure 20-8). The same phenomenon is

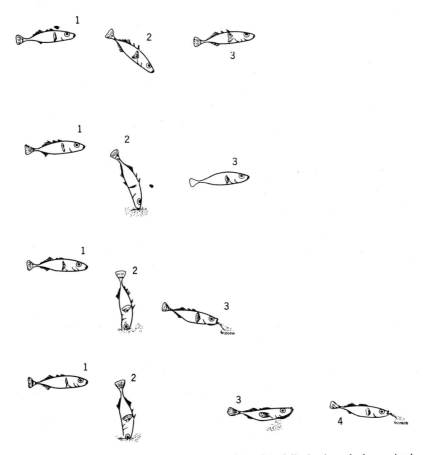

Figure 20-8   Four increasingly complete versions of sand digging in male three-spined sticklebacks. After Tinbergen 1951.

indicated in Craig's description of "incipient" consummatory actions of nest building in doves which are fragmentary versions of the "complete consummatory actions" to follow.

Measures of the intensity of behavior have a wide application in many fields. Experimental measures are sometimes used, such as the force of pulling on a harness or the kind of obstruction which an animal will overcome. Other measures are the minimal stimulus strength necessary to elicit a response, or the learning rate that results.

Direct descriptive measures fall into two categories. One is concerned with the internal patterning of the acts in time and space. Acts vary in intensity or vigor. There may be (1) variations in the number and completeness of components, (2) variations in the force, extent (or amplitude), and duration, and (3) variations in duration of an act.

Measures can also be derived from the overall pattern in time. They include (1) the intervals between various points in a behavioral sequence; examples are the intervals between the start of the sequence and the first appearance of a certain action (latency); the intervals between successive appearances of the same act; intervals between one type of act and another, or intervals between sequences; (2) frequency measures of the number of acts in various units of time; either one or several types of behavior patterns may be included; (3) measures of the total duration of activity or inactivity in a given period; and (4) measures of the quantity of some physical commodity involved in the behavior such as food, water, or nest material (Russell, Mead, and Hayes 1954, Hinde 1960a).

A review of these methods reminds us that there is not one measure of behavioral 'intensity' or 'vigor' but many. The conclusions to be drawn from an investigation depend very much on the measures adopted, as we have noted in studies of feeding behavior (page 130). A bout of behavior may be more intense than another by one measure and less intense by a different measure (Hinde 1958, 1959). Care must also be taken in interpreting measures which are dependent on each other. Cane (1961) has found several cases in which unawareness of subtle interdependence has led to misinterpretation of results.

◆ *Progressive Changes in Sequence Composition.* We have discussed behavior that is temporally grouped as though the composition of sequences were constant, but this is clearly not the case. Even within a very short time span sequence composition can vary widely in several ways. As the time span covered by the observations is increased to weeks or months, trends in sequence patterns may appear. Habits of feeding and locomotion show seasonal and life cycle changes. Reproductive behavior changes with the season and may disappear entirely on an annual or seasonal basis. Imposed on these long-term changes, there are often short-term fluctuations in sequence composition related to such things as cyclic egg production and raising of young. Fluctuations may occur at different times of day. More or less irreversible changes may also take place in the course of development. Thus an account of sequence structure may only be appropriate for the particular time at which the records were taken. In any case caution is required in merging data taken over a long period of time. Contrary to the view that is often favored, it is not always advantageous to mass data, at least not before extracting the maximum of information from the separate items.

DESCRIPTION AND CAUSAL ANALYSIS

Behavior is a product of physiological processes. We may hope eventually to explain it in physiological terms. Much of the material discussed in this book has been physiological, and such work clearly must proceed hand in hand with behavioral analysis. Students of animal behavior sometimes even seem to feel that behavioral analysis is no more than preliminary if it does not include physiological methods.

How far can a descriptive analysis of behavior proceed in deriving causal explanations of the temporal patterns of behavior without experimental intervention? The basic methods are two. One arises directly from the descriptions of temporal patterning of behavior. The other centers on the fact that while an investigator is recording behavior he can also record changes taking place in the animal's environment, building up a record of external stimuli impinging on behavior.

Both methods ultimately depend on establishing temporal correlations between different phenomena. Given an adequate description of the sequential patterning of a group of actions, correlations can be sought between the different measures of the pattern. For example, if the interval between sequences is longer than the average, how does this relate to sequence duration, to the number and frequency of certain acts within the sequence, or to the completeness of the acts? Or conversely, if certain sequences are longer than average, or include more than the usual number of certain acts, how does this relate to the duration of the subsequent interval or to the composition of the next bout? Correlations can also be looked for between different measures of the temporal properties of the same sequence. We may ask, for example, how variations in frequency and in the completeness of acts are related.

Answers to such questions have a direct bearing on an understanding of the causal mechanism underlying the behavior. If we find that two properties are positively correlated, we hypothesize that they are facilitated by similar causes, immediate or distant, or that they facilitate each other. If there is a negative correlation, it may be that the factors which facilitate one inhibit the other, or vice versa. If there is no correlation we assume an absence of immediate relationship. In the same way, the inclusion of data on environmental changes in the temporal record makes possible a further series of correlations between variables. Account may be taken of changes in the physical environment, changes in the social stimuli presented by other animals, or changes which are generated by the animal's own behavior. The wider the range of things observed, the more complete the understanding of the causal basis of behavior becomes.

The central concern in causal analysis is with motivation. If we are right in phrasing the ultimate aim of motivational analysis as the explanation and prediction of the temporal patterning of behavior, the way to begin is with a meticulous description of the temporal pattern. This does not mean that temporal analysis is more than a part of the whole investigation. Experimental manipulation of the variables involved, whether they are behavioral variables, stimuli from the physical environment, or physiological factors, is an essential step in any scientific investigation. Nevertheless, the observation of temporal patterning is in a sense basic to the other approaches. It can serve both as a description of what other methods seek to explain and as a source of hypotheses about what variables need to be controlled in the course of experimental analysis.

REFERENCES

Altmann, S. A. 1962. A field study of the sociobiology of rhesus monkeys *Macaca mulatta. Ann. N.Y. Acad. Sci.,* **102:**338–435.

———. 1965. Sociobiology of rhesus monkeys. II: stochastics of social communication. *J. Theoret. Biol.,* **8:**490–522.

———. In press. The structure of primate communication.

Aronson, L. R. 1949. An analysis of reproductive behavior in the mouthbreeding cichlid fish, *Tilapia macrocephala* (Bleeker). *Zoologica,* **34:**133–158.

Baerends, G. P., R. Brouwer, and H. Tj. Waterbolk. 1955. Ethological studies on *Lebistes reticulatus* (Peters). I. An analysis of the male courtship pattern. *Behaviour,* **8:**249–334.

Beach, F. A. 1956. Characteristics of masculine "sex drive." *Neb. Symp. Motiv.,* **4:**1–32.

Bol, A. C. A. 1959. A consummatory situation. The effect of eggs on the sexual behaviour of the male three-spined stickleback (*Gasterosteus aculeatus* L.). *Experientia,* **15:**115.

Cane, V. 1961. Some ways of describing behaviour. In *Current Problems in Animal Behaviour,* ed. by W. H. Thorpe and O. L. Zangwill: 361–388. Cambridge University Press, Cambridge.

Craig, W. 1918. Appetites and aversions as constituents of instincts. *Biol. Bull.,* **34:**91–107.

Daanje, A. 1950. On the locomotory movements in birds and the intention movements derived from them. *Behaviour,* **3:**48–98.

Darling, F. Fraser. 1937. *A Herd of Red Deer.* Oxford University Press, London.

Denenberg, V. H. and E. M. Banks. 1962. Techniques of measurement and evaluation. In *The Behaviour of Domestic Animals,* ed. by E. S. E. Hafez: 201–243. The Williams and Wilkins Company, Baltimore.

Eisenberg, J. 1962. Studies on the behavior of *Peromyscus maniculatus gambelii* and *Peromyscus californicus parasiticus. Behaviour,* **19**:177–207.

———. 1963. The behavior of heteromyid rodents. *Univ. Calif. Publ. Zool.,* **69**:1–114.

Fabricius, E. and A. Jansson. 1963. Laboratory observations on the reproductive behaviour of the pigeon (*Columba livia*) during the pre-incubation phase of the breeding cycle. *Anim. Behav.,* **11**:534–547.

Gray, J. 1953. *How Animals Move.* Cambridge University Press, Cambridge.

Hinde, R. A. 1952. Behaviour of the great tit (*Parus major*) and some other related species. *Behaviour Suppl.,* **2**:1–201.

———. 1953. Appetitive behaviour, consummatory act, and the hierarchical organisation of behaviour—with special reference to the great tit (*Parus major*). *Behaviour,* **5**:189–224.

———. 1954. Factors governing the changes in strength of a partially inborn response, as shown by the mobbing behaviour of the chaffinch (*Fringilla coelebs*). I. The nature of the response, and an examination of its course. *Proc. Roy. Soc. Lond., B,* **142**:306–331.

———. 1958. The nest-building behaviour of domesticated canaries. *Proc. Zool. Soc. Lond.,* **131**:1–48.

———. 1959. Unitary drives. *Anim. Behav.,* **7**:130–141.

———. 1960a. Some recent trends in ethology. In *Psychology: A Study of a Science,* ed. by S. Koch, Vol. 2:561–610. McGraw-Hill Book Company, New York.

———. 1960b. Factors governing the changes in the strength of a partially inborn response, as shown by the mobbing behaviour of the chaffinch (*Fringilla coelebs*). III. The interaction of short-term and long-term incremental and decremental effects. *Proc. Roy. Soc. Lond., B,* **153**:398–420.

Iersel, J. J. A. van. 1953. An analysis of the parental behaviour of the male three-spined stickleback (*Gasterosteus aculeatus* L.). *Behaviour Suppl.,* **3**:1–159.

——— and A. C. A. Bol. 1958. Preening of two tern species. A study on displacement activities. *Behaviour,* **13**:1–88.

Isaac, D. and P. Marler. 1963. Ordering of sequences of singing behaviour of mistle thrushes in relationship to timing. *Anim. Behav.,* **11**:179–188.

Kavanau, J. 1963. Continuous automatic monitoring of the activities of small captive animals. *Ecology,* **44**:95–110.

Kruger, W. 1958. Bewegungstypen. *Handb. Zool.,* 8:15, Teil 6(3):1–56.

Lack, D. 1956. *Swifts in a Tower.* Methuen and Company, London.

Larsson, K. 1956. Conditioning and sexual behavior in the male albino rat. *Acta Psychol. Gothoburg.,* **1**:1–269.

Lorenz, K. 1941. Vergleichende Bewegungsstudien an Anatinen. *J. Orn.,* Suppl. III. [Festschrift Oskar Heinroth] : 194–293.

———. 1950. The comparative method in studying innate behaviour patterns. *Symp. Soc. Exp. Biol.,* **4**:221–268.

Marler, P. R. 1956. Behaviour of the chaffinch, *Fringilla coelebs. Behaviour Suppl.,* **5**:1–184.

Morgan, C. T. 1957. Physiological mechanisms of motivation. *Neb. Symp. Motiv.,* **5**:1–35.

Morris, D. 1958. The reproductive behaviour of the ten-spined stickleback (*Pygosteus pungitius* L.). *Behaviour Suppl.,* **6**:1–154.

Neil, E. H. 1964. An analysis of color changes and social behavior of *Tilapia mossambica. Univ. Calif. Publ. Zool.,* **75**:1–58.

Nelson, K. 1964a. The temporal patterning of courtship behavior in the glandulocaudine fishes (Ostariophysi, Characidae). *Behaviour,* **24:**90–146.

———. 1964b. Behavior and morphology in the glandulocaudine fishes (Ostariophysi, Characidae). *Univ. Calif. Publ. Zool.,* **75:**59–152.

Nissen, H. W. 1951. Phylogenetic comparison. In *Handbook of Experimental Psychology,* ed. by S. S. Stevens: 347–386. John Wiley and Sons, New York.

Richter, C. P. 1927. Animal behavior and internal drives. *Quart. Rev. Biol.,* **2:**307–343.

Russell, W. M. S., A. P. Mead, and J. S. Hayes. 1954. A basis for the quantitative study of the structure of behaviour. *Behaviour,* **6:**153–205.

Schneirla, T. C. 1950. The relationship between observation and experimentation in the field study of behavior. *Ann. N.Y. Acad. Sci.,* **51:**1022–1044.

Scott, J. P. 1950. Methodology and techniques for the study of animal societies. *Ann. N.Y. Acad. Sci.,* **51:**1001–1121.

Sevenster-Bol, A. C. A. 1962. On the causation of drive reduction after a consummatory act. *Arch. Néerl. Zool.,* **15:**175–236.

Sherrington, C. 1906. *The Integrative Action of the Nervous System.* Charles Scribner's Sons, London.

Spurway, H. and J. B. S. Haldane. 1954. The comparative ethology of vertebrate breathing. I. Breathing in newts, with a general survey. *Behaviour,* **6:**8–34.

Tinbergen, N. 1951. *The Study of Instinct.* Oxford University Press, London.

———. 1952. "Derived" activities; their causation, biological significance, origin, and emancipation during evolution. *Quart. Rev. Biol.,* **27:**1–32.

Wiepkema, P. R. 1961. An ethological analysis of the reproductive behaviour of the bitterling (*Rhodeus amarus* Bloch). *Arch. Néerl. Zool.,* **14:**103–199.

Weiss, P. 1941. Self-differentiation of the basic patterns of coordination. *Comp. Psychol. Monogr.,* **17**(4):1–96.

———. 1950. Experimental analysis of coordination by the disarrangement of central-peripheral relations. *Symp. Soc. Exp. Biol.,* **4:**92–111.

AUTHOR INDEX

SUBJECT INDEX